Inspection Manual

Seventh Edition

National Fire Protection Association
Batterymarch Park
Quincy, MA 02269

Seventh Edition
J2 2130101

Product Manager: Richard Wallace
Copy Editor: Laurie Beaulieu
Cover Design: Dinardo Design
Illustrations: George Nichols
Text Processing: Louise Grant and Marilyn Lupo
Composition: Devlin Graphics
Production: Donald McGonagle and Debra Rose
The following are the registered trademarks of the National Fire
Protection Association:
Life Safety Code and 101
National Electrical Code and NEC
National Fire Codes

NFPA IM-94
ISBN 0-87765-393-3
Library of Congress Card No. 93-087250
Printed in the United States of America

99   98   97   96   95   5   4   3   2

Contents

Contributors

T he National Fire Protection Association is grateful to the professionals who have contributed to this manual. The knowledge and experience they have gained from conducting hundreds of fire inspections will be invaluable to every inspector.

As a body, the NFPA is not responsible for the content of this *Manual* because the Association's full membership has not had an opportunity to review the contents before publication. Some of the opinions and recommendations expressed in the *Manual* are those of the contributors and do not necessarily reflect the views and recommendations of the National Fire Protection Association.

The editors wish to thank the following people who contributed or reviewed materials for publication in this *Manual:*

David M. Banwarth, Prince Georges County Fire Department, Upper Marlboro, MD (Lodging or Rooming Houses)

Donald G. Bathurst, General Services Administration, Washington, DC (Business Occupancies)

Robert P. Benedetti, National Fire Protection Association, Quincy, MA (Storage and Handling of Flammable and Combustible Liquids)

Howard Boyd, Tennessee State Fire Marshal's Office-Retired (Apartment Buildings)

William J. Bradford, Consultant, Brookfield, CT (Chemicals)

Harry L. Bradley, Maryland State Fire Marshal's Office, Bel Air, MD (One- and Two-Family Dwellings)

Francis L. Brannigan, Professor-Retired, Montgomery College, Rockville, MD (Building Construction)

Arval W. Bridges, Jr., Louisiana State Fire Marshal, Baton Rouge, LA (Educational Occupancies)

Kenneth E. Bush, Maryland State Fire Marshal's Office, Easton, MD (Health Care Facilities)

John Caloggero, National Fire Protection Association, Quincy, MA (Electrical Systems)

Wayne Carson, Carson Associates, Inc., Warrenton, VA (Hotels and Occupancies in Special Structures)

Bert M. Cohn, Bert Cohn Associates, Inc., Chicago, IL (Plastics and Rubber)

Mark T. Conroy, National Fire Protection Association, Quincy, MA (Special Agent Extinguishing Systems and Portable Fire Extinguishers)

Ron M. Coté, National Fire Protection Association, Quincy, MA (Life Safety Considerations)

Richard J. Davis, Factory Mutual Research, Norwood, MA (Construction, Alteration, and Demolition Operations)

Philip J. DiNenno, Hughes Associates, Inc., Columbia, MD (Hazards of Special Occupancies)

John Echternacht, Fire Safety Consultants, Houston, TX (Industrial Occupancies)

Russell P. Fleming, National Fire Sprinkler Association, Patterson, NY (Water Supplies)

Dennis N. Gage, ISO Commercial Risk Services, Inc., Parsippany, NJ (Venting Systems for Commercial Cooking Appliances)

Casey C. Grant, National Fire Protection Association, Quincy, MA (Special Agent Extinguishing Systems and Heat-Utilization Equipment)

Greg Haley, CIGNA Loss Control, Philadelphia, PA (Storage Occupancies)

Clifford Harvey, Boulder Fire Department, Boulder, CO (Assembly Occupancies and Mercantile Occupancies)

J. Edmund Hay, U.S. Department of the Interior, Bureau of Mines, Pittsburgh, PA (Explosives and Blasting Agents)

A. Larry Iseminger, Jr., Maryland State Fire Marshal's Office, Hagerstown, MD (Detention and Correctional Occupancies)

Joseph N. Knapp, McDonalds Corporation, Oak Brook, IL (Venting Systems for Commercial Cooking Appliances)

Kenneth L. Kosanke, PyroLabs, Inc., Whitewater, CO (Fireworks and

Pyrotechnics)

James K. Lathrop, Koffel Associates, Niantic, CT (Residential Board and Care Occupancies)

Theodore C. Lemoff, National Fire Protection Association, Quincy, MA (Gas Hazards)

August Manz, A.F. Manz Associates, Union, NJ (Welding and Cutting)

Walter Maybee, Los Alamos National Laboratory, Los Alamos, NM (Radioactive Materials)

Jeffrey Moore, Consultant, Cincinnati, Ohio (Protection of Openings in Fire Barriers)

Michael E. Mowrer, Professional Loss Control, Inc., Kingston, TN (Waste-Handling Systems and Materials-Handling Systems)

Steven Sawyer, National Fire Protection Association, Quincy, MA (Occupancy Inspection Forms)

Don R. Scarbrough, Nordson Corporation, Westlake, OH (Spray Painting and Powder Coating)

William A. Schmidt, Consultant, Bowie MD (Heating Systems and Air Conditioning and Ventilating Systems)

Richard F. Schwab, Allied-Signal, Inc., Morristown, NJ (Combustible Dusts)

Michael J. Serapiglia, AT&T, Basking Ridge, NJ (Hazards of Special Occupancies)

L. Charles Smeby, Jr., National Fire Protection Association, Quincy, MA (The Fire Inspector and Inspection Procedures)

Walter Smittle, III, West Virginia State Fire Marshal, Charleston, WV (Foreword)

Robert E. Solomon, National Fire Protection Association, Quincy, MA (Automatic Sprinkler and Other Water-Based Fire Protection Systems and General Storage)

Walter Sterling, National Fire Protection Association, Quincy, MA (Interior Finish)

Harry H. Stultz, Metro-Dade County, Miami, FL (Venting Systems for Commercial Cooking Appliances)

Bob Tapscott, New Mexico Engineering Research Institute, Albuquerque, NM (Metals)

Dean K. Wilson, Industrial Risk Insurers, Hartford, CT (Fire Alarm Systems and Housekeeping Practices)

Acknowledgments

*I*t would be difficult to thank all of the individuals whose contributions to fire prevention and fire protection are used herein. For their indispensable assistance, particular appreciation is due:

L. Charles Smeby, Jr.

James K. Lathrop

Foreword

A fire safety inspection program is vital to our society. The fire safety inspector evaluates a building or structure and determines what measures are necessary for a building or structure to meet a reasonable level of safety.

The fire service must deliver an adequate fire safety inspection program to improve the quality of life. To avoid a haphazard program and major problems, especially failure, the fire service must be committed to an efficient and effective program for improving the fire safety environment. These inspection guidelines will provide you, the inspector, with the necessary knowledge and skills to develop such an inspection program.

The inspection program must have strong support of the administration, including the necessary mechanism for enforcement. With the administration's endorsement, these guidelines provide a reliable means for reducing loss of life and property from fire.

These guidelines concentrate on identifying unsafe conditions or deficiencies in buildings and structures related to current codes and standards. These unsafe conditions include, but are not limited to, obstructed or locked exits, inoperative fire alarm and sprinkler systems, fire doors blocked open, and improper storage to name a few. These unsafe conditions can be caused by renovations or alterations of existing buildings and structures; new construction projects not conforming to code requirements; deterioration of the existing buildings; existing buildings built prior to modern codes; changes in occupancy; improper interior finish; improperly separated hazardous areas; and unenclosed vertical openings. The fire service has recognized these unsafe conditions or deficiencies in fire safety for years. The elimination of these deficiencies, be they human or environmental, depends on the implementation of the inspection program.

These inspection guidelines provide the necessary information for evaluating the fire safety conditions of buildings and structures on a regular and systematic basis. You will also have the personal satisfaction of recognizing the benefits of reducing fire losses in the future.

NFPA *101®*, *Life Safety Code®*, and NFPA 1, *Fire Prevention Code,* provide the most up-to-date guidelines for conducting fire safety inspections. These NFPA codes and standards address hazards of fires and other emergencies. Inspectors should be properly trained in using these codes. Another valuable document for reference in evaluating the fire safety of buildings and structures is the NFPA *Fire Protection Handbook,* and as an inspector you should become familiar with it. Finally, the master index for the NFPA *National Fire Codes®* is an excellent source for locating specific requirements in the more than 280 NFPA codes and standards.

The fire safety inspection program will deliver lasting benefits. Reducing life and fire losses is a matter of priority. If you emphasize the importance and sell fire safety to everyone, the results will be forthcoming, but instant results will not occur overnight. It takes commitment, time, and hard work to achieve success. Use the resources available to you to develop, implement, and maintain a viable fire safety inspection program.

CHAPTER 1

The Fire Inspector

*F*ire inspectors must possess excellent communications skills and be knowledgeable about property and its contents, operations, and fire protection provisions of building and fire codes. They must have exceptional judgment and should understand their role in life safety and property conservation. Fire inspectors are part detective, part reporter, part technical consultant, part missionary, and part salesperson.

Physical Condition

While conducting an inspection, you might have to climb ladders or stairs in tall buildings, crawl into confined spaces, and lift or push heavy objects. Thus, you should have enough strength, agility, and stamina to perform such physical activities.

Comunications Skills

A vital part of the inspection process is discussing the problems or violations discovered and their potential solutions with owners, property managers, architects, engineers, lawyers, contractors, vendors, the fire service, and representatives from the insurance industry. You also will have to record the conditions found and actions taken. Therefore, you must be able to communicate clearly, both orally and in writing, and should use tact and discretion to maintain authority. This is critical to an effective, smoothly run fire prevention program.

Authority

When you are not able to gain compliance by using your communications skills, you may have to take legal action to force compliance, such as serving the property owner with a series of written notices of violation, each with a deadline for compliance.

If, after serving violations you still are not able to gain compliance, you probably will have to consult with a local or state government's attorney to start the appropriate legal action specified in the fire safety legislation.

In some situations, policy may require immediate compliance, such as unlocking exit doors in an assembly occupancy. In other situations you may have to issue a violation notice similar to a traffic ticket.

The organization you represent must support you with clear authority and consistent policy enforcement. In addition, only enforceable and nationally recognized codes and standards, such as the *NFPA National Fire Codes®*, should be the basis for the jurisdiction's fire safety ordinances and laws.

If you end up in litigation, standards designated as American National Standards (ANSI) offer you the best chance of convincing a court of the seriousness and credibility of the violation. ANSI assures that the approved standards and codes are developed by a fair consensus process and keep pace with technology and innovation.

NFPA codes and standards are ANSI approved.

Knowledge

The breadth of knowledge you need as a fire inspector is determined by the types of facilities you will be inspecting, the materials contained in them, and the operations they house. You also must be familiar with construction practices, nationally recognized fire safety standards, and other agencies that you can consult for advice, solutions to problems, or corrections for specific hazards.

Most important is to know your own limitations and when to ask questions. As is often said, there are no stupid questions, only stupid mistakes. If an owner asks a question to which you do not know the answer, don't try to fake it. Tell the owner that you will research it and get back to him or her.

Construction with the introduction of new processes, product lines, or tenants, the interior layouts of a building often are altered. During periods of construction, renovation, or demolition, properties are especially vulnerable to fire. You should have sufficient knowledge of building construction and materials to recognize potentially hazardous conditions and to recommend temporary steps that can be taken during construction or renovation to provide for the fire safety of the structure.

Building Services

Building services can represent a fire hazard if they are not installed and maintained properly. You should be familiar with the fire hazards associated with electrical systems, heating systems, air conditioning and ventilating systems, waste-handling systems, and materials-handling systems.

Hazardous Materials

You should be familiar with the proper handling, storage, and protection of a wide variety of hazardous materials that might be encountered during an inspection. Typical hazardous materials include flammable and combustible liquids, compressed or liquefied flammable gases, explosives, corrosives, reactive materials, unstable materials, toxic materials, oxidizers, radioactive materials, natural and synthetic fibers, combustible metals, and combustible dusts.

Process Hazards

Industrial processes can introduce unusual hazards. You should be able to recognize those hazards, know how to minimize them, and understand the fire protection methods appropriate for the hazards. This may require you to seek out industry experts or other written sources of hazardous processes.

Fire Protection Equipment

A variety of fire protection equipment might be installed or available on the premises. The most common are portable fire extinguishers, sprinkler systems, and standpipe and hose systems. However, some areas and processes may be protected by special fixed extinguishing systems. For example, a dipping or coating process might be protected by a system that uses carbon dioxide, dry chemical, or foam as the extinguishing agent. You should understand the application and operation of any extinguishing system equipment on the premises. You also should be able to evaluate the operational readiness of the private or public water supply systems.

A property also might be equipped with heat, smoke, and flame detection equipment. They may provide early warning of developing fire, and fire alarm systems and devices may alert the occupants and summon the fire department. You should be acquainted with the purpose and operation of such devices and systems.

Bibliography

Cote, A. E., ed., *Fire Protection Handbook*, 17th edition, National Fire Protection Association, Quincy, MA 1991.

NFPA *National Fire Codes*

NFPA 1031, *Standard for Professional Qualifications for Fire Inspector.* Specifies the minimum level of professional competence required for Fire Inspector, I, II, and III.

NFPA 1035, *Standard for Professional Qualifications for Public Fire and Life Safety Educator.* Specifies the minimum level of professional competence required for Public Fire Educator I, II, and III.

CHAPTER 2

Inspection Procedures

*A*s pointed out in Chapter 1, fire inspectors are part detective, part reporter, part technical consultant, part missionary, and part salesperson. An inspection should inspire others to take action to reduce fire hazards, encourage an improved attitude toward fire safety by management and employees, and provide a record of the findings and actions resulting from the inspection.

Inspectors' Equipment

In order to conduct the fire inspection safely and efficiently, you should have the proper equipment. Among the equipment you will need is a visible means of identification, such as an identification card or badge, and you should wear a uniform or other appropriate business attire.

Personal Equipment

When inspecting dirty or hard-to-reach areas, you may need coveralls and perhaps overshoes to protect your street clothes. You may need to wear boots when conducting waterflow tests.

You should be equipped with and use the personal safety equipment required of the employees working in the area being inspected. This could include a hard hat, safety shoes, safety glasses, gloves, and ear protection. In some environments you may have to use respiratory protection devices.

Aids to Inspection

The basic tools you will need as a fire inspector are a flashlight, a notebook or clipboard in which to make sketches or record observations, report forms, and a pen or pencil. If a sketch is to be drawn, the accuracy of dimensions measured by pacing is often adequate. When greater accuracy is required, you will find a 6-foot ruler or a 50-foot measuring tape helpful. You also may ask the owner if he or she has "as built" blueprints from which you can find accurate measurements.

More sophisticated equipment that you might need occasionally includes gauges and connections for making waterflow measurements and a combustible gas detector for testing potentially hazardous environments.

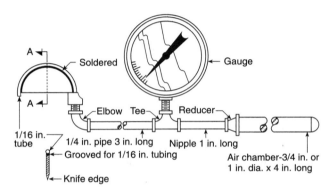

Figure 2-1. Pitot tube assembly used for making waterflow measurements.

Preparation

If you inspect residential properties, you will need little in the way of preparation after you have made a few inspections; you might only need to remind yourself of chronic trouble areas that need to be watched carefully. If you inspect nonresidential properties, however, you should prepare yourself by reviewing previous inspection reports, surveys, and any construction plans; learning about the operations and activities carried out on the premises; and preparing a list of the more important points to be investigated before starting the inspection. The appropriate occupancy chapter in this Manual is a good place to start.

If you are inspecting a property for the first time, you can add items to the inspection list from the NFPA *Fire Protection Handbook;* the local building codes; the NFPA *Life Safety Code,* if applicable; and other NFPA standards on specific occupancies, hazards, or fire protection features, such as sprinklers and standpipes. You may not have to do much preparation before inspecting small properties, such as one-story mercantile establishments or gasoline service stations. However, you should review information on larger, more complex properties and the processes they contain before you begin the inspection.

Inspections usually are conducted during normal business hours, although advance arrangements can be made for inspections at other hours. For example, you may visit a property at night to observe conditions during the night shift or at other times to check on the security guards. Normal business hours for many occupancies such as night clubs or theaters may be at night.

The element of surprise can be effective in determining true operating conditions. If an inspection time is likely to harm a good relationship between you and the owner or manager, it might be prudent to reschedule the inspection, provided there is no evidence of an immediate fire or life hazard. Checking a restaurant's hood and duct system during meal time is a good example of when not to conduct an inspection. Briefly walking through the facility to make sure exits are not blocked in the dining area during this busy time is appropriate, however.

Introductions

Some general observations can be noted mentally as you enter the property. You can observe the general occupancy, the condition of exterior housekeeping and maintenance, some building construction features, and the height of the facility. However, you should not begin an exterior inspection without first introducing yourself to management and seeking permission to inspect the property.

If you are not part of the facility's staff, you should make an effort to create a favorable impression in order to ensure cooperation and courteous treatment. You should enter the premises by the main entrance, seek out someone with authority, introduce yourself, and state the nature of your business. As a visiting inspector, you should ask for permission to inspect the premises, not demand it. You have no reason to be irritated if you have to wait before receiving attention, especially if you have arrived without an appointment. The person you need to see may have other important matters to attend to first.

It would be wise for you to spend a reasonable amount of time making sure that whomever is in charge of the property understands why the facility is being inspected and answering any questions the property owner or manager might have, particularly during the first inspection of a property. Most properties have been inspected at some time, and records of such inspections usually can be obtained from your agency's files. The records often contain plans that could save you much time or work.

Inspections by outside inspectors always should be conducted in the company of the property owner or a designated representative. This representative will help you gain access to all parts of the property and will obtain answers to necessary questions. Of course, if you are an employee of the occupant, there will be no need for a guide once the initial inspection has been made. You should work in pairs when inspecting residential properties to eliminate any potential complaints of inpropriety.

Inspection Observations

You either have or will be developing your own technique and methodology for inspecting a facility, and this methodology must be flexible to allow for variations and unexpected observations during the inspection. Either before or during the inspection, you must ascertain both general and specific information in order to review and generate the appropriate recommendations or code compliance requirements. In addition to the specific information you will obtain about the specific occupancy classification, you must determine several general facts before you can completely evaluate the occupancy and determine which code requirements it must meet.

Occupancy Classification

You should evaluate how the facility is used and determine which specific occupancy classification it falls under. This will enable you to choose the appropriate checklist and code requirements in order to accurately conduct the inspection and make the appropriate evaluations. Chapter 4 of the NFPA *Life Safety Code* or the local building code will help you classify the occupancy.

Sequence

In a large property, you should start by touring the outside of the facility to observe how the buildings relate to one another and to adjacent properties. A site plan of the property will also help you visualize the layout of the premises. It also might be helpful to obtain an overall view of the property from the top of the tallest building.

Whether a building is inspected from top to bottom or from bottom to top is of little consequence; it is your choice. It is important is that your inspection be done systematically and thoroughly. No area should be omitted. Every room, closet, attic, concealed space, basement, or other place where fire could start should be inspected. If you are barred from an area for security reasons, you should note it on the inspection report.

The following gives a general indication of what you should look for while going through the property. More specific information is contained in subsequent chapters and from the list you prepared in your preliminary research.

Exterior

While touring the exterior areas of the property, you can record the address, the names and types of occupancies, exterior housekeeping and maintenance, exterior evidence of building construction type, and the building height. You should note the location and character of potential exposures and the arrangement and condition of outdoor storage. You should note conditions affecting fire department response and fireground operations, including the location of public fire hydrants.

Accessibility is an important factor. Fire lanes should be well marked and unobstructed. Vehicular activity should be limited to the pick up and discharge of passengers, and parking should be prohibited in these areas. Fire lanes must be wide enough to allow fire apparatus to pass. Hydrants and other sources of water must be accessible. Sprinkler valves must be open, and sprinkler and standpipe connections must be capped, free of debris, and accessible. You should determine in which direction flammable liquids will flow should they be spilled, and what sort of drainage facilities are provided.

Construction Classifications

An important point of all inspections is to determine accurately the construction classification of the building or structure. This normally will be based on NFPA 220, *Standard on Types of Building Construction,* or the local building code. You will need to be familiar with the definitions of the individual construction types defined in NFPA 220 or the local building code in order to accurately classify the different types of construction you will be inspecting.

Once you are familiar with the exact definitions of the different construction types, you need to determine the similarities and distinguishing features of each category. A facility often will be composed of multiple construction types, and it is common for construction classifications to change as the building undergoes renovations, including alterations and additions. These factors can make the overall classification process complicated, and it may be impossible to determine one overall construction classification if the building is composed of multiple construction types. However, you can simplify the classification process by dividing the structure during your inspection into sections based on building configurations and construction, renovations, alterations, and additions. It is essential that you classify the structure accurately because the construction classification(s) will significantly affect the code requirements for the overall level of life safety and property conservation that can be provided inherently within the structure.

The type of construction and the materials used will influence the ease of ignition and the rate of fire spread. The integrity of fire-resistive walls and floor/ceiling assemblies must be assured. Openings in fire-rated walls must be protected to retard or prevent the spread of fire. Doors in fire-rated walls must be kept closed or close automatically to ensure a reasonably safe avenue of escape for the occupants and to restrict fire spread. If holes are made in these assemblies for the passage of services and utilities and the voids are not sealed, they could allow fire to spread horizontally and vertically throughout the facility.

Inspecting the integrity of exit enclosures is very important. Check the door into each exit enclosure while inspecting each floor. Then inspect each exit stair enclosure for its full length. In taller buildings it is recommended that this be done from the top down for ease. Use a different elevator to go back to the top each time, using this opportunity to note if Phase II fire fighter service is provided for that elevator car. (See Chapter 15 for more information on exit enclosures.)

Many of these items are not readily obvious, and you may find it necessary to examine concealed spaces, such as the voids above suspended ceilings, the interiors of shafts, and stair enclosures to make sure that the integrity of these fire protection features has not been breached.

Building Facilities

Water distribution systems, heating systems, air conditioning and ventilating systems, electrical distribution systems, refuse-handling equipment, and conveyor systems all play an important role in the fire hazard potential of a premises. They must be properly installed, used, and maintained in order to minimize the hazard. While you are not responsible for maintaining such systems, you should be able to determine whether or not the equipment is being properly used and maintained. This may mean reviewing the equipment's maintenance records as part of the inspection process.

Hazards of Contents

The level of hazard of the contents of a building are categorized as low, ordinary, and high in Chapter 4 of the *Life Safety Code.* Your evaluation of the hazard level of the building contents will have a significant impact on the fire safety evaluation and the resulting recommendations. Therefore, it is critical for you to be familiar with the following definitions of each category. (See Section 4-2 of the *Life Safety Code* for the exact definitions.)

Low Hazard Contents: Contents of such low combustibility that no self-propagating fire therein can occur, and thus the only probable danger requiring the use of emergency exits will be from panic, fumes, smoke, or fire from some external source.

Ordinary Hazard Contents: Contents that are liable to burn with moderate rapidity or that give off a considerable volume of smoke, but probably will not produce poisonous fumes or explode in the event of a fire.

High Hazard Contents: Hazards that are liable to burn with extreme rapidity or from which poisonous fumes or explosions are possible in the event of fire.

Be aware that the classifications used by NFPA 13, *Standard for the*

Installation of Sprinkler Systems, may be different. For example, an office occupancy will have "ordinary hazard contents" as defined by the *Life Safety Code;* however, NFPA 13 will define an office as a "light hazard occupancy."

At the time of your inspection, you must determine the hazard level of the building's contents based on your observations of the actual contents of the building or structure. Controlling the hazards of materials depends on storing, handling, using, and disposing of them properly. In this regard, you should pay particular attention to housekeeping and storage practices. You also should be familiar with any process that might cause a fire hazard or any special features of the property that might present special problems. You are evaluating the actual contents and fuel loading within the structure, not the structure's construction or any of its features.

During the inspection, you might want to use the process of elimination to accurately determine the hazard level of the contents. You should begin by asking the question "could a self-propagating fire occur within that space?" This question should be based on the type and burning characteristics of the fuel located in the building and its specific arrangement in relation to other fuel stations. The low hazard level of contents category does not imply that no fire can occur; it only implies that fire will not spread from one combustible item to another. Low hazard contents are rarely found in occupancies; thus this condition normally would not be a major classification during most inspections.

Because the vast majority of structures have contents classified as ordinary hazards, normally it is best to skip this category and determine if the contents fall into the high hazard category.

When making this determination you must use a great deal of judgment based on your experience in the field and your ability to make observations and assess burning characteristics of various fuels. To classify contents as having a high hazard, they would have to burn at a very fast rate and have dramatic burning characteristics that could render the occupied space unsafe at a faster rate than the occupants could evacuate. High hazard contents could explode in the occupied area and also produce significant and unusual amounts of poisonous fumes, thus exposing the occupants to a high level of personal hazard. Flammable liquids, gases, dusts, or solid combustibles with a very high rate of heat release are included in this category.

Many times you will be able to easily eliminate categories of low and high hazard contents, which leaves only contents of ordinary hazard. To ascertain if contents fail under this classification, you need to determine if the contents in the building are liable to burn with moderate rapidity or give off a considerable volume of smoke, but would not produce poisonous fumes or explosions. This classification includes typical combustion products such as carbon monoxide and hydrogen cyanide.

It is commonly believed that the most hazardous classification will prevail as the overall classification for the building, but this is not usually the case. Normally, when some contents are of a high hazard, the area is protected as a subcategory, but it will not be the determining overall hazard level of contents classification. You must make sure that the provisions of special protection are provided and adequate before areas of high hazard contents can be segregated from the overall classification.

To make this concept tangible, consider the following example of an educational facility. In a college, typical classrooms and office areas normally would have a sufficient amount of fuel in a configuration that would allow a self-propagating fire to occur, but neither poisonous fumes nor explosions would be produced. As a result, this area would be classified as having ordinary hazard contents.

Air-handling equipment rooms and restrooms probably have some amount of fuel that could allow a fire to begin, but in the appropriate type of construction the fire most likely would burn without significantly affecting the structure or the egress time of the occupants. As a result, these areas can be classified appropriately as having low hazard contents. There also will be laboratories that utilize high-pressure reactors for research purposes, considerable amounts of flammable liquids or flammable gases, as well as a host of other hazardous materials that would classify the occupancy as having high hazard contents.

If the following requirements are met, then the appropriate hazard level of contents classification would be ordinary, but you must consider all three classifications when making your evaluation:

1. The high hazard items are appropriately protected and segregated.
2. The low hazard items do not contribute significantly to the overall square footage of the facility.
3. The ordinary hazard items predominate.

It is very common for a structure to have either two or all three hazard categories because the hazard level of contents may change as you move through the facility. Determining the hazard level of contents will allow you to make a more precise assessment of the facility, and the correct occupancy classification will direct you to the use of the appropriate code requirements.

Fire Detection and Alarm Systems

Often, a property will be equipped with fire detection and alarm devices and systems. The purpose of such equipment is to detect the presence of fire, alert the occupants, notify the fire department, or a combination of these functions. You should understand the function of, and be able to identify, the major components of these systems. Routine inspections should ensure that manually operated fire alarm devices are clearly marked, accessible to occupants, and are properly maintained. Tests should be performed by a representative of the owner and witnessed by you to confirm that the systems are in operating condition. For further information on fire detection alarm systems see Chapter 10.

Fire Suppression Equipment

You should carefully check the fire suppression equipment on the premises. Typical equipment includes sprinklers and standpipe systems and portable fire extinguishers. Routine inspections should determine that sprinkler valves are open, sprinklers are unobstructed, that the system has not been altered, and that the sprinkler system has been extended to cover building additions. Standpipes should be checked for proper operation and that caps are in place with hose valves closed.

You also should determine that portable fire extinguishers of the proper size and type are provided for any given hazard, and that they are serviceable, clearly identified, and accessible to the occupants. You should check special extinguishing systems for special hazards to ensure that they have been maintained and are serviceable, and you should conduct or witness periodic operational tests of fire extinguishing equipment. See Chapters 12, 13, and 14 for further information on these systems.

Surveying and Mapping

During the initial inspection, you should gather information that will be used to prepare a site plan if one does not already exist. Such information will include construction features, occupancy data, fire protection features, and exposures.

The site plan is a scaled drawing that indicates the locations and dimensions of the buildings, fire protection equipment (including water-distribution systems), and the specific hazards and hazardous processes in each building. To show details of the fire protection features, it might be necessary for you to draw a series of side sketches, which need not be drawn to scale. These maps should be incorporated into the fire department prefire plan.

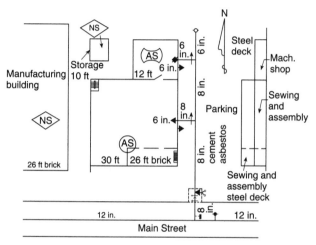

Figure 2-2. A typical site plan. "NS" means nonsprinklered; "AS" means automatic sprinkler.

Closing Interview

At the conclusion of the facility tour, you should discuss the results with someone in authority. You might have found conditions that seriously jeopardize the safety of the occupants and the property itself and should be corrected immediately. If you are an in-house fire inspector, you or your supervisor often have the authority to remedy hazardous situations. However, all inspectors will have to rely on their regulatory authority or on persuasion to convince the owner or the representative that corrective action should be taken at once.

Reports

There will be times when items that do not present an immediate threat to life safety will have to be corrected at a substantial cost to the owner. In such cases, you should go back to your office, research the adopted codes and standards to ensure that you have accurately noted the code violation, and produce a typewritten correction order. Call the owner or the owner's representative and schedule a meeting. Deliver the correction order in person, and fully explain the reasoning behind the requirement.

During the inspection process, you may be asked to clarify a provision of a code or standard, or be asked a technical question. In a field of knowledge as complex and diversified as fire protection, it is impossible for anyone to know all the answers. For example, NFPA publishes more than 280 codes and standards. It is better for you to admit you are not familiar with the answer, than try to bluff your way through. Remember, you must have the trust of those responsible for making and financing corrections to violations. To gain trust, you must always be completely honest.

Write down the question, the name and telephone number of the individual, and tell the person that you will respond with an answer. You now have the time needed to research the question, consult with other enforcement officials, your supervisor, or call the organization responsible for the requirement. As soon as possible, return an answer.

For less urgent conditions or conditions that will take time to correct, your recommendations should be explained clearly so that the owner fully understands the problem and the options available to correct it. Your view should be expressed in easy-to-understand terms, and you should not engage in arguments, technicalities, or petty fault-finding, any of which will antagonize the people you most want to influence. In all cases, you should explain any appeal process or procedures for granting equivalencies.

A written report should be prepared for each inspection. The amount of detail required will depend on the character and purpose of the inspection. In general, every report should include the following information:

1. Date of inspection.
2. Name of inspector.
3. Name and address of property, noting the name and title of the person(s) interviewed, and phone numbers.
4. Name and address of owner (or agent if a different location), and phone number.

5. Names of tenants of a multiple occupancy building (but not necessarily the name of every tenant in an apartment building or office building).
6. Type of occupancy. If mixed occupancy, state each principal occupancy and its location. In the case of industrial plants, state the principal items of raw materials and finished product.
7. Dimensions of buildings, including height and construction type.
8. Factors that could contribute to fire spread inside buildings, such as stairways, elevator and utility shafts, and lack of vertical and horizontal cutoffs.
9. Common fire hazards, such as open flames, heaters, and inaequate wiring.
10. Special fire hazards, such as hazardous materials and their storage, handling, use, and processes.
11. Extinguishing, detection, and alarm equipment.
12. Employee fire safety organization.
13. Exits (adequacy and accessibility).
14. Exposures, including factors making fire spread possible between buildings.
15. Recommendations or notations of violations.

The purpose of this report is to describe the property and its use, hazards, and fire protection without going into unnecessary detail. An inspection report should give the reader a clear understanding of the conditions found and the corrections needed.

A checklist might be adequate for routine procedures such as determining whether a sprinkler valve is open. When a measurement, such as water or air pressure, is to be checked, however, provision should be made for entering the actual measurement.

Hazardous practices and conditions are best treated in the narrative form. Inspectors who are required to describe the conditions they have observed are likely to do a more thorough job than those who merely complete a checklist. A checklist cannot be devised to take into account every situation that could conceivably arise, and an inspector could easily miss some hazard that a checklist does not include. Some agencies computerize data from the inspections they conduct. In these situations the terminology and data classifications contained in NFPA 901, *Uniform Coding for Fire Protection,* can be helpful.

Your recommendations or correction orders for reducing hazards and improving protection constitute an important part of the reporting process. Recommendations or correction orders can be prepared as a separate document and submitted to the property owner or manager for consideration. A copy should be filed with the inspection report.

If the purpose of the inspection is code enforcement, you should identify the code violations and give a date by which compliance is expected. Follow-up inspections should then be conducted to ensure proper compliance with the requirements.

Daily Inspection

In many facilities, there are items that should be checked daily or at some other periodic interval. These items should be compiled into a list that you can use to guide you and to ensure that each item is checked. The following is a partial list that might apply to an individual facility:

1. Check that exit doors are not locked.
2. Check the control valves, fire department connections, and gauges on sprinkler and standpipe systems.
3. Check the pilot light on fire pump control panels to be certain the equipment is energized.
4. Check the pilot lights and trouble lights on the fire alarm panels.
5. Check that all fire doors are closed.

In addition, there could be other items in the various departments of the facility that require a daily or periodic check. One convenient routine is to provide a card for each item to be checked. These cards should be kept at the location to be checked, and the employee responsible for the inspection should be required to initial, check, and record the necessary observations on the appropriate card. Entries should show the date, the time, and the name of the person making the observation. Bar code readers also can be used for this purpose in many cases.

It is not enough for management to specify that daily checks must be conducted. The individuals assigned to make the checks must feel that if the matter is important enough to be recorded, it must be done correctly. The property manager or the fire inspector should review the cards or records weekly, and the results should be summarized in the weekly report of loss prevention activities.

Bibliography

Cote, A. E., ed., *Fire Protection Handbook,* 17th edition, National Fire Protection Association, Quincy, MA, 1991. Section 10, Chapter 5, contains the specific information needed to make a survey, as well as mapping symbols and common abbreviations used in mapping.

NFPA Codes, Standards, and Recommended Practices

NFPA 1, *Fire Prevention Code.* Provides a basis for enforcement and administration of a fire prevention program; references other NFPA standards and codes for detailed guidance.

NFPA *101, Life Safety Code.* A code designed to reduce and eliminate life loss due to fire.

NFPA 170, *Standard for Firesafety Symbols.* Uniform fire protection symbols for use in property and structure diagrams for fire loss or risk analysis.

NFP 901, *Uniform Coding for Fire Protection.* A glossary of terms that the inspector can use to provide standardized terms in inspection reports and a system for classifying data from inspection reports.

NFPA 1031, *Standard for Professional Qualifications for Fire Inspector.* Specifies the minimum level of professional competence required for Fire Inspector I, II, and III.

NFPA 1201, *Recommendations for Developing Fire Protection Services for the Public.* Describes the basics of a fire prevention program.

NFPA 1452, *Guide for Training Fire Service Personnel to Make Dwelling Fire Safety Surveys.* Basic guide for establishing a local fire safety program for both single- and multifamily dwellings in rural and urban areas.

Inspection Fieldnotes

This is a sample of the type of form that can be used in the field. It is not intended to be an inspection report, but rather a tool to aid in the gathering of data. This form should be modified to reflect local conditions of use and should be used in conjunction with the reminder checklists at the ends of Chapters 16–29.

Administrative data

Name of facility: _____

Address: _____

City, state, zip code: _____

Inspection conducted by: _____

Date and time of inspection: _____

Building representative

Name: _____

Title: _____

Phone No.: _____

Property use

Occupancy classification: _____

Location and size of assembly area: _____

Height, area, and construction

Number of stories: _____

Number of sublevels: _____

Ground floor area: _____

Structural framing and protection: _____

Exterior wall construction: _____

Roof covering: _____

Floor construction: _____

Integrity of area separation: _____

Integrity of occupancy separation: _____

Interior finish: _____

Vertical shafts and protection: _____

Fire detection and alarm system

Type of system: _____

Supervised properly: _____

Initiation methods: _____

    Occupants: _____

    Fire dept.: _____

Where alarm is received:_____

Extent of coverage: _____

Any areas to which system should be extended: _____

System properly tested and maintained: _____

Sprinkler system

Type of system: _____

Extent of coverage: _____

Fire department connection

    accessible and maintained: _____

Valves open and sealed: _____

Type of valve supervision: _____

Type of waterflow alarm: _____

Are any pressure regulating devices used: _____

   Are they properly set: _____

   Are they properly maintained: _____

System properly tested and maintained: _____

Any areas to which sprinkler system should
   be extended: _____

Any system extensions that have not
   been documented previously: _____

Standpipe system

Type of system: _____

Arrangement of system: _____

Fire department connection
   accessible and maintained: _____

Are any pressure regulating devices used: _____

   Are they properly set: _____

   Are they properly maintained: _____

Occupant hose serviceable: _____

System properly tested and maintained: _____

Fire pump

Type and size of pump: _____

Suction supply adequate and
   properly maintained: _____

Valves open: _____

Power
   Primary: _____

   Secondary: _____

Pump properly tested and maintained: _____

Fire extinguishers

Adequate number and distribution: _____

Appropriate type for hazards: _____

Fire extinguishers properly
   tested and maintained: _____

Special hazard system
Type of system: _____
Hazard protected: _____
System appropriate and adequate
   for the hazard: _____
System properly tested and maintained: _____

Exit doors
Adequate number: _____
Adequate size: _____
Correct door, hardware, and swing: _____
Door, frame, and hardware serviceable: _____

Corridors
Adequate width: _____
Arrangement (length, dead ends,
   smoke barriers, and so on): _____
Integrity of walls and doors: _____

Fire doors
Rating appropriate for location: _____
Door, frame, and hardware serviceable: _____
Closing and latching devices operational: _____

Exit illumination
Adequate lighting levels in all exits:_____
Signs illuminated: _____
Emergency power system
   maintained and tested: _____

Stairways
Width adequate: _____
Integrity of walls and doors: _____
Guardrails: _____
Handrails provided and serviceable: _____
Discharge arrangement adequate
   and clear: _____

HVAC systems
Type and arrangement of system proper: _____
Fuel properly arranged: _____
Dampers and detectors in ducts
   properly arranged and maintained: _____
Automatic controls working properly: _____
System properly maintained: _____

Electrical system
Circuit protection and wiring adequate: _____
Temporary wiring and extension cords limited: _____
Grounding of circuits and machinery maintained: _____
Meter and panel board clear and maintained: _____

Housekeeping
Storage properly arranged: _____
Rubbish picked up and stored properly: _____
Smoking controlled: _____
Spills of flammable or combustible liquids
   properly cleaned up: _____
Weeds and rubbish controlled on exterior: _____
Adequate general maintenance: _____

Flammable or combustible liquids
Type and amount: _____
Properly stored and handled: _____

Other Items:

Notes by: _____
Date: _____

CHAPTER 3

Building Construction

*T*he type of construction and the materials used in a building influence the building's life safety and fire protection requirements. As an inspector, you have a major responsibility in determining that those requirements are met at all times. In order to discharge that responsibility, you must know the functions of the various structural elements of a building and understand the significant characteristics of the various construction types.

Space in this manual is limited. The 17th edition of the Fire Protection Handbook, and the 3rd edition of Building Construction for the Fire Service, by F. Brannigan, both published by NFPA, contain significant additional information.

Structural Elements

In general, the structural components of a building can be divided into two groups: those elements that support the structure, or its framing members, and those that enclose the working, storage, and living spaces—that is, its walls, floors, ceilings, and roofs.

Framing Members

The framing members form the skeleton of a building, which supports the building and everything attached to it. This is known as the "dead load." The frame also supports the "live load," or the building's contents, load," or the building's contents, its occupants, and the forces of earthquake, wind, snow, ice, and water.

The structural frame is supported on footings, which transfer the weight of the building to the earth below. Columns or load-bearing walls are located on top of these footings and support the floor or floors above and the roof.The failure of a column or columns from fire exposure is critical because it can result in the collapse of thebuilding.

Trusses, beams, girders, joists, and rafters are all horizontal structural members that support a ceiling, floor, or roof. In the past, trusses were used only when a large, open area was needed, as they are in a gymnasium or an exhibition hall. In recent years, however, they have been used widely because they save on weight and labor at the job site.

Trusses can be constructed of steel, wood, wood and steel, or concrete, and are composed of a series of triangles connected together to span large distances and to transmit the load to the building's columns or walls. Because of their relatively light weight and multiple connections, trusses may fail early in a fire.

A beam is a relatively large horizontal structural member capable of spanning long distances and into which other members, such as joists, can be framed. If a beam is supported only at its ends, it usually is called a "simple span beam." If it spans three or more supports, it is a "continuous span beam."

A girder is a large beam, generally one into which other beams are framed.

A joist is one of a series of smaller, parallel members used to directly support either the floor, in which case they are called floor joists, or the ceiling, where they are ceiling joists. Joists generally are framed into beams or load-bearing walls.

A rafter is similar to a joist except that it supports the roof. Rafters are closely spaced and usually are framed into beams or load-bearing walls.

Walls

Walls serve a variety of functions and can be classified as bearing, nonbearing, common or party, shear, or fire walls.

A bearing wall supports more than its own weight, such as a floor or roof, while a nonbearing wall supports only its own weight.

A common, or party, wall is a single wall that is common to two separate buildings. In some cases, the wood floor joists of both buildings that share a common wall are placed in the same opening, providing a hidden path for fire to spread.

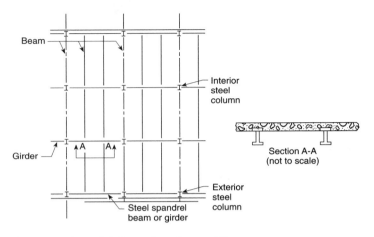

Figure 3-1. A partial floor plan of a steel-frame structure.

A shear wall acts to brace a portion of a building against the forces of the wind or an earthquake. It resists, by its stiffness, the forces applied parallel to its length.

Finally, a fire wall is used to divide a building or buildings or to isolate a special hazard within a building, such as a flammable liquids storage area. Openings in these walls are protected with automatic closing devices. Fire walls usually range in fire-resistance rating from 1 to 4 hours, although some rate as low as 30 or 45 minutes. They also vary in strength and stability. Fire walls should remain structurally sound and should not permit the spread of fire through, under, over, or around the wall, even if the structure on one side of it burns out and collapses. The efficiency of a fire wall depends on its own integrity and on the reliability of its closing devices.

The term "fire wall" is currently the subject of much debate. The actual term "fire wall" generally is reserved for fire-resistance rated walls of higher fire-resistance, usually 2, 3, or 4 hours, that are structurely independent. "Fire barriers" have fire-resistance ratings ranging from 20 minutes on up, but usually they are not structurally independent. "Smoke barriers" may or may not have a fire-resistance rating, but are primarily intended to restrict the passage of smoke. Other terms commonly used are "building separation walls," "area separation walls," "fire partitions," and "occupancy separation walls."

A veneered wall consists of a single wythe, or thickness, of brick facing attached to a backing; the two materials are not bonded together to act as a unit under load. These walls may look like fire walls from the outside. The backing usually is wood, but it may be steel, concrete, or masonry. If the backing wall is affected by fire, the veneer is likely to collapse. In any case, the entire wall must be rebuilt. The veneer cannot be saved.

Floor/Ceiling Assemblies

Fire safety in buildings is influenced by the floor/ceiling assemblies that must support the live load placed on them. Some assemblies have been tested in accordance with nationally recognized standards and have received a specific fire-resistance rating. This rating does not mean that they are impervious to fire, however. For example, rated steel floor assemblies easily can be made ineffective by removing ceiling tiles. The installed assembly should be identical to the assembly listed for maximum benefit. Rated assemblies of wood construction are tested only against fire from below when, in fact, fire can enter an assembly without hindrance either laterally or from above. When a floor/ceiling or roof/ceiling assembly is given a fire-resistance rating it is a rating for the total assembly, not the ceiling itself.

Other assemblies may be combustible in themselves and may contain concealed spaces that are difficult to access and that allow for rapid fire spread. The space above a ceiling also can contain combustible materials, or it may be used as part of the building's air-handling system.

Roofs

Roofing assemblies are constructed of a combination of materials and in a variety of configurations. Basically, a roof consists of supports, such as beams or rafters; a deck; insulation; and a covering. The live load on the roof—snow, ice, or water—is carried by the roof deck and is transmitted along rafters and beams to the columns, footings, and soil below. Typical roof deck materials are concrete, gypsum, steel, and wood.

Insulation generally is adhered or mechanically fastened to the top of the roof deck and is covered on top by a roof covering that provides weatherproofing. Roof coverings can be prepared, built-up, or single-ply membranes. Examples of fire-resistive coverings are fire-retardant-treated wood shingles, brick, concrete, tile, and slate. Untreated wood shingles have been used in the past but are now prohibited in many communities because they ignite readily and can produce flying brands, which may ignite other combustibles.

A built-up roof membrane typically consists of three to five layers, known as "plies," of roof membrane attached to the roof deck or insulation and to each other at the job site using hot asphalt or some other adhesive to secure the layers. Built-up roofs laid directly on metal decking present a special fire problem.

Single-ply roof membranes generally consist of flexible, water-resistant sheets of a variety of plastic- or rubber-based products. These membranes, which typically are applied over insulation, usually are attached with mechanical fasteners, full adhesion, or a combination of the two, or they are ballasted with large gravel or paving blocks.

Elastomeric coatings such as hypalon, acrylic, silicone, and so on also are used as roof coverings over urethane foam insulation, which is sprayed in place on top of the roof. Single-ply roofs present certain hazards both in construction and during a fire in the building.

Torch-applied roof systems are bituminous roofing systems that are heated with a torch, which melts the asphalt that saturates the membrane. The membrane is then immediately secured to the substrate, usually insulation, below.

Nationally recognized standards exist to evaluate roof assemblies for combustibility, surface burning over the top surface, wind resistance, and hail resistance.

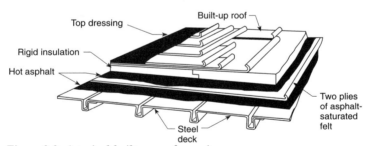

Figure 3-2. A typical built-up roof covering.

See Chapter 2 of *Building Construction for the Fire Service* and Section 7 of the *Fire Protection Handbook* for additional information on structural elements.

Types of Construction

There are five fundamental construction types. Type I is fire-resistive construction. Type II is noncombustible. Type III is exterior-protected combustible (formerly known as ordinary). Type IV is heavy timber. And Type V is wood frame construction. These classifications are not hard and fast, and many buildings depart from the characteristics given here. The specific definitions of each type and a numerical system for defining their required fire resistance may be found in NFPA 220, *Standard on Types of Building Construction.* Not all codes use the same definitions.

Type I, or Fire-Resistive, Construction

Type I construction—the use of the term "fire-resistive construction" is not encouraged—is the preferred type of construction due to its on combustibility and its ability to remain structurally sound during a fire. This type of construction contains structural members that are of non-combustible or limited combustible[1] material and have a high fire-resistance rating, generally 2 to 4 hours. There are two subtypes of Type I construction; the basic difference between them is the level of fire protection specified for the structural frame. Monolithic reinforced concrete construction, precast concrete construction, and protected steel-frame construction all qualify as fire-resistive when designed, constructed, and maintained properly.

Only noncombustible materials are permitted for the structural elements of a building, but the use of some combustible materials for some elements is permitted for practical reasons. These combustible materials, which include roof coverings, some types of insulating materials, and limited amounts of wood for interior finish and flooring, do not add significantly to the fire hazard when properly regulated. However, the use of some combustibles, such as wood or other paneling, may not be adequately regulated. For example, paneling is sometimes added by a tenant without the knowledge of the building or fire departments. Extensive wood paneling, which is often found in ornate offices, club rooms, and restaurants, may be mounted on furring strips, which creates a hidden

---

[1]See NFPA 220, *Standard on Types of Building Construction*, or *Building Construction for the Fire Service*, p. 41, for a definition of limited combustibility.

void. And heavy decorative wood planking on ceilings may not be secured by anchors that are resistant to fire failure.

Type I construction is concerned principally with structural stability and with limiting the spread of fire by physical barriers. By itself, it does not limit the spread of toxic smoke, which has caused many deaths in Type I buildings. Nor does it guarantee limited property damage. The direct and indirect losses suffered in recent fires in typical high-rise, Type I office buildings are staggering, and the effort required to control such fires manually have overwhelmed the strongest fire department.

In 1975, *The Bulletin of The Society of Fire Protection Engineers* warned that the building codes had not anticipated modern fire loads. Thus, every effort should be made to provide automatic sprinkler protection for Type I buildings that have high fire loads of material and equipment with a high rate of heat release, particularly if there is serious risk to life. The argument that the cost of retrofitting sprinklers is excessive might be countered by making a distinction between the cost of installing the **necessary** system and the often greater cost of hiding the piping, an **aesthetic** cost which is the option of the building owner and is not required for life safety.

Type II, or Noncombustible, Construction

The materials that make up buildings classified as Type II construction do not contribute to the development or spread of fire. This classification consists of noncombustible materials that do not meet the requirements of Type I construction. Typical of this class of construction are metal-framed, metal-clad buildings and concrete-block buildings with metal deck roofs supported by unprotected open-web steel joists.

A serious disadvantage of unprotected noncombustible construction is its inability to withstand fire temperatures for short periods without being damaged or failing structurally. Such construction should only be used where the anticipated fire severity is low or where fire suppression agents and equipment are available to deal successfully with the most severe fire that could be expected to occur.

It should be noted here that the term "noncombustible" must not be taken literally. Many noncombustible buildings contain substantial combustible elements, such as combustible metal deck roofs, balconies, mansards, and so on.

Type III, or Exterior Protected, Combustible Construction

Type III construction, formerly known as "ordinary construction," is widely used for mercantile buildings, schools, churches, motels, and apartment houses. In this type of construction, the exterior bearing walls and bearing portions of exterior walls consist of noncombustible or limited-combustible materials, such as brick, concrete, or reinforced concrete. They carry hourly fire-resistance ratings, and they exhibit stability when exposed to fire. Nonbearing exterior walls are also made of noncombustible or limited-combustible materials. To restrict the potential for conflagration, some cities enforce so called "fire limits," within which all structures must have masonry exterior walls.

The floors, roofs, and interior framing of buildings of Type III construction are made entirely or partly of wood but in smaller dimensions than are required for heavy timber construction. Unprotected steel also is used in conjunction with wood structural members and is quite common in newer buildings.

Floor joists in this type of construction are much closer together than are the floor beams in heavy timber construction, thus creating more channels beneath the floors. Sheathing the wall and floor framing with gypsum wallboard to provide them with some fire protection also will create concealed wall and ceiling spaces in which fire might originate or through which fire might spread. Firestopping thus becomes an important factor in a building's ability to resist the spread of fire.

In industrial occupancies or other buildings where appearance is not a factor, one might encounter open joist construction. Although the absence of sheathing increases the area of exposed wood, fighting fires in joist channels becomes easier, provided the involved channels are accessible to fire fighters.

Older buildings of Type III construction often have wood or steel truss roofs, while newer buildings may have truss roofs and floors. Truss floors provide voids that are interconnected from floor to floor through utility channels. These voids may provide a path over which fire may spread rapidly throughout the building.

Many Type III buildings have been restored and rehabilitated, which may create additional fire protection problems. Typically, new, lower ceilings create huge voids between themselves and the floor joists above them. In addition, unprotected steel is often used to replace deteriorated wood interior supports, and mercantile and office live loads may be carried without proper reinforcement on structures that were originally designed as residences.

Type IV, or Heavy Timber, Construction

Heavy timber construction in the United States is typified by the textile mills built in New England during the nineteenth century. One of the more desirable characteristics of this type of construction is that it will resist structural collapse better than other forms and materials of construction. In addition, the surface char that develops on the burning timbers acts as insulation and slows heat penetration into the timbers.

To qualify as heavy timber, or Type IV, construction, a building must meet several requirements. First, the bearing walls and the bearing portions of walls must be of noncombustible materials, have a fire-resistance rating of 2 hours or more, and remain stable when exposed to fire. All exterior walls, bearing and nonbearing, must be made of noncombustible materials.

Floors and roofs must be built of wood, generally without concealed spaces. Where concealed spaces are permitted, they must be closed with tightly fitting wooden covers.

In order to qualify as heavy timber construction, columns, beams, girders, and roof deck planks must have specified minimum dimensions. Structural components of specified sizes made of materials other than wood must have a fire-resistance rating of at least 1 hour.

There have been a number of major fires in heavy timber structures that demanded huge commitments of fire suppression forces and stripped large areas of normal fire service. This record clearly demonstrates that complete, adequate automatic sprinkler protection is the only fire suppression method that is effective in these structures once they become involved in fire. The "slow burning" characteristic of this type of construction is of value only as long as the fire department can maintain an offensive operation. When the fire suppression forces are forced to withdraw and to operate defensively, the huge amount of fuel available even in an empty structure cannot be controlled until most of it has been consumed.

In modern heavy timber construction glued, laminated timbers are used. Timbers such as this that conform to the specifications of the American Forest Products Association have performed in a manner similar to that of solid beams of a similar size. Unfortunately, glued, laminated timbers are supported in many cases on unprotected steel columns. Buildings in which this is the case cannot be considered to be Type IV construction.

Type V, or Wood Frame, Construction

Construction in which the exterior walls are principally or entirely made of wood or some other combustible materials and that does not qualify as Type III or Type IV is known as "wood frame" or simply "frame" construction.

In this type of construction, walls and partitions typically are framed with 2- by 4-inch wood studs attached to wood sills and plates. Wood boards, plywood sheets, various composition boards, or foamed plastic are then nailed to the studs. Over this underlayment is placed a layer of building paper, then the finishing material. The exterior wall covering can be any one of a variety of materials, including wood or cement-asbestos shingles; clapboards of wood, plastic, or metal; matched boards; brick veneer; sheet metal cladding; stucco; and cement-asbestos corrugated sheets.

A chief disadvantage of wood frame construction is that it necessarily creates hidden combustible voids through which toxic gases and fire can travel undetected. The movement of fire through these voids can be slowed or stopped by firestopping, but it is very difficult to provide the complete barrier necessary to stop the flow of heated gases moving under pressure. A single gap can render the firestopping useless, something that many who build or maintain buildings do not understand. And even when it is well installed, firestopping is often compromised by the passage of utilities through it. In addition, there are no standards for firestopping. Thin plywood or gypsum board just "buttered" into place without support might be adequate to stop ordinary drafts, but they do not appear to present any barrier to a serous fire. Solid pieces of dimension lumber cut to a tight fit are probably the best material to use.

The recent introduction of trusses and wooden I-beams as floor joists has made a tremendous change in the fire protection situation in this type of construction. By their nature, sawn joists provide a firestop at each joist. Trusses, however, provide a continuous void, and the thin plywood webs of wooden I-beams are allowed to contain sizable holes to permit the passage of metal or plastic heat ducts. Even if firestopping is provided at specified boundaries, the entire bounded area is subject to early collapse.

While some work is being undertaken to mitigate the collapse potential of wood trusses during a fire, the hazard of the void, as a means of extending fire and as a reservoir of explosive and toxic carbon monoxide gas, remains.

Bibliography

Brannigan, F. L., *Building Construction for the Fire Service,* 3rd edition, National Fire Protection Association, Quincy, MA, 1992.

Cote, A. E., ed., *Fire Protection Handbook,* 17th edition, National Fire Protection Association, Quincy, MA, 1991. Section 6, Chapter 2 provides a detailed description of the standard types of building construction. Section 6, Chapter 3 discusses structural raming elements and describes the various floor, wall, and roof assemblies used in building construction.

Fire Resistance Directory, Underwriters Laboratories, Inc., Northbrook, IL. Issued annually. Contains hourly fire-resistance ratings for beams and columns, as well as floor, roof, wall, and partition assemblies that have been subjected to standard fire tests.

Building Materials Directory, Underwriters Laboratories, Inc., Northbrook, IL. Issued annually. A listing of building materials and hardware that have been subjected to fire tests and, as a result, have been found suitable for use in building construction.

NFPA Codes, Standards, and Recommended Practices

NFPA 203, *Guideline on Roof Coverings and Roof Deck Constructions.* Provides general information about roof coverings and their fire characteristics.

NFPA 220, *Standard on Types of Building Construction.* Specifies types of building construction, including "limited combustible" and "noncombustible" building construction materials.

NFPA 241, *Standard for Safeguarding Construction, Alteration, and Demolition Operations.* Covers fire safety procedures during the erection, alteration, or demolition of buildings.

NFPA 251, *Standard Methods of Fire Tests of Building Construction and Materials.* Specifies methods for determining the fire-resistive abilities of building members and assemblies.

NFPA 255, *Standard Method of Test of Surface Burning Characteristics of Building Materials.* Guidelines for determining the comparative flame-spread rate and smoke density of building materials.

NFPA 256, *Standard Methods of Fire Tests of Roof Coverings.* Methods for measuring relative fire characteristics of roof coverings when fire originates outside a building.

NFPA 703, *Standard for Fire Retardant Impregnated Wood and Fire Retardant Coatings for Building Materials.* Criteria for defining and identifying certain types of wood that have undergone pressure impregnation or surface-coating processes to retard flame spread.

CHAPTER 4

Construction, Alteration, and Demolition Operations

*A*s a fire inspector, you frequently will be faced with hazards introduced during construction, alteration, and demolition operations. Most buildings are more vulnerable to fire at these times than at any other because the amount of combustibles and hazardous materials present usually is greater than usual, the number of potential ignition sources often is greater than usual, and the facility's fire protection systems may be impaired or even inoperative. Many of the comments to follow could apply to two or even all three of these operations.

Construction

Construction projects progress more rapidly in areas important to fire protection in the latter stages than they do in the early stages. Thus, they should be inspected more frequently after framing is underway. However, planning and scheduling water supplies for fire control during construction must be reviewed during the planning and permit stages so that the various installations needed, such as access roads, water mains, temporary water storage, sprinkler systems, hydrants, standpipes for multistory buildings, hand extinguishers for contractors and watch services, and fire walls, are properly planned and physically in place when needed. Making sure that fire protection during construction is clearly laid out in the plans and specifications or included in the permit conditions can prevent many problems, ranging from disagreements to major fire loss during construction. The building owner or contractor should appoint one individual to oversee all fire protection duties.

Site Preparation

In large projects, site preparation should include not only the removal of vegetation and combustible debris from the site, but also the appropriate layout of the contractors' temporary buildings, trailers, and material storage yards so that they will be neither a fire exposure to new construction nor obstruct access routes for fire fighters and their equipment. Most codes contain provisions that can be invoked to cover problem areas, but such after-the-fact solutions are seldom as satisfactory as planned layouts.

Roadways with an all-weather driving surface should be provided for fire apparatus. They should be at least 20 feet wide and have at least 13 feet 6 inches of clearance.

If permanent water mains and hydrants cannot be installed during the site preparation and foundation phases of the project, temporary water supplies such as on-site tanks or tank trailers, temporary or surface mains, and pumps may have to be included in the project. Aboveground swimming pools make excellent temporary water storage and can be moved easily as needed. It is important that these items, which could involve substantial cost, be included in the contracts. Temporary water supplies must be properly located to protect against damage from construction equipment or activities, and they should be designed with protection against freezing or other site-specific perils.

If special equipment, such as pumps or normally closed lines, are present, guards or other persons on site 24 hours per day must know how to operate it. This means knowing not only how to start a pump but how to prime it and understanding which valves need to be kept opened or closed.

Temporary Structures

Nearly all temporary structures associated with construction projects are made of combustible construction, whether they have a metal or plywood skin or ride on trailer wheels or skids. They will burn rapidly and can be the source of a major loss.

In the worst situation, a temporary structure, such as a job office, a tool or supply shed, a warming or locker room, or a carpenter or paint shop, is set up within the structure under construction. A fire in such a temporary structure will immediately involve the major structure. Because this approach is favored by contractors for ease of travel, security, economy, and weather protection, it can become the norm unless the regulatory agencies resist it. The situation is more difficult to handle at an urban site, where space in the streets is limited or nearby buildings must be rented at significant cost. If space is available, the temporary units should be separated by 30 or more feet from the main building and from each other to minimize the loss potential from a "shack" fire. However, this amount of space can easily require many acres, so a compromise generally is necessary, depending on the hazard, value, protection, and construction features of both the temporary and permanent structures.

Temporary enclosures of fabric or plastic often are used to protect workers and construction operations from the weather until the building is enclosed. If fabric is used, the inspector should make sure that it is fire-retardant-treated tarpaulin. If plastic is used, it should be flame-resistant and pass the large-scale test noted in NFPA 701, *Standard Methods of Fire Tests for Flame-Resistant Textiles and Films*. In either case, the material should be fastened securely to a rigid steel or wood frame to prevent it from coming in contact with an ignition source, such as a temporary heater. The tarpaulin or plastic sheet should be anchored properly so that it cannot be torn by the wind.

Process Hazards

While some process hazard is inherent in such job-site shops as carpenter, welding, pipe, and paint facilities, you, the inspector, can encourage segregation of incompatible uses, such as carpentry and welding, and discourage the accumulation of flammable liquid in paint, fuel, and lubrication areas. Substandard heating appliances, stovepipes, bonfires, and substandard liquid- or gas-fuel-handling systems are proven fire hazards and should not be tolerated.

If local fire codes do not provide the authority to cope with these problems, work toward the adoption of stronger codes. NFPA codes and standards that provide specific fire safety criteria addressing specific hazards are available to you (see Bibliography).

Housekeeping

Prompt removal of trash from a construction or remodeling site is critical to fire safety. Because it is an overhead cost to the contractor, however, you, the inspector, must often take a firm stand to ensure reasonable compliance. If trash chutes are used, they should be located on the outside of the building. They should be of noncombustible construction and as straight as possible to prevent debris from piling up inside.

Storage of new material on site can present both a fire exposure and an obstruction to emergency access. To prevent this from happening, large amounts of combustible materials should be well separated from the building. As an inspector, you can have considerable influence on material storage and delivery practices.

Theft and Vandalism

While there is no sure prevention measure, a clean job site that is fenced, secured, lighted where needed, and attended by guards is much less likely to experience a fire started by a thief or vandal. Again, a realistic balance of cost and exposure is necessary.

Other Hazards

Recently, there has been a dramatic increase in both the number and size of engine-driven fork lifts, crew lifts, excavators, and so on, all of which must be refueled on site and all of which contain hot exhaust systems capable of igniting trash, spilled fuel, or flapping weather enclosures. The person handling job-site safety for the general contractor should enforce and require in writing job-site safety rules on fuel storage and handling, equipment shutdown during fueling, and fire extinguisher availability.

A fuel dump arrangement and fuel handling rules also must be designed for the site. Fuel should be stored separately from the building under construction and from major temporary structures, and indoor fueling should be restricted to devices that cannot be moved readily. Only those fueling systems that minimize accidental spills, such as safety cans, automatic shut-off nozzles, and approved pump systems, should be used, and a sizable hand extinguisher with a rating of at least 40 B-C should be provided at the fueling site.

Further discussion of fuel storage and handling can be found in Chapter 35 of this book and in NFPA 395, *Standard for the Storage of Flammable and Combustible Liquids at Farms and Isolated Sites.*

Open-flame and spark-producing equipment must be strictly controlled. Those who operate this equipment, from cutting torches and arc welders to soldering, grinding, or roofing fusion machines, generally seem to feel that they do their jobs safely and that the problems lie either with apprentices or some other trade. Be this as it may, the basics of fire prevention in these areas are simple: Combustibles in or below work areas must be controlled, the equipment used must have the proper safety controls, a fire watch must be used, extinguishers and hoses must be handy, and horseplay must be limited. Still, work fires in construction projects are frequent. Further discussion of hot work hazards and controls can be found in NFPA 51, *Standard for the Design and Installation of Oxygen-Fuel Gas Systems for Welding, Cutting, and Allied Processes;* NFPA 51B, *Standard for Fire Prevention in Use of Cutting and Welding Processes;* and NFPA 241, *Standard for Safeguarding Construction, Alteration, and Demolition Operations.*

Roofing materials, whether the older hot-mopped felt, tar, and gravel system, the torch-applied modified bitumen, or the cold-applied cut back asphalt system, all have a common problem: Much of the work is done with flammable materials that are heated near or above their flash points. Workers careless with torches, inaccurate or nonexistant controls for asphalt pots, punklike action of fiber insulation, or cigarette smoking are all potential sources of ignition. Do not allow torches to be used near areas in which combustible dusts or oils may accumulate, such as exhaust hoods. Propane tanks on which frost has built up should not be heated with the torch flame. Instead, a larger tank should be recommended. Strict controls are necessary on the location and temperature control for asphalt pots. The pots should never be placed on the roof or under roofs or canopies, and their temperature controls must be automatic and working properly.

NFPA 241 contains guidelines for fire-safe roofing operations. For additional information refer to Factory Mutual Engineering and Research Corporation, *Technical Advisory Bulletin 1-29, Safeguarding Torch-Applied Roof Installations.*

Needless to say, application and kettle areas must have a sizable (2-A : 20-B:C) hand extinguisher within 30 feet—20 feet for torch-applied equipment—of the immediate work area because a roofing fire can be just as hot and rapid as any flammable liquid fire. Where practical, charged hose lines should be available. If attempts to extinguish a kettle fire with hand extinguishers are unsuccessful, water from a hose line must be applied in a fine spray due to the potential frothing action of hot asphalt. Roofing mops soaked with tar have been known to ignite spontaneously and cause fires. Used mops should not be left indoors or near ignition sources or combustible materials. Rather, they should be "spun" or cleaned thoroughly and safely stored.

Fire Protection

When the code requires that a building have standpipes, they should be installed on a floor-by-floor basis. The standpipe can be either temporary or permanent (and rigged as a dry standpipe in cold climates) until the building is enclosed. In most cases, the fire department connection must be temporary because the permanent location will not be completed and might not be accessible during much of the construction. Regardless of the building, hand extinguishers must be provided in rating and spacing suitable to the construction activity and in accordance with NFPA 10, *Standard for Portable Fire Extinguishers.*

Sprinklers should be put into service and fire walls should be built as soon as possible after the building shell is finished. Only steel or limited amounts of combustible formwork, scaffolding, or shoring are acceptable in unsprinklered areas.

Alterations and Additions

More and more older buildings are being altered or renovated, some to preserve the architecture of an age gone by. As older buildings are rehabilitated, every effort should be made to bring them into compliance with present-day building and fire codes. However, this is not always possible. In such cases, equivalent protective measures might be acceptable in lieu of meeting certain code requirements. These equivalencies might involve the installation of automatic sprinkler protection, smoke detection systems, and smoke control features. Your responsibility as a fire inspector is to police those protection systems as you would those in a new building.

Sometimes renovations have to be made while a building is partially occupied. It is extremely important to life safety that exits for occupants are properly maintained. It is your job to make sure that the exits are accessible and have been properly identified. In addition to exits for occupants, sufficient exits should be provided for construction workers in the area under renovation. You should be just as diligent in inspecting these exits as you are in inspecting the public exits.

If a building addition blocks an existing exit, an alternate means of egress must be provided You must inspect the alternate route as part of your normal procedure. The exit should be free of debris or stored materials. It should be properly identified and lighted. The exit discharge should be clear of parked vehicles and other objects.

If the alterations involve hot work, such as cutting, welding, and heating, a permit system should be used; for further information see NFPA 51B. Whenever practical, combustibles should be removed from at least 35 feet in all directions. If this cannot be done, you should recommend covering combustibles with a fire-resistant tarp, sweeping up combustible dusts, and wetting down wood floors. A fire watch provided with extinguishers or hoses should be assigned to the area for at least 30 minutes after the work has been finished; this should be extended to 60 minutes in torch-applied roof installations.

Demolition

Demolition operations have many of the attendant hazards of construction operations, as well as a few others. The hazards of cutting torches, flammable liquids, and trash accumulations are as common in demolition operations as they are in construction operations.

Before demolition begins, gas pipes should be turned off and capped outside the building. Explosives should be stored and used in accordance with NFPA 495, *Explosive Materials Code.*

Early in a demolition project, flammable liquids and combustible oils should be drained from tanks and machinery and immediately removed from the building. The removal of residue and sludge deposits also is important, especially in areas where cutting torches are used. Torches should not be used to cut through walls, floors, ceilings, or roofs containing combustible materials.

Fixed fire protection systems and fire walls should be maintained for as long as possible. Sprinkler and standpipe systems should be modified so they can be dismantled floor by floor as demolition progresses downward from the top floor or system by system in large one-story buildings. This will preserve protection on the adjacent floors. Either type of protection can be converted readily from a wet-pipe system to a dry-pipe system, if minimal heat (40°F) cannot be maintained at remote parts of the building.

Generally, chutes are provided to carry demolition rubble and debris from the upper floors to trucks or mobile trash receptacles below. These should be constructed as described under "Housekeeping." The use of inside chutes, which would necessitate cutting holes in the floor thereby creating an unprotected vertical opening through which fire could spread rapidly from floor to floor, should be discouraged.

Bibliography

"Collapse of the Hotel Vendome, Nine Fire Fighters Killed, Boston, Massachusetts," *Fire Journal,* Vol. 67, No. 1 (Jan. 1973), pp. 34–41. This is an account of the collapse of an old Boston hotel during rehabilitation operations.

Cote, A. E., ed., *Fire Protection Handbook*, 17th edition, National Fire Protection Association, Quincy, MA, 1991. Section 6, Chapter 14 discusses the fire hazards of construction, alteration, and demolition of buildings.

Factory Mutual Engineering and Research Corporation, *Technical Advisory Bulletin 1–29, Safeguarding Torch-Applied Roof Installations.*

Herbstman, Donald, "Fire Protection During Construction," *Fire Journal,* Vol. 64, No. 1 (Jan. 1970), pp. 29–32, 89. This describes the procedures, practices, and equipment used to protect the World Trade Center in New York during its construction.

Sharry, John A., "Group Fire Indianapolis, Indiana," *Fire Journal,* Vol. 68, No. 4 (July 1974), pp. 13–16. A fire originating on the top floor quickly spread throughout a partially demolished building and involved four other buildings.

NFPA Codes, Standards, and Recommended Practices

NFPA 10, *Standard for Portable Fire Extinguishers.* Covers the minimum requirements for selecting, installing, inspecting, maintaining, and hydrostatically testing portable extinguishing equipment.

NFPA 30, *Flammable and Combustible Liquids Code.* Covers safe storage and handling requirements, including bulk storage in tanks, piping systems and valves, warehousing of containers, incidental use, and operations.

NFPA 51, *Standard for the Design and Installation of Oxygen-Fuel Gas Systems for Welding, Cutting, and Allied Processes.* Applies to acetylene and oxygen cylinder storage and use. Covers MAP, other stable gases, and acetylene generation.

NFPA 51B, *Standard for Fire Prevention in Use of Cutting and Welding Processes.* Covers practices and precautions for cutting and welding processes involving electric arcs and oxy-fuel gas flames.

NFPA 54, *National Fuel Gas Code.* Covers safety procedures regarding the installation of fuel gas piping systems, fuel gas utilization equipment, and related accessories.

NFPA 58, *Standard for the Storage and Handling of Liquefied Petroleum Gases.* Covers safety procedures regarding the shipping, storage, and installation of liquefied petroleum gas equipment.

NFPA 241, *Standard for Safeguarding Construction, Alteration, and Demolition Operations.* Covers fire safety procedures during the erection, alteration, or demolition of buildings.

NFPA 395, *Standard for the Storage of Flammable and Combustible Liquids at Farms and Isolated Sites.* Covers storage of hazardous materials in rural areas, where isolation from other structures makes it unnecessary to adhere to the more rigid requirements of NFPA 30.

NFPA 495, *Explosive Materials Code.* Provides guidance on the storage and use of explosive materials, which will be helpful to workers in the demolition and construction industry.

NFPA 701, *Standard Methods of Fire Tests for Flame-Resistant Textiles and Films.* Covers fire test criteria for plastic films used for temporary enclosures at construction, alteration, or demolition sites.

. . . .

CHAPTER 5

Protection of Openings in Fire Barriers

*O*ne method of limiting the spread of fire in a structure is to divide the interior into compartments using fire barriers and rated floor/ceiling assemblies. However, fire barriers can be expected to delay the spread of fire from the room or area of origin to other parts of the structure only if they are constructed and maintained properly and if the openings in them are properly protected.

The Hazard

It is not uncommon for heated, unburned pyrolysis products to flow out of the area of initial involvement, mix with air, and ignite. Such flame extension can even occur over noncombustible surfaces. Flames can heat interior finish materials to the point at which they release pyrolysis products of their own, which also ignite and contribute to the intensity of the extending flame.

Properly maintained protection in fire barrier openings is essential to contain a fire until manual fire suppression operations are begun. Part of your responsibility as an inspector, therefore, is to determine that these openings are properly protected and that nothing has been done to nullify their protection.

Forms of Protection

A variety of methods for protecting openings in fire barriers is available. The method selected will depend on the type, function, and configuration of the opening. Typical protection measures include firestopping, fire-resistive construction, fire doors, and wired glass, although special problems may require other forms of protection.

Vertical Openings

Unprotected openings in floors and ceilings, referred to as vertical openings, may permit the extension of fire from one floor to another.

Floor/Ceiling Penetrations

Unsealed gaps created when holes are made through floor/ceiling assemblies for routing cables, conduits, or pipes permit the passage of fire and smoke from floor to floor. One method used to seal these gaps involves modular devices sized for the pipe, conduit, or cable that contain an organic compound that expands when heated to seal the penetration. Other methods of sealing such penetrations include the use of foamed-in-place fire-resistant elastomers, various caulking materials, and poured- or troweled-in-place compounds. In addition, there are bags of fire-resistant material that can be placed around penetrating pipes, cable, or conduit. When exposed to fire, these bags expand and fuse to prevent the passage of the fire products.

Many of these materials have been tested and listed or approved, and all can provide the required protection if they are properly installed and maintained.

The penetrating objects should be supported well enough to keep them from placing any mechanical stress on the seal that could pull the sealant from the opening. Where "temporary" routing of utilities or control cables is a fairly common occurrence, workers tend to neglect to seal the gaps. Be alert for such conditions. Often, utility lines are hidden in closets or above drop ceilings and are not obvious during a casual visual inspection. Learn the locations of these concealed, but accessible, fire-barrier penetrations so that you do not overlook them during the inspection process.

Stair Enclosures, Shafts, and Chutes

Certain vertical openings cannot be sealed because their functions require that they communicate between floors. Examples include stair enclosures, elevator shafts, utility shafts, and chutes for packages, laundry, or trash. Such openings should be enclosed in fire-resistive construction. Openings in the walls of utility shafts should be protected construction. Openings in the walls of utility shafts should be protected with self-closing fire doors or access doors approved or listed for the purpose. Openings in the walls of stair enclosures and elevator shafts must be protected by rated self- or automatic-closing fire door assemblies.

It is not uncommon for occupants to prop open stair doors for the sake of convenience. Wood blocks, wedges, or pieces of wire or rope near a fire door indicate that the occupants are blocking or holding the fire door open. This, of course, defeats the purpose of a fire door and is a condition that must be corrected immediately. If this situation becomes common and impossible to enforce, you may consider requiring the installation of magnetic hold-open devices with appropriate actuation devices.

Escalators

Holes made in floor/ceiling assemblies to accommodate escalators present a unique protection problem because enclosing them in fire-resistive construction is not practical. However, there are alternative forms of protection. In a fully sprinklered building, NFPA 13, *Standard for the Installation of Sprinkler Systems,* provides a protection of escalators known as the sprinkler-draft curtain method.

Another method relies on a combination of automatic fire-or smoke-detection equipment, an automatic exhaust system, and an automatic water curtain. Another method involves filling the opening with a dense water spray pattern from open, high-velocity water-spray nozzles. The water-spray system is operated automatically by heat or smoke detection and is equipped with manual control valves to minimize water damage. (Details on these systems can be found in the *Life Safety Code Handbook.*) You should examine the control valves in these systems as you would those in other water-spray and sprinkler systems to make sure that they are open.

Another method is to protect the opening with a partial enclosure of fire-resistive construction in a "kiosk" configuration. This enclosure is equipped with self-closing doors. Check that the doors are in operating condition and that the self-closing feature has not been circumvented in any way.

Horizontal Openings

If left unprotected, openings in fire walls and partitions, called "horizontal openings," will permit fire to spread in the horizontal plane throughout the floor of origin. Corridors, in particular, must be protected, not only because they are a path for the horizontal spread of fire, smoke, and toxic gases, but also because they are a part of the means of egress through which the occupants must pass to escape the building.

Fire Door Assemblies

One of the most widely used means of protecting openings in fire-resistive walls is the fire door assembly. Tests conducted by independent testing laboratories determine the suitability of a fire door assembly.

Fire doors are given an hourly rating, and the openings in which they are placed are given an alphabetical letter designation of A, B, C, D, or E, depending on the type and location of the wall. The alphabetical classification of the opening does not apply to the fire door. In practice, however, the distinction between opening classification and door rating is rarely maintained. A 3-hour fire door for use in a Class A opening is commonly called a Class A door.

Listed fire doors must be identified by a label, a listing mark, or a classification mark that is readily visible. Labels or classification marks may be of metal, paper, or plastic, or they may be stamped or diecast into the item. Very large fire doors may not have a listing mark if they exceed the size of the door the testing laboratory can physically test. However, the laboratory may furnish the door with a certificate of inspection that states that it conforms to the same requirements of design, materials, and construction as a rated fire door, even though it has not been subjected to an actual test.

Ratings: Each fire door classification has specific applications. Where a wall separates two buildings or divides a building into two fire areas, the Class A opening might require the use of a 3-hour fire door. Openings in walls enclosing hazardous areas also can be protected with fire doors. Depending on the local codes or ordinances in effect, the fire-resistance rating required for a specific application may vary from those given here.

Doors in openings in exterior walls that might be subjected to severe fire exposure from outside the building and doors protecting openings in 2-hour enclosures of vertical building openings each carry a 1 1/2-hour fire-resistance rating. One-hour stair enclosures are protected by 1-hour fire doors. Rated 3/4-hour fire doors are used to protect openings in the exterior walls of buildings that might be subjected to a light or moderate fire exposure from outside the building. Rated 3/4-hour fire door assemblies are used in some room-to-corridor openings, especially to isolate a hazardous area from the corridor.

Fire doors with 1/2- and 1/3-hour ratings are intended primarily for smoke control. They are used across corridors in which a smoke barrier is required and to protect openings in partitions with fire-resistance ratings of up to 1 hour that are installed between a habitable room and a corridor.

Construction: Several types of construction are used in the manufacture of fire doors.

Composite doors are flush doors made of a manufactured core material with chemically impregnated wood edge banding. They are faced with untreated wood veneer or laminated plastic, or they are encased in steel.

Hollow metal doors are made in flush and panel designs of 20-gauge or heavier steel. Metal-clad or Kalamein® doors are flush or panel-design swinging doors with metal-covered wood cores or stiles and rails and insulated panels covered with 24-gauge or lighter steel. Sheet metal doors are made in corrugated, flush, or panel designs of 22-gauge steel or lighter, while rolling steel doors are fabricated of interlocking steel slats or plate steel.

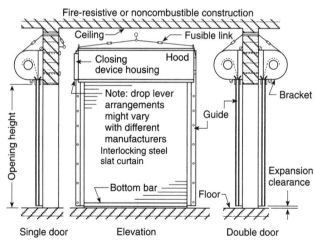

Figure 5-1. Surface-mounted rolling steel doors. Fusible links are required on both sides of wall. Source: Figure B-48, **NFPA 80, Standard for Fire Doors and Fire Windows,** *NFPA, Quincy, MA, 1992.*

Tin-clad doors are of two- or three-ply wood core construction. They are covered with 30-gauge galvanized steel or terne plate with a maximum size of 14 by 20 inches or with 24-gauge galvanized steel sheets with a maximum width of 48 inches.

Curtain-type doors consist of interlocking steel blades or a continuous formed-spring steel curtain installed in a steel frame.

Wood core doors consist of wood, hardboard, or plastic face sheets bonded to a wood block or a wood particle board core material with untreated wood edges.

Special-purpose fire door assemblies called horizontal sliding accordion or folding doors also are available. They are self- or automatic-closing doors, and some of them are power-operated. Under some codes, folding doors are permitted within a means of egress as horizontal exits or in smoke barriers under certain restrictions. Materials used in these types of doors vary.

Door Closing: Fire doors must be self-closing or close automatically in the event of fire. A suitable door holder/release device can be used, provided the automatic-release feature is actuated by a combination of automatic fire detection devices, such as smoke detectors. Generally, automatic release that is accomplished with fusible links is permitted only in limited areas.

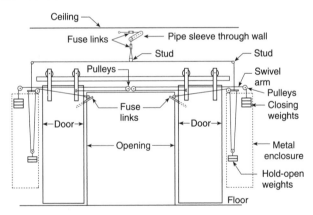

Figure 5-2. Closing devices for center-parting, horizontally sliding doors. Fusible links are required on both sides of wall.
Source: Figure B-38, NFPA 80, Standard for Fire Doors and Fire Windows, NFPA, Quincy, MA, 1992.

Automatic-closing fire doors sometimes are required to begin closing not more than 10 seconds after the release device has actuated. Where applicable, this should be verified because a door holder/release device with an excessive time-delay feature could allow a large volume of smoke to pass through the opening before the door closes.

Maintenance and Inspection: Fire doors that normally are open during working hours should be closed during nonworking hours. Highly combustible material that is likely to produce a flash fire should not be stored near an opening in a fire wall because the fire might spread through the opening before the protective device can operate.

Make sure that fire doors are not obstructed or blocked in any way or intentionally wedged open so that self-closing is not possible.

Should you find that fire doors have been intentionally blocked or wedged, determine the reason for it and take appropriate action. Where doors have been fastened open to improve ventilation, other ventilating means should be provided. Guards or railings should be provided where necessary to prevent damage from material handling equipment. This also discourages employees from piling stock against or near the door. Be sure that the movement of balance weights is free and unobstructed and that fusible links are of the proper temperature rating. See to it that fusible links have not been made inoperative by paint, corrosion, or other external conditions. For example, have wires that would prevent closure even if the links did activate rendered the elements inoperative? Self-closing and automatic-closing fire doors should be tested to ensure that they are operational and that they latch when closed.

Be aware that heat-actuated closing devices are suitable only when property protection is desired and life safety is not being considered.

Tin-clad doors have some special features that require attention. Make sure that the door has proper lap over the opening. The binders are sometimes filled with blocking to make the door easier to open. These blocks must be removed. The door should have chafing strips, which add to its fire resistance. Note the condition of the door. Is the tin covering corroded, torn, or battered? Is there evidence of dry rot? Indications of dry rot include edges caving in and screws pulling out. Tapping the door with a weighted object such as a hammer can give some indication of the extent of the rot damage.

When inspecting any fire door except rolling steel doors, you should perform an operating test to make sure it does not jam or stick and that the hardware is complete and undamaged. Check the automatic-closing mechanism by lifting the counterbalance weight or dropping the suspended weight. When door closers are equipped with a fusible link, the test is limited to general observation of the device. Make sure the fusible link is not corroded or coated with dirt or paint that could interfere with its operation. It is also important to ensure that the link is exposed so heat can reach it. Rolling steel doors should be tested during nonworking hours so that any malfunction that might occur will not interfere with the normal activities on the premises.

Fire Shutters

Fire shutters are used to protect openings in exterior walls. If the potential fire exposure from outside the building is severe, 1 1/2-hour shutters are used. Where the potential fire exposure is moderate or light, 3/4-hour shutters are used. If fire shutters are installed on the outside of the opening, they should be protected against the weather to ensure proper operation. Shutters must be equipped to close automatically in case of fire.

Do not overlook these devices on your inspection tour. Although fire shutters are no longer used to any great extent in new construction, they are still found on older structures.

Wired Glass

Wired glass is used as the glazing material in 3/4-hour fire-resistance-rated windows. Fire windows are designed to protect openings in corridor and room partitions and in exterior walls where the potential exposure is moderate or light. Some fire windows are equipped with automatic closing devices that are actuated by automatic fire detection equipment. When inspecting fire windows, be sure the closing devices are in operating condition.

Wired glass frequently is used as a vision panel in smoke-stop barriers and in fire doors that protect stairway enclosures. While conducting your inspection, be alert for situations in which plain window glass might have been used to replace broken wired glass. However, you should be aware that a recently introduced glazing that does not contain wire has been tested successfully for specific hourly fire rating. Two layers of glazing sandwich a gel-like material, making the glass considerably thicker than other types of conventional glazing. Another fire-rated glazing product is made of a ceramic material and looks like single-thickness plate glass.

Sills

Criteria prohibiting the extension of combustible material through an opening protected by a fire door assembly have been revised. Combustible floor coverings can now extend through openings protected by 1 1/2-, 1-, 3/4-, 1/2-, or 1/3-hour fire door assemblies, as long as the floor covering has at least a Class II interior floor-finish rating and the clearance between the covering and the bottom of the door does not exceed 1/2 inch.

Special Problems

Duct and conveyor systems that penetrate walls, partitions, floors, and ceilings contribute to both the horizontal and vertical spread of fire. Duct systems are discussed in Chapter 9, "Air Conditioning and Ventilating Systems" and Chapter 47, "Venting Systems for Commercial Cooking Equipment," and conveyors are discussed in Chapter 33, "Materials-Handling Systems."

Bibliography

Cote, A. E., ed., *Fire Protection Handbook,* 17th edition, National Fire Protection Association, Quincy, MA, 1991.

Life Safety Code Handbook, 5th edition, National Fire Protection Association, Quincy, MA, 1991.

NFPA Codes, Standards, and Recommended Practices

NFPA 80, *Standard for Fire Doors and Fire Windows.* Describes the use, installation, and maintenance of fire doors, windows, glass blocks, and shutters.

NFPA 80A, *Recommended Practice for Protection of Buildings from Exterior Fire Exposures.* Provides the minimum guidelines for protecting openings in exterior walls from exposure fires.

NFPA 82, *Standard on Incinerators, Waste, and Linen Handling Systems and Equipment.* Contains requirements for reducing fire hazards associated with the installation and use of compactors, incinerators, waste-handling and linen-handling systems, and waste storage rooms and containers.

NFPA 90A, *Standard for the Installation of Air Conditioning and Ventilating Systems.* Specifies installation requirements to restrict the spread of smoke, heat, and fire through duct systems in order to minimize ignition sources and permit the use of the system for emergency smoke control.

NFPA 90B, *Standard for the Installation of Warm Air Heating and Air Conditioning Systems.* Provides installation requirements for supply ducts, controls, clearances, heating panels, return ducts, air filters, heat pumps, and other components for one- and two-family dwellings or spaces that do not exceed volumes of 25,000 cubic feet.

NFPA 91, *Standard for Exhaust Systems for Air Conveying of Materials.* Covers safety requirements for fans, ducts, direct clearances, design, and dust-collecting systems for removing or conveying flammable vapors, corrosive fumes, dust stock, and refuse.

NFPA 92A, *Recommended Practice for Smoke-Control Systems.* Addresses smoke control using barriers, airflows, and pressure differentials in order to confine the smoke of a fire to the zone of fire origin and thus maintain a tenable environment in other zones.

NFPA 101, *Life Safety Code.* Specifies the required hourly ratings for openings in fire-rated barriers, and contains criteria for fire and smoke barriers, interior finish, and protection of floor openings.

NFPA 105, *Recommended Practice for the Installation of Smoke-Control Door Assemblies.* Recommends parameters for door performance that will limit smoke spread through a door opening.

NFPA 204M, *Guide for Smoke and Heat Venting.* Defines principles of natural venting, types of vents, venting ratios, curtain boards, inspection and maintenance, and heat release data.

NFPA 252, *Standard Methods of Fire Tests of Door Assemblies.* Outlines methods of testing fire resistance of door assemblies in wall openings.

NFPA 257, *Standard for Fire Tests of Window Assemblies.* Methods for testing glass block and other light-transmitting assemblies.

CHAPTER 6

Interior Finish

A s an inspector, you must be constantly aware of the different types of interior finishes that can be installed within a building. Interior finishes have been a significant factor in rapid flame spread for many of the deadliest fires in recent decades.

Interior finishes traditionally are considered to consist of those materials or combinations of materials that form the exposed interior surfaces of walls and ceilings in a building. Interior floor finishes are the exposed floor surfaces of buildings and include floor coverings, such as carpets and floor tiles, that may be applied over or in lieu of a finished floor. Furnishings, which in some cases may be secured in place for functional reasons, should not be considered interior finish. Decorations and furnishings generally are not considered interior finishes but are handled separately. Furnishings will be addressed later in this chapter.

Interior finish relates to a fire in four ways. It can affect the rate of a fire build up to flashover conditions, contribute to fire extension by flame spread over its surface, add to the intensity of a fire by contributing additional fuel, and produce smoke and toxic gases that contribute to life hazard and property damage. Controlling the type of interior finish in an occupancy or a building will ultimately increase the occupants' safety.

Wall and Ceiling Finishes

Interior wall and ceiling finishes are the exposed interior surfaces of buildings, including, but not limited to, fixed or moveable walls and partitions, columns, and ceilings.

There are numerous types of interior finish materials, including some commonly used materials such as plaster, gypsum wallboard, wood, plywood paneling, fiber ceiling tiles, plastics, and a variety of wall coverings. Interior wall and ceiling finishes should be tested under conditions that simulate the actual installation. For proper evaluation classifications, assemblies of interior finish material must be tested as they will actually be installed. If they are not, the test findings may not be accurate. For example, the flame spread rating of an interior finish material tested without the adhesive that is actually used to apply it may be more favorable than it is when the adhesive is used.

It is important to realize that the type and end use of a material determines the fire test it will undergo. A material that is used as a wall covering must have a flame spread rating. The same material used as a drape or a curtain must have a flame propagation resistance through vertical burn characteristics. And if the material is used on upholstered furniture, it must undergo an appropriate fire test for resistance to cigarette ignition. When a material that is used ordinarily on the floor, such as a carpet, is applied to a wall or ceiling it must be tested with a fire test appropriate for such an installation or application. Synthetic fabric carpeting, when applied to walls or ceilings, must be tested using a "room corner test." The fire tests for such applications will be covered later in this chapter.

Interior wall and ceiling finishes are classified in accordance with the results of actual fire tests, which record the flame spread and smoke development of the material. Flame spread ratings offer a general indication of the speed with which fire may spread across the surface of the material, while smoke development is the degree of obscurity associated with the smoke the product develops.

The tests used for wall and ceiling finishes typically are measured in the Steiner Tunnel Test, also known as NFPA 255, *Standard Method of Test of Surface Burning Characteristics of Building Materials,* and ASTM *E-84, Standard Test Method for Surface Burning Characteristics and Building Materials.* The material to be tested is placed face down on the top of the inside of the test furnace. A gas burner is then ignited, and flame travels over the bottom face of the test specimen. The specimen is observed through the sealed windows on one side of the furnace for 10 minutes. The distance the flame has spread across the test specimen in this time is then calculated against the distance flame spreads across two arbitrarily selected materials. These materials are inorganic reinforced cement board and select-grade red oak flooring, which represent a flame spread of 0 and 100 respectively. These values are the benchmarks against which all other materials tested are classified.

The flame spread rating is indexed into three classifications:

Flame Spread	Smoke Development
Class "A": 0–25	0–450
Class "B": 26–75	0–450
Class "C": 76–200	0-450

The smoke development value is based solely on obscuration and was determined using research done to evaluate various stages of observation of illuminated exit signs in a test room that was gradually filling with the smoke generated in a tunnel test chamber. The numerical value of 450 was chosen as the point at which the means of egress may become obscured. Some codes refer to "A" "B," and "C" as "I" "II," or "III," but the flame spread and smoke development ratings are the same.

It should be noted that the ways in which occupants use a facility dictate the type of minimum threshold for interior finish classification. One should review each occupant's use of a space to determine the appropriate finish ratings. As indicated earlier, the classification of an interior finish is that of the basic material used either by itself or in combination with other materials. The material should be tested in exactly the same configuration in which it will be used in a facility.

Paint or wall coverings applied after the interior finish has been installed are not subject to interior finish requirements if they are no thicker than 1/28 of an inch. However, such materials would require a flame spread rating if they or their applications produced significant flame spread or smoke development in and of themselves. It should be noted that multiple layers of wall coverings can contribute to a rapid fire growth and that they should be subject to the requirements for the interior finish of the type of occupancy in which they are used.

Textile materials with a napped, tufted, looped, woven, nonwoven, or similar surface should not be applied to walls or ceilings unless they have been appropriately documented for the application through fire testing. Even if this type of material receives a Class A rating when tested in accordance with the requirements of NFPA 255, its fire behavior is not reliably predictable for all aspects of application. The appropriate test for this application is the room corner fire test, which demonstrates the product in its final form using the actual mounting system, including the adhesive, with which it will be installed in an occupancy.

The application of cellular or foamed plastic materials on interior walls and on ceilings should not be permitted unless fire tests can reasonably substantiate the combustibility characteristics of the materials for the particular uses under actual fire conditions. Cellular or foamed plastics may be used as trim if they do not exceed 10% of the wall or ceiling.

Trim or incidental finish applied to interior walls or ceilings may be of a Class C material, even when the interior wall or ceiling finish is required to be of a Class A or B material, as long as they are not applied to more than 10% of the aggregate wall area. The purpose of this provision is to permit the use of wood trim around doors and windows as a decoration or as functional molding. The belief is that this type of trim would be distributed uniformly throughout a room, rather than concentrated in one area.

Interior finish materials that do not have the appropriate interior flame spread rating can be modified by applying fire-retardant coatings. These coatings must be applied in accordance with the manufacturers' instructions and should possess the desired degree of permanency, remaining effective when in actual use.

Most fire-retardant paints and coatings require an application rate three to four times greater than that of ordinary paints. The treatment must be reapplied or renewed periodically because the retardant's overall effectiveness could be reduced by regular maintenance, washing, or cleaning. Fire-retardant treatments should comply with the requirements of NFPA 703, *Standard for Fire Retardant Impregnated Wood and Fire Retardant Coatings for Building Materials.*

Interior Floor Finish

Interior floor finish are the exposed floor surfaces of a building, including coverings, that are applied over the normal finished flooring or stairs, including risers. To obtain a rating for interior floor finish, the Flooring Radiant Panel Test Method is used. This test method is also known as NFPA 253, *Standard Method of Test for Critical Radiant Flux of Floor Covering Systems Using a Radiant Heat Energy Source,* and ASTM E-648, *Standard Method of Test for Critical Radiant Flux of Floor Coverings Systems Using a Radiant Heat Energy Source.* The test results measure burning that occurred on a sample. The results are then converted into a value, known as the "critical radiant flux," of W/cm^2.

A Class I interior floor finish has a critical radiant flux of at least .45 W/cm², while a Class II interior floor finish has a minimum .22 W/cm². The greater the critical radiant flux value, the more resistant the floor finish is to flame promulgation.

Since April 1991, the federal government has required that all carpets manufactured in the United States meet a flammability standard known as the Federal Flammability Standard, FF-1-70 Pill Test, or simply the Pill Test. The Pill Test consists of eight 9-inch-square sections of a carpet that are secured in a test chamber. A methanamine tablet is ignited and placed in the center of the specimen. If the flame advances to any point within 1 inch of the edge of the sample, the specimen fails the test.

The appropriate floor finish rating is determined by the way in which the facility is used and the location of the finish within the facility—that is, in exits and corridors. Interior floor finish ratings only apply when floor finish presents an unusual hazard or where the floor finish requirements are specified because of occupant use.

Automatic Sprinklers

The presence of an automatic sprinkler system in a facility provides a degree of safety that is incorporated into the interior finish requirements. The rating of an interior finish can be reduced by one level if a sprinkler system is installed in the facility. When the automatic sprinklers are used, however, the rating cannot be reduced below the minimum flame spread rating for that occupancy.

Furnishings and Decorations

Furnishings and decorations are not considered interior finishes when one is discussing flame spread characteristics. But these items can contribute fuel to fire in an occupancy and are required under certain conditions to meet certain fire tests. Draperies, curtains, and other similar, loosely hanging furnishings or decorations that must be flame resistant because of the occupancy in which they are used are required to pass both the small- and large-scale test of NFPA 701, *Standard Methods of Fire Tests for Flame-Resistant Textiles and Films.* This test applies to textiles and films that are hung. If the material is applied to the surface of a building or to backing materials as an interior finish, it should be treated as interior finish and tested in accordance with the requirements of NFPA 255.

Upholstered furniture also contributes to the fire loading in a facility. Depending on the type of occupancy in which the furniture is placed, it may have to undergo a fire test.

Many different types of tests are available to determine the fire characteristics of upholstered furniture. NFPA 260, *Standard Methods of Tests and Classification System for Cigarette Ignition Resistance of Components of Upholstered Furniture*, and NFPA 261, *Standard Method of Test for Determining Resistance of Mock-Up Upholstered Furniture Material Assemblies to Ignition by Smoldering Cigarettes,* are just two of these test standards. Depending on the way the occupants use the facility, upholstered furniture may be required to meet a certain threshold for rates of heat release. NFPA 264A, *Standard Method of Test for Heat Release Rates for Upholstered Furniture Components or Composites and Mattresses Using an Oxygen Consumption Calorimeter,* provides the necessary testing procedures to obtain these rates of heat release. As with interior finishes, upholstered furniture need not be tested if an automatic sprinkler system has been installed in the facility.

The faster a fire develops, the greater the threat it presents to the occupants of a building. Interior finishes and furnishings have a major influence on how fast a fire will develop and how intense it will become. By establishing minimum criteria for interior finish requirements, we can raise the level of safety for building occupants.

Bibliography

Combustible Properties of Treated Wood by the Crib Test, ASTM E-160, American Society for Testing and Materials, Philadelphia, PA.

Combustible Properties of Treated Wood by the Fire Tube Apparatus, ASTM E-69, American Society for Testing and Materials, Philadelphia, PA.

Fire Retardancy of Paints (Cabinet Method), ASTM D-1360, American Society for Testing and Materials, Philadelphia, PA.

Flammability of Finished Textile Floor Covering Materials, ASTM D-2859, American Society for Testing and Materials, Philadelphia, PA.

Rate of Burning and/or Extent and Time of Burning of Flexible Plastics in a Vertical Position, ASTM D-568, American Society for Testing and Materials, Philadelphia, PA.

Rate of Burning and/or Extent and Time of Burning of Flexible Thin Plastic Sheeting Supported on a 45-Degree Incline, ASTM D-1433, American Society for Testing and Materials, Philadelphia, PA.

Rate of Burning and/or Extent and Time of Burning of Self-Supporting Plastics in a Horizontal Position, ASTM D-635, American Society for Testing and Materials, Philadelphia, PA.

Standard Test Method for Flame Height, Time of Burning, and Loss of Weight of Rigid Thermoset Cellular Plastics in a Vertical Position, ASTM D-3014, American Society for Testing and Materials, Philadelphia, PA.

Standard Test Method for Measuring the Minimum Oxygen Concentration to Support Candle-Like Combustion of Plastics (Oxygen Index), ASTM D-2863, American Society for Testing and Materials, Philadelphia, PA.

Standard Test Method for Surface Burning Characteristics of Building Materials, ASTM E-84, American Society for Testing and Materials, Philadelphia, PA.

Test for Surface Burning Characteristics of Building Materials, UL 723, Underwriters Laboratories, Inc., Northbrook, IL.

Test Method for Critical Radiant Flux of Floor-Covering Systems Using a Radiant Heat Energy Source, ASTM E-648, American Society for Testing and Materials, Philadelphia, PA.

Cote, A. E., ed., *Fire Protection Handbook,* 17th edition, National Fire Protection Association, Quincy, MA, 1991. Section 6, Chapter 4 deals with the types of interior finish, their application and role in building fires, and fire test methods.

"Carpets and Rugs—Notice of Standard," *Federal Register,* Vol. 35, No. 74 (April 16, 1970). Standard for the surface flammability of carpets and rugs (Pill Test).

NFPA Codes, Standards, and Recommended Practices

NFPA 35, *Standard for the Manufacture of Organic Coatings.* Outlines the standard processes involving fire hazards in organic coating manufacturing.

NFPA *101, Life Safety Code.* Included are definitions of interior finish, materials that are and are not acceptable as interior finish, and classifications, fire-retardant coatings, and automatic sprinklers as they relate to interior finish.

NFPA 253, *Standard Method of Test for Critical Radiant Flux of Floor Covering Systems Using a Radiant Heat Energy Source.* A procedure for measuring critical radiant flux behavior of horizontally mounted floor covering systems exposed to a flaming ignition source in a graded radiant heat energy environment in a test chamber.

NFPA 255, *Standard Method of Test of Surface Burning Characteristics of Building Materials.* Contains the specifications and procedures for testing building materials with the Steiner Tunnel Test.

NFPA 258, *Standard Research Test Method for Determining Smoke Generation of Solid Materials.* Intended for research purposes only. Specifies procedures for measuring smoke generation from solid materials in thicknesses up to 1 inch.

NFPA 260, *Standard Methods of Tests and Classification System for Cigarette Ignition Resistance of Components of Upholstered Furniture.* Contains the specification and procedures to evaluate ignition resistance of upholstered furniture components when exposed to smoldering cigarettes under specific conditions.

NFPA 261, *Standard Method of Test for Determining Resistance of Mock-Up Upholstered Furniture Material Assemblies to Ignition by Smoldering Cigarettes.* Contains the specifications and procedures to measure the performance of upholstered furniture when exposed to a smoldering cigarette.

NFPA 264A, *Standard Method of Test for Heat Release Rates for Upholstered Furniture Components or Composites and Mattresses Using an Oxygen Consumption Calorimeter.* Provides procedures to determine the ignitability and the release rates of heat.

NFPA 701, *Standard Methods of Fire Tests for Flame-Resistant Textiles and Films.* Contains specifications and procedures for testing flame resistance of materials used in draperies, decorations, tents, and air-supported structures.

CHAPTER 7

Electrical Systems

*E*lectrical systems are best examined and tested by qualified electrical inspectors because they have the special skills needed to correct electrical system deficiencies that may cause fires. Because fire inspections are carried out more frequently than electrical inspections, however, it is likely that a fire inspector, rather than an electrical inspector or a qualified electrician, will detect potential problems. Thus, you, as a fire inspector, must be aware of the signs and symptoms of the potential fire hazards presented by electrical systems.

The causes of electrical fires can be placed in four broad categories: damaged electrical equipment, improper use of electrical equipment, accidents, or defective installations. By learning to recognize the signs of potential trouble, you will go a long way toward eliminating electrical failures as a cause of fire.

Wiring and Apparatus

Electrical fires are due principally to arcing and overheating. Arcing occurs when the electrical current or energy tries to take an unintended route over small breaks in a conducting wire, at splices and terminals that have become loose, or between a live conductor to grounded metal in very close proximity. Arcing produces enough heat to ignite nearby combustible materials, such as insulation, and can throw off particles of hot metal that also can cause ignition. Arcing also can melt metal conductors and produce sparks.

The conditions that create an arc usually cause protective devices, such as fuses and circuit breakers, to operate, making the heat exposure brief. However, intermittent arcing, such as might occur in ground faults, can sometimes happen without tripping such devices.

Overheating is more subtle, harder to detect, and slower to cause ignition, but it is equally capable of causing a fire. Conductors and other electrical equipment may generate a dangerous level of heat when they carry a current in excess of rated capacity. Overloading deteriorates insulation to the point at which it becomes conductive and overheats, causing nearby combustible materials to ignite. Insulation failure caused by overheating also can lead to arcing between conductors or between conductors and adjacent grounded objects.

Common Faults

Conduits, Raceways, and Cables: Among the obvious faults are badly deteriorated and improperly supported conduits, raceways, and cables. Where these items enter boxes, cabinets, and other equipment, they should be terminated in proper fittings that hold them securely in place without damaging the conductor insulation. Conduits that are not supported properly may pull apart and expose conductors and insulation to damage.

Cables should be protected from mechanical damage where they pass through walls or floors. They also should be protected from overload, which is not as immediately obvious as mechanical damage. One way to determine whether a cable is overloaded is to touch it. Depending on the load, it may feel abnormally warm or even hot. If this is the case, you should make sure that a qualified electrician investigates the problem and corrects the situation.

Circuit Conductors: Single conductors usually are installed in race-ways, but they may be installed on insulators in free air or in cable trays. Open conductors are more common in industrial occupancies and in older buildings. Like cables, branch circuit conductors must be supported properly along their length and at the point at which they terminate in junction, switch, and outlet boxes. Conductors should not be exposed to excessive external heat, which will hasten the deterioration of their insulation. Circuit conductors also may be subject to electrical overload where fuses or circuit breakers are of the incorrect value. To detect overloaded conductors, look for discoloration of the terminals or of the surfaces of conduits and boxes.

Flexible Cords: There are a number of several unsafe practices involving flexible cords that may result in fires. Among these are using them in place of fixed wiring. Extension cords should be used only to connect portable equipment that is being used temporarily, not as part of the permanent wiring of a building. Nor should they be used to supply equipment that will load them beyond their rated capacity. Flexible cords should not be nailed, tacked, or stapled to woodwork or tied or taped to pipes. Nor should they be spliced or repaired: A damaged cord should be replaced with a new cord of the proper size and type. The termination of a cord should not be relied on to provide mechanical support. Rather, cords should be clamped in a connector or knotted in an approved manner where they enter appliances to keep them from placing stress on the terminations. Flexible cords should never be left where they can be damaged by vehicles, carts, or pedestrian traffic. Nor should they be left coiled or hanked or run under rugs or carpets.

Boxes and Cabinets: Outlet, switch, and junction boxes and cabinets are used to protect the equipment and connections they house. All such boxes should be equipped with the proper cover. Boxes and cabinets are made with prepunched "knockouts" that can be removed to allow the installation of cable connectors and the entrance of a cable. Only those "knockouts" that are necessary to accommodate the conductors entering the box should be removed. The number of wires in a box or cabinet must not exceed the number for which it was designed.

When observing outlet and switch boxes, look for cracked or broken switch and outlet assemblies, discolored devices, or covers that indicate overheating. If you find any, make sure they are replaced promptly.

Switchboards and Panelboards: On some switchboards and panelboards, there are exposed live parts from which occupants must be protected. This can be done by placing a cage or barrier around these open switchboards. Such boards usually also employ bus bars, which should be adequately supported. During your inspection, you should check switchboards and panelboards for deterioration, dirt, moisture, tracking, and poor maintenance. You should also make sure that the area around them is kept clear to allow quick and ready access. Nothing should be stored in this working space or on top of switchboards or panelboards.

Lamps and Light Fixtures: Light fixtures are subject to deterioration and poor maintenance. With age, the insulation on fixture wires can dry, crack, and fall away, leaving bare conductors. Sockets may become worn and defective, and the fixtures themselves may loosen in the mountings.

Fixtures should not be mounted directly on combustible ceilings. Since lamps often operate at temperatures high enough to ignite combustible material, they should be mounted far enough away from materials such as paper or cloth, which may be used as shades or placed nearby, so that their continuous operation does not ignite them. Oversized lamps cause excessive temperatures in fixtures, and these temperatures can damage the supply conductors or ignite nearby combustibles. You should take care to ensure that lamps are of the proper size and type and that the fiberglass thermal barrier is in the fixture canopy. Discolored globes or lenses can indicate improper lamp size. Newer, recessed fixtures have thermal protectors that will turn the fixture off if incorrect lamp size results in high temperatures. Unguarded portable lamps may ignite ordinary combustibles if placed in contact with them, and a broken lamp may ignite combustible dust in suspension or flammable vapors in the atmosphere.

Grounding

Lightning, accidental contact with a high voltage source, surface leakage due to conductive dirt or moisture, and breakdown of insulation on conductors can cause hazardous voltages in electrical distribution systems and equipment. If the affected equipment is permitted to "float" at a dangerous voltage, anyone who comes in contact with it and a point of different potential, such as ground, will receive a serious, if not fatal, shock.

Grounding facilitates the operation of the overcurrent devices installed in ungrounded conductors. One of the system's conductors is grounded, and all the metal parts that could be energized are connected to it through equipment-grounding conductors and bonding jumpers. If a ground fault occurs, this will provide a path to the grounded system conductor, which will cause the overcurrent device to operate.

Metal cable armor, raceways, boxes, and fittings, as well as the frames and housings of electrical machinery, must be grounded. Certain electrical tools and cord-and-plug-connected appliances, such as washers, dryers, air conditioners, pumps, and so on, must be grounded through a third contact in the line plug.

A grounding electrode is connected to the system to stablize the voltage to ground and to limit voltages due to lightning, line surges, or unintentional contact with higher voltage lines. A metallic underground

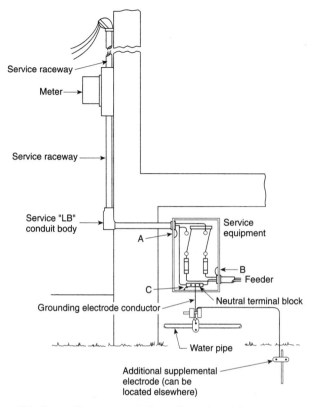

Figure 7-1. Grounding at a typical small service (AC, single-phase, three-wire, 120/240 v). A—supply-side bonding jumper; B—load-side bonding jumper; C—main bonding jumper.

water piping system must be used as the grounding electrode where it is available and where the buried portion of the pipe is more than 10 feet long. If a metal underground water pipe is the only grounding electrode, it must be supplemented by an additional electrode to ensure the integrity of the grounding electrode system.

Ground clamps and connectors should be checked periodically to ensure that they are tight and that the ground connection is being maintained. When new electrical machinery or equipment is installed on the premises, it should be inspected to see that it has been connected properly to the grounding system.

Overcurrent Protection

Conductors and equipment are provided with overcurrent protection that opens a circuit if the current reaches a value that will cause an excessive or dangerous temperature in the conductor or the conductor insulation. Fuses and circuit breakers are the most commonly used overcurrent devices for the protection of feeders and circuits and of equipment. Thermal overload devices are used to protect equipment such as motors.

Plug Fuses: There are two types of plug fuses, the Edison base and the type S. Both can be either of the quick-acting or the time-delay type. The Edison base plug fuse is familiar to most people. The type S plug fuse is designed to prevent the use of pennies or other bridging schemes to bypass the fuse and to prevent the use of incorrectly sized fuses.

Cartridge Fuses: Cartridge fuses are made in quick-acting and time-delay types. They are also made for one-time use or with renewable links. However, the renewable link cartridge fuses have two drawbacks: Two or three links can be installed at one time, thereby increasing the fusing current and defeating the purpose of the fuse, and the fuse can be left with loose connections when a link is replaced, which results in overheating.

Circuit Breakers: Circuit breakers are available in a number of styles. The most common has two nonadjustable trips, one of which is thermal to detect overloads and the other magnetic to detect short circuits. Another type has adjustable trip units, which may have either conventional or solid-state sensing units. Some circuit breakers have shunt-trip features that allow them to be operated from remote locations. An example is the type of circuit breaker used to shut down equipment under kitchen hoods in restaurants. Among the special types of circuit breakers used are motor-operated breakers, ground-fault sensing breakers, and motor-circuit protectors. Any of these devices may feel warm under normal loads, but none should be too hot to touch.

Thermal Overload Devices: These devices are not intended to protect against short circuits. Rather, they protect against overload. Examples are the thermal overload protection for electric motors or the thermal protection in recessed light fixtures.

Ground-Fault Circuit-Interrupters: These devices sense when the current passes to ground through any path other than the proper path. When this occurs, the ground-fault circuit-interrupter (GFCI) trips almost instantly, stopping all current flow in the circuit. GFCIs are extremely important for life protection in wet locations. GFCI protection is provided by a special circuit breaker located in the panelboard or by a GFCI receptacle installed in the outlet box.

Industrial Equipment

Transformers

Dry-type and fluid-filled transformers are used in both industrial and large commercial occupancies. Dry-type transformers are the most common in newer commercial constructions although other types may be encountered, while fluid-filled transformers are more common in industrial plants or older buildings. In most cases, dry-type transformers do not require a separate room or vault, but they must be separated from combustible materials and the area in which they are located must be adequately ventilated. Oil-filled transformers usually are required to be installed in a vault with 3-hour fire-rated floor, walls, doors, ceilings, and sills to contain the contents of the transformer should they spill.

New transformer fluids, classified as less flammable or nonflammable, are available. When these new fluids are used, the requirements for vaults are reduced or eliminated. Some older transformers might contain askarel and will have to be marked and eventually replaced due to environmental concerns.

Under conditions of full load, transformers operate at elevated temperatures. Many will be too hot to touch for more than a few seconds. All transformers should be provided with adequate ventilation, and the clearance requirements marked on the transformer should be maintained. Materials should not be stored on top of transformer enclosures.

Outdoor transformers should be located in such a way that leaking fluids will drain away from buildings or be contained in place. They should be placed in such a way that they will not expose exits or windows to fire in the event of transformer failure.

Motors

Motors and rotating machines can cause mechanical injury as well as a shock hazard and should be treated with caution. Many motors start automatically, so even a motor at rest should be treated as though it were running.

The sparks or arcs that result when a motor short circuits can ignite nearby combustibles. Bearings can overheat if they are not properly lubricated. And dust deposits or accumulations of textile fibers can prevent heat from dissipating from the motor.

Your inspection of motors should indicate that there are no combustibles in the immediate vicinity of the motor or its controls, that the equipment is cleaned properly and maintained, and that it has the proper overcurrent protection. Motors are designed to operate without overheating under normal conditions, but they also are designed to operate with a temperature rise well above ambient under normal full-load conditions. A hot casing may indicate a potential problem and should be examined closely.

Medium Voltage Equipment

Most of the equipment discussed above can operate on medium-voltage, as well as low-voltage, systems. Medium voltage usually is considered to be in excess of 1,000 volts. Equipment rated as high as 15,000 volts is common in large buildings and industrial complexes. Because of the severe shock hazard associated with this equipment, you must use caution when inspecting it.

Hazardous Areas

Electrical hazardous areas are those in which flammable liquids, gases, combustible dusts, or readily ignitible fibers or flyings are present in sufficient quantities to represent a fire or explosion hazard. Special electrical equipment is necessary in these areas. Complete definitions of the classes and divisions of hazardous locations and of the wiring methods and types of electrical equipment to be used in each are covered in Article 500 of the *National Electrical Code®* (NFPA 70).

Class I, Division 1

Class I, Division 1 locations include areas in which ignitible concentrations of flammable gases or vapors exist under normal conditions; areas in which ignitible concentrations of flammable gases or vapors may exist frequently because of repair or maintenance operations or leakage; and areas in which the breakdown or faulty operation of equipment or processes may cause the simultaneous failure of electrical equipment.

Electrical equipment used in these locations must be the explosion-proof type or the purged-and-pressurized type approved for Class I locations.

Class I, Division 2

These locations include areas in which volatile flammable liquids or flammable gases, which normally are confined to closed containers or systems that allow them to escape only during accidental rupture, breakdown, or abnormal operation of equipment, are handled, processed, or used. They also include areas in which positive mechanical ventilation normally prevents the development of ignitible concentrations of gases or vapors that could become hazardous should the ventilating equipment fail or operate abnormally, as well as areas adjacent to, but not cut off from, Class I, Division 1 locations to which ignitible concentrations of gases or vapors could be communicated.

Class II, Division 1

These classified locations include areas in which combustible dust is, or may be, in suspension in the air continuously, intermittently, or periodically under normal operating conditions in large enough quantities to produce explosive or ignitible mixtures. Areas in which mechanical failure or abnormal operation of equipment might result in explosive or ignitible mixtures and provide a source of ignition through simultaneous failure of electrical equipment are also classified as Class II, Division 1, as are areas in which combustible dusts of an electrically conductive nature might be present. Class II, Division 1 locations also include areas in which a buildup of dust on horizontal surfaces over a 24-hour period exceeds 1/8 inch.

Class II, Division 2

These classified locations include areas in which combustible dust normally is not suspended in the air in quantities sufficient to produce explosive or ignitible mixtures and in which dust accumulations normally are not sufficient to interfere with the normal operation of electrical equipment or other apparatus. They also include areas in which the infrequent malfunction of handling or processing equipment might result in dust in suspension in the air and in which these dust accumulations could be ignited by the abnormal operation or failure of electrical equipment or other apparatus. Areas in which a buildup of dust on horizontal surfaces is 1/8 inch or less deep, obscuring the surface color of the equipment, are also classified as Class II, Division 2 locations.

Class III, Division 1

This classified location includes areas in which easily ignitible fibers or materials producing combustible flyings are handled, manufactured, or used.

Class III, Division 2

These locations include areas in which easily ignitible fibers are stored or handled, except during the manufacturing process.

Static Electricity

Precautions against sparks from static electricity should be taken in locations in which flammable vapors, gases, or dusts or easily ignited materials are present. Only qualified persons should be allowed to test for static charges in these locations, since unintended discharges can ignite the hazardous atmosphere.

Measures that will bring the hazard of static electricity under reasonable control are humidification, bonding, grounding, ionization, conductive floors, or a combination of these methods.

Humidification

Humidity alone is not a completely reliable means of eliminating static charges. To reduce the danger of static, however, the relative humidity should be high. If practical, relative humidities should be as high as possible, even up to 75%, as long as this does not create undue hardship.

Some industrial operations cannot be performed at humidities high enough to mitigate the danger of static.

Bonding and Grounding

Bonding minimizes the differences in electrical potential between metallic objects. There is practically no difference between two metal objects connected by a bond wire, which generally carries a small current.

The term "grounding" describes connections made to minimize the difference in electrical potential between objects and the ground and to provide a low-resistance path to actuate the overcurrent device. In such cases, the ground wire can carry a current from power circuits that is much larger than the static current. You should check the ground connections when they are installed and frequently thereafter to detect corrosion, loose connections, or damage.

Flowing gases, liquids, or granular solids, such as sand, generate static. Thus, their containers should be bonded or grounded. When gasoline is

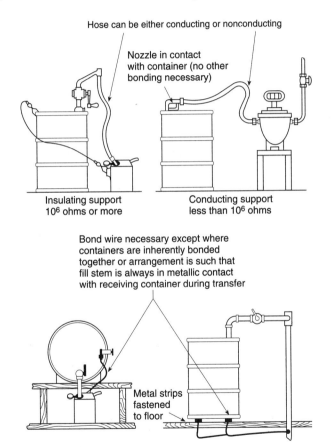

Figure 7-2. Recommended methods of bonding flammable liquid containers during container filling. Source: Figure 4-8.4, NFPA 77, **Recommended Practice on Static Electricity, NFPA, Quincy, MA, 1993.**

ELECTRICAL SYSTEMS 71

transferred from a drum to a can, for example, the drum and the can should be bonded together by an electrically conductive tube that is firmly in contact at both ends or securely attached to a grounding wire before the liquid is transferred.

In general, bonding and grounding connections should be of substantial construction so that they are not broken easily, and the connections should be installed in such a way that you can readily see that they are in place and intact.

Ionization

Ionization is the process of increasing the conductivity of air so that it will conduct static charges away from the area.

One ionization technique employs the tendency of static to concentrate on the surface of least radius of curvature, such as a sharp point. A metal bar with needle points (static comb) or with metallic tinsel removes static from moving sheet materials. Another technique uses a so-called electrical neutralizer, which produces an alternating electrical field through which the electrified sheet material passes. Yet another technique, used on printing presses, uses a flame to ionize the surrounding air. Static may also be ionized by alpha radiation from a radioactive surface.

The hazards introduced by these various techniques, as well as their respective effectiveness in removing static charges, must be considered.

Lightning Protection

Lightning protection systems are installed to provide an alternate, nondestructive path for lightning to follow to earth. When lightning follows this path, building materials are spared the heat and mechanical forces that result when the energy of the lightning stroke passes through a structure. Any part of a building that is likely to be struck, such as chimneys, ventilators, steeples, dormers, and other projections, should be protected. This is done by installing a series of air terminals, down conductors, and secondary conductors and ground terminals. Surge arrestors also may be installed to protect the building's electrical system.

Air terminals are installed on the edges of a building's roof and on its projections and connected by conductors. Down conductors are used to provide at least two paths to the ground terminals. Metal objects nearby are bonded to the system with secondary conductors, which prevent damage from sideflashing. All of these conductors are constructed of heavy-gauge copper or aluminum to resist corrosion.

Because the materials used for lightning protection systems are strong, they require very little maintenance, so you may not have to inspect these systems as frequently as you do other systems. In fact, NFPA 780, Lightning Protection Code, recommends inspecting them every five years. When you do inspect them, check conductors for excessive corrosion or mechanical damage. Down conductors near the ground may be damaged by vehicles, and connections to ground terminals may be disturbed by mowers or other groundskeeping tools. Be sure to check connections throughout for tightness, and inspect air terminals to make sure they are secure and in place.

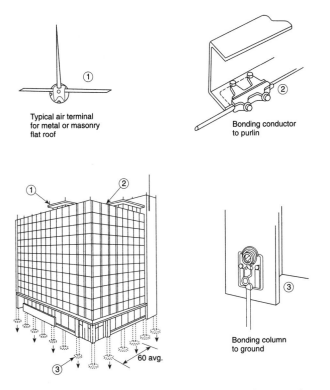

Figure 7-3. Grounding and bonding of lightning down conductors. Water pipe grounds (if pipes are metallic) can be made at 1, 2, or 3.

Bibliography

Cote, A. E., ed., *Fire Protection Handbook,* 17th edition, National Fire Protection Association, Quincy, MA, 1991.

Electrical Appliance and Utilization Equipment Directory, Underwriters Laboratories, Inc., Northbrook, IL. Issued annually. This is a listing of the electrical appliances and devices that have been tested and found to be safe for use.

Electrical Construction Materials Directory, Underwriters Laboratories, Inc., Northbrook, IL. Issued annually. A directory of tested and listed construction materials such as circuit breakers, wires, transformers, industrial control equipment, electrical service equipment, and fixtures and fittings.

Hazardous Location Equipment Directory, Underwriters Laboratories, Inc., Northbrook, IL. Issued annually. A listing of electrical components and equipment that have been tested and listed for use in hazardous atmospheres.

NFPA Codes, Standards, and Recommended Practices

NFPA 70, *National Electrical Code.* Contains the requirements for safe electrical systems.

NFPA 70B, *Recommended Practice for Electrical Equipment Maintenance.* Preventive maintenance for industrial- and commercial-type electrical systems and equipment.

NFPA 70E, *Standard for Electrical Safety Requirements for Employee Workplaces.* Includes installation requirements, work practices, and maintenance requirements necessary to provide practical and safe work areas for employees.

NFPA 77, *Recommended Practice on Static Electricity.* Explains the hazards of static accumulation and the means of diminishing or eliminating them.

NFPA 79, *Electrical Standard for Industrial Machinery.* Applies to the electrical/electronic equipment, apparatus, or systems of industrial machinery or mass-production industrial equipment.

NFPA 325M, *Fire Hazard Properties of Flammable Liquids, Gases, and Volatile Solids.* A tabulation of the fire hazard properties of more than 1,600 substances listed alphabetically by chemical name.

NFPA 496, *Standard for Purged and Pressurized Enclosures for Electrical Equipment.* Requirements for the design and operation of purged and pressurized electrical equipment enclosures to reduce or eliminate the hazardous location classification within the enclosures.

NFPA 497A, *Recommended Practice for Classification of Class I Hazardous (Classified) Locations for Electrical Installations in Chemical Process Areas.* Guidelines for classifying areas in which flammable gases or vapors, flammable liquids, or combustible liquids are processed or handled and in which they could be ignited by electrical systems or equipment if released into the atmosphere.

NFPA 497B, *Recommended Practice for the Classification of Class II Hazardous (Classified) Locations for Electrical Installations in Chemical Process Areas.* Guidelines for classifying areas in which combustible dusts are produced, processed, or handled and in which electrical systems or equipment may ignite dust in the atmosphere or on surfaces.

NFPA 497M, *Manual for Classification of Gases, Vapors, and Dusts for Electrical Equipment in Hazardous (Classified) Locations.* Covers the selection of special electrical equipment for hazardous (classified) areas.

NFPA 780, *Lightning Protection Code.* Contains the protection requirements to safeguard persons and property from lightning hazards.

CHAPTER 8

Heating
Systems

*L*arge Buildings

Most large buildings use oil- or gas-fired hot water or steam boilers to generate building heat. Hot water or steam piping systems distribute this heat to air conditioning units, unit heaters, finned tube radiation units, and, in some cases, ice- and snow-melting systems.

There have been major changes in building heating systems since the middle 1970s as a result of both the energy crisis and stricter environmental regulations for flue gas exhaust emissions. Many buildings have abandoned their heavy oil-and coal-fired boiler plants because installing and operating the necessary pollution abatement devices costs too much. In many cases, the savings in the cost of fuels simply could not offset the higher operating costs. Nor could space always be found to store the quantities of coal necessary to run such plants. And in large cities, removing the coal ash became a major cost and environmental problem.

Building owners became acutely aware of energy costs as they saw their utility bills skyrocket. They added insulation to exterior walls, replaced single-pane windows with insulating glass, and covered minimally insulated or noninsulated pipe with energy-saving insulation. They repaired and replaced leaking and noninsulated chimneys and exhaust flues and replaced boilers and heating units with more efficient units so that less energy escaped up the stacks.

Many of these changes supported greater fire safety and contributed to building safety. For example, the added insulation on pipes and other hot surfaces reduced the transmission of heat to adjacent surfaces, which reduced the likelihood of building fires. Efficient boilers and heating units reduced the temperatures of the stacks, which lessened the chances of chimney chase and roof fires. While the fire hazard from heating systems in new buildings has been reduced, however, the problem remains in a large inventory of existing buildings. Systems used for industrial processes and power generation are discussed in Chapter 43, "Heat-Utilization Equipment."

Residential and Small Buildings

Most small buildings use a warm-air furnace and air conditioning unit to control temperature, and these systems have been engineered so that they are very energy efficient. In fact, the flue gas temperatures of some units have become so low that condensation within the flue has become a major problem. Check the flue pipes of such combustion-efficient systems for any sign of acid corrosion. Furnaces and ductwork have been insulated to increase operating efficiencies, but proper clearance between such devices and surrounding materials should still be maintained.

Despite these generally positive conditions, the energy crisis, with its high fuel costs, has created a new hazard within buildings: Occupants increasingly use portable devices to provide individual or area heating. These devices are not built into the building systems, and the building owners may not even be aware that they are being used. Where they are permitted, the cords and extensions should be inspected. Portable electrical heaters with undersized cords and extensions overheat and cause fires. Unvented portable kerosene heaters, which have caused numerous deaths and fires, should not be permitted in places of public assembly. The *Life Safety Code* prohibits such devices in educational occupancies, day-care facilities, health-care occupancies, detention and correctional occupancies, and in all residential occupancies except one- and two-family dwellings.

Burner Controls and Boilers

Fuel that is permitted to collect in the combustion chamber of a furnace in the absence of an ignition source could explode if it is ignited. There-fore, safety considerations require that fuel burners be equipped with controls to cut off the fuel supply in the event of a malfunction.

Primary safety controls shut off the fuel supply in the event of flame or ignition failure. Interlock circuits shut off the fuel supply if an induced or forced draft fails, if atomization fails, if dangerous fluctuations in fuel pressure occur, or if the oil temperature in burners requiring heated oil falls below the required minimum. You should verify that all of these controls operate satisfactorily by checking the operators' logs to confirm that periodic tests are being performed.

Because boiler rooms often become storage areas for building materials and chemicals, good housekeeping practices should be enforced. In addition, building detection and fire suppression systems should be installed in such equipment rooms. Be sure to confirm that these systems are tested periodically.

Oil

There are a number of grades of fuel oil in use today, No. 1 and No. 2 being the most common. Nos. 5 and 6 fuel oil are known as "heavy" oils and must be heated if they are to flow. As a result, systems using Nos. 5 and 6 fuels have a complex system for oil heating that usually requires extensive pollution-abatement equipment to deal with the impurities in the oils. You should verify that this equipment is tested periodically.

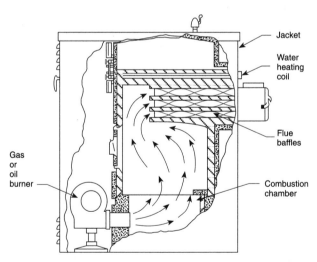

Figure 8-1. An oil-fired steam boiler (National Fuel Oil Institute, Inc.).

Oil leaks and spills should be kept to a minimum and cleaned when necessary. Sawdust should not be used on spills because it adds to the risk of fire.

Gas

LP-Gas, an LP-Gas-air mixture, and natural gas also are used to fuel heat-producing devices. Because LP-Gas vapors are heavier than air, the inspection of such equipment in below-grade indoor locations is especially critical.

Natural gas generally is preferred as a fuel because it is clean-burning, it usually is available, and it requires no storage facilities. Leaks usually are detected quickly because of the odor added by gas companies.

Many burners can use either gas or oil. In some areas, customers switch to oil when gas supplies run low.

Furnaces

Central warm-air furnaces are either of the gravity type or the forced-air type. Gravity furnaces are mounted on the floor and heat only the spaces above them. They should be equipped with high-temperature-limit controls that shut off the fuel supply when the temperature of the discharge air reaches a predetermined level.

Forced warm-air furnaces are equipped with plenums, which can become hot enough to ignite adjacent combustibles. Such furnaces should

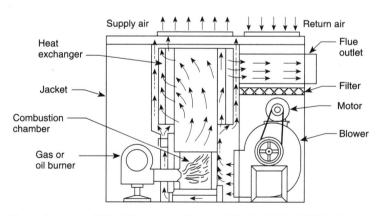

Figure 8-2. An oil-fired forced-air furnace (National Fuel Oil Institute, Inc.).

be equipped with a limit control to shut down the fuel supply when the temperature in the plenum or at the entrance to the supply duct reaches a predetermined level. As with all warm-air furnaces, it is important to maintain adequate clearances from combustibles.

Self-contained indirect-fired gas or oil heaters installed in or on a wall are called wall furnaces. They supply heated air by gravity or with the aid of a fan, and they are either directly vented or connected to a vent or chimney. Wall furnaces also should have high-temperature-limit controls.

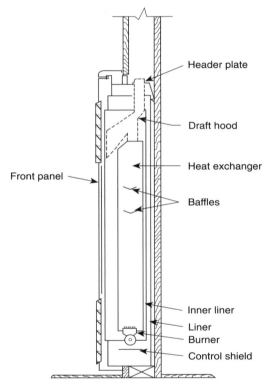

Figure 8-3. A typical gas-fired wall furnace.

Unit heaters are self-contained, automatically controlled, chimney- or vent-connected air heating appliances equipped with a fan for circulating air. They can be mounted on the floor or suspended, and they are equipped with limit controls. Unit heaters connected to a duct system can be considered central-heating furnaces and should have the same safeguards.

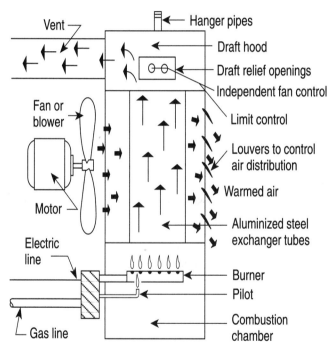

Figure 8-4. A typical gas-fired unit heater.

A heat pump is a forced-air heating system that uses refrigeration equipment so the hazards of such an arrangement are those of electrical, refrigeration, and heating equipment. When heat is wanted, it is taken from a heat source and given up to the conditioned space. When cooling is desired, the heat is removed from the space. Heat pumps that use supplemental heating units are equipped with an interlock that prevents the compressor from operating when the indoor air-circulating fan is not operating. Heat pumps usually are equipped with temperature-limit controls. Be sure to check periodically the high-limit controls for all types of furnaces.

Heat Distribution

Warm-Air Systems

Horizontal supply ducts, vertical ducts, risers, boots, and register boxes can reach hazardous temperatures if the high-temperature-limit control malfunctions. Thus, it is essential that combustibles be kept away from them. NFPA 90B, *Standard for the Installation of Warm Air Heating and Air Conditioning Systems,* contains required clearances for many warm-air ductwork configurations.

Steam and Hot Water Systems

Hot water pipes and radiators in systems operating with a maximum temperature of 150°F require no installation clearances. Those supplied with hot water up to 250°F or with steam at a pressure up to 15 psig require a clearance of 1 inch from combustibles. Where these pipes pass through a floor, wall, or ceiling, the clearance at the opening through the finish boards must be at least 1/2 inch and covered with a plate of noncombustible material.

Installation

A major consideration in the installation of any heat-producing appliance is its effect on nearby combustibles. Wood and other combustibles can ignite at temperatures well below their usual ignition temperatures if they are continually exposed to moderate heat over long periods of time. For this reason, installation clearances are of the utmost importance, as is insulating combustible surfaces. Extensive information on clearances is given in Section 2, Chapter 4, of the *Fire Protection Handbook*, 17th edition. Check these distances during an inspection.

Listings of tested heating equipment indicate the materials upon which the equipment can be mounted, such as combustible floors, fire-resistive floors extending specific distances beyond the equipment, masonry floors, or metal-over-wood floors. The *Fire Protection Handbook* covers these materials thoroughly by type of appliance, while laboratory listings cover them by manufacturer's model. You should check the materials and consult the references.

As a result of the energy crisis, buildings are being insulated more thoroughly, and cracks and crevices are being sealed. However, there should be enough air available for combustion and ventilation. An oxygen-starved fire is a dirty and inefficient fire that will lead quickly to maintenance problems. Additional air for ventilation also helps carry away the heat that develops on the surface of the equipment.

Equipment rooms that contain combustion equipment should be inspected for a positive means of combustion air. This is especially important if there are any exhaust fans operating in the area because they could draw a reverse flow down the stack or flue. NFPA 54, *National Fuel Gas Code,* contains specific recommendations on how to supply the air required for combustion and ventilation.

Chimney and Vent Connectors

Chimney and vent connectors are those lengths of pipe or conduit that connect the heat-producing appliance to the chimney or vent. Connectors are made of noncombustible, corrosion-resistant material, such as steel or refractory masonry, that can withstand flue gas temperatures and resist physical damage. Connectors must be short, well fitted and supported, and continuously pitched toward the chimney or vent. They also should have adequate clearance from combustibles.

Vents

Vents are used with specific types of heat-producing equipment. In buildings in which vertical openings must be protected, vents should be enclosed in fire-resistive construction. For buildings less than four stories high, the construction must have a 1-hour fire-resistance rating. For buildings of four stories or more, the construction must have a 2-hour rating.

Chimneys

There are three major types of chimneys: masonry, factory-built, and metal.

Masonry Chimneys: A masonry chimney should be inspected along its entire length, so far as it is accessible. You can examine the inside of the chimney by placing a mirror in a connector opening and catching the sunlight. On the roof, note the condition of the mortar, the chimney lining, and the flashing, and look for evidence of cracking or settling. Note the number of flues. In the attic and the basement, check for cracks and loose mortar. On other floors, check chimney connections.

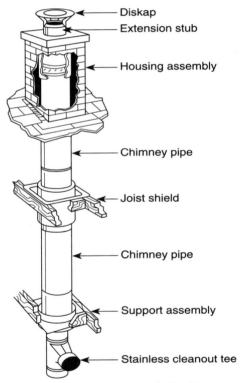

Diskap

Extension stub

Housing assembly

Chimney pipe

Joist shield

Chimney pipe

Support assembly

Stainless cleanout tee

Figure 8-5. A typical factory-built chimney. (Metalbestos Division, Wallace-Murray Corporation)

One simple method of determining whether a chimney is unsafe is to hold your hand against it while it is in use. If it is too hot for comfort, no combustible material should be permitted to come in contact with it. You also should check the mortar. If it has begun to fall from between the bricks, openings can be expected to develop all the way through the wall. You can tell it is time to rebuild the chimney if you can push a sharp instrument through the wall. The tops of chimneys are the places most likely to need rebuilding.

Factory-Built Chimneys: Factory-built chimneys are lightweight assemblies and good draft producers. Some types resemble Type B gas vents, but they are larger and heavier. The materials used in their construction meet certain requirements for heat- and corrosion-resistance, and, where applicable, they have passed physical tests for crushing and for freezing and thawing. Factory-built chimneys are available in listed assemblies for low- and medium-heat appliance service.

Metal Chimneys: Metal chimneys are suitable for all classes of appliances, but they are not subjected to safety testing of any kind. The major hazard to look for when inspecting these chimneys is inadequate clearance from combustibles where they penetrate floors, ceilings, and roofs. The conditions under which metal chimneys can be used are quite limited and are spelled out in detail in NFPA 211, *Standard for Chimneys, Fireplaces, Vents, and Solid Fuel-Burning Appliances.*

Checklist of Chimney Defects

The following is a list of common and important chimney defects that, individually or in combination, constitute sufficient reason for requiring that a masonry chimney be repaired or rebuilt.

1. The design or proportionate dimensions of the chimney are structurally unsound.
2. There is evidence of settling or cracking due to inadequate footings or other causes.
3. The chimney rests upon, or is wholly or partly carried by, wooden floors, beams, or brackets, or it is hung by metal stirrups from wooden construction. The chimney is used to support any wooden floor or roof beams.

4. The chimney increases in size, has projecting masonry, or is set back within 6 inches above or below the rafters or roof joists.
5. The chimney is unlined, and its walls are not as thick as required.
6. The masonry is unbonded or improperly bonded, or the sections are not properly anchored or reinforced.
7. The mortar is weak.
8. Old mortar is decayed, due to the action of the flue gases, or it is weathering. The chimney is not properly finished at top.
9. The brickwork is not laid up around the lining. In other words, the lining was dropped into place after walls were constructed.
10. Linings are cracked or broken.
11. There is no fire clay or metal thimbles at the openings for connec tors.
12. Connector openings are found in more than one story for a single flue, and no provision has been made effectively closing unused openings.
13. The flues show leakage in a smoke test.
14. Flue linings are not complete from 8 inches below the connector openings to the top of the chimney.
15. There is a reduction in the cross-sectional area of a flue at any point.
16. The flue is positioned at greater than 30° angle with vertical.
17. The chimney does not extend at least 3 feet above a flat roof or 2 feet above the edge of a gable or hipped roof.
18. Woodwork, particularly beams and joists, is within 2 inches of the outside surface of the entire chimney.
19. Combustible material or construction is located near an ash pit or the cleanout doors, or access to such doors is blocked.

Bibliography

Boiler and Pressure Vessel Code, Section IV, American Society of Mechanical Engineers, New York, NY. Defines low-pressure boilers and hot-water boilers.

Chimneys, Factory-Built Residential Type and Building Heating Appliance, ANSI/UL 103, Underwriters Laboratories, Inc., Northbrook, IL. A testing standard for factory-built chimneys.

Cote, A.E., ed., *Fire Protection Handbook,* 17th edition, National Fire Protection Association, Quincy, MA, 1991. Section 2, Chapter 4 is a detailed treatment of heating systems and appliances.

Gas and Oil Equipment Directory, Underwriters Laboratories, Inc., Northbrook, IL. Issued annually. A directory of tested and listed oil- and gas-fired heating equipment.

Medium Heat Appliance Factory Built Chimneys, ANSI/UL 959, Underwriters Laboratories, Inc., Northbrook, IL. A safety test standard for chimneys.

NFPA Codes, Standards, and Recommended Practices

NFPA 30, *Flammable and Combustible Liquids Code*. Requirements for tank storage, valves and fittings, container storage, industrial plants, bulk plants, and processing plants.

NFPA 31, *Standard for the Installation of Oil-Burning Equipment*. Requirements for stationary and portable oil-burning equipment, tanks, piping, and accessories.

NFPA 54, *National Fuel Gas Code*. General criteria for safe design, installation, operation, and maintenance of gas piping in buildings and gas appliances in residential, commercial, and industrial applications.

NFPA 58, *Standard for the Storage and Handling of Liquefied Petroleum Gases*. Covers LP-Gas systems, liquid transfer, truck transportation, engine fuel systems, and buildings or structures housing LP-Gas distribution facilities.

NFPA 70, *National Electrical Code*. Contains wiring requirements for furnaces.

NFPA 85C, *Standard for the Prevention of Furnace Explosions/Implosions in Multiple Burner Boiler-Furnaces*. Covers design, installation, operation, and maintenance requirements.

NFPA 86C, *Standard for Industrial Furnaces Using a Special Processing Atmosphere*. Covers Class C industrial furnaces that use a special processing atmosphere, including salt baths and integral quench furnaces. Sets requirements for location, construction, heating system, safety controls, operation, and fire protection.

NFPA 86D, *Standard for Industrial Furnaces Using Vacuum as an Atmosphere*. Applies to the design, construction, and protection of Class D industrial furnaces that operate at above ambient temperatures to over 5,000°F and at pressures normally below atmosphere to 10-8 Torr.

NFPA 90B, *Standard for the Installation of Warm Air Heating and Air Conditioning Systems*. Installation requirements for supply ducts, controls, clearances, heating panels, return ducts, air filters, heat pumps, and other components for one- and two-family dwellings of 25,000 cubic feet or less.

NFPA 97, *Standard Glossary of Terms Relating to Chimneys, Vents, and Heat-Producing Appliances*. Defines terms.

NFPA 211, *Standard for Chimneys, Fireplaces, Vents, and Solid Fuel-Burning Appliances*. Requirements for safe installation and use in residential, commercial, and industrial applications.

NFPA 8501, *Standard for Single Burner Boiler Operation*. Covers design, installation, operation, and maintenance requirements.

NFPA 8503, *Standard for Pulverized Fuel Systems*. Details requirements for the design, installation, operation, maintenance, and personnel safety around pulverized fuel systems.

CHAPTER 9

Air Conditioning and Ventilating Systems

*A*ir conditioning systems control the temperature and humidity of air, clean it, and distribute it to meet the requirements of a conditioned space. There are many types of air conditioning systems, such as those that provide filtered, cooled, and dehumidified air in summer and heated, humidified air in winter.

Air conditioning systems have three major components: the air intake system, the conditioning equipment, and the distribution system.

Air-Intake System

Some systems mix fresh air with recirculated air, while others use fresh air exclusively. In either case, there must be an air-intake duct to introduce fresh air into the system. The opening of this duct should be protected with a grill or screen to prevent foreign materials from entering the system. Make sure that the duct is not broken, clogged, or missing and that it is free of rubbish and debris.

Conditioning Equipment

Fans, air heating and cooling units, and filters should be installed in a room that is separated from the rest of the building by construction with a 1-hour fire-resistance rating. This enclosure also should be equipped with a 3/4-hour fire door with closer. Automatic sprinklers can be used in lieu of fire separation, however.

Some systems use smoke detectors to stop the fan and close dampers during a fire. These devices should be inspected and tested periodically.

You also should inspect equipment rooms to make sure they are clean and that nothing is being stored in them. Such enclosures often are used to store air filters, paper products, and light bulbs; they should not be.

Fans

Lack of lubrication and accumulations of dust are two of the greatest enemies of fans and motors. Both can cause the equipment to overheat so much that it actually becomes an ignition source.

Check the fan belts for wear, and have them replaced if necessary. Although fans often are located in places that are difficult to reach, they should nonetheless be included in the inspection program.

Heating and Cooling Equipment

The hazards of cooling equipment are related to the hazards of electrical installations—proper wiring and grounding are discussed in Chapter 7, "Electrical Systems"—and to those of the refrigerant itself. Most common refrigerants are at least slightly toxic so a leak in the system will be hazardous to health and life safety. Some refrigerants present a combustibility hazard, as well. However, the greatest problem associated with refrigeration units is the explosion hazard of the pressurized refrigerant.

The fire experience of air conditioning refrigeration units generally is good as long as the cooling equipment is properly installed and maintained. In your inspection, be sure to check the quality of maintenance performed on the equipment and the housekeeping in the vicinity of the equipment. Because equipment rooms traditionally are used to store chemicals, lawn and snow removal equipment, and supplies, they may warrant protection with smoke detection and fire extinguishing systems. Recommendations for the installation of mechanical refrigeration equipment are contained in the *Safety Code for Mechanical Refrigeration* (see Bibliography).

The hazards of air-heating equipment depend on the method of heating used. Heating equipment is discussed in Chapter 8, "Heating Systems."

Air-Cleaning Equipment

The purpose of filters and air cleaners is to remove entrained dust and other particulate matter from the air stream. The filtered particles accumulate in the filter or on the air-cleaner collector plates and, if ignited, could burn and produce a large volume of smoke. The products of combustion could be circulated throughout the building by the air-distribution system, posing a threat to life.

Many systems have draft gauges that visibly or audibly indicate an excessive pressure drop across the filters, letting the occupants know that the filters should be cleaned or replaced. Filters should have either a Class 1 or Class 2 rating in accordance with UL 900, *Test Performance of Air Filter Units.* Most systems have disposable filters, which should be discarded when dirty and then replaced. Other systems have a washable medium, which should be cleaned in accordance with the manufacturer's instructions and recoated with adhesive. This adhesive must have a flash point not lower than 325°F as measured in the Pensky-Martens closed tester (ASTM D 93, *Standard Test for Flash Point by Pensky-Martens Closed Tester).*

Electronic air cleaners use electrostatic precipitation to remove particulate matter. Entrained particles pass through electrostatic fields and are collected either on a filter or on charged plates. Because electronic air cleaners use lethal voltages and currents, they are equipped with interlocks that shut down the unit if a door or access panel is opened. As you make your inspection, note that the interlocks are intact and have not been bypassed. Some systems have an automatic wash and recoating cycle for proper plate operation. These systems should be checked to ensure they are operating properly and to ascertain that the correct cleaning solvents and adhesives are being used. Other systems use disposable filters, which are simply discarded when dirty and replaced.

Distribution Equipment

Conditioned air is distributed throughout the building through the duct system. During a fire, the same duct system could disperse smoke and toxic gases instead of breathable air throughout the building.

Generally, ducts are of metal, masonry, fiberglass, or other approved materials. The Sheet Metal and Air Conditioning Contractors National Association (SMACNA) publishes information about the construction of ducts.

UL 181, *Factory-Made Air Ducts and Connectors,* classifies duct materials according to flame spread, smoke development, and flame

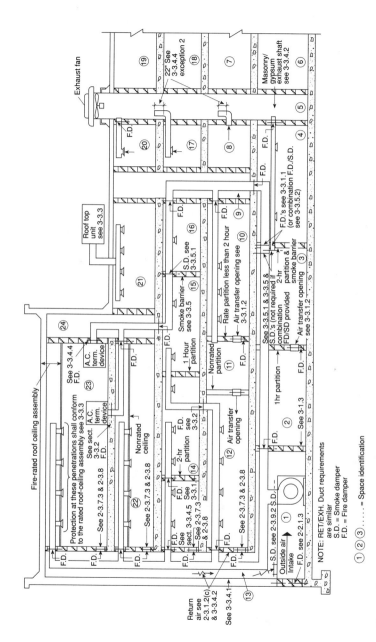

Figure 9-1. A typical installation of an air conditioning system showing penetration protection in a building. (Paragraph numbers refer to NFPA 90A, and explanations can be found in that standard.) Source: Figure 3-3, NFPA 90A, Standard for the Installation of Air Conditioning and Ventilating Systems, NFPA, Quincy, MA, 1993.

penetration. Class O materials have a flame spread and smoke development rating of O. Class 1 materials have a flame spread rating of 25 or less, with no evidence of continued progressive combustion, and a smoke development rating of not more than 50. Class 2 materials have a flame spread rating greater than 25 but not more than 50, with no evidence of continued progressive combustion, and a smoke development rating of not more than 50 for the inside surface of the duct and not more than 100 for the outside surface. Class O and Class 1 materials must pass a 30-minute flame penetration test, and Class 2 materials must pass a 15-minute flame penetration test.

Ducts can create both vertical and horizontal openings in structural fire barriers. As a fire inspector, your interest is in seeing that, where the ducts pass through fire barriers or fire walls, adequate firestopping has been provided to seal the space between the duct walls and the edges of the opening. If properly installed and firestopped, sheet metal ducts in the gauges commonly used can protect an opening in a fire barrier for up to 1 hour. Openings in a fire wall, ceiling, or floor may have to be protected with a fire damper. These should be inspected, cleaned, and tested for proper operation every four years. Fire dampers should be listed in accordance with UL 555, *Fire Dampers and Ceiling Dampers.*

Smoke Control

Two recognized approaches to controlling smoke in buildings make use of the air conditioning system. The passive approach requires that fans be shut down and that smoke dampers in ductwork be closed during a fire. In the active approach, the air conditioning system is used to exhaust the products of combustion to the outdoors to prevent smoke migration from the fire area.

When the active approach is used, most of the smoke and fire dampers may be omitted from the system. Smoke dampers used in the passive form of smoke control should be installed in ducts at the main fan room. They also should be installed in ducts that penetrate smoke partitions and controlled by smoke detectors located in the ducts or the occupied space.

Smoke dampers should be listed in accordance with UL 555S, *Leakage Rated Dampers for Use in Smoke Control Systems.* NFPA 92A, *Recommended Practice for Smoke-Control Systems,* and NFPA 92B, *Guide for Smoke Management Systems in Malls, Atria, and Large Areas,* contain recommendations for periodically testing smoke control systems.

Ventilating Systems

Special ventilation systems often are needed to remove flammable vapors, corrosive vapors or fumes, grease-laden air from cooking equipment, or combustible dusts from an occupancy. Among the hazards such systems present is the possibility that sparks generated by fans, foreign materials in the air stream, or overheated bearings will ignite the flammable materials or vapors.

To reduce the hazard of fire, fans should be of noncombustible construction, accessible for maintenance, and structurally sound enough to resist wear. Occupants also should be able to shut the fans down by remote control. In systems used to exhaust flammable solids or vapors, fan blades and housing should be constructed of nonferrous metal to minimize the possibility of spark generation.

These special exhaust systems should be independent of other ventilating systems and of one another. They should be vented directly outdoors by the shortest route and should not pass through fire walls. For specific hazards, these systems might contain special extinguishing systems. A schedule for inspecting, testing, and cleaning the system should be developed if one is not already in use. Commercial kitchen exhaust systems are discussed in Chapter 47, "Venting Systems for Commercial Cooking Equipment."

Maintenance

A maintenance and cleaning schedule is the key to safely operating air conditioning and ventilating systems. As you inspect the equipment, look for signs of rust and corrosion, especially on moving parts. Check the condition of the filters and the electrical wiring, and examine air ducts for accumulations of combustible dust and lint. Recommend cleaning if necessary.

The fire protection devices associated with the system—that is, the fire suppression and smoke control equipment, the alarms, the fire and smoke dampers, and so on—should be tested periodically as part of the maintenance program. If you do not witness these tests or conduct them yourself, ask to see the records of the tests that were performed.

Bibliography

Cote, A. E., ed., *Fire Protection Handbook,* 17th edition, National Fire Protection Association, Quincy, MA, 1991. Section 6, Chapter 13; Section 6, Chapter 7; and Section 6, Chapter 19, are detailed treatments of air conditioning, smoke control, and air-moving equipment.

Factory-Made Air Ducts and Connectors, UL 181, Underwriters Laboratories, Inc., Northbrook, IL.

Fire Dampers and Ceiling Dampers, UL 555, 3rd edition, Underwriters Laboratories, Inc., Northbrook, IL.

Leakage Rated Dampers for Use in Smoke Control Systems, UL 555S, Underwriters Laboratories, Inc., Northbrook, IL.

Linville, J. L., ed., *Industrial Fire Hazards Handbook,* 2nd edition, National Fire Protection Association, Quincy, MA, 1984. Chapter 45 deals with the design, hazards, and equipment of air-moving systems.

Safety Code for Mechanical Refrigeration, ANSI 15, American National Standards Institute, New York, NY. Describes the requirements for the installation of air conditioning equipment and ducts.

Standard Test for Flash Point by Pensky-Martens Closed Tester, ASTM D 93, American Society for Testing and Materials, Philadelphia, PA.

Test Performance of Air Filter Units, UL 900, Underwriters Laboratories, Inc., Northbrook, IL.

NFPA Codes, Standards, and Recommended Practices

NFPA 70, *National Electrical Code.* Contains wiring and grounding requirements for electrical equipment.

NFPA 90A, *Standard for the Installation of Air Conditioning and Ventilating Systems.* A standard to restrict the spread of smoke, heat, and fire through duct systems to minimize ignition sources and permit the system to be used for emergency smoke control.

NFPA 91, *Standard for Exhaust Systems for Air Conveying of Materials.* Covers safety requirements for fans, ducts, direct clearances, design, and dust-collecting systems for removal or transport of flammable vapors, corrosive fumes, dust stock, and refuse.

NFPA 92A, *Recommended Practice for Smoke-Control Systems.* Covers smoke control using barriers, airflows, and pressure differentials so as to confine smoke to the zone of fire origin and thus maintain a tenable environment in other zones.

NFPA 92B, *Guide for Smoke Management Systems in Malls, Atria, and Large Areas.* Covers the complex problem of maintaining a tenable condition within large zones of fire origin and the physics involved in such spaces.

NFPA 96, *Standard for the Installation of Equipment for the Removal of Smoke and Grease-Laden Vapors from Commercial Cooking Equipment.* Covers the design, installation, and use of exhaust system hoods, grease-removal devices, ducts, dampers, air-moving devices, and fire extinguishing equipment.

NFPA 101, *Life Safety Code.* Covers established minimum requirements that will provide a reasonable degree of safety from fire, smoke, fumes, or panic.

CHAPTER 10

Fire Alarm Systems

F ire alarm systems perform several functions vital to limiting life and property losses during fires. They can provide fire detection, early warning for evacuation, and local fire brigade or public fire department notification.

Inspecting a fire alarm system while it is being installed will allow you to determine whether the system is being installed in accordance with the manufacturer's plans and specifications and in compliance with the requirements of NFPA 72, *National Fire Alarm Code.*

Once the installation has been completed, an inspection and a functional acceptance test of the system will identify any part that is not working properly. Periodic inspections and functional tests throughout the life of the fire alarm system help determine if any part of the system has failed. Although fire alarm systems have power supplies and means of interconnecting the components "monitored for integrity," the advent of solid state electronic components in these systems has introduced numerous unsupervised components and junctions that can fail without notification of the failure. Such a failure can impair part or all of the system without any apparent change in the system's status.

Types of Fire Alarm Systems

There are six general types of commercial and industrial fire alarm systems—central station, local, auxiliary, remote station, proprietary, and emergency voice/alarm communication—and they all share some basic features. Each has alarm initiating device circuits that provide a means of interconnecting the fire alarm control unit with manual fire alarm boxes, waterflow-actuated alarm initiating devices, automatic fire detectors, or other fire alarm initiating devices. The control unit has both a primary, or main, power supply and a secondary, or standby, power supply.

Local and emergency voice/alarm communication systems have one or more notification appliance circuits that connect audible and visible alarm notification appliances to the fire alarm control unit. These alarm notification appliances notify people at the protected property of the fire. Depending on the needs of the property protected, the audible or visible alarm notification appliances may consist of bells, horns, sirens, chimes, loudspeakers, incandescent or stroboscopic lamps, annunciators, punch tape registers, alpha-numeric printers, or digital displays on a visual display unit.

Central station, auxiliary, remote station, and proprietary systems have signaling line circuits that connect the fire alarm control unit with a supervising station that monitors the signals from the fire alarm system.

Table 10-1 describes the differences between the various fire alarm systems, all of which must comply with the requirements of NFPA 72,

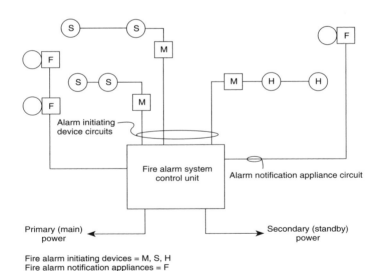

Figure 10-1. Basic components of a local fire alarm system.

Table 10-1. Types of fire alarm systems.

Type	Description	Comments
1. Central station fire alarm system	A system, or group of systems, in which the operation of circuits and devices are transmitted automatically to, recorded in, maintained by, and supervised from a listed or approved central station having competent and experienced servers and operators who, upon receipt of a signal take such action as required by the standard. Such service is to be controlled and operated by a person, firm, or corporation whose business is the furnishing, maintaining, or monitoring of supervised signaling systems.	This system protects property by allowing operators at the central station to retransmit fire alarm signals to the public fire service communication center. It also permits the monitoring of supervisory signals from other protective systems, including guard patrol tours. NFPA 72, *National Fire Alarm Code*, Chapter 3, states the requirements for the premises portion of this system, while Chapter 4 states the requirements for the off-premises portion. Chapters 1, 5, 6, and 7 also apply and cover fundamentals, initiating devices, notification appliances, and testing and maintenance, respectively.
2. Local fire alarm system	A system sounding an alarm at the protected premises as the result of the manual operation of a fire alarm box or the operation of protection equipment or systems, such as water flowing in a sprinkler system and the discharge of carbon dioxide, the detection of smoke, or the detection of heat.	This system notifies building occupants of a fire so they may evacuate. It may also notify the local fire brigade of the location of a fire so they may promptly respond. NFPA 72, *National Fire Alarm Code*, Chapter 3, states the requirements for this system. Chapters 1, 5, 6, and 7 also apply and cover fundamentals, initiating devices, notification appliances, and testing and maintenance, respectively

Continued

Table 10-1. Types of fire alarm systems *(Continued)*

Type	Description	Comments
3. Auxiliary fire alarm system	A connection to the municipal fire alarm protective signaling system for transmitting an alarm of fire to the public fire service communication center. Fire alarms from an auxiliary fire alarm system are received at the public fire service communication system on the same equipment and by the same methods as alarms transmitted manually from municipal fire alarm boxes located on the streets.	This system protects property by transmitting fire alarm signals to the public fire service communication center. NFPA 72, *National Fire Alarm Code*, Chapter 3, states the requirements for the premises portion of this system, while Chapter 4 states the requirements for the off-premises portion. Chapters 1, 5, 6, and 7 also apply and cover fundamentals, initiating devices, notification appliances, and testing and maintenance, respectively.
4. Remote station fire alarm system	An installation using a digital alarm communicator system or supervised dedicated circuits, installed in accordance with the standard to transmit alarms supervisory and trouble signals from one or more protected premises to a remote location at which appropriate action is taken.	This system protects property by transmitting fire alarm signals to the public fire service communication center, or other location acceptable to the authority having jurisdiction. NFPA 72, *National Fire Alarm Code*, Chapter 3, states the requirements for the premises portion of this system, while Chapter 4 states the requirements for the off-premises portion. Chapters 1, 5, 6, and 7 also apply and cover fundamentals, initiating devices, notification appliances, and testing and maintenance, respectively.

Continued

Table 10-1. Types of fire alarm systems *(Continued)*

Type	Description	Comments
5. Proprietary fire alarm system	An installation of fire alarm systems that serve contiguous and noncontiguous properties under one ownership from a proprietary supervising station located at the protected property, where trained, competent personnel are in consultant attendance. This includes the proprietary supervising station, power supplies, signal initiating devices, initiating device circuits, signal notification appliances, equipment for the automatic, permanent visual recording of signals, and equipment for initiating the operation of emergency building control devices.	This system protects property by transmitting fire alarm signals to the proprietary supervising station where operators will retransmit those signals to the public fire service communication center. NFPA 72, *National Fire Alarm Code,* Chapter 3, states the requirements for the premises portion of this system, while Chapter 4 states the requirements for the off-premises portion. Chapters 1, 5, 6, and 7 also apply and cover fundamentals, initiating devices, notification appliances, and testing and maintenance, respectively.
6. Emergency voice/alarm communication system	A fire alarm system that provides dedicated manual and automatic facilities for the origination, control, and transmission of information and instructions pertaining to a fire emergency to the occupants of a building, and to fire department personnel operating at that building.	This system notifies building occupants of a fire so they may evacuate or relocate to an area of refuge within the building. It may also notify the local fire brigade of the location of a fire so they may promptly respond. NFPA 72, *National Fire Alarm Code,* Chapter 3, states the requirements for this system. Chapters 1, 5, 6, and 7 also apply and cover fundamentals, initiating devices, notification appliances, and testing and maintenance, respectively.

National Fire Alarm Code. Chapter 1 of the code covers the fundamentals of signaling systems. Chapter 2 covers household fire warning equipment, Chapter 3 protected premises fire alarm systems, and Chapter 4 off-premises fire alarm systems. Chapter 5 addresses initiating devices for fire alarm systems. Chapter 6 covers notification appliances for fire alarm systems, and Chapter 7 covers testing and maintenance of fire alarm systems.

Generally, local and emergency voice/alarm communication systems provide life safety protection by notifying occupants that they should evacuate or relocate during a fire. Such systems may also provide property protection by notifying members of the guard force or the local fire brigade of the need to respond to the location of a fire.

In contrast, central station, auxiliary, remote station, and proprietary systems provide property protection by summoning the public fire department. Proprietary systems also may summon the local private fire brigade. These systems may provide life safety protection if they interface with a local or emergency voice/alarm communication system.

You should be familiar with the *National Fire Alarm Code* so that you can determine whether the installer has selected the appropriate alarm initiating devices and notification appliances and has installed them in accordance with the requirements of the code.

Modern fire alarm systems can do much more than transmit a fire alarm. They can operate smoke-control equipment, control elevator recall, control exit doors, or actuate special extinguishing systems. Combination systems can integrate fire alarm functions with burglar alarms, door-entry controls, paging systems, or building energy-management systems.

Chapter 2 of the *National Fire Alarm Code,* "Household Fire Warning Equipment," covers the requirements for fire alarm systems protecting residential occupancies. In many cases, this protection consists of single-station or multiple-station smoke detectors, each powered by a connection to 120 vac or by a 9-volt battery. This self-contained chapter covers all aspects of residential fire alarm protection.

Manual Fire Alarm Boxes

You should verify that the installer has installed manual fire alarm boxes at unobstructed, readily accessible locations throughout the protected area, putting at least one box on each floor. NFPA *101* requires that a manual fire alarm box be located near each required exit. The travel distance to a box should be no more than 200 feet from any point in the area, and the box should be positioned in the normal path of egress. The installer should mount each box so that the bottom of the box is between 3.5 feet and 5 feet from the floor.

Chapter 7 of the *National Fire Alarm Code* specifies the testing frequency for manual fire alarm boxes. When testing, follow the manufacturer's operating instructions (see Fig. 10-2).

Waterflow-Actuated Fire Alarm Initiating Devices

The fire alarm system should monitor the operation of automatic sprinkler systems or other fire extinguishing or suppression systems by means of listed fire alarm initiating devices. When the automatic sprinkler system operates, the waterflow-actuated fire alarm initiating device will initiate a fire alarm signal.

The fire alarm system also should monitor the normal standby condition of these extinguishing or suppression systems by means of listed supervisory initiating devices. If someone closes a sprinkler system control valve or otherwise impairs the protective system, the supervisory initiating device will cause the fire alarm system control unit to indicate a "supervisory off-normal condition." When the valve is reopened or the impairment is cleared, the supervisory initiating device will cause the fire alarm system control unit to indicate a "supervisory restoration to normal" signal.

Automatic Fire Detectors

Fire produces well-defined signatures, most commonly heat, smoke, and radiant energy. Fire alarm system designers should select automatic fire detectors to detect these signatures in accordance with the requirements of Chapter 5 of the *National Fire Alarm Code*. This chapter not only details the selection of detectors, it also sets forth the rules for spacing and installing them.

Chapter 7 of the code discusses the initial acceptance tests, the periodic tests, and the routine maintenance of the detectors and all other

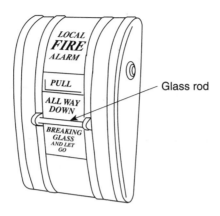

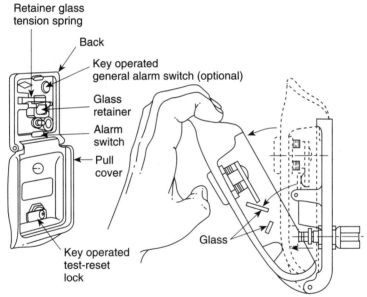

Figure 10-2. Breakglass and single-action manual fire alarm boxes.

fire alarm system components. You should review the records of previous
tests and compare them with the current test results to be sure that all
parts of the system continue to function properly.

Automatic fire detectors may protect a defined number of square feet immediately around the detector—this is the spot-type detector—or an area along the entire length of a detector—this is the line-type detector.

Heat Detectors

Heat detectors respond to the thermal energy signature of a fire and generally are located on or near the ceiling. They respond when the detecting element reaches a predetermined fixed temperature or when a specified rate of temperature rise occurs. You should know the difference between types of detectors.

All detectors should be tested periodically. Restorable detectors can be tested by applying a safe source of heat, while nonrestorable detectors must be tested mechanically or electrically. It is important that you know which types of heat detectors are installed so that you can test all restorable heat detectors; do not test the fusible elements of nonrestorable detectors.

Fixed-Temperature Heat Detectors

These detectors initiate an alarm when the detecting element reaches a predetermined fixed temperature. By the time the detector actually operates, the temperature of the air surrounding the detector has always extended considerably higher than the set point of the detector because of inherent thermal lag.

One form of spot-type fixed-temperature detector uses a fusible element made from a eutectic metal alloy that melts rapidly at a predetermined temperature, commonly 135°F. The fusible links of automatic sprinklers and fire dampers and doors commonly use a similar material. Operation destroys either the entire unit—or at least the operating element—which the system maintainer must replace. Another form of spot-type fixed-temperature heat detector uses a bimetallic element. After operating, the bimetallic type automatically restores when the temperature falls to a point below the set point of the detector.

Rate-of-Rise-Compensated Fixed Temperature Detector

In a slowly developing fire, this form of detector responds when the temperature of the air surrounding it reaches a predetermined level. In a rapidly developing fire, the detector anticipates that the air temperature will reach the operating point, accelerating the operation of the detector. This produces a fixed temperature detector with virtually no thermal lag.

Rate-of-Rise Detector

A rate-of-rise detector will operate when the rate of temperature increase from a fire exceeds a predetermined level, typically around 5°F in 20 seconds or 15°F per minute. Small, normal changes in ambient temperature that can be expected under nonfire conditions will not cause the detector to operate. These detectors are available as both line- and spot-type detectors, and they are restorable.

Combination Detector

Detectors can contain more than one element to respond to a fire. Examples of such detectors include a combination rate-of-rise and fixed-temperature heat detector and a combined smoke and heat detector.

Testing Heat Detectors

A restorable heat detector and the restorable element of a combination detector should be tested by exposing the detector to a safe heat source, such as hot water, a hairdryer, or a shielded heat lamp, until it responds. The detector should reset automatically after each heat test. Precautions should be taken to avoid damaging the nonrestorable fixed-temperature element of a combination rate-of-rise/fixed-temperature detector.

Smoke Detectors

The results of full-scale fire tests, using typical fires in family living units, have shown that detectable quantities of smoke precede detectable levels of heat in nearly all cases. Thus, fire alarm system designers use smoke detectors more extensively today. Three common categories of smoke detectors include the ionization smoke detector, the photoelectric smoke detector, and the air-sampling smoke detector.

Ionization Smoke Detector

An ionization smoke detector contains a small amount of radioactive material that ionizes the air in the sensing chamber, thus rendering it conductive and permitting a current flow through the air between two charged electrodes. When smoke particles enter the chamber, they attach themselves to the ionized air molecules and decrease the conductivity between the electrodes. This decrease in conductivity can be measured by an electronic circuit that initiates a fire alarm signal when the reduction in conductivity reaches a preset threshold.

Photoelectric Light-Scattering Smoke Detector

In a photoelectric light-scattering smoke detector, a light source and a photosensitive sensor are arranged so that the rays from the light source do not normally fall on the photosensitive sensor. When smoke particles enter the light path, they scatter some of the light by reflection and refraction onto the sensor, causing the detector to initiate a fire alarm signal.

Photoelectric Linear Projected Beam Smoke Detector

In a photoelectric linear projected beam smoke detector, a light source and a photosensitive sensor are arranged across a protected space so that the rays from the light source normally fall on the photosensitive sensor. When smoke particles enter the light path, the intensity of the light is reduced, causing the detector to initiate a fire alarm signal.

Air-Sampling Smoke Detector

In an air-sampling smoke detector, a system of tubing and sampling ports draws a sample of air from a protected space into a detection unit. When smoke particles in the air sample enter the detection chamber, their presence causes the detector to initiate a fire alarm signal.

Heat detectors have a listed spacing; smoke detectors do not. The manufacturer of the smoke detector determines the recommended spacing. If the manufacturer does not recommend a spacing, then Chapter 5 of the *National Fire Alarm Code* recommends a spacing of 30 feet.

Testing Smoke Detectors

The person testing the smoke detectors should inspect each detector visually and introduce smoke or some other aerosol acceptable to the manufacturer into the detector at its installed location to ensure that smoke can enter the chamber and initiate an alarm. Some testing companies use a bee smoker as one source of relatively safe smoke. Residential smoke detectors have an integral test means that permits the homeowner to test the detector.

Chapter 5 of the *National Fire Alarm Code* requires that the sensitivity of a smoke detector be tested periodically to ensure that it has remained within the sensitivity listed and marked on the detector. The code permits several methods of testing sensitivity but does not permit the use of unmeasured amounts of an aerosol. In all cases, the person testing should follow the manufacturer's instructions for testing the smoke detectors.

Radiant Energy Sensing Fire Detectors

Designers specify flame and spark/embers detectors for sophisticated detection applications. Custom-engineered for each particular protected space, these detectors often actuate special hazard fire extinguishing or suppression systems.

Testing Radiant Energy Sensing Fire Detectors

Chapter 7 of the *National Fire Alarm Code* states the requirements for testing radiant energy sensing fire detectors. Every six months, the person testing the system should use a source of radiant energy to simulate a fire, spark, or ember and test the operation of each detector. The person testing the system should verify the sensitivity of each detector annually in accordance with the manufacturer's instructions.

Location of Heat and Smoke Detectors

While inspecting a fire alarm system, you should review the location of the heat detectors to make sure that they are in accordance with the requirements of Chapter 5 of the *National Fire Alarm Code*. The installer should have mounted detectors on the ceiling not less than 4 inches from the side wall or on the side walls with 4 inches to 12 inches between the ceiling and the top of the detector. Experts normally consider the space where the ceiling and side wall meet to be a "dead air pocket" or a "void" (see Fig. 10-3). In room fire development, the concentration of fire heat and smoke probably will be low in this dead air space, so detectors should not be located here.

The installer should base the spacing of detectors on the listed spacing modified to take into account ceiling height and the type of ceiling

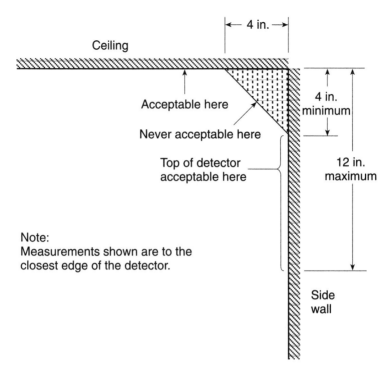

Figure 10-3. Mounting of detectors with respect to dead air space. Source: Figure A-2-5.2.2(b), NFPA 72, National Fire Alarm Code, NFPA, Quincy, MA, 1993.

construction. The distance between the detector measured perpendicular to an end wall, side wall, or partition extending to within 18 inches of the ceiling should not exceed one half the selected spacing. And no point on the ceiling should be more than 0.7 times the final selected spacing from a detector. This allows detectors placed on smooth ceilings in irregularly shaped areas to extend beyond their listed spacing provided the maximum spacing from a detector to the farthest point on a side wall, end wall, or corner is no more than 0.7 times the listed spacing (see Fig. 10-4).

Installers should always mount detectors on the bottoms of joists. However, detectors normally should not be located on the lower flange of

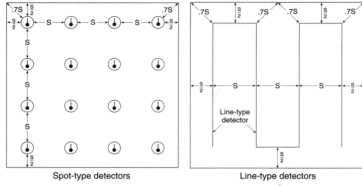

| Spot-type detectors | Line-type detectors |

(🌡) Heat detector

S Spacing between detectors

Figure 10-4. Heat detector spacing. Source: Figures A-5-2.5.1(b) and A-5-2.7.1, NFPA 72, National Fire Alarm Code, NFPA, Quincy, MA 1993.

beams or suspended from the ceiling by conduit. Detectors can be installed on the bottoms of beams that are less than 12 inches deep and less than 8 feet on center.

For peaked or shed ceilings, the installer must first mount detectors within 3 feet of the highest point of the ceiling, measured horizontally from that highest point. The installer then must mount the other detectors following the selected spacing as if mounting the detectors parallel with the floor. In correcting for ceiling height, use the average height above the floor if the slope of the peaked or shed ceiling with respect to the floor exceeds 30 degrees. If the slope is 30 degrees or less, use the height of the highest point.

Instead of adjusting detector spacing following the rigid rules found in Chapter 5 of the *National Fire Alarm Code,* the designer of a fire alarm system can follow the performance approach found in Appendix C of the code. Based on actual fire tests conducted by the Fire Detection Institute, Appendix C bases detector spacing on the fire growth rate and the fire size at which the designer desires detection.

Location of Heat Detectors

Correction for ceiling height must follow the requirements of Table 10-2. For joisted ceilings where the solid joists are more than 4 inches deep and 3 feet or less apart, the spacing corrected for ceiling height should be reduced by half in the direction perpendicular to the joists. For beamed ceilings where the solid beams are more than 4 inches deep and more than 3 feet apart, the spacing corrected for ceiling height should be reduced by one-third in the direction perpendicular to the beams. If the beams are more than 8 inches deep and more than 8 feet apart, the installer should treat each bay formed by the beams as a separate area.

Location of Smoke Detectors

Correction for ceiling height must follow the dictates of engineering judgment. For joisted ceilings where the solid joists are more than 8 inches deep and 3 feet or less apart, the spacing corrected for ceiling height should be reduced by one-third in the direction perpendicular to the joists. For beamed ceilings where the solid beams are more than 4 inches deep and more than 3 feet apart, the spacing corrected for ceiling height should be reduced by following the dictates of engineering judgment. If the beams are more than 8 inches deep and more than 8 feet apart, the installer should treat each bay formed by the beams as a

Table 10-2.

Ceiling Height (ft) Above	Up To	Percent of Listed Spacing
0	10	100
10	12	91
12	14	84
14	16	77
16	18	71
18	20	64
20	22	58
22	24	52
24	26	46
26	28	40
28	30	34

Exception: Table 10-2 does not apply to the following detectors, which rely on the integration effect: Line-type electrical conductivity detectors, pneumatic rate-of-rise tubing, series connected thermoelectric effect detectors. In these cases, the manufacturer's recommendations shall be followed for appropriate alarm point and spacing. *Source:* Table 5-2.7.1.2, NFPA 72, *National Fire Alarm Code,* NFPA, Quincy, MA, 1993.

separate area. In addition, the installer must consider the effects of air flow, reducing the spacing in accordance with Figure 10-5 or Table 10-3. Installers should avoid mounting smoke detectors in the direct air stream of a supply register (see Fig. 10-6).

Location of Radiant Energy Sensing Fire Detectors

A designer must carefully plan the location of radiant energy sensing fire detectors based on the size and location of the expected fire, spark, or ember. Such a design must account for the line of sight between the fire location and the detectors and for the field of view of each detector.

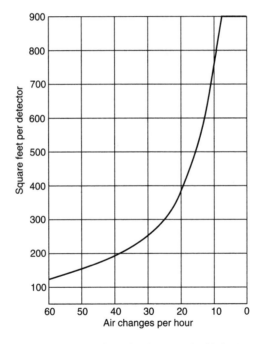

Figure 10-5. Use of smoke detectors in high air movement areas (not to be used for under floor or above ceiling spaces). Source: Figure 5-3.7.6.3, NFPA 72, **National Fire Alarm Code,** *NFPA, Quincy, MA, 1993.*

Table 10-3.

Minutes/Air Change	Air Changes/Hour	Sq Ft/Detector
1	60	125
2	30	250
3	20	375
4	15	500
5	12	625
6	10	750
7	8.6	875
8	7.5	900
9	6.7	900
10	6	900

Source: Table 5-3.7.6.3, NFPA 72, *National Fire Alarm Code,* NFPA, Quincy, MA, 1993.

Wiring Inspection

The installer should install all fire alarm system wiring in accordance with the requirements of NFPA 70, *National Electrical Code.* Depending upon the design of the power supply for the listed fire alarm system, circuits extending from the system control unit will be designated either nonpower-limited or power-limited. Article 760 of the *NEC®* describes in detail the wiring methods permitted for each designation. It also states

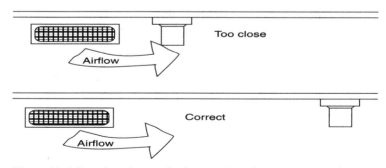

Figure 10-6. Locations for smoke detectors in relation to air supply registers.

requirements for the type of wire and cable permitted, the marking of terminals and of wire and cable, the number of strands permitted for stranded wire, and the proximity of fire alarm wiring to other wiring for other systems. You should review carefully the fire alarm system to determine if it complies with the requirements of Article 760 of the *NEC.*

Monitoring Integrity of Installation Conductors

The integrity of the conductors that interconnect external devices and appliances with the fire alarm system control unit usually is monitored by passing a small current through each wire and through an end-of-line device installed across the end of each circuit. To achieve continuity of the monitoring, no branch circuits are permitted.

A check of the wiring to the supervised fire alarm initiating devices and fire alarm notification appliances should reveal wiring as shown in Figure 10-7, not wiring as shown in Figure 10-8. Furthermore, a check of the riser diagram and the wiring of the risers in the system should reveal that each circuit is wired as shown in Figure 10-9, not as it is shown in Figure 10-10.

In place of this more traditional method, the periodic multiplex interrogation and response communication between individually address-able fire alarm initiating devices and the fire alarm control unit monitors

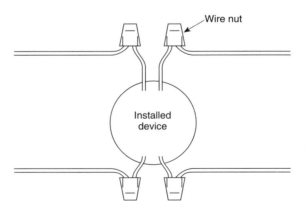

Figure 10-7. Correct wiring method for pigtail connections.

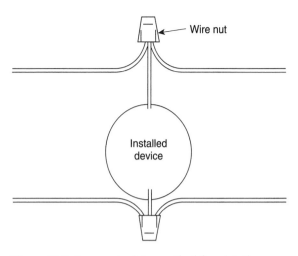

Figure 10-8. Incorrect wiring method for pigtail connections.

the integrity of the interconnecting wiring. Because the system control unit addresses the alarm initiating devices individually, some systems permit the use of branch circuits and eliminate the need for an end-of-line device.

Notification Appliances for Fire Alarm Systems

Local and emergency voice/alarm communication systems both must employ audible and visible alarm notification appliances. Chapter 6 of the *National Fire Alarm Code* contains the details on how to properly locate these appliances so that they will be clearly heard and clearly seen by all occupants. It also gives specific output levels that the appliances must deliver. In addition, Chapter 3 of the *National Fire Alarm Code* specifies that after July 1, 1996, the signal specified in ANSI S3.41, *American National Standard Audible Emergency Evacuation Signal*, must be used.

A distinctive sound that will not be confused with some other signal must be used. Audible alarm notification appliances must produce a sound level that either exceeds the average ambient sound level by at least 15 dBA, or exceeds the maximum sound level by 5 dBA. The average ambient sound level is the root mean square A-weighted sound

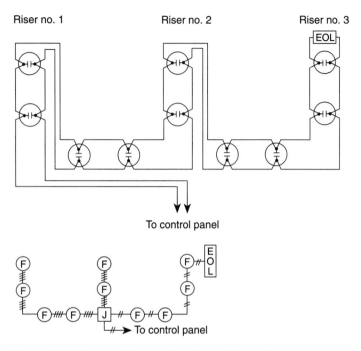

Figure 10-9. Correct wiring method for multiriser circuit.

pressure measured over a 24-hour period. The maximum sound level is a sound pressure level at least one minute in duration that routinely occurs. Temporary sound sources not normally found continuously in the occupied area need not be considered. In sleeping areas, the appliance must produce at least 70 dBA up to a maximum of 15 dBA above the average ambient sound level. In mechanical equipment rooms, a minimum of 85 dBA must be used for the average ambient sound level. Average sound levels above 115 dBA require the use of visible notification appliances.

Where ceiling heights permit, a wall-mounted audible alarm notification appliance must have its top at least 90 inches above the finished floor and at least 6 inches below the finished ceiling. Ceiling-mounted appliances may be used.

The bottom of a visible alarm notification appliance must be between 80 inches and 96 inches above the finished floor. Ceiling-mounted

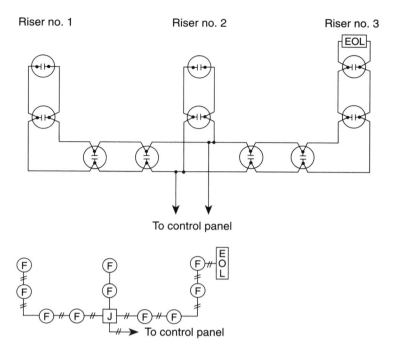

Figure 10-10. Incorrect wiring method for multiriser circuit.

appliances may be used. In sleeping rooms, the visible alarm notification appliance must be located within 16 feet of the pillow. If the distance from the top of the visible notification appliance to the ceiling is 24 inches or greater, then the visible notification appliance must deliver an effective intensity of 100 candelas (cd). If the distance from the top of the appliance to the ceiling is less than 24 inches, then the visible notification appliance must deliver an effective intensity of 177 cd.

In corridors that do not exceed 20 feet in width, one 15 cd visible notification appliance may serve up to 30 feet of corridor, two 15 cd units up to 130 feet of corridor, three 15 cd units up to 230 feet of corridor, four 15 cd units up to 330 feet of corridor, five 15 cd units up to 530 feet of corridor, and six 15 cd units up to 530 feet of corridor.

In rooms, one 15 cd unit may serve an area 20 feet by 20 feet (see Figure 10-11 and Table 10-4)

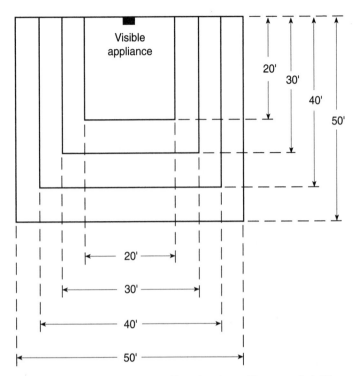

Figure 10-11. Room spacing allocation for wall-mounted visible appliances. NOTE: The above is based on the visible signaling appliance at the halfway distance of the longest wall. In square rooms with appliances not centered or nonsquare rooms, the effective intensity (cd) from one visible signaling appliance shall be determined by maximum room size dimensions obtained either by the distance to the farthest wall or by double the distance to the farthest adjacent wall, whichever is greater, as shown in Table 10-4. Source: Figure 6-4.4.1, NFPA 72, National Fire Alarm Code, NFPA, Quincy, MA, 1993.

Fire Alarm System Testing

Finally, you should test the entire fire alarm system as follows.

First, test the fire alarm system control unit to verify that it is in the normal supervisory condition, as detailed in the manufacturer's instruc-

Table 10-4. Room spacing allocation for wall-mounted visible appliances.

		Minimum Required Light Output, Candela (cd) (Effective Intensity)	
Maximum Room Size	One Light Per Room (cd)	Two Lights per Room (Located on Opposite Walls) (cd)	Four Lights per Room (One Light per Wall) (cd)
20′ X 20′	15	—	—
30′ X 30′	30	15	—
40′ X 40′	60	30	15
50′ X 50′	95	60	30
60′ X 60′	135	95	30
70′ X 70′	185	110	60
80′ X 80′	—	140	60
90′ X 90′	—	180	95
100′ X 100′	—	—	95
110′ X 110′	—	—	135
120′ X 120′	—	—	160
130′ X 130′	—	—	185

Source: Table 6-4.4.1(a), NFPA 72, *National Fire Alarm Code,* NFPA, Quincy, MA, 1993.

tion manual. Then test each initiating device circuit and notification appliance circuit to confirm that the system control unit is monitoring the integrity of the installation conductors. Open the connection at enough initiating devices and notification appliances to ensure a thorough test. Next, test each initiating device and notification appliance for operation and proper response at the system control unit. Test all functions, including all supplementary functions, in accordance with the manufacturer's manual. Finally, test the primary, or main, power supply and the secondary, or standby, power supply.

If anyone makes additions or other changes to the fire alarm system, you should witness a re-acceptance test on all affected portions. This will help ensure the continued integrity of the fire alarm system.

Additional information on fire alarm systems can be found in the publications listed in the Bibliography.

Bibliography

Cote, A. E. ed., *Fire Protection Handbook,* 17th edition, National Fire Protection Association, Quincy, MA, 1991. Section 4 discusses fire alarm systems and fire detection devices.

Bukowski, R. W., O'Laughlin, R. J., and Zimmerman, C. E., *Fire Alarm Signaling Systems Handbook,* National Fire Protection Association, Quincy, MA, 1987.

Carson, W. G. and Klinker, R. L., *Fire Protection Systems: Inspection, Test, and Maintenance Manual,* 2nd edition, NFPA, Quincy, MA, 1992.

The Moore-Wilson Signaling Report. Published by Focus Publishing Enterprises, Bloomfield, CT. This bimonthly newsletter presents a comprehensive listing of questions and answers relating to various fire alarm codes and standards.

NFPA Codes, Standards, and Recommended Practices

NFPA 70, *National Electrical Code.* Contains comprehensive electrical safety requirements for all types of electrical installations. Article 760 contains the specific wiring requirements for fire alarm systems.

NFPA 72, *National Fire Alarm Code.* This code contains the requirements for the installation, testing, maintenance, and use of the various types of fire alarm systems.

CHAPTER 11

Water Supplies

A facility's water supply arrangements should be inspected before any of its water-based fire extinguishing systems are inspected. A general understanding of the piping layout will help you evaluate the level of protection provided by the individual sprinkler, standpipe, water spray, or foam-water systems.

Using NFPA 25

In 1992, the National Fire Protection Association published the first edition of NFPA 25, *Standard for the Inspection, Testing, and Maintenance of Water-Based Fire Protection Systems.* This was a significant development, since it established for the first time a set of definitive minimum requirements relating to the inspection of water-based systems, including their water supply components.

As an inspector, you should become familiar with the requirements of NFPA 25. You also should be aware that standardized forms are now available for use in inspecting automatic sprinkler systems, standpipe systems, private fire service mains, fire pumps, water storage tanks, water spray fixed systems, and foam-water sprinkler systems in accordance with the requirements of NFPA 25.

Where NFPA 25 is enforced, you should check to make sure that the property owner is keeping the records required by the standard to demonstrate compliance with all inspection, testing, and maintenance requirements. It is understood, however, that you may not be the party responsible for inspection procedures in accordance with NFPA 25.

Water Supply Sources and Arrangements

The first step in inspecting a facility's water supply is to identify the sources of the supply. This can begin during the initial exterior inspection as you note the locations of hydrants and exterior control valves and determine whether elevated water storage tanks, ground water storage reservoirs, or other sources of water exist. You also should note the location of exterior fire department connections, since these devices are considered auxiliary sources of water supply. Visible external attachments of sprinkler systems, such as water motor alarm gongs and drains, can help you locate the position of system control equipment within a building complex.

When identifying the sources of the water supply, you may find building site plans and previous inspection reports extremely helpful, as they may point out unlikely sources of supply, such as swimming pools or decorative ponds. Property owners or their representatives also can be of assistance in this regard. For large facilities or industrial complexes, maps and other information regarding the water supplies should be available at the facility, the local fire department, or from an insurance rating bureau.

In a city or developed suburban area, the water for fire protection commonly comes from a public water supply system. In rural areas, it may come from private water systems, which can consist of a combination of tanks, reservoirs, and pumps. In many locations, the fire protection supplies are a combination of public and private supplies. It is common to augment the pressure of a public water supply with a private fire pump that supplies the water pressures needed to effectively operate the water-based fire extinguishing system.

Sources of water supply may include surface lakes, rivers, and impounded supplies, but these are considered acceptable for fire protection use only if they are available on a year-round basis. For this reason, you should make a special effort to inspect these sources during periods of freezing weather and drought.

Water supplied to private fire systems from a public water supply is sometimes metered. To allow accurate metering of small flows while avoiding high pressure losses for large flows, the meters often are equipped with a bypass feature. The normal water flow is through the small metered bypass. In the event of a fire and a large flow demand, the large flow will lift a weighted clapper in the main waterway, allowing water to flow unobstructed through the system. Obviously, the fire flow is not metered in such a case; fire flow from public fire hydrants is never metered.

Backflow Protection for Public Water Supplies

Whatever the arrangements, the water used for fire protection must be segregated by valves from the potable water that is delivered through the public water supply system. This is necessary to prevent backflow, a reverse flow of water that could take place if the pressure of the public water supply system dropped below that of the private fire protection systems it serves.

A number of studies have shown that potable water from a public supply stored in the piping of a fire extinguishing system over a long period can become aesthetically objectionable. While the water does not pose a health risk, its backflow into a public supply is obviously undesirable. For this reason, private fire protection systems traditionally have been separated from public water supplies by means of check valves, which permit only one-way flow into the fire protection systems. Control valves generally are located at the same places to isolate the systems and to permit repair of the check valves.

Special backflow prevention devices generally are required where fire protection systems are served by additional water supply sources or where additives, such as antifreeze or corrosion inhibitors, are used. These devices usually are either double check valve assembly backflow preventers or reduced-pressure principle backflow prevention assembly (RPBA) devices. The more elaborate RPBA-type devices generally are required only where contamination of the public water supply is a possibility. This would be the case where the additional water supply source was an open reservoir or where antifreeze or other additives were mixed into the water supply.

The fire department connection to a sprinkler or standpipe system does not warrant the use of a backflow prevention device unless the fire department's pre-fire planning includes provisions for supplying the connection from an open pond or other potential source of contamination.

The appendix of NFPA 24, *Standard for the Installation of Private Fire Service Mains and Their Appurtenances,* addresses the need for backflow prevention equipment on fire protection systems. Because backflow prevention devices have inherent pressure losses, they should not be installed on existing fire protection water supply mains unless the available water supply pressures and system demands have been analyzed by a qualified fire protection contractor or fire protection engineer. Otherwise, the system's ability to perform its intended fire suppression function could be impaired.

Inspecting Valves

The single most important feature you can check is the position of control valves. Water supply system control valves must be in the "open" position.

Post indicator valves used in yards indicate their position by means of an "open" or "shut" sign visible through a window in the valve face. Outside stem and yoke (OS & Y) valves indicate their position by means of the valve screw or stem. Because a visible screw or stem means the valve is open, the valve is sometimes referred to as an "open screw and yoke" valve. Other types of valves use indicating markers. Since the key-operated gate valves frequently used by public water utilities are not indicating valves, water must often be flowed through the fire protection system to verify whether these valves are open.

Each control valve must be identified and have a sign indicating the system or portion of the system it controls. NFPA 25 requires that each valve be secured in its normal open or closed position by means of a seal or a lock, or that it be electrically supervised in accordance with the applicable NFPA standards. An exception waives this requirement for valves controlling flow to wall and roof outlets.

NFPA 25 requires that all types of valves be inspected weekly, including hose valves, pressure regulating valves, and the valves that isolate backflow prevention devices. An exception permits monthly inspections for valves secured with locks and valves supervised in accordance with applicable NFPA standards.

When you inspect a valve, you must verify that the valves are in the normal open or closed position, and that they are properly sealed, locked, or supervised. The valves also must be accessible, free from external leaks, and provided with appropriate identification and the appropriate wrenches.

Control valves must be tested quarterly, with the valve opened until spring or torsion is felt in the rod. This indicates that the rod has not

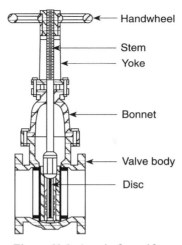

Figure 11-1. A typical outside screw and yoke (OS & Y) valve. This one is currently in the closed position. Note that the screw stem is not extending past the handwheel. Source: Figure A-9-1(f), NFPA 25, **Standard for the Inspection, Testing, and Maintenance of Water-Based Fire Protection Systems,** *NFPA, Quincy, MA, 1992.*

become detached from the valve. Each control valve must be operated through its full range and then returned to its normal position annually.

Inspecting Fire Department Connections

Fire department connections must be inspected monthly to verify that they are visible and accessible, that couplings and swivels have not been damaged and rotate smoothly, and that plugs or caps are in place and undamaged. Gaskets should be in place and in good condition, and the automatic drain valve should be in place and operating properly. Identification signs also should be in place. Finally, the check valve should be examined to make sure it is not leaking.

If you find that the plugs or caps are not in place, you must inspect the interior of the fire department connection for possible obstructions and verify that the valve clapper is operational over its full range.

Inspecting Private Fire Service Mains and Yard Hydrants

A private fire service main is piping on private property located between a source of water and a sprinkler system, standpipe system, water spray system, foam-water system, hydrant, or monitor nozzle. When connected to a public water system, the private fire service main begins at a point designated by the public water utility, usually at a manually operated valve near the property line.

In some cases, there may be no exclusive private fire service main. This is the case with residential sprinkler systems, for example. Instead, a combined service main might serve both domestic and fire protection demands. Special care must be taken in these situations to ensure that the water needed for fire protection purposes will be available even in times of peak domestic demand. NFPA 13R, *Standard for the Installation of Sprinkler Systems in Residential Occupancies Up to and Including Four Stories in Height,* provides a means of estimating simultaneous domestic demand through combined supply piping. A similar situation may also exist in industrial facilities if a combined service main serves both fire protection and process demands.

In other cases, a private fire service main might serve a system of yard hydrants or monitor nozzles protecting an factory complex, tank farm, or other special hazard. This system could include hose/hydrant houses, located over or next to hydrants to provide ready access to hose nozzles, hose wrenches, gaskets, and spanners.

The authority having jurisdiction determines the needed fire flow and hydrant locations for a yard hydrant system, but NFPA 24 limits hose lengths to 500 feet. The standard also specifies that, for average conditions, hydrants must be placed at least 40 feet from buildings. Hydrant outlets must have the NH standard external threads for the size outlet supplied, as specified in NFPA 1963, *Standard for Screw Threads and Gaskets for Fire Hose Connections.* Where local fire departments do not use the NH threads, however, the authority having jurisdiction designates the connection to be used.

NFPA 25 calls for monthly inspections of any hose/hydrant houses to check accessibility, repair physical damage, and replace missing equipment. Dry barrel and wall hydrants must be inspected semiannually; wet hydrants must be inspected at least annually. All hydrants also should be checked after each operation. In addition to ensuring that hydrants are accessible and wrenches available, you should confirm that the outlets are tight and that the nozzle threads and hydrant operating nut are not worn. Leaks in outlets or at the top of the hydrant should be repaired.

You must check drainage from the barrel of dry barrel and wall hydrants. The presence of water or ice may indicate a faulty drain, a leaky hydrant valve, or a high groundwater table.

You may use the following checklist when inspecting hydrants:

1. Check that the hydrant is set up plumb with outlets approximately 18 inches above the ground. The hydrant should be unobstructed and easily accessible, and it should be clear of snow in the winter.

2. Open and close the hydrant to verify that it is working properly. Note the direction of turn and number of turns needed to open it fully. It is useful to post a sign on the hydrant showing this information.

3. Check that the hydrant drains properly. If the drain is working properly, you should be able to feel a suction at the outlets immediately after you close the valve. There is a small drain in the base of the barrel of frost-proof types. This drain is closed when the main valve is open, but it is arranged in such a way as to permit water to drain out of the barrel when the main valve is shut. If the hydrant has been installed properly (with about a barrel of small stones under it), water will drain away. If the drain is working properly and the main valve is tight, any problems due to water freezing in the barrel will be avoided.

4. Check for leaks. The main valve should close tight. When the main valve is open wide with the hydrant outlets capped, there should be no flow from the drain valve. You should look for leaks in mains near the hydrant; there are stethoscope-like listening devices you can use for this purpose.

5. Check the hydrants for freezing during cold weather. You can do this by "sounding," or striking one of the open outlets with your

hand. Water or ice in the barrel shortens the length of the "organ tube" and raises the pitch of the sound. With experience, you can detect the presence of ice or water. Sometimes, you can also detect water or ice in the barrel by lowering a weight on a stout cord into the barrel. If you find any water in the barrel, it must be pumped out and the defective drains or valves repaired. Using salt or antifreeze in the barrels is of limited value in preventing freezing, and the corrosive effect can impair the operation of the hydrant. If the hydrant is only slightly bound by ice, tapping the arm of a wrench on the nut can release the stem. Only moderate blows should be used to prevent breaking the valve rod.

As with dry barrel and wall hydrants, monitor nozzles must be inspected semiannually. Leakage and damage must be repaired, and corrosion must be cleaned and the nozzle lubricated or otherwise protected.

If the private fire service mains contain a mainline strainer, you must inspect it annually to make sure it is not plugged or fouled. If it is, it must be cleaned. The strainer also must be cleaned after each significant system flow. If corrosion is evident, the strainer must be repaired or replaced.

Since most private fire service main piping is located underground, it is not easy to inspect. However, the results of required flow testing at 5-year intervals can indicate whether the available water flow has deteriorated. Exposed portions of private fire service mains must be inspected annually, and leaks, damage, or weaknesses in restraint methods must be repaired. Corroded piping must be cleaned or replaced and coated.

As mentioned above, you should make sure that the property owner is keeping records on the above inspection items and on the annual maintenance of hydrants, hose/hydrant houses, monitor nozzles, and mainline strainers. These records should include evidence of the required annual tests of hydrants, the semiannual tests of monitor nozzle range and operation, and the 5-year piping flow tests.

Inspecting Fire Pumps

The centrifugal-type pump is the pump of choice for providing water under pressure to fire protection systems.

These are single- or multi-stage pumps, depending on the number and arrangement of the impellers. Horizontal and vertical centrifugal pumps are available in capacities up to 5,000 gpm, with pressures ranging from 40 to 200 psi for horizontal pumps and 75 to 280 psi for vertical pumps. Pump capacity is rated on the discharge of one stage in gallons per minute; pressure rating is the sum of the pressures of the individual stages, minus a small head loss.

Horizontal shaft centrifugal fire pumps should be operated under positive suction head, especially with automatic or remote-control starting. If the location requires suction lift, a vertical turbine-type pump should be used.

The vertical turbine pump can operate without priming, and often it is used in streams, ponds, and pits. Such a pump consists of a motor of right-angle gear drive, a column pipe and discharge fitting, a drive shaft, a bowl assembly housing the impellers, and a suction strainer. Its operation is similar to a multi-stage horizontal pump.

A fire pump assembly includes the water supply suction and discharge piping and valving; the pump; the driver, which may be an electric motor, a diesel engine, or a steam turbine; the controller; and auxiliary equipment. The auxiliary equipment includes the shaft coupling; the automatic air release valve; pressure gauges; the circulation relief valve, which is not used for diesel drive with heat exchanger; pump test devices; the pump relief valve and piping; alarm sensors and indicators; right-angle gear sets for engine-driven vertical shaft turbine pumps; and the pressure maintenance, or jockey, pump, and accessories.

A fire pump assembly usually is inspected weekly to verify that it is in proper condition. This is done in conjunction with a weekly test of an electric, diesel, or steam-driven pump. The test for electric motors should last for at least 10 minutes, while the test for diesel engines should run for a minimum of 30 minutes. These tests are conducted with an automatic start, but without flowing water.

Tables 11-1 and 11-2, taken from NFPA 25, summarize the weekly inspection observations and the weekly test procedure.

Fire pumps also are tested annually at "no load," "rated load," and "peak load" flow conditions. These three flow points relate to the three points on a head-discharge curve that any fire pump is required to meet. The first point of a head-discharge curve is churn or shut-off, with the pump operating at rated speed with the discharge valve closed; the total

Table 11-1. Weekly inspection observations.

Pump House Conditions

Heat adequate, not less than 40°F (70°F for pump room with diesel pumps without engine heaters)
Ventilating louvers free to operate

Hydraulic System Conditions

Pump suction and discharge, and bypass valves fully open
Inspect for piping leaks
Suction line pressure gauge reading normal
System line pressure gauge reading normal
Suction reservoir full

Electrical System Conditions

Controller pilot light (power on) illuminated
Transfer switch normal pilot light illuminated
Isolating switch closed—standby (emergency) source
Reverse phase alarm pilot light off, or normal phase rotation pilot light on
Oil level in vertical motor sight glass normal

Diesel Engine System Conditions

Fuel tank two-thirds full
Controller selector switch in AUTO position
Batteries (2) voltage readings normal
Batteries (2) charging current readings normal
Batteries (2) pilot lights on or battery failure (2) pilot lights off
All alarm pilot lights off
Engine running time meter reading
Oil level in right angle gear drive normal
Crankcase oil level normal
Cooling water level normal
Electrolyte level in batteries normal
Battery terminals free from corrosion
Water-jacket heater operating

Steam System Conditions

Steam pressure gauge reading normal

NOTE: Visual indicators other than pilot lights may be used for the same purpose. Source: Table 5-2.2, NFPA 25, *Standard for the Inspection, Testing, and Maintenance of Water-Based Fire Protection Systems,* NFPA, Quincy, MA, 1992.

Table 11-2. Weekly test procedure.

Hydraulic System Procedure

Record system suction and discharge pressure gauge readings
Check pump packing glands for slight discharge
Adjust gland nuts if necessary
Check for unusual noise or vibration
Check packing boxes, bearings, or pump casing for overheating
Record pump starting pressure

Electrical System Procedure

Observe time for motor to accelerate to full speed
Record time controller is on first step (for reduced voltage or reduced current starting)
Record time pump runs after starting (for automatic stop controllers)

Diesel System Procedure

Observe time for engine to crank
Observe time for engine to reach running speed
Observe engine oil pressure gauge, speed indicator, water, and oil temperature indicators
  periodically while engine is running
Record any abnormalities
Check heat exchanger for cooling water flow

Steam System Procedure

Record steam pressure gauge reading
Observe time for turbine to reach running speed

Source: Table 5-3.2.4, NFPA 25, *Standard for the Inspection, Testing, and Maintenance of Water-Based Fire Protection Systems,* NFPA, Quincy, MA, 1992.

head at shutoff must not exceed 140% of the rated head at 0% capacity. The second point is rating; the curve should pass through or above the rated capacity and head, providing at least 100% of the rated head at 100% capacity. And the third point is overload; at 150% of rated capacity, the total head should not be less than 65% of rated total head.

When inspecting any fire pump, you should first read the manufacturer's rating data and compare the data to the records of recent tests. Records should be maintained on suction pressure, discharge pressure, pump RPM, flow (based on Pitot pressure readings from flowing nozzles or on a test meter), and current and voltage of the electric driving motor, using a number of different flow points, including the churn and overload conditions.

When inspecting fire pumps, test any pump that is supposed to start automatically by opening a test connection. Have the pump started and watch for signs of leakage, overheating, and irregular performance. Make sure all alarms and relief valves operate satisfactorily. Note whether the pump is aligned correctly with the driving motor or turbine and whether the stuffing box glands are leaking. Watch pressure gauges for erratic performance, which could indicate poor suction, obstructions, inadequate water supply, or insufficient immersion of the suction pipe. Finally, close all outlets, including the relief valve, and note whether the pump shuts off at the correct pressure.

Table 11-3, taken from NFPA 25, outlines the annual test procedure with regard to flow conditions.

The purpose of the annual test is to compare the performance of the pump assembly against the performance recorded in earlier tests and at

Table 11-3. Annual test procedure.

At No Flow Condition (Churn)
(Conduct this Test First)

Check circulation relief valve for operation to discharge water (see 9-5.4 of NFPA 25)
Check pressure relief valve (if installed) for proper operation (see 9-5.4 of NFPA 25)
Continue test for one-half hr

At Each Flow Condition

Record electric motor voltage and current (all lines)
Record pump speed in rpm
Record simultaneous (approximately) readings of pump suction and discharge pressures and pump discharge flow
Observe operation of any alarm indicators or any visible abnormalities (see 9-5.4.1.1 of NFPA 25)

Source: Table 5-3.3.2, NFPA 25, *Standard for the Inspection, Testing, and Maintenance of Water-Based Fire Protection Systems,* NFPA, Quincy, MA, 1992.

the time of initial field acceptance. Thus, to verify that all inspections and test results are being properly recorded and retained, it is important to interpret the results correctly. Reduced pumping capacity and adjustments for changes in pump speed must be evaluated against the fire protection system demand.

Engine generator sets supplying emergency or standby power, as well as transfer switches, must be tested in accordance with NFPA 110, *Standard for Emergency and Standby Power Systems.*

You must make sure that the fire pump room is kept clean, dry, orderly, and free of miscellaneous stored materials and that proper temperatures are maintained. Diesel-driven pumps must be ventilated adequately to supply air to the engine and to remove hazardous vapors.

Check the condition and reliability of any storage, of the lubrication systems, and of the oil and fuel supplies. If the pump is taking suction from a public water supply, you should make sure that the operation of the pump does not reduce the suction pressure at the pump below the minimum pressure permitted by local authorities; this is generally 10 to 20 psi.

In areas subject to earthquakes, you also should make sure that the fire pump assembly and its associated piping and valving are properly braced and supported to withstand the possible horizontal and vertical forces.

Inspecting Water Storage Tanks

Three types of tanks are used to store fire protection water: gravity tanks; ground tanks, both suction and embankment-supported; and pressure tanks.

Gravity tanks generally are made of steel or wood. Steel tanks range in capacity from 5,000 to 500,000 gallons, while the capacity of wood tanks ranges from 5,000 to 100,000 gallons. Depending on the requirements, these tanks may be located on the roof of a building or raised on an independent steel tower so that the tank's bottom capacity line is 75 to 150 feet above ground. Reinforced concrete towers may also be used. In some cases, concrete tanks have been constructed within the buildings or other structures they supply.

For a complete inspection of a gravity tank, usually it is necessary to climb the tower and descend into the tank itself to check the condition of the interior. If you are not an experienced inspector, however, you should not attempt to climb a tank or tower until you have been instructed by an appropriately experienced person and have practiced doing it.

Ground suction tanks are made of steel, wood, or concrete and are set on a foundation of concrete, crushed stone, or sand. The foundation usually is surrounded by a concrete ring wall.

Embankment-supported rubberized-fabric tanks also are used as ground suction tanks. They are available in 20,000- and 50,000-gallon sizes, and in 100,000-gallon increments up to 1 million gallons. These tanks have a reservoir liner with an integral flexible roof and are designed to be supported by earth on the bottom and on four sides.

For both elevated and ground suction tanks, a valve pit or house usually is built to contain valves, tank heaters, and other fittings. You should check these houses or pits for appropriate waterproofing and drainage and for a water-level indicator or a high- and low-water electrical alarm. The gauge normally is installed in a heated room where it is readily accessible. There should be an overflow pipe at least 3 inches in diameter.

Pressure tanks, whose capacities range from 2,000 to 15,000 gallons, are used to supply sprinkler and standpipe systems, hose lines, and water spray systems. Sometimes they are connected to fire pumps and gravity tanks. The tank normally is kept about two-thirds full of water, with an air pressure of at least 75 psi. Tanks should be housed in noncombustible structures unless they are installed in a heated room within a building.

When inspecting a pressure tank, you should read the water level in the sight gauge, check the pressure gauge, and compare these readings to previously recorded readings and to the fire protection system demand criteria. You should also make sure that the pump is operating correctly to fill the tank, and examine the air compressor for capacity and maintenance condition.

NFPA 25 requires that the water level and the condition of the water in storage tanks be checked monthly or daily during cold weather. The water temperature must never be permitted to drop below 40°F. Temperature can be maintained with a heat exchanger and water-circulation system.

The exterior of a tank should be checked for signs of damage or weakening at least monthly. The area that surrounds the tank and its support structure also must be checked monthly to ensure that it is free of combustible storage, debris, and other material that could present a fire exposure; accumulated material that could accelerate corrosion or rot;

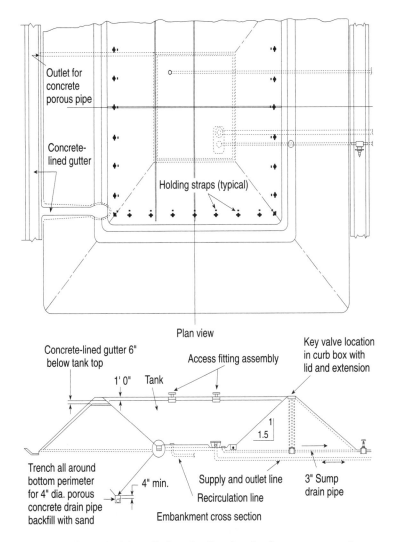

Figure 11-2. Typical installation details of embankment-supported rubberized-fabric tanks, including fittings. Source: Figure B-5, NFPA 22, **Standard for Water Tanks for Private Fire Protection,** *NFPA, Quincy, MA, 1993.*

and ice build-up. The supporting embankments of embankment-supported tanks should be inspected for signs of erosion.

Exterior surfaces that have been painted, coated, or insulated should be checked at least annually for signs of degradation. Provided expansion joints also should be inspected for leaks and cracks annually. Check the hoops and grillage of wooden tanks at least every other year.

The interior of most tanks must be inspected at least every 5 years. However, the interior of steel tanks that have no corrosion protection must be checked every 2 years. The interior of pressure tanks should be inspected at 5-year intervals at the most, and air pressure is to be checked monthly.

You must make sure that the required testing and maintenance is being carried out and recorded. During cold weather, this includes monthly tests of the low-water temperature alarms and the high-water temperature limit switches on tank heating systems. High- and low-water-level alarms must be tested at least semiannually, and pressure gauges and water level indicators must be tested for accuracy at 5-year intervals.

Tank drain valves should be fully opened and closed at least annually and the tank vents cleaned. Cathodic protection, if provided, must be maintained in accordance with manufacturer's instructions. Sediment is to be drained or flushed from tanks at least semiannually.

In areas subject to earthquakes, you also should make sure that the tank and its support structure are braced to withstand the possible horizontal and vertical forces. Water supply piping from the tank to the system should be braced at appropriate intervals, but the piping also should be flexible where needed to accommodate differential building movement.

The following checklist can be followed when inspecting all storage tanks:

1. Note the name of the tank manufacturer and the installing company. Features of structural design, foundations, and wind and earthquake loadings must be addressed during initial installation.

2. Note whether the tank site is clear of weeds, brush, rubbish, and piles of combustible material, which might cause the steelwork to fail through fire or corrosion. Determine whether the tank would be safe should a fire occur in nearby buildings.

3. Note whether the tank is used for any purpose other than fire service.

4. Read the mercury gauge or other water level indicator and consult the records kept of such readings throughout the year.

5. Find out whether the tank has an overflow; this does not apply to pressure tanks. Ask that the tank be filled to overflow to test the water-level indicators and the tank-filling arrangements.

6. Note the general maintenance of the tank structure, the tank itself, and its accessories.

7. Ask how recently the owner has had the tank completely in spected by an experienced tank contractor. Where water conditions make frequent cleaning necessary, ask when the tank was last cleaned.

8. Consult the records of weekly valve inspections. Note whether the valves were found to be wide open and properly sealed. Be sure each valve has been given an operating test.

9. Inspect every valve pit. Their construction and arrangement should be satisfactory, with adequate clearance around the pipes. The valves in the pit, the manhole, and the ladder should be in good repair. The pit should be waterproof and drain properly.

10. Consult the daily records of tank temperature readings kept during cold weather. Ask if the heating system is checked daily in cold weather and find out when the plant is closed.

11. Ask about any experiences with ice on any part of an outdoor tank structure.

12. Inspect the tank heating system, particularly any separate above-grade heater house. Note the construction of the heater house, and determine whether the roof will properly support frost-proof casing and any other loads imposed on it.

13. Review the records of tank painting and estimate the condition of the paint. Note whether the paint surface inside the tank has been checked within 2 years.

14. If a steel tank has cathodic protection, ask when the supplier last inspected the equipment.

15. For pressure tanks, make sure that the pressure is at least 75 psi.

Minimum Water Supplies for Fire Fighting

A number of formulas have been used to determine needed fire flow in municipalities, but there are many variables that influence the calculations. For facilities protected by water-based fire protection systems, the system design generally dictates the minimum water supply requirements. NFPA 1231, *Standard on Water Supplies for Suburban and Rural Fire Fighting*, contains the minimum requirements for fire flow for facilities located in areas without public water supply systems. NFPA 419, *Guide for Master Planning Airport Water Supply Systems for Fire Protection,* provides similar guidance for airport water supply systems.

In general, the plumbing and health codes in North America require that public water supply pressures not be reduced below minimum positive pressures of 10 to 20 psi. For this reason, it is common to evaluate the capacity of both public and private water mains and hydrants as the flow available at a minimum net positive pressure of 20 psi. Some large municipal water supply systems, such as that of Chicago, have fairly large flows available, but only at pressures of 30 to 40 psi. Other municipal water supplies are kept at pressures exceeding 100 psi. The combination of available flows and pressures determines whether a particular water supply can meet the demand of a fire protection system or whether pumps or on-site tanks will be needed.

Flow Testing Water Main

The following test procedure can be used to flow test hydrants on a water main, using two hydrants nearest the point at which the building fire service connects to the main. Be sure to secure permission for the test from the water utility when public mains are involved.

First, attach the gauge to Hydrant A and obtain the static pressure. Then attach a second gauge to Hydrant B and remove the cap from one of its 2 1/2-inch outlets.

While Hydrant B is uncapped, measure the diameter of the outlet to check its size. Although the inside diameter of the hydrant opening usually is close to 2 1/2 inches, some butts are sufficiently different to require a fairly close measurement. For convenience, this should be taken to the nearest hundredth of an inch. Feel inside the outlet to determine its shape—that is, either smooth, right angle, or projecting.

Then open Hydrant B and read the pressure on both hydrants. Make sure the full opening is filled with the water flowing because full flow is needed for accurate measurement.

The accuracy of the test is slightly better if you read the pressure on a gauge on a Pitot tube held in the flowing stream instead of on a gauge on

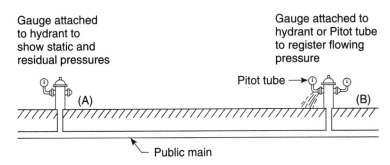

Figure 11-3. Test set-up for flow testing water main. Source: Figure A-7-2.1, NFPA 13, Standard for the Installation of Sprinkler Systems, NFPA, Quincy, MA, 1994.

Hydrant B. The position of the tube in the stream should be varied to get the most representative reading. In most openings, the Pitot reading will be best with the tube near the middle of the stream, held about half the outlet diameter away from the face of the outlet.

If accurate results are needed, attach a 50-foot length of 2 1/2- inch rubber-lined cotton hose to each of the 2 1/2-inch connections on Hydrant B. Each hose line should have a playpipe and a smooth cone nozzle tip 1 1/8 inches or larger. Turn on both lines together and read the pressure at the nozzles with a Pitot tube and gauge. Discharges can be measured quite closely with good nozzles, and the total discharge is the sum of the discharge computed for each nozzle. Measure the nozzle diameters with a scale that can be read to hundredths of an inch. If it is desirable to know how much water is available at a selected residual pressure, take readings at two or more flows and plot a flow curve.

Discharge is computed using the formula below or estimated from Table 11-4. You can compute the static pressure difference at the top line of sprinklers by deducting from the minimum reading of the gauge on Hydrant A 0.434 psi for each foot the highest sprinklers are above the gauge.

Discharge from hydrant opening or nozzle is computed using the formula:

$$Q = 29.83 \ cd^2 \sqrt{p}$$

where Q is gallons per minute, c is a coefficient of discharge for the opening, d is its diameter in inches, and p is the pressure read at the gauge on the hydrant flowing or on the Pitot tube gauge in pounds per square inch.

The values in Table 11-4 are computed using the above formula with $c = 1.00$. This corresponds to a smooth outlet. If the outlet meets the hydrant barrel with a sharp edge, or right angle, a c value of 0.9 should be used. If the outlet edge projects into the hydrant barrel, a c value of 0.8 should be used. These factors should be used to modify the flow calculations appropriately.

Flow Testing a Yard System

Figure 11-4 shows a yard system fed by a city connection, which is used as an example of how water flow in such a system is checked. Friction losses in pipes can be estimated from Tables 11-5 and 11-6.

In Figure 11-4, Gauge No. 1 shows street pressure. Gauge No. 2 is located as close to the street connection and the meter as possible. The amount by which the reading of Gauge No. 2 differs from that of Gauge No. 1 shows the loss in the connection. Meters frequently cause large pressure drops.

Gauge No. 3 gives readings at the point at which water is flowing during a test. The difference in pressure should be explained by the expected friction losses in the piping system between Gauge No. 3 and Gauge No. 2.

The pressure for a specific flow at the end of the system at Gauge No. 3 should be the same as it is for the same flow at Gauge No. 1, less

Table 11-4. Theoretical discharge through circular orifices.

Pressure, psi	Head, ft	Diameter of orifice, inches			
		1	1-1/8	2-1/2	4
		Flow, gpm			
15	34.6	116	146	722	1849
30	69.3	164	207	1022	2616
45	104	200	253	1253	3203
60	138	231	293	1445	3700
90	208	283	358	1770	4531
120	277	327	414	2044	5232

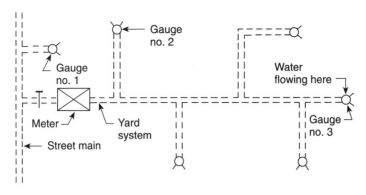

Figure 11-4. Gauge connections for yard system flow tests.

calculated losses in the piping between Gauges No. 1 and No. 3. If observed pressure is less than calculated, you should take readings at other outlets between Gauges No. 1 and No. 3 and calculate the pressure losses to be expected for a given flow until the obstruction is located.

With tests such as these, you can plot a hydraulic-grade line for a given run of piping that often will show otherwise undetectable sources of pressure drop. The value of a careful check of a private system of underground piping is shown by the following list of defects that have been found in water supply systems:

The system was never connected to the city main.

The system was connected to the city main, but the gate valve was never opened or was only partly open.

The meters were broken or clogged.

The mains were smaller than indicated on plans.

Flow areas in the mains were seriously reduced because of sedimentation, mud, or hard deposits on the inside.

There was serious leakage in the underground systems.

The mains or valves were frozen.

The hydrants were inoperative.

The valves were entirely or partly closed due to improper or careless operation.

The check valves were installed in the wrong direction.

The check valves leaked.

Table 11-5. Friction loss in pipe.

Pounds per square inch per 100 feet of pipe
Hazen-Williams C = 100*

Actual diameter of pipe 1/2 through 3-1/2 in.†
Nominal diameter of pipe for 4 through 30 in.

Gpm	1/2	3/4	1	1-1/4	1-1/2	2	2-1/2	3	3-1/2	4
5	17.9	4.55	1.40	.369	.174	.052	—	—	—	—
10	64.5	16.4	5.06	1.33	.629	.186	.078	.030	—	—
15		34.7	10.7	2.82	1.33	.394	.166	.064	.028	—
20	*5*	59.1	18.2	4.89	2.27	.671	.282	.109	.048	.027
30	.019	*6*	38.6	10.2	4.80	1.42	.598	.231	.102	.057
40	.033	—	65.8	17.3	8.17	2.42	1.02	.393	.174	.097
50	.050	.020	*8*	26.2	12.3	3.66	1.54	.593	.263	.147
60	.069	.029	—	36.6	17.3	5.12	2.16	.831	.369	.206
70	.092	.038	—	48.7	23.0	6.81	2.87	1.11	.490	.274
80	.118	.049	—	62.4	29.4	8.72	3.67	1.41	.628	.350
90	.147	.060	—	77.6	36.6	10.8	4.56	1.76	.781	.435
100	.178	.074	—	*10*	44.5	13.1	5.55	2.14	.949	.529
120	.250	.103	—	—	62.3	18.5	7.77	3.00	1.33	.741
140	.333	.137	.034	—	82.9	24.6	10.3	3.98	1.77	.986
160	.426	.175	.043	—	106.0	31.4	13.2	5.10	2.26	1.26
180	.529	.218	.054	.018	*12*	39.1	16.5	6.34	2.81	1.57
200	.643	.265	.065	.022	—	47.5	20.0	7.71	3.42	1.91
220	.768	.316	.078	.026	—	56.7	23.9	9.19	4.08	2.28
240	.902	.371	.091	.031	.013	*14*	28.0	10.8	4.79	2.67
260	1.05	.430	.106	.036	.015	—	32.5	12.5	5.56	3.10
280	1.20	.493	.122	.041	.017	—	37.3	14.4	6.37	3.55
300	1.36	.562	.138	.047	.019	—	42.3	16.3	7.24	4.04

Flow										*16*	*18*	*20*	*24*	*30*
350	21.7	9.63	5.37	1.81	.746	.184	.062	.026	.012	—	—	—	—	—
400	27.8	12.3	6.88	2.32	.955	.235	.079	.033	.015	—	—	—	—	—
450	34.6	15.3	8.55	2.88	1.19	.292	.099	.041	.019	—	—	—	—	—
500	42.0	18.6	10.4	3.51	1.44	.353	.120	.049	.023	.012	—	—	—	—
550	50.1	22.2	12.4	4.18	1.72	.424	.143	.059	.028	.015	—	—	—	—
600	58.8	26.1	14.6	4.91	2.02	.498	.168	.069	.033	.017	—	—	—	—
650	68.2	30.3	16.9	5.70	2.34	.577	.195	.080	.038	.020	—	—	—	—
700	—	34.7	19.4	6.53	2.69	.662	.223	.092	.043	.023	—	—	—	—
750	—	39.4	22.0	7.42	3.05	.752	.254	.104	.049	.026	—	—	—	—
800	—	44.5	24.8	8.36	3.44	.848	.286	.118	.056	.029	—	—	—	—
850	—	49.7	27.7	9.35	3.85	.948	.320	.132	.062	.032	—	—	—	—
900	—	—	30.8	10.4	4.28	1.05	.356	.146	.069	.036	—	—	—	—
950	—	—	34.1	11.5	4.73	1.17	.393	.162	.076	.040	—	—	—	—
1,000	—	—	37.5	12.6	5.20	1.28	.432	.178	.084	.044	—	—	—	—
1,250	—	—	—	19.1	7.85	1.94	.653	.269	.127	.066	—	—	—	—
1,500	—	—	—	—	11.0	2.71	.914	.376	.178	.093	—	—	—	—
1,750	—	—	—	—	—	3.61	1.22	.501	.236	.123	—	—	—	—
2,000	—	—	—	—	—	4.62	1.56	.641	.303	.158	.089	.053	.022	.007
2,250	—	—	—	—	—	—	1.94	.797	.376	.196	.111	.066	.027	.009
2,500	—	—	—	—	—	—	2.35	.969	.457	.239	.134	.081	.033	.011
2,750	—	—	—	—	—	—	2.81	1.16	.545	.285	.160	.096	.040	.013
3,000	—	—	—	—	—	—	3.30	1.36	.641	.334	.188	.113	.046	.016
4,000	—	—	—	—	—	—	—	2.31	1.09	.569	.321	.192	.079	.027
5,000	—	—	—	—	—	—	—	3.49	1.65	.860	.485	.290	.119	.040

* To convert friction loss at $C = 100$ to other values of C, see Table 11-6.

† Schedule 40 pipe sizes 1/2 through 3-1/2 in. steel pipe.

Table 11-6. Conversion factors for friction loss in pipe for values of coefficient other than 100.

C	Factor	C	Factor	C	Factor
150	0.472	110	0.838	70	1.93
145	0.503	105	0.914	65	2.22
140	0.537	100	1.00	60	2.57
135	0.574	95	1.10	55	3.02
130	0.615	90	1.22	50	3.61
125	0.662	85	1.35	45	4.38
120	0.714	80	1.51	40	5.48
115	0.772	75	1.70	35	6.97

Unknown valves and meters existed.

Suction on the fire pump was blocked.

The drop pipe on a gravity tank was frozen, as were other tank connections.

Bibliography

Cote, A. E., ed., *Fire Protection Handbook,* 17th edition, National Fire Protection Association, Quincy, MA, 1991. Section 5, Chapters 2 through 8 cover many aspects of water supplies and distribution systems for fire protection.

Backflow Protection for Fire Sprinkler Systems, National Fire Sprinkler Association, Patterson, NY, 1990. Discusses history of backflow protection of fire protection systems, including information on sampling studies of water quality.

Carson, W. G. and Klinker, R. L., *Fire Protection Systems: Inspection, Test and Maintenance Manual,* NFPA, Quincy, MA, 1992.

NFPA Codes, Standards, and Recommended Practices

NFPA 13, *Standard for the Installation of Sprinkler Systems.* Contains minimum requirements for the design and installation of automatic sprinkler systems, including water supply requirements.

NFPA 13D, *Standard for the Installation of Sprinkler Systems in One- and Two-Family Dwellings and Mobile Homes.* Covers the design and installation of low-cost life-safety-oriented sprinkler systems for dwelling units.

NFPA 13E, *Recommendations for Fire Department Operations in Properties Protected by Sprinkler and Standpipe Systems.* Outlines fire department inspection and pre-fire planning, fireground operations, and post-fire operations in buildings with fire protection systems.

NFPA 13R, *Standard for the Installation of Sprinkler Systems in Residential Occupancies Up to and Including Four Stories in Height.* Covers the design and installation of economical life-safety-oriented residential sprinkler systems for low-rise apartment buildings, lodging and rooming houses, board and care facilities, hotels, motels, and dormitories.

NFPA 14, *Standard for the Installation of Standpipe and Hose Systems.* Contains minimum requirements for the design and installation of standpipe and hose systems, including water supply requirements.

NFPA 15, S*tandard for Water Spray Fixed Systems for Fire Protection.* Contains minimum requirements for the design and installation of water spray systems, including water supply requirements.

NFPA 16, *Standard on the Installation of Deluge Foam-Water Sprinkler and Foam-Water Spray Systems.* Contains minimum requirements for the design and installation of foam water deluge systems, including water supply requirements.

NFPA 16A, *Recommended Practice for the Installation of Closed-Head Foam-Water Sprinkler Systems.* Gives recommendations for the design and installation of automatic foam-water sprinkler systems, including water supply requirements.

NFPA 20, *Standard for the Installation of Centrifugal Fire Pumps.* Contains minimum requirements for selecting and installing pumps supplying water for private fire protection, including water supplies, power sources and controls, acceptance tests, and operation.

NFPA 22, *Standard for Water Tanks for Private Fire Protection.* Contains minimum requirements for the design, construction, and installation of tanks supplying water for private fire protection.

NFPA 24, *Standard for the Installation of Private Fire Service Mains and Their Appurtenances.* Contains minimum requirements for the installation of private fire service mains supplying automatic sprinkler systems, open sprinkler systems, water spray fixed systems, foam-water systems, private hydrants, monitor nozzles, or standpipe systems, with references to water supplies, private hydrants, and hose houses.

NFPA 25, *Standard for the Inspection, Testing, and Maintenance of Water-Based Fire Protection Systems.* Contains minimum requirements for the periodic inspection, testing, and maintenance of water-based fire protection systems, including water supplies that are part of these systems, valves controlling system flow, and impairment handling and reporting.

NFPA 291, *Recommended Practice for Fire Flow Testing and Marking of Hydrants.* Covers testing procedures, classification, and color coding of hydrants.

NFPA 419, *Guide for Master Planning Airport Water Supply Systems for Fire Protection.* Covers methods of calculating and designing airport water supply systems.

NFPA 1231, *Standard on Water Supplies for Suburban and Rural Fire Fighting.* Contains minimum requirements for water supplies needed for fire fighting based on building construction, occupancy, exposure, and fire protection systems. Also contains guidance on the construction and use of dry hydrants and cisterns as water supply sources.

NFPA 1962, *Standard for the Care, Use, and Service Testing of Fire Hose Including Couplings and Nozzles.* Contains requirements for use, inspection, storage, service testing, and record keeping for fire department, industrial, and forestry fire hose.

NFPA 1963, *Standard for Screw Threads and Gaskets for Fire Hose Connections.* Contains dimensional requirements for screw thread connections, gauges, gaskets, and gasket seats.

CHAPTER 12

Automatic Sprinkler and Other Water-Based Fire Protection Systems

*I*n 1992, NFPA adopted the new Standard, NFPA 25, *Standard for the Inspection, Testing, and Maintenance of Water-Based Fire Protection Systems,* which discusses water supply systems, sprinkler systems, standpipes, fire pumps, water storage tanks, water spray systems, and foam water sprinkler systems. This chapter addresses these same fixed systems.

Because water is an efficient and almost universally available and acceptable agent, the use of water in water-based fire protection systems is continually increasing. Residential sprinkler systems are becoming more practical, and newer, more effective systems are being designed for warehouses and other large occupancies. In fact, the hazards of a particular building are an important factor in determining what kind of fire protection is needed for that building. This chapter describes some of these systems and provides information on inspecting them properly.

Sprinkler systems are found much more often now than they used to be, due both to code requirements and as an equivalent alternative to those code requirements. Therefore, it is very important for you to verify that any sprinkler system in the building is in service and fully operational. More and more often, communities are allowing trade-offs for some of the code requirements if the building is protected throughout with a sprinkler system. With this in mind, you should recognize that some items required by the code might not be present when a sprinkler system has been installed in lieu of them. This "voluntary" sprinkler system then becomes a required system due to its use as an equivalent alternative, and it should meet all the standards required by NFPA 13, *Standard for the Installation of Sprinkler Systems.*

Classifying the Occupancy

For simplicity's sake, occupancies are classified into three basic hazard categories when the installation of automatic sprinkler systems are contemplated: light hazard, ordinary hazard, and extra hazard. These categories are used when sprinkler systems are designed and installed in accordance with the requirements of NFPA 13.

The light hazard class includes occupancies such as dwellings, apartments, churches, hotels, schools, offices, and public buildings, where the quantity of combustible materials is relatively low and fires are expected to have a low rate of heat release.

The ordinary hazard class includes ordinary mercantile, manufacturing, and industrial occupancies, and these fall into two groups. Ordinary hazard Group 1 occupancies are those in which the combustibility of the contents is relatively low, the quantity of materials is moderate, stockpiles are no higher than 8 feet, and fires are expected to release heat at a moderate rate. Ordinary hazard Group 2 occupancies include properties in which the quantity and combustibility of the contents is moderate to high, stockpiles are no higher than 12 feet, and fires are expected to have moderate to high rates of heat release. This group includes cereal mills, textile and printing plants, shoe factories, feed mills, piers and wharves, and paper manufacturing plants.

The extra hazard class includes two main groups. Group 1 includes occupancies that contain little or no flammable or combustible liquids but that may nonetheless have severe fires. These include die casting and metal extruding plants, sawmills, rubber production facilities, and upholstering operations using plastic foams. Extra hazard Group 2 includes occupancies that contain moderate to substantial amounts of flammable or combustible liquids. These include buildings that house asphalt saturating, flammable-liquid spraying, open-oil quenching, solvent cleaning, plastics processing, or varnish and paint dipping processes.

In addition to these hazard groupings, there are special occupancy conditions that require consideration. Such conditions include high-piled combustibles, a variety of flammable and combustible liquids, combustible dusts, chemicals, aerosols, and explosives.

In occupancies containing such high-hazard items, water may not be an effective extinguishing agent unless it is combined with an additive. For most occupancies, however, water is the primary media for controlling or suppressing fires. Water-based fire protection systems can be designed to meet a variety of situations, but they must have an automatic and reliable water supply source. As with any fire protection system, a sprinkler system must be operable at all times.

There are two occasions when you, as an inspector, must be at your most observant and critical: when a new sprinkler or some other water-based fire protection system is being installed and when the installed system is shut down for repairs, inspection, or modification. During these periods, the occupancy will lack its principal means of automatic fire protection.

When systems must be shut down for any reason, the proper authorities—that is, the fire department, the insurance company, and the corporate safety office—should be notified. This will allow the fire department to alter the response and the type of equipment that is dispatched to the fire. If the impairment is planned, all the necessary replacement parts and equipment should be in place to minimize the amount of "down time" for the system. NFPA 25 provides a regimented protocol for taking a fire protection system out of service and a procedure for placing the system back into service once repairs have been completed.

As an inspector, you should determine whether the building you are inspecting is covered by NFPA 13. You also should determine whether it is a light, ordinary, or extra hazard occupancy or a structure that may be covered by some other occupancy-based code or standard. This will help you assess the capability of the automatic sprinkler system. Most of the flaws or errors will be fundamental and easy to find; you might discover others in routine tests. Remember, inspections, testing, and maintenance should be documented to ensure compliance with NFPA 25.

Sprinkler System Water Supplies

When sprinkler systems fail to control a fire, generally there are two primary reasons: the water supply was insufficient for the particular hazard or a valve on the supply line was closed. Therefore, one of your first acts during an inspection is to verify that there is enough water available to the sprinkler system. The system plans, the site plans, and other data developed before and after the system was installed should indicate the flows and pressures throughout the system, the piping layout, and the location of the valves. You should arrange to have each valve operated while you observe in order to verify that it performs well. Be sure to note if there is a sign or some other indication that the valve should remain open or closed.

The fire department connection, if there is one, merits your attention next. This is considered an auxiliary water supply source. Remove the outlet caps and examine the threads, then examine the interior for rags and other debris. Note whether the threads are compatible with those of the local fire department or if adaptors are needed.

Check the condition of any yard hydrants and indicator post valves outside the facility, and and make sure they are easy to operate. Determine if OS & Y (outside stem and yoke) valves are supposed to be locked in the open position or if they are supervised open by some other means. Make sure the valve pit is kept clean and is well maintained.

Make sure that the appropriate keys or wrenches to any underground valves are readily accessible. If the property contains municipal hydrants, check with the local fire department to determine how they will be operated during a fire. The fire department should plan to support the system through the fire department connections.

Central station, proprietary, and remote supervisory services are available to provide continual electrical surveillance of the valves in water systems. You should determine if the building or plant you are inspecting has such services and, if they do, the extent and effectiveness of the supervision.

If the valves are not supervised by means of a signaling service to a remote location or some other constantly attended point, they should either be locked open or sealed. Sealed valves should be located within fenced enclosures under the control of the owner and inspected weekly.

Inspection reports on valve conditions should identify the valve number and note whether it is normally open or closed. The report also should note whether the valve is sealed properly or locked and whether it is in good operating condition and free of leaks. In addition, this report should discuss the valve's accessibility and note whether the valve key or wrench is in place.

The Sprinkler System

All automatic fire sprinklers, regardless of the type of system, should be clean. They must not be caked with dust, grease, or paint, particularly on the heat-responsive element. They should not be bent or otherwise damaged, and guards should be provided for sprinklers located in areas prone to damage or abuse. The sprinkers should not be obstructed by light fixtures, HVAC equipment, cables, stored materials, or the movement of overhead doors or windows. NFPA 25 requires that this type of evaluation be performed once a year. If the sprinklers are installed in an inaccessible area, however, the yearly inspection is not required.

Sprinklers should be free of corrosion. Listed corrosion-resistant or special coated sprinklers should be used in areas in which enough chemicals, moisture, or corrosive vapors exist to cause corrosion. Such coatings must be applied only by the sprinkler manufacturer; field application of any type of plating or coating is not acceptable.

When you are inspecting the sprinkler system, be sure to check the temperature ratings of any sprinklers near such heat sources as ovens, unit heaters, and skylights. NFPA 13 provides detailed information on the need to install color-coded intermediate or higher rated sprinklers in such areas. Sprinklers with ordinary temperature ratings installed in such areas may operate inadvertently and discharge over time.

You also should check the orientation of sprinklers to make sure that upright sprinklers have been installed in the upright position, pendent sprinklers in the pendent position, and sidewall sprinklers in the proper position with respect to their coverage area.

All sprinklers made before 1920 should be replaced, and representative samples of sprinklers in all systems should be submitted for operational testing after a certain period of service. For most sprinklers, this period is 50 years. However, there are two exceptions.

Sprinklers with temperature ratings of 325°F and higher that have been exposed on a regular basis to the maximum allowable ambient temperatures should be tested at 5-year intervals. And fast response sprinklers, such as residential and quick-response sprinklers, should be tested first after 20 years of service and at 10-year intervals thereafter.

Make sure that a sufficient supply of spare sprinklers of each type and rating used on the system is stored on the premises in a cabinet where it will not be exposed to corrosion or high temperatures. The cabinet also should contain any special wrenches needed to replace the sprinklers.

Piping should be checked once a year when the sprinklers are being inspected to make sure that it is in good condition, that it is free from mechanical damage, and that it is not being used to support fixtures, ladders, or any other loads. Hangers and seismic bracing should be tight and intact. If the atmosphere is corrosive, the piping should be protected by an appropriate covering. Where mechanical fittings are used, the protective covering should extend to the bolts connecting them.

Be sure to examine any records available to determine whether the interior of the piping has been examined recently. Piping systems should be examined internally when abnormal conditions are detected during routine system tests. These conditions include, but are not limited to, defects on intake screens from a raw water supply source; foreign objects in the pump suction lines, dry-pipe valves, or deluge valves; obstructions in the sprinkler pipe due to system alterations; and, in a dry-pipe system, false trips. Systems whose piping or sprinklers are plugged, systems that discharge foreign material during tests, and systems that show other signs of obstruction should be flushed and re-examined at intervals of not more than 5 years. Flushing connections are provided at the ends of the mains on all newer systems, and flushing procedures for various configurations of sprinkler systems are described in NFPA 25.

You should record pressure gauge readings of the system and compare them with the information provided during the acceptance test and with previously recorded readings. There are ways to test alarm valves and waterflow devices, and you should arrange for such tests, as described later in this chapter. You also should have somebody operate the main

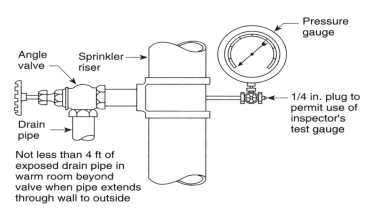

Figure 12-1. Tests and drain connection for a wet-pipe sprinkler system riser. Source: Figure 4-6.3.4, NFPA 13, **Standard for the Installation of Sprinkler Systems, NFPA, Quincy, MA, 1994.**

drain and auxiliary drain connections during an inspection. NFPA 25 requires that the pressure gauges of wet-pipe systems be read monthly and that those of dry-pipe, preaction, and deluge systems be read weekly. If the air pressure in dry-pipe and preaction systems is supervised at a constantly attended location, however, monthly inspections are permitted. The pressure gauges that monitor the air pressure in systems of this type also must be inspected and the air pressure recorded.

Dry-Pipe Systems

Dry-pipe systems differ from basic wet-pipe systems in several ways. First, the water is kept from reaching the sprinklers by the pressure of compressed air or nitrogen acting on the system side of the valve. Water does not enter the system until the system air pressure drops below a predetermined point. When one or more sprinklers operate in the area of a fire, the air pressure drops, the dry-pipe valve automatically opens, and water enters the system. Water is then discharged from any open sprinklers.

Another difference between dry- and wet-pipe sprinklers involves the use of pendent sprinklers. In areas subject to freezing, the dry-pipe pendent-type sprinkler can be used; standard pendent sprinklers are allowed only on return bends in heated areas.

Check valves are sometimes installed in the branches of older dry-pipe systems to improve the water delivery time to open sprinklers. In such cases, drain valves are connected by a bypass around each check valve to allow the system to be drained. This practice is no longer permitted on newer systems.

Dry-pipe systems with a capacity of more than 500 gallons must have quick-opening devices. Gridded dry-pipe systems, no longer permitted for new installations, are required to have a quick-opening device when the system's volume exceeds 350 gallons. This quick-opening device usually is an accelerator placed close to the dry-pipe valve. There also will be a soft disc globe or angle valve in the connection between the dry-pipe sprinkler riser and the accelerator. Quick-opening devices are inspected and tested at the same frequency as the dry-pipe valve. The dry-pipe valve and the supply pipe must be protected against cold temperatures and mechanical injury. A heated enclosure is required for this purpose.

The air pressure in the dry-pipe system may come from a shop system or an automatic compressor. Check that the air pressure in the system corresponds to that listed on the instruction sheet for the dry-pipe valve or is 20 psi above the valve's calculated trip pressure. The same requirement applies to nitrogen.

Pressure gauges are installed on the water and air sides of the dry-pipe valve, at the source of air pressure, in each independent pipe from the air supply to the system, and at the exhausters and accelerators. You can identify these gauges and their purpose using the system installer's plans or the manufacturer's literature.

The inspection procedures for dry-pipe systems are much like those for wet-pipe systems, as described in Chapter 11, except that you will have to evaluate the source of the air pressure and examine the ancillary equipment unique to this type of system.

Preaction and Deluge Systems

Preaction and deluge systems use a supplemental detection system to initiate the flow of water. In a preaction system, only one or a few sprinklers will open; in a deluge system, all the sprinklers discharge simultaneously.

When checking the location and spacing of fire detection devices, as well as the functions of the system, you should refer to the manufacturer's literature, the listing criteria, and the appropriate installation standards such as NFPA 72, *National Fire Alarm Code*. If there are more than 20 sprinklers on a preaction system, the sprinkler piping and fire detection devices must be supervised automatically. Because a preaction system cannot have more than 1,000 closed sprinklers, very large areas will require more than one preaction valve. The fire detection devices and systems of a deluge system also must be supervised automatically, regardless of the number of sprinklers on the system.

If the fire detection devices in the circuits are not accessible, additional testing devices for each circuit must be accessible, and they must be connected to the circuit at a point that will ensure an adequate test.

The system should include testing apparatus that will produce enough heat or impulse to operate any normal fire detection device. In hazardous locations where explosive materials or vapors are present, you may use hot water, steam, or another nonignition method.

Water Spray Systems

Water spray systems are designed to control and extinguish fires and to protect exposures in special situations; they are not meant to replace sprinkler systems, although they are similar to sprinkler systems except for the pattern of spray discharge. Water spray can be designed for a variety of discharge rates and patterns, including ultra high-speed response in milliseconds. The type of system used depends on the extent of the hazard and the required water discharge.

Water spray systems commonly are used to protect vessels in which flammable liquids and gases are stored, as well as electrical transformers, oil switches, rotating electrical machinery, electrical cable trays and runs, conveyor systems, wall openings, and similar fire problems. They consist of fixed piping and water spray nozzles designed specifically to discharge and distribute water over the area to be protected.

Water flow is started manually or automatically, usually by the actuation of separate detection equipment. Water spray systems have a heavy demand for water because simultaneous, high-density discharge from many nozzles often is needed. As with sprinkler systems, it is important that the water supplies for water spray systems be adequately designed and reliably maintained.

Steam Smothering Systems

Steam smothering systems were used many years ago, but they are rare today and are not recommended for fire protection. They can be used to

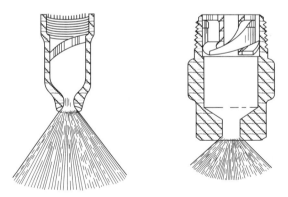

Figure 12-2. Water spray nozzles with internal spiral passages. (Spraying Systems Co., type H, and "Automatic" Sprinkler Corp. of America, type MA)

protect ovens or cargo spaces on ships, aircraft engine test facilities, and coal pulverizer systems. An accepted application is 8 pounds of steam per minute for each 100 cubic feet of volume.

Testing a Sprinkler System

Sprinkler systems must maintained in accordance with NFPA 25. The water supply pressure, indicated by a gauge located above the indicator gate valve controlling the system but below the system alarm or dry valve, should be observed. If the system does not rely on a pump, you may use this rule of thumb to estimate the water pressure: the readings should be at least 30 psi for a one-story building and 5 psi for each additional story.

If the system riser contains an alarm check valve, as it does in a wet system, or a dry-pipe valve, as it does in a dry system, note the reading of the system pressure gauge, which usually is located at or immediately above the alarm or dry valve. On a wet-pipe system, the system gauge should read the same or, in some cases, slightly higher than the supply gauge. On a dry-pipe system, the system pressure is the pressure of the air or nitrogen and usually is considerably less than the water supply pressure.

A test known as the "main drain test" should be conducted quarterly using the following procedure, established in NFPA 25. Record the pressure on the water supply gauge. If the system is equipped with an alarm check valve, close the alarm line. Then open the main drain valve. When the flow has stabilized, record the residual pressure from the water supply gauge. You may then close the main drain valve, noting the time it takes the gauge to reach its original static reading. Once you have completed these steps, you must place the valve on the alarm line back in its normal open position.

No flow measurements are taken during this test, only readings from the pressure gauges. The pressures noted should be compared to the results from previous tests. This test simply provides a comparison with the original main drain test pressure values and can be used to detect a deterioration in the system water supply.

The gauges used on a sprinkler system must be replaced or tested every 5 years to verify their accuracy. A calibrator, or inspectors, gauge should be used to determine whether the system gauge is accurate to within 3% of the full-scale reading of that gauge. If the system gauge is not accurate to within 3%, it must be recalibrated or replaced.

Testing Preaction and Deluge Systems

The same basic procedures used to test wet-pipe systems may be applied to preaction and deluge systems. The interior of the deluge valve housing should be inspected annually to determine whether there has been any corrosion or other deterioration that might impair operation of the device. The level of preaction valves that use priming water must be checked quarterly.

Preaction and deluge systems must be flow tested annually to ensure that all the valves and devices perform as intended. Special arrangements must be made to flow test the deluge system. Equipment that is subject to damage must be removed or protected so that the discharge of water from the system will not affect it. Under special circumstances, this test may be postponed for as long as 3 years. If the test must be postponed, you can complete a trip test without discharging water into the system.

Double interlock preaction systems have the attributes of both dry-pipe and preaction systems. Thus, they are inspected, tested, and maintained in the same manner as a dry-pipe or a preaction system. Because double interlock systems are somewhat more complex than other types of sprinkler systems, you will need to take extra time to ensure that they are operating normally.

Combined dry-pipe and preaction systems must be constructed so that either system will still operate if the fire detection system fails and the fire detection system will operate if either of the sprinkler systems fail.

Chapters 2 and 9 of NFPA 25 provide additional information on inspecting, testing, and maintaining sprinkler systems. Table 12-1 outlines the basic elements of those items associated with the inspection, testing, and maintenance of sprinkler systems.

Inspecting Water Spray Systems

These systems must be inspected and maintained regularly. When inspecting a water spray system, make sure that the operating and maintenance instructions and layouts are available or are posted at the control equipment and at the plant's fire headquarters. Among the items to be inspected are strainers, piping, control valves, heat-actuated devices, detectors, and spray nozzles, especially those with strainers. You

Table 12-1. Summary of minimum inspection, testing, and maintenance.

Item	Activity	Frequency
Gauges (dry, pre-action deluge systems)	Inspection	Weekly/Monthly
Control Valves	Inspection	Weekly/Monthly
Alarm Devices	Inspection	Monthly
Gauges (wet pipe systems)	Inspection	Monthly
Hydraulic Nameplate	Inspection	Quarterly
Buildings	Inspection	Annually (prior to freezing weather)
Hanger/Seismic Bracing	Inspection	Annually
Piping	Inspection	Annually
Sprinklers	Inspection	Annually
Fire Department Connections	Inspection	
Valves (all types)	Inspection	
Alarm Devices	Test	Quarterly
Main Drain	Test	Quarterly
Antifreeze Solution	Test	Annually
Gauges	Test	5 years
Sprinklers—High Temp.	Test	5 years
Sprinklers—Fast Response	Test	20 years and every 10 years thereafter
Sprinkler	Test	50 years and every 10 years thereafter
Valves (all types)	Maintenance	Annually or as needed
Obstruction Investigation	Maintenance	5 years or as needed

Source: Table 2-1, NFPA 25, *Standard for the Inspection, Testing, and Maintenance of Water-Based Fire Protection Systems,* NFPA, Quincy, MA, 1992.

should verify the position and alignment of nozzles as they are directional-type spray nozzles, and it is important that the small water passages be kept clear. If spray nozzles are subject to paint vapors and other coatings, blowoff caps should be used to protect them against foreign matter and corrosion.

Operational flow tests of water spray systems are required annually to ensure that the spray nozzles are not obstructed and that they are positioned properly to protect the intended hazard. During the test, be sure to record the time it takes the detection system to actuate the deluge valve and the time it takes the water to reach the nozzle system. You also should record the pressure readings at the remote spray nozzles to establish that they have enough pressure to project the necessary pattern.

Chapter 7 of NFPA 25 provides information on inspecting, testing, and maintaining water spray systems. Table 12-2 outlines which elements of the system must be inspected, tested, and maintained at what intervals.

Foam Extinguishing Systems

Fire fighting foam is a combination of water and concentrated liquid foaming agent. It floats on the surface of flammable and combustible liquids and forms a covering that excludes air, cools the liquid, and seals the layer of vapor. It also can form a blanket over transformers and other irregularly shaped items to smother flames. There are several kinds of foaming agents, and their effectiveness varies with the type of application and the properties of the fire being considered.

Foam can be applied by portable devices or fixed extinguishing systems. In either type of application, the resultant solution must be at the right proportion, and the application must be continuous and consistent. Foam breaks down and its water content vaporizes when it is directly exposed to heat and flame. If it is applied in sufficient volume, however, it can overcome this loss and can control and eventually extinguish the fire. The smothering layer also can be broken and dispersed by mechanical or chemical action or by turbulence from air or fire gases. Nevertheless, automatic extinguishing systems can apply foam efficiently.

Types of foaming agents include aqueous film-forming, fluoroprotein foaming, film-forming fluoroprotein, protein foaming, high expansion foaming, synthetic hydrocarbon surfactant foaming, low temperature

Table 12-2. Inspection, test, and maintenance frequencies.

Item	Activity	Frequency
Check Valves	Inspection	
Control Valves	Inspection	Weekly (sealed)
Control Valves	Inspection	Monthly (locked, supervised)
Deluge Valve	Inspection	
Detection Systems	Inspection	
Detector Check Valves	Inspection	
Drainage	Inspection	Monthly
Electric Motor	Inspection	
Engine Drive	Inspection	
Fire Pump	Inspection	
Fittings	Inspection	Monthly
Fittings (Rubber Gasketed)	Inspection	Monthly
Gravity Tanks	Inspection	
Hangers	Inspection	Monthly
Heat (Deluge Valve House)	Inspection	Monthly
Nozzles	Inspection	Monthly
Pipe	Inspection	Monthly
Pressure Tank	Inspection	
Steam Driver	Inspection	
Strainers	Inspection	Mfg Instruction
Suction Tanks	Inspection	
Supports	Inspection	Monthly
Water Supply Piping	Inspection	
Backflow Preventer	Inspection	
Heat (Deluge Valve House)	Inspection	Weekly
Check Valves	Maintenance	
Control Valves	Maintenance	Annually
Deluge Valve	Maintenance	
Detection Systems	Maintenance	
Detector Check Valve	Maintenance	
Electric Motor	Maintenance	
Engine Drive	Maintenance	
Fire Pump	Maintenance	
Gravity Tanks	Maintenance	
Pressure Tank	Maintenance	
Steam Driver	Maintenance	
Strainers	Maintenance	Annually
Strainers (baskets/screen)	Maintenance	5 years
Suction Tanks	Maintenance	
Water Spray System	Maintenance	Annually
Backflow Preventer	Maintenance	

(Continued)

Table 12-2 *(Continued)*

Item	Activity	Frequency
Check Valves	Operational Test	
Control Valves	Operational Test	Quarterly
Deluge Valve	Operational Test	
Detection Systems	Operational Test	
Detector Check Valve	Operational Test	
Electric Motor	Operational Test	
Engine Drive	Operational Test	
Fire Pump	Operational Test	
Flushing	Operational Test	Annually
Gravity Tanks	Operational Test	
Main Drain Test	Operational Test	Quarterly
Manual Release	Operational Test	Annually
Nozzles	Operational Test	Annually
Pressure Tank	Operational Test	
Steam Driver	Operational Test	
Strainers	Operational Test	Annually
Suction Tanks	Operational Test	
Water Flow Alarm	Operational Test	Quarterly
Water Spray System Test	Operational Test	Annually
Water Supply Flow Test	Operational Test	
Backflow Preventer	Operational Test	

Source: NFPA 25, *Standard for the Inspection, Testing, and Maintenance of Water-Based Fire Protection Systems,* NFPA, Quincy, MA, 1992.

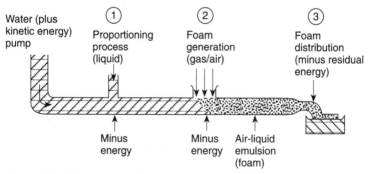

Figure 12-3. The steps in air-foam generation.

foaming, "alcohol-type," chemical agents, and powders. These last two are practically obsolete and are not used in newly designed systems.

Foam-water sprinkler and spray systems are effective in protecting areas in which flammable and combustible liquids are processed, stored, and handled. These include aircraft hangars, oil-water separators, pump areas and oil piping manifolds, petroleum piers, warehouses containing large quantities of combustible and flammable liquids, and similar installations. The foam is discharged in essentially the same pattern as water is discharged from a nozzle designed to discharge water.

When inspecting such equipment, you should watch for indications of corrosion. You also should make sure that orifices are not clogged, valves do not stick, and electrical parts do not malfunction. In addition, you should review test results.

The foam system should meet the requirements of fire protection standards and should otherwise show evidence of regular inspections and maintenance. Regular tests should confirm the dimensions and configuration of the discharge pattern, the percent of foam concentrate in the finished solution, the degree of foam expansion in the finished compound, the rate at which water drains from the foam after discharge, and the film-forming ability of the foam concentrate. You should inspect the system's mechanical equipment as you would a sprinkler system's. Chapter 8 of NFPA 25 provides the requirements for properly inspecting and testing foam-water sprinkler systems. Table 12-3 outlines the basic elements associated with inspecting, testing, and maintaining foam-water sprinkler systems.

Standpipe and Hose Systems

Standpipe and hose systems provide a means of manually applying water to fires in buildings. However, they do not take the place of automatic fire protection systems. They usually are needed where automatic protection is not provided and in areas to which hose lines from outside hydrants cannot easily reach.

Types of Systems

There are five types of standpipe systems. The most common is an automatic wet system, which is charged at all times. Another is a semiautomatic dry system, which is equipped with remote control devices at

Table 12-3. Inspection, test, and maintenance frequency.

System/Component	Activity	Frequency
Discharge Device Location	Inspection	Monthly
Discharge Device Position	Inspection	Monthly
Discharge Device Obstruction	Inspection	Monthly
Foam Concentrate Strainer(s)	Inspection	Monthly
Drainage in System Area	Inspection	Monthly
Proportioning System(s)-All	Inspection	Monthly
Foam Concentrate Pump—Power	Inspection	Monthly
Pipe Corrosion	Inspection	Quarterly
Pipe Damage	Inspection	Quarterly
Fittings Corrosion	Inspection	Quarterly
Fittings Damage	Inspection	Quarterly
Hangers/Supports	Inspection	Quarterly
Water Supply Tank(s)	Inspection	See Chapter 6, NFPA 25
Fire Pump(s)	Inspection	See Chapter 5, NFPA 25
Water Supply Piping	Inspection	See Chapter 4, NFPA 25
Control Valve(s)	Inspection	See Chapter 9, NFPA 25
Deluge/Preaction Valve(s)	Inspection	See Chapter 9, NFPA 25
Detection System	Inspection	See NFPA 72
Discharge Device Location	Test	Annually
Discharge Device Position	Test	Annually
Discharge Device Obstruction	Test	Annually
Foam Concentrate Strainer(s)	Test	Annually
Proportioning System(s)—All	Test	Annually
Complete Foam-Water System(s)	Test	Annually
Foam-Water Concentrate	Test	Annually
Manual Actuation Device(s)	Test	Annually
Backflow Device	Test	Annually
Fire Pump(s)	Test	See Chapter 5, NFPA 25
Water Supply Piping	Test	See Chapter 4, NFPA 24
Control Valve(s)	Test	See Chapter 9, NFPA 25
Strainer(s)—Mainline	Test	See Chapter 7, NFPA 25
Deluge/Preaction Valve(s)	Test	See Chapter 9, NFPA 25
Detection System	Test	See NFPA 72
Backflow Preventer	Test	See Chapter 9, NFPA 25
Water Supply Tank(s)	Test	See Chapter 6, NFPA 25
Water Supply Flow Test	Test	See Chapter 4, NFPA 25
Foam Concentrate Pump Running	Maintenance	Monthly
Foam Concentrate Strainer(s)	Maintenance	Monthly
Foam Concentrate Samples	Maintenance	Annually

(Continued)

Table 12-3 *(Continued)*

System/Component	Activity	Frequency
Proportioning System(s)		
Standard Pressure Type		
Ball Drain (Automatic Type)		
Drain Valves	Maintenance	5 Years
Foam Concentrate Tank—		
Drain and Flush	Maintenance	10 Years
Internal Corrosion & Hydro.	Maintenance	10 Years
Bladder Tank Type		
Sight Glass	Maintenance	10 Years
Foam Concentrate Tank—Hydro.	Maintenance	10 Years
Line Type		
Foam Concentrate Tank—		
Corrosion and Pickup Pipes	Maintenance	10 Years
Foam Concentrate Tank—		
Drain and Flush	Maintenance	10 Years
Standard Balance Pressure Type		
Foam Concentrate Pump(s)	Maintenance	5 Years*
Balancing Valve Diaphragm	Maintenance	5 Years
Foam Concentrate Tank	Maintenance	10 Years
In-Line Balance Pressure Type		
Foam Concentrate Pump(s)	Maintenance	5 Years*
Balancing Valve Diaphragm	Maintenance	5 Years
Foam Concentrate Tank	Maintenance	10 Years
Water Supply Tank(s)	Maintenance	See Chapter 6, NFPA 25
Fire Pump(s)	Maintenance	See Chapter 5, NFPA 25
Water Supply Piping	Maintenance	See Chapter 4, NFPA 25
Backflow Preventer(s)	Maintenance	See Chapter 9, NFPA 25
Detector Check Valve(s)	Maintenance	See Chapter 9, NFPA 25
Check Valve(s)	Maintenance	See Chapter 9, NFPA 25
Control Valve(s)	Maintenance	See Chapter 9, NFPA 25
Deluge/Preaction Valves	Maintenance	See Chapter 9, NFPA 25
Strainer(s)—Mainline	Maintenance	See Chapter 9, NFPA 25
Detection System	Maintenance	See NFPA 72

*Also refer to manufacturer's instructions and frequency.
Maintenance intervals other than preventive maintenance are not given, as they depend on the results of the visual inspections and operational tests. For foam-water systems in aircraft hangars refer to inspection, test, and maintenance requirements in NFPA 409, Table 6-1.1.
Source: NFPA 25, *Standard for the Inspection, Testing and Maintenance of Water-Based Fire Protection Systems,* NFPA, Quincy, MA 1992.

each hose station that admits water into the system. A third type is an automatic dry-pipe system for unheated buildings. In this system, which is similar to a dry-pipe sprinkler system, a dry-pipe valve prevents water from entering the system until the stored air pressure in the discharge side falls below the water supply pressure. The fourth type of standpipe system is a manual dry system, which has no permanent water supply. It is composed of a pipe that contains air at atmospheric pressure and receives its water supply from a fire department pumper. The fifth type of system is a manual wet system. This has no permanent water supply, either. Instead, a small-diameter water supply pipe is connected to the system to keep it filled at all times, and the water supply for both flow and pressure is provided by a fire department pumper.

In some buildings, a combined sprinkler/standpipe system riser can be used. For some combined riser arrangements, the water supply and the pressure for the sprinkler system must be adequate, but the flow and pressure for the standpipe system might have to be provided through the fire department connection. This type of arrangement is considered a manual wet standpipe system because it uses a fire department pumper to maintain the appropriate standpipe pressures.

Inspections and Tests

Periodic inspection of all portions of standpipe systems is essential. You should make sure that the valves in the automatic sources of water are open and test the supervisory means of such valves. Examine the threads at the fire department connection and be sure that the waterway is not clogged with any foreign material.

Check the valve at each discharge outlet or hose station for leakage and examine the hose threads. Where hose is provided for occupant use, check its condition and the condition of the nozzle and see to it that the hose is stored properly. Any pressure regulating valves provided must be tested once every 5 years to ensure that they are properly set and adjusted. Chapter 3 of NFPA 25 provides information on inspecting, testing, and maintaining standpipes (see Table 12-4).

Inspecting and Testing Hose Threads and Fire Hose

Fire hose found in commercial or industrial environments generally is intended either for occupant use in dealing with incipient fires or for use

Table 12-4.

Item	Activity	Frequency
Hose/Hydrant Houses	Inspection	Monthly
Hydrants (Dry Wall)	Inspection	Semiannually & after each operation
Monitor Nozzles	Inspection	Semiannually
Hydrants (Wet)	Inspection	Annually & after each operation
Mainline Strainer	Inspection	Annually & after each significant flow
Piping (Exposed)	Inspection	Annually
Piping (Underground)	Inspection	*
Monitor Nozzles	Test	Flow-Annually (Range-Operation) Semi-annually
Hydrants	Test	Annually
Piping (Exposed and Underground)	Flow Test	5 Year
Mainline Strainer	Maintenance	Annually & after each operation
Hose/Hydrant Houses	Maintenance	Annually
Hydrants	Maintenance	Annually
Monitor Nozzles	Maintenance	Annually

Source: Table 4-1, NFPA 25, *Standard for the Inspection, Testing, and Maintenance of Water-Based Fire Protection Systems,* NFPA, Quincy, MA, 1992.

by trained fire fighters or fire brigade members in attacking a fire. The former is known as occupant use hose and the latter as attack hose. It is important that you understand the differences between them, as their testing requirements differ.

Inspection Requirements for Fire Hose

When inspecting fire hose, first you should determine if the proper amount of hose is available, where it will be used, and whether it is stored in hose houses, on racks or reels, or on some type of cart or vehicle. You also should make certain that it is the proper type of hose. Attack hose can be used in an occupant use environment, but occupant use hose should not be used where attack hose is required.

Occupant use hose manufactured after July 1987 will have a service test pressure of 150 psi stenciled on the jacket. Occupant hose manufactured before July 1987 will be either single-jacket hose stenciled with a proof pressure of 300 psi or will be unlined standpipe hose.

Next, you should make sure that the hose has no mechanical damage, such as an abrasion or a cut, and that it has not been damaged by heat, mildew or mold, acid, gasoline or oil, rodents, or any other environmental condition. If there is evidence that the hose has been subject to any of these conditions, inspect it carefully and test it to determine whether it still can be used. You also should make sure that the hose is stored in such a way as to protect it from these conditions.

Then you should inspect all couplings to make sure that they have not been damaged. Physically connect or disconnect all the hose stored at a particular location to ensure that the couplings turn freely and are not out of round; that the threads have not been damaged; and that all the threads, including those on the nozzles and hydrant outlets, are compatible. Make sure there are no signs of corrosion, that the coupling has not slipped on the hose, and that there is no other sign of damage from use or misuse. Only those lubricants specified by the coupling manufacturer should be used on the couplings.

Next, check the gaskets in the couplings to make sure that they fit properly, are flexible, have not deteriorated or been cut or torn, and do not protrude into the waterway.

You also should determine whether the hose has been service tested at the required frequency. In addition, the hose should be stretched out periodically for inspection, then repacked or refolded so that folds are not in the same place.

After hose has been used, it must be dried. Make sure that suitable facilities, such as hose racks, hose towers, or drying cabinets, are available for this. Hose should not be laid out to dry on a hot surface such as concrete or asphalt.

Finally, make sure that the hose threads used throughout the facility are the same. If they are not compatible with the threads used by the local public fire department or with the threads on municipal hydrants, make sure there is an adequate supply of adaptors available where they will be needed.

Testing Requirements for Fire Hose

Attack hose must be tested annually, while occupant use hose must be tested 5 years after the date of purchase and every 3 years after that.

Hose manufactured after July 1987 will be stenciled with the service test pressure. For occupant use hose, this will be a minimum of 150 psi (1,034 kPa). Attack hose has a minimum service test pressure of 300 psi (2,070 kPa).

If the hose was manufactured before July 1987, a table in NFPA 1962, *Standard for the Care, Use, and Service Testing of Fire Hose Including Couplings and Nozzles,* specifies the test pressure. For older hose, the pressure stenciled on the hose is the proof pressure*that is, the pressure to which new hose is tested after being coupled. The hose should not be service tested to the proof test pressure.

The procedure for service testing fire hose is outlined in NFPA 1962. Essentially, it involves stretching the hose out in lengths no longer than 300 feet, connecting it to a water pressure source, and flooding it and expelling all the air. The pressure then should be partially raised while the hose is checked for leaks and marked at the couplings. Next, the pressure is raised to the test pressure and held there for 5 minutes. The hose is then checked for slippage at the couplings, and the test is concluded. Because testing fire hose can be dangerous, particularly if the details of the test procedure are not followed, you should not try to perform a test without carefully following the instructions in NFPA 1962.

Bibliography

Cote, A. E., ed., *Fire Protection Handbook*, 17th edition, National Fire Protection Association, Quincy, MA, 1991. Section 5, Chapter 3 deals with water supplies for fire protection; Section 5, Chapters 9,10, 14, and 15 covers water-based extinguishing systems; and Section 5, Chapter 20 discusses foam extinguishing agents and systems.

Carson, W. G. and Klinker, R. L., *Fire Protection Systems: Inspection, Test and Maintenance Manual,* 2nd edition, NFPA, Quincy, MA, 1992.

NFPA Codes, Standards, and Recommended Practices

NFPA 11, *Standard for Low Expansion Foam and Combined Agent Systems.* Provides the minimum requirements for inside hazards, exterior storage tanks, indoor and outdoor processing areas, spray foam systems, and monitor and hose systems.

NFPA 11A, *Standard for Medium- and High-Expansion Foam Systems.* Outlines the minimum requirements for design, installation, testing, operation, and maintenance.

NFPA 11C, *Standard for Mobile Foam Apparatus.* Outlines the minimum requirements for the design, approval, testing, inspection, operation, and maintenance of mobile foam apparatus.

NFPA 13, *Standard for the Installation of Sprinkler Systems.* Explains the complete requirements for various types of sprinkler systems, including inside and outside protection, water supplies, system components, types of systems, and specialized units, such as hydraulically designed and high-rise systems.

NFPA 13D, *Standard for the Installation of Sprinkler Systems in One- and Two-Family Dwellings and Mobile Homes.* Covers the design and installation of automatic sprinkler systems and provides information on water supply, systems design, and other important technical considerations.

NFPA 13E, *Recommendations for Fire Department Operations in Properties Protected by Sprinkler and Standpipe Systems.* Outlines fire department inspection, planning, water supply, operations, and reports.

NFPA 13R, *Standard for the Installation of Sprinkler Systems in Residential Occupancies Up to and Including Four Stories in Height.* Covers the design and installation of automatic sprinklers in low-rise residential occupancies such as apartments, condominiums, dormitories, hotels, and motels.

NFPA 14, *Standard for the Installation of Standpipe and Hose Systems.* Describes the required components, delivery systems, sizes, number, outlets, water supplies, piping, and location of hose stations.

NFPA 15, *Standard for Water Spray Fixed Systems for Fire Protection.* Covers system components, design, installation, tests, hydraulic calculations, and automatic-detection equipment.

NFPA 16, *Standard on the Installation of Deluge Foam-Water Sprinkler and Foam-Water Spray Systems.* Covers regular and spray systems, from water supply to testing and maintenance.

NFPA 16A, *Recommended Practice for the Installation of Closed-Head Foam-Water Sprinkler Systems.* Covers system components, water supplies, system design and installation, acceptance tests, periodic testing, and maintenance.

NFPA 24, *Standard for the Installation of Private Fire Service Mains and Their Appurtenances.* Details of yard piping that supplies water to automatic sprinkler systems, yard hydrants, standpipes, and other systems.

NFPA 25, *Standard for the Inspection, Testing, and Maintenance of Water-Based Fire Protection Systems.* Provides requirements for the periodic inspection, testing, and maintenance of all water-based fire protection systems. Covers frequencies, procedures, and retention of records.

NFPA 1961, *Standard for Fire Hose.* Covers construction, diameter and length, and hydrostatic pressure capacity for fire department, industrial, and forestry fire hose.

NFPA 1962, *Standard for the Care, Use, and Service Testing of Fire Hose Including Couplings and Nozzles.* Defines requirements for use, inspection, storage, service testing, and record keeping for fire department, industrial, and forestry fire hose.

NFPA 1963, *Standard for Screw Threads and Gaskets for Fire Hose Connections.* Covers dimensions for screw threads, gauges, gaskets, and gasket seats.

NFPA 1964, *Standard for Spray Nozzles (Shutoff and Tip).* Applies to portable adjustable-pattern nozzles intended for general fire department use or for use with hoses attached to standpipe systems.

CHAPTER 13

Special Agent Extinguishing Systems

*T*he most widely used special agent extinguishing systems are carbon dioxide, halogenated agents, and dry chemicals. Because systems employing these agents use a fixed supply, it is important that all hazard areas that could possibly be involved in a single fire be protected simultaneously.

Systems using these special agents consist of detection and control equipment, agent release devices, agent storage containers, agent distribution systems such as pipes and nozzles, and ancillary devices such as door closures and damper releases.

These systems initially are designed for a defined hazard. However, changes in the hazard, such as the layout of the equipment being protected; changes to the enclosure surrounding the hazard; and changes in the type of fuel could affect the system's ability to extinguish a fire.

Application Systems

Three basic methods are used to apply extinguishing agents: total flooding systems, local application systems, and hand hose lines.

Total flooding systems discharge enough extinguishing agent into an enclosure to provide a uniform fire extinguishing concentration throughout the entire enclosure. Openings in the enclosure sometimes can be compensated for by providing automatic closure devices controlled by the fire protection system, which is the more common method, or by adding extinguishing agent.

Local application systems discharge the agent directly onto the burning material or object without relying on an enclosure to retain the agent. These systems typically are used to protect printing presses, dip and quench tanks, spray booths, oil-filled electric transformers, vapor vents, and so on.

Hand hose line systems consist of a supply of extinguishing agent, such as carbon dioxide, halon 1211, or dry chemical, and one or more hand hose lines that allow manual delivery of the agent to the fire. The hose lines are connected to the agent container either directly or by means of intermediate piping.

Both engineered and pre-engineered systems are available. An engineered system is one in which individual calculations and design are required to determine the agent flow rate, the size of the piping, nozzle pressures, and so on. A pre-engineered system, sometimes called a package system, is one in which minimum and maximum parameters have been predetermined and confirmed by an independent testing agency. Installation within the listed limits ensures adequate flow rate, pressure, and pattern coverage without individual calculation.

Inspection and Maintenance

These systems should be thoroughly inspected and tested for proper operation by competent personnel. The manufacturer, installing contractor, or other qualified organization should provide regular service contracts.

The tables given in this chapter for each type of system outline the main aspects of the inspection and maintenance procedure and should be used for guidance only. For more details on these procedures and on the frequency of the different verifications and tests, refer to the applicable NFPA standards (see Bibliography) and to the manufacturers' manuals.

Ideally, you should witness the tests and verifications conducted when the system is serviced regularly. If this is not feasible, however, you should be informed that the tests were conducted and be given access to the reports. In addition to inspecting the system and the protected hazard, you should verify that the personnel using and operating the system or any personnel who might become involved during a fire in the protected area have been trained adequately.

Carbon Dioxide Systems

A number of properties make carbon dioxide a desirable fire extinguishing agent. It does not react with most substances, it does not conduct electricity, and it provides its own discharge pressure. As a gas, carbon dioxide can penetrate the fire area and it leaves no residue.

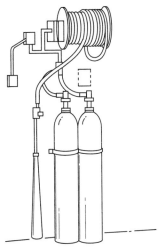

*Figure 13-1. Carbon dioxide hand
hose extinguishing system with
hose mounted on a reel. (Walter
Kidde & Company, Inc.)*

Carbon dioxide is effective as an extinguishing agent primarily because it reduces the oxygen content of the atmosphere by dilution to a point at which the atmosphere no longer supports combustion. Under suitable conditions, the available cooling effect also can be helpful, especially in local application.

Safety Considerations

Carbon dioxide can produce unconsciousness and death when present in the amounts needed to extinguish a fire. Therefore, carbon dioxide total flooding systems should not be used in spaces that normally are occupied. To prevent accidental discharge, a "lock-out" is provided when persons not familiar with the systems and their operation are present in a protected space. Authorities responsible for continuity of fire protection must be notified of lock-out and subsequent restoration of the system. For total flooding hazards that normally are not occupied but in which personnel might be present for maintenance or other purposes, there must be some means of warning the occupants of an impending discharge and of ensuring that they can be evacuated before the discharge occurs. It might be difficult to ensure evacuation if the space is large or if egress is impeded in any way by obstacles or complicated passageways. Escape is even more difficult after the discharge starts because the noise can cause confusion and visibility is greatly reduced.

Type of Storage

The carbon dioxide supply can be stored in high- or low-pressure containers. High-pressure containers, usually cylinders, are designed to store liquid carbon dioxide at ambient temperature. Because the temperature affects the pressure, it is important to store the cylinder in an area where temperatures will be within the listed limits. Low-pressure containers are pressure vessels designed to maintain the temperature of carbon dioxide at about 0°F by means of insulation and refrigeration. These containers can hold 500 pounds to 100 tons or more of agent.

Inspection and Maintenance

Table 13-1 lists the main points of the inspection and maintenance procedure. Refer to NFPA 12, *Standard on Carbon Dioxide Extinguishing Systems,* and to the system manufacturer's manual for more complete information. Inspection and maintenance should be carried out by competent personnel only.

Halogenated Agents Systems

Halogenated extinguishing agents, or halons, have a number of unique fire protection qualities. In addition to their ability to extinguish flames, they leave no residue to clean up after a fire, and they do not cause thermal shock to delicate equipment. The two halons most widely used in North America are halon 1301 [bromotrifluoromethane (CF_3Br)] and halon 1211 [bromochlorodifluoromethane (CF_2ClBr)].

Fire protection halons currently are the focus of worldwide attention because they have been linked to the destruction of the Earth's stratospheric ozone layer. The global production of halons is being phased out by the Montreal Protocol, a far-reaching treaty signed by most countries of the world. Because future supplies of fire protection halons will be very limited, all unnecessary emissions should be eliminated. Meanwhile, many halon systems exist, and they must be inspected periodically and maintained.

Table 13-1. Testing guidelines for carbon dioxide systems. Note: For all of these verifications and tests, the actuating controls must be removed from the agent containers to avoid accidental discharge. Frequency is minimum recommended.

Verification or test	Frequency
1. The system	
Overall physical appearance	Every 30 days
Check if there have been any changes in the size or type of hazard	Every 6 months
2. Supervised circuits	Every year
3. Control panel (all functions)	Every year
4. Power supply	Every Year
5. Emergency power	Every year
6. Detectors (test, clean, and check wiring)	Every year
7. Verification of the time delay	Every year
8. Alarms (operation, warning signs properly displayed)	Every year
9. Selector valves (if applicable)	Every year
10. Ancillary functions (closure of dampers and doors, shutdown of equipment, and so on)	Every year
11. Manual releases (operation, accessibility)	Every year
12. Piping (supports, blockage, integrity, and so on)	Every year
13. Nozzles	Every year
14. Containers (physical condition, weight)	Every 6 months
15. Release devices	Every year
16. Testing of hoses	Every 5 years
17. Hydrostatic testing of high-pressure containers	12 years; after a discharge if more than 5 years since last test.
18. Liquid level gauge of low-pressure containers	Every week

Safety Considerations

Experience and testing have shown that personnel can be exposed to halon 1301 and halon 1211 vapors in low concentration for brief periods without serious risks. However, unnecessary exposure is not recommended. Exposure to high concentrations—10% for halon 1301 and 4% for halon 1211—can present a hazard to personnel. Halon 1211 should not be used as a total flooding agent in enclosures that normally are occupied.

Type of Storage

Total flooding systems can have a modular design or a central storage design. In modular systems, a nozzle is connected to a halon container with little or no piping. Containers are located throughout the space to be protected so that the concentration of the agent will be uniform upon discharge. In central storage systems, halon containers are connected to a manifold, and the halon is delivered to discharge nozzles through a piping network.

Inspection and Maintenance

Table 13-2 gives the main items of the inspection and maintenance procedure. Refer to NFPA 12A, *Standard on Halon 1301 Fire Extinguishing Systems* and to the system manufacturer's manual for more complete

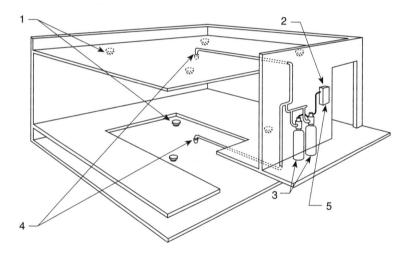

1. Automatic fire detectors installed both in room proper and in underfloor area.
2. Control panel connected between fire detectors and cylinder release valves.
3. Storage containers for room proper and underfloor area.
4. Discharge nozzles installed both in room proper and in underfloor area.
5. Control panel might also sound alarms, close doors, and shut off power to the area.

Figure 13-2. A total flooding halogenated extinguishing agent system installed in a room with a raised floor. (The Ansul Company)

Table 13-2. Testing guidelines for halogenated agents systems. Note: For all of these verifications and tests, the actuating controls must be removed from the agent containers to avoid accidental discharge. Frequency is minimum recommended.

Verification or test	Frequency
1. Detection and actuation system	Every 6 months
Detectors checked and cleaned	
Supervision features checked	
Operation of actuating controls (removed from containers)	
Operation of manual operating controls	
2. Containers	
Visual examination	Every 6 months
Verification of agent quantity and pressure	Every 6 months
3. Piping and nozzles	
Visual verification for any evidence of corrosion or obstruction, and proper position and alignment of nozzles	Every 6 months
Visual inspection of hoses	Every 6 months
Hydrostatic testing of hoses	Every 5 years
4. Auxiliary equipment	Every 6 months

information. Full inspection and maintenance should be carried out by competent personnel only.

Dry Chemical Systems

Dry chemical extinguishing agents are known as ordinary dry chemicals and multipurpose dry chemicals. The former are used to combat fires involving flammable liquids (Class B) and electrical equipment (Class C). The latter are effective on ordinary combustibles (Class A), on flammable liquids (Class B), and on electrical equipment (Class C).

Typical dry chemical agents include sodium bicarbonate, potassium bicarbonate, monoammonium phosphate, potassium chloride, or urea

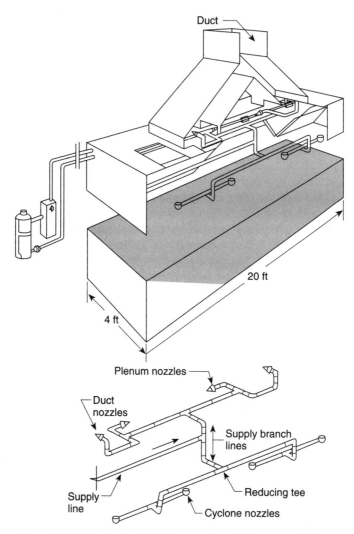

Duct

Duct

20 ft

4 ft

Plenum nozzles

Duct
nozzles

Supply branch
lines

Supply
line

Reducing tee

Cyclone nozzles

Figure 13-3. A typical, single 30-pound cartridge-operated dry chemical system with fusible links for automatic operation that was engineered for kitchen range, hood, duct, and fryer fire protection. (The Ansul Company)

potassium bicarbonate as base materials. Dry chemical extinguishing agents should not be confused with dry powder agents, which were developed for use on combustible metals. Extinguishing agents used on combustible metal fires are discussed in Chapter 38.

Extinguishing Properties

Ordinary dry chemical is used primarily to extinguish flammable liquids fires. However, its use might not result in permanent extinguishment if reignition sources, such as hot metal surfaces, are present. Dry chemicals might not extinguish deep-seated Class A fires, and they are not suitable for fires in materials that supply their own oxygen for combustion.

Dry chemicals should not be used in installations containing delicate electronic equipment because the insulating properties of the chemicals can render such equipment inoperative. Some dry chemicals are slightly corrosive, especially monoammonium phosphate base, and should therefore be removed from all undamaged surfaces as soon as possible after extinguishment.

Safety Considerations

The discharge of large amounts of dry chemicals can create hazards to personnel. They may reduce visibility and temporarily make breathing difficult.

Type of Storage

Dry chemicals are stored in pressure containers either at atmospheric pressure until the system is actuated—these are cylinders or cartridge-operated containers—or at the pressure of the internally stored expellant gas—these are stored pressure containers.

Inspection and Maintenance

Table 13-3 lists the main points of the inspection and maintenance procedure. Refer to NFPA 17, *Standard for Dry Chemical Extinguishing Systems,* and to the system manufacturer's manual for more complete information. Full inspection and maintenance should be carried out by competent personnel only.

Table 13-3. Testing guidelines for dry chemical systems. Note: For all of these verifications and tests, the actuating controls must be removed from the agent containers to avoid accidental discharge. Frequency is minimum recommended.

Verification or test	Frequency
1. Check location of the extinguishing system	Every month
2. Manual actuators are not obstructed	Every month
3. Tamper indicators and seals are intact	Every month
4. Maintenance tag or certificate is in place	Every month
5. No obvious physical damage	Every month
6. Pressure gauge(s), if any, in operable range	Every month
7. No modification of the hazard	Every 6 months
8. Examine all detectors, containers, releasing devices, piping, hose assemblies, nozzles, alarms, and auxiliary equipment	Every 6 months
9. Verify that agent distribution piping is not obstructed	Every 6 months
10. Examine the dry chemical:	
Atmospheric pressure systems	Every 6 months
Stored pressure systems	Every 6 years
11. Operational test of the system and all of its functions (excluding discharge)	Every 6 months
12. Replacement of the fusible links	Every year
13. Hydrostatic test	Every 12 years

Wet Chemical Systems

For a complete discussion of wet chemical systems, see Chapter 47, "Venting Systems for Commercial Cooking Equipment."

Bibliography

Cote, A. E., ed., *Fire Protection Handbook,* 17th edition, National Fire Protection Association, Quincy, MA, 1991. Carbon dioxide, halogenated agent, and dry chemical agent extinguishing systems are discussed in considerable detail in Section 5, Chapters 17, 18, and 19.

Carson, W. G. and Klinker, R. L., *Fire Protection Systems: Inspection, Test and Maintenance Manual,* 2nd edition, NFPA, Quincy, MA, 1992.

NFPA Codes, Standards, and Recommended Practices

NFPA 12, *Standard on Carbon Dioxide Extinguishing Systems*. Covers design, installation, testing, approval, operation, and maintenance for total flooding, local application, and hose line systems.

NFPA 12A, *Standard on Halon 1301 Fire Extinguishing Systems*. Provides the minimum requirements for design, installation, testing, inspection, and maintenance of bromotrifluoromethane systems.

NFPA 12B, *Standard on Halon 1211 Fire Extinguishing Systems*. Provides the minimum requirements for design, installation, testing, inspection, and maintenance of bromochlorodifluoromethane systems.

NFPA 17, *Standard for Dry Chemical Extinguishing Systems*. Provides minimum requirements and discusses total flooding, local application, hand hose line systems, and pre-engineered systems.

NFPA 17A, *Standard for Wet Chemical Extinguishing Systems*. Covers the design, installation, operation, testing, maintenance, and minimum requirements of wet chemical pre-engineered fire extinguishing systems that discharge wet chemical from fixed nozzles and piping by means of expellant gas.

NFPA 75, *Standard for the Protection of Electronic Computer/Data Processing Equipment*. Provides standard requirements for installations needing fire protection or special building construction, rooms, areas, or operating environments.

CHAPTER 14

Portable Fire Extinguishers

*P*ortable fire extinguishers are installed in many occupancies to give the building occupants a means of fighting a fire manually. Not all occupancies are required to have portable fire extinguishers. Normally, a building code, NFPA *101, Life Safety Code,* or insurance company standard will have a provision that states, "Portable fire extinguishers shall be installed in accordance with NFPA 10, *Standard for Portable Fire Extinguishers.*" Once it has been established that portable fire extinguishers are required, you must ensure that they are properly selected, placed, and serviced.

Selecting Extinguishers

The size and type of portable fire extinguisher is based on the total amount of Class A combustible materials, the total amount of Class B flammables, or, for some occupancies, a combination of both. For many areas, the extinguishing agent also must be compatible with energized electrical equipment.

NFPA 10 provides the following criteria for determining the classification of hazards.

Light (Low) Hazard

Light hazard occupancies are locations in which the total amount of Class A combustible materials, including furnishings, decorations, and contents, is minor. These occupancies may include buildings or rooms occupied as offices, classrooms, churches, assembly halls, the guest rooms of hotels or motels, and so on. This classification anticipates that most of the contents of the occupancy are either noncombustible or that they have been arranged in such a manner that a fire is not likely to spread rapidly among them. Small amounts of Class B flammables used in duplicating machines, art departments, and the like are included, provided they are kept in closed containers and are stored safely.

Ordinary (Moderate) Hazard

Ordinary hazard occupancies are locations in which the total amount of Class A combustibles and Class B flammables are present in greater amounts than may be expected in light hazard occupancies. These occupancies may consist of dining areas, mercantile shops and their allied storage, light manufacturing facilities, research operations, auto showrooms, parking garages, the workshop or support service areas of light hazard occupancies, and warehouses containing Class I or Class II commodities, as defined by NFPA 231, *Standard for General Storage.*

Extra (High) Hazard

Extra hazard occupancies are locations in which the total amount of Class A combustibles and Class B flammables present in storage, in production, or as finished products is over that expected in ordinary hazard occupancies. These occupancies may consist of woodworking shops, vehicle repair areas, aircraft and boat servicing facilities, cooking areas, product showrooms, convention center displays, and areas that house storage and manufacturing processes, such as painting, dipping, and coating. Also included is warehousing or in-process storage of commodities other than Class I and II commodities.

Distributing Extinguishers

After the hazard classification of an occupancy has been determined, the portable extinguishers can be distributed. Extinguishers should be placed in locations that are readily available, provide easy access and are relatively free from temporary blockage, are near normal paths of travel, are near exits and entrances, and are free from the potential of physical damage.

Mounting Extinguishers

Most extinguishers are mounted on walls or columns by securely fastened hangers so that they are supported adequately, although some extinguishers are mounted in cabinets or wall recesses. In any case, the operating instructions must face outward, and the extinguisher should be placed so that it can be removed easily. Cabinets should be kept clean and dry.

In areas where extinguishers may become dislodged, brackets specifically designed to cope with this problem should be used. In areas such as warehouse aisles, where they are subject to physical damage, they should be protected from impact. In large open areas such as aircraft hangars, extinguishers can be mounted on movable pedestals or wheeled carts whose proper locations should be marked on the floor to maintain the pattern of distribution.

NFPA 10 specifies floor clearance and mounting heights, based on extinguisher weight. Extinguishers with a gross weight of no more than 40 pounds should be installed so that the top of the extinguisher is not more than 5 feet above the floor. Extinguishers with a gross weight greater than 40 pounds (except wheeled types) should be installed so that the top of the extinguisher is not more than 3 1/2 feet above the floor. In no case should the clearance between the bottom of the extinguisher and the floor be less than 4 inches.

When extinguishers are mounted on industrial trucks, vehicles, boats, aircraft, trains, and so on, special mounting brackets, available from the manufacturer, should be used. It is important to install an extinguisher at a safe distance from a hazard so that it will not become involved in a fire.

Distribution for Class A Hazards

Table 14-1, which was taken from NFPA 10, provides the requirements for determining the minimum number and rating of extinguishers needed in any particular area to cope with Class A fires. Sometimes, extinguishers with ratings higher than those indicated in this table will be necessary, due to process hazards or building configuration. In no case, however, should the recommended maximum travel distance be exceeded.

The first step in calculating how many Class A extinguishers are needed is to determine whether an occupancy is a light, an ordinary, or an extra hazard occupancy. Next, the extinguisher rating should be matched with the occupancy hazard to determine the maximum area an extinguisher can protect. Table 14-1 also specifies the maximum travel distance, or actual walking distance, allowed; for Class A extinguishers, it is 75 feet. Thus, a 2 1/2-gallon stored-pressure water extinguisher rated

Table 14-1. Minimum number and rating of extinguishers for Class A fires. Two 2-1/2-gallon water-type extinguishers can be used to fulfill the requirements of one 4-A rated extinguisher.

	Light (Low) Hazard Occupancy	Ordinary (Moderate) Hazard Occupancy	Extra (High) Hazard Occupancy
Minimum rated single extinguisher	2-A	2-A	4-A
Maximum floor area per unit of A	3000 sq ft	1500 sq ft	1000 sq ft
Maximum floor area for extinguisher	11,250 sq ft	11,250 sq ft	11,250 sq ft
Maximum travel distance to extinguisher	75 ft	75 ft	75 ft

Source: Table 3-2.1, NFPA 10, *Standard for Portable Fire Extinguishers*, NFPA, Quincy, MA, 1990.

2-A will protect an area of 3,000 square feet in an ordinary hazard occupancy, but only 2,000 square feet in an extra hazard occupancy.

Table 14-2, which was taken from NFPA 10, was developed from Table 14-1 and summarizes what was intended by the second and third rows of Table 14-1. The following examples show how to place extinguishers in accordance with these tables.

The first example demonstrates placement at the maximum protection area limits of 11,250 square feet allowed in Table 14-1 for each class of occupancy. Installing extinguishers with higher ratings will not affect distribution or placement.

Example 1:

$$\frac{67,500}{11,250} = 6$$

4-A Extinguishers for Light Hazard Occupancy
10-A Extinguishers for Ordinary Hazard Occupancy
20-A Extinguishers for Extra Hazard Occupancy

Table 14-2. Maximum area to be protected per extinguisher, sq ft.

Class A Rating Shown on Extinguisher	Light (Low) Hazard Occupancy	Ordinary (Moderate) Hazard Occupancy	Extra (High) Hazard Occupancy
1A	—	—	—
2A	6,000	3,000	—
3A	9,000	4,500	—
4A	11,250	6,000	4,000
6A	11,250	9,000	6,000
10A	11,250	11,250	10,000
20A	11,250	11,250	11,250
30A	11,250	11,250	11,250
40A	11,250	11,250	11,250

Note: 11,250 is considered a practical limit. Source: Table E-3-4, NFPA 10, *Standard for Portable Fire Extinguishers,* NFPA, Quincy, MA, 1990.

This placement along outside walls would not be acceptable because the travel distance rule clearly has been violated (see Figure 14-1). Relocation or additional extinguishers are needed.

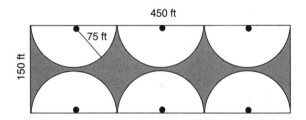

Figure 14-1. A diagrammatic representation of extinguishers located along the outside walls of a 450- by 150-feet (137-by 46-meters) building. (The dots represent extinguishers.) The shaded areas indicate "voids" that are further than 75 feet (227 meters) to the nearest extinguisher. Source: Figure E-3-6, NFPA 10, **Standard for Portable Fire Extinguishers, NFPA, Quincy, MA, 1990.**

Example 2 deals with extinguishers with ratings that correspond to protection areas of 6,000 square feet. This example shows just one of the many ways these extinguishers can be placed. Meeting the travel distance requirement generally becomes less of a problem as the number of lower-rated extinguishers increases.

Example 2:

$$\frac{67,500}{6,000} = 12$$
2-A Extinguishers for Light Hazard Occupancy
4-A Extinguishers for Ordinary Hazard Occupan
6-A Extinguishers for Extra Hazard Occupancy

Extinguishers could be mounted on exterior walls or on building columns or interior walls, as shown in Figure 14-2, and conform to both distribution and travel distance rules.

NFPA 10 also allows up to half the complement of extinguishers for Class A fires to be replaced by uniformly spaced small hose (1 1/2-inch) stations. However, the hose stations and the extinguishers should be located so that the hose stations do not replace more than one of every two extinguishers previously used.

Distribution for Class B Hazards

In areas in which flammable liquids are not expected to reach an appreciable depth, extinguishers should be provided according to Table 14-3, which was taken from NFPA 10. The basic maximum travel

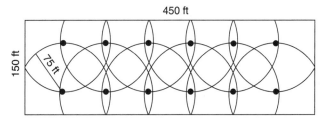

450 ft

150 ft

75 ft

Figure 14-2. Requirements for both travel distance and extinguisher distribution are met in this configuration representing 12 extinguishers mounted on building columns or interior walls. Source: Figure E-3-8(a), NFPA 10, Standard for Portable Fire Extinguishers, NFPA, Quincy, MA, 1990.

distance to Class B extinguishers is 50 feet, as opposed to 75 feet for Class A extinguishers, because flammable liquids fires reach their maximum intensity almost immediately, and thus the extinguisher must be used earlier. With lower-rated extinguishers, the travel distance drops to 30 feet.

Where flammable liquids are likely to reach an appreciable depth, a Class B-rated fire extinguisher must be provided on the basis of at least two numerical units of Class B extinguishing potential per square foot of flammable liquid surface of the largest tank hazard in the area. The travel distances specified by Table 14-3 also should be used to locate extinguishers to protect spot hazards. Sometimes, a single extinguisher can be installed to provide protection against several different hazards, provided that travel distances are not exceeded.

Extinguishers selected to protect deep-fat fryers must be of either the sodium-bicarbonate- or potassium-bicarbonate-based dry-chemical-type. These extinguishing agents react chemically with the cooking oils to form a type of soap on the liquid surface that effectively prevents the grease from reigniting.

Table 14-3. Travel distances to Class B extinguishers. The specified ratings do not imply that fires of the magnitudes indicated by these ratings will occur, but rather the ratings give the operators more time and agent to handle difficult spill fires that could occur.

Type of Hazard	Basic Minimum Extinguisher Rating	Maximum Travel Distance to Extinguishers (ft)
Light (low)	5-B	30
	10-B	50
Ordinary (moderate)	10-B	30
	20-B	50
Extra (high)	40-B	50
	80-B	50

Source: Table 3-3.1, NFPA 10, *Standard for Portable Fire Extinguishers,* NFPA, Quincy, MA, 1990.

Distribution for Class C Hazards

Extinguishers with a Class C rating are installed where there is live electrical equipment. This sort of extinguisher contains a nonconducting agent, usually carbon dioxide, dry chemical, or halon. Once the power to live electrical equipment has been cut off, the fire becomes a Class A or Class B fire, depending on the nature of the burning electrical equipment and the burning material in the vicinity.

Distribution for Class D Hazards

It is particularly important that the proper extinguishers be available for Class D fires. Because the properties of combustible metals differ, even a Class D extinguishing agent can be hazardous if it is used on the wrong metal. Agents should be chosen carefully according to the manufacturer's recommendations.

The amount of agent needed normally is figured according to the surface area of the metal plus the shape and form of the metal, which can contribute to the severity of the fire and cause the agent to "bake-off." For example, fires in magnesium filings are more difficult to put out than fires in magnesium scrap, so more agent is needed for fires in magnesium filings. The maximum travel distance to all extinguishers for Class D fires is 75 feet.

Types of Fire Extinguishers

Listed fire extinguishers are classified into seven major types. These are stored pressure water extinguishers, dry chemical extinguishers, halon 1211 extinguishers, carbon dioxide extinguishers, foam extinguishers, loaded stream extinguishers, and extinguishers and agents used on combustible metals.

Stored pressure water extinguishers use plain water as the agent, with stored pressure in the same chamber as the water. Typically, they have a 2 1/2-gallon capacity and a rating of 2-A.

Dry chemical extinguishers are of the stored-pressure type or the cartridge- or cylinder-operated type. Dry chemical extinguishing agents include ordinary dry chemical, which is sodium-bicarbonate-based; multipurpose dry chemical, which is monoammonium-phosphate-based; or dry chemicals with the other base ingredients of potassium bicarbonate, potassium chloride, and urea-based potassium bicarbonate.

Halon 1211 extinguishers use halon 1211 as the extinguishing agent and are of the stored-pressure type. When using this type of extinguisher in confined spaces, precautions should be taken to avoid breathing the gases or vapors that are released. The agent is very "clean," which is useful when using it on electronic equipment. Ratings for small units are for Class B and C fires. However, larger units that contain 9 pounds or more of agent also carry Class A ratings.

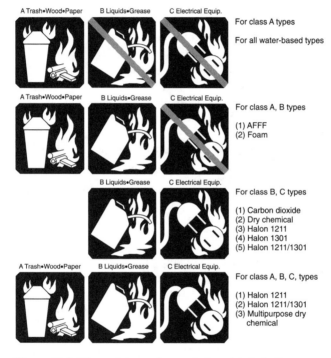

Figure 14-3. These pictographs are designed to help the user determine at a glance the proper use of an extinguisher. When an application is prohibited, the background is black, and the slash is bright red. Otherwise, the background is light blue. Class B,C extinguishers have limited effectiveness on Class A fires so no picture is shown in that category. Source: Table B-2-1, NFPA 10, **Standard for Portable Fire Extinguishers,** *NFPA, Quincy, MA, 1990.*

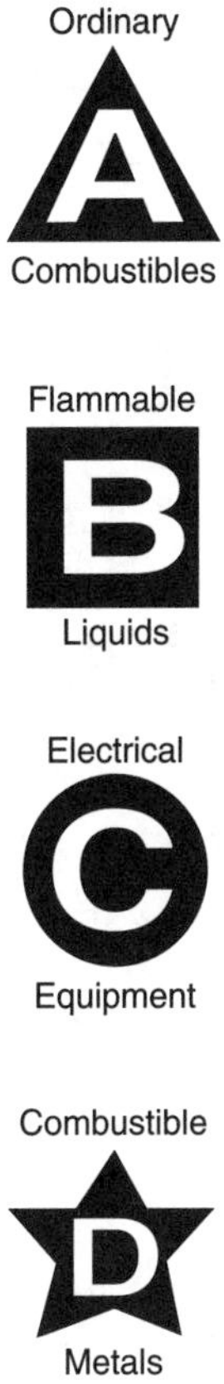

Ordinary

Combustibles

Flammable

Liquids

Electrical

Equipment

Combustible

Metals

Figure 14-4. These letter-shaped symbol markings are no longer recommended but are still found on many extinguishers in use. Source: Table B-2-2, NFPA 10, **Standard for Portable Fire Extinguishers,** *NFPA, Quincy, MA, 1990.*

Carbon dioxide (CO_2) extinguishers use steel cylinders rated for 1,800 psi or higher. The carbon dioxide is stored as a liquid in the cylinder with a vapor space at the top. When the agent is discharged, it vaporizes

PORTABLE FIRE EXTINGUISHERS

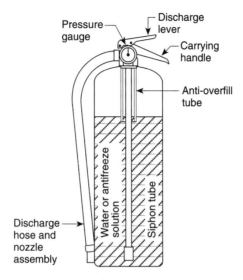

Figure 14-5. Stored-pressure water extinguisher.
Source: Figure D-4-1.1, NFPA 10, **Standard for**
Portable Fire Extinguishers, NFPA, Quincy, MA,
1990.

quickly so the range is relatively short. CO_2 is a nonconductor of
electricity and can be effective on Class B and C fires. Typical ratings
range from 5-B:C to 20-B:C.

Foam fire extinguishers are either of the stored-pressure type or of the
cylinder-operated type and are intended for use on Class A and B fires.
They contain an aqueous film-forming foam (AFFF) or film-forming
fluoroprotein foam (FFFP) solution as the agent. The 2 1/2-gallon stored-
pressure units are rated 3-A:40-B. The 33-gallon cylinder-operated units,
rated 20-A:160B, are provided on wheels and are most commonly used in
factories and warehouses.

Loaded stream extinguishers are stored-pressure water-based extinguishers that use antifreeze solutions for use in low temperatures. An
additive consisting of alkali-metal salt solutions—the loaded stream— is
added to the water. These extinguishers usually have a 2 1/2-gallon
capacity and a rating of 2-A.

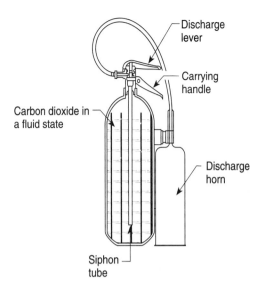

Discharge
lever

Carrying
handle

Carbon dioxide in
a fluid state

Discharge
horn

Siphon
tube

Figure 14-6. Carbon dioxide fire extinguisher.
Source: Figure D-4-3(a), NFPA 10, **Standard**
for Portable Fire Extinguishers, *NFPA,*
Quincy, MA, 1990.

Extinguishers and agents for use on combustible metals can be applied from an extinguisher, a scoop, or a shovel. The metals on which these extinguishers and agents can be used are specified in the individual listings (see Chapter 38).

In addition to these major listings, there are listings for extinguishers containing dry chemical and halon mixtures, for miscellaneous extinguishers (such as those containing wetting agents), for special purpose extinguishers, and for pump tank water extinguishers.

As of 1969, manufacture of inverting fire extinguishers was discontinued. These included soda-acid extinguishers and chemically generated foam units. Fire extinguishers of this type should not be hydrostatically tested. In fact, they should be destroyed. They can severely injure the operator because the sudden pressurization of a cylinder that is only stressed when activated presents the potential for explosion.

Examples of the different classifications and ratings of portable extinguishers follow.

Description	Rating
2.5 gal water, stored pressure	2-A
20 lb carbon dioxide	10-B : C
5 lb dry chemical (ammonium phosphate)	2-A : 10-B : C
10 lb dry chemical (sodium bicarbonate)	60-B : C
10 lb dry chemical (potassium bicarbonate)	80-B : C
125 lb dry chemical (ammonium phosphate)	40-A : 240-B : C
33 gal aqueous film-forming foam	20-A : 160-B
5 lb halon 1211	10-B : C
9 lb halon 1211	1-A : 10-B : C
1.5 lb halon 1211/1301	1-B : C

Inspection, Maintenance, and Hydrostatic Testing

Inspection and maintenance have very specific meanings within the
context of portable fire extinguishers. According to NFPA 10, an "inspection" is a quick check intended to give you reasonable assurance that an
extinguisher is available, is fully charged, and is operable. You do this by

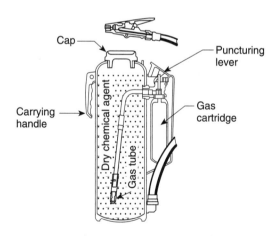

*Figure 14-7. Cartridge-operated dry chemical
extinguisher. Source: Figure D-4-5(b), NFPA 10,*
Standard for Portable Fire Extinguishers, *NFPA,
Quincy, MA, 1990.*

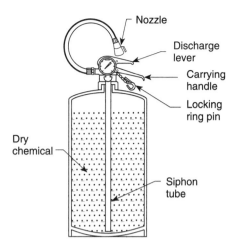

Figure 14-8. Stored-pressure dry chemical extinguisher. Source: Figure D-4-5(a), NFPA 10, Standard for Portable Fire Extinguishers, NFPA, Quincy, MA, 1990.

seeing that the extinguisher is in its designated place, that it has not been actuated or tampered with, and that there is no obvious physical damage or condition that would prevent its operation.

"Maintenance," on the other hand, is a thorough check of an extinguisher intended to give maximum assurance that it will operate effectively and safely. Maintenance includes a thorough examination and any necessary repair or replacement. It normally will reveal the need for hydrostatic testing.

Maintenance must be performed annually by a servicing company or by a trained industrial safety or maintenance person. There are two lists of items in the appendix of NPFA 10 that must be checked during maintenance.

Cartridge-operated, cylinder-operated, and loaded stream extinguishers are the only types that are required to be examined internally on an annual basis. Extinguishers with a five-year hydrostatic test interval are examined internally on the same five-year basis. Those with a 12-year interval are examined internally on a 6-year basis.

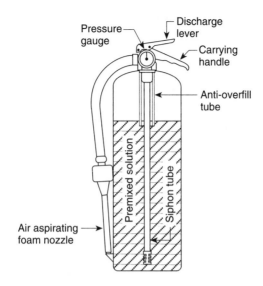

Figure 14-9. Stored-pressure aqueous film-forming foam (AFFF) liquid extinguisher. Source: Figure D-4-2.1(a). NFPA 10, **Standard for Portable Fire Extinguishers,** *NFPA, Quincy, MA, 1990.*

Nonrechargeable extinguishers are neither examined internally nor hydrostatically tested. They are removed from service 12 years from the date of manufacture.

Maintenance tags or labels must be attached to fire extinguishers to indicate the month and year that they were last serviced. A separate label is required to record information on the six-year teardown requirement.

"Hydrostatic testing" is performed by personnel who have been specifically trained. Untrained people should not attempt the procedure because serious safety hazards can easily develop.

The purpose of hydrostatically testing fire extinguishers is to protect against the unexpected failure of the cylinder. Table 14-4 provides the test intervals for fire extinguishers.

The cylinders of high-pressure extinguishers that pass the hydrostatic test must be stamped with the month, the year, and the DOT identification number. Low-pressure extinguishers are not stamped, but a self-destructive label listing the month, the year, and the identification of the person or company performing the test is affixed to the cylinder.

Inspection, maintenance, and hydrostatic testing must be carried out according to the minimum requirements established in NFPA 10 and in strict conformance with the manufacturers' recommendations. The minimum frequency for inspections is at 30-day intervals. Extinguishers must be maintained annually.

For each type of extinguisher, you should carefully read the manufacturer's instructions regarding periodic examination and maintenance. The following checklist can be useful during inspections.

1. Is the extinguisher clean and well cared for?
2. Has it been charged and hydrostatically tested within the pre scribed periods and tagged to show the dates?

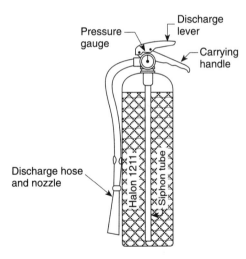

Figure 14-10. Halon 1211 stored-pressure fire extinguisher. Source: Figure D-4-4.1, NFPA 10, **Standard for Portable Fire Extinguishers, NFPA, Quincy, MA, 1990.**

Table 14-4. Hydrostatic test interval for extinguishers.

Extinguisher Type	Test Interval (Years)
Stored-pressure water and/or antifreeze	5
Wetting agent	5
AFFF (Aqueous Film-Forming Foam)	5
FFFP (Film-forming Fluoroprotein Foam)	5
Loaded stream	5
Dry chemical with stainless steel shells	5
Carbon dioxide	5
Dry chemical, stored-pressure, with mild steel shells, brazed brass shells, or aluminum shells	12
Dry chemical, cartridge or cylinder operated, with mild steel shells	12
Halogenated agents	12
Dry powder, cartridge or cylinder operated, with mild steel shells	12

Source: Table 5-2, NFPA 10, *Standard for Portable Fire Extinguishers,* NFPA, Quincy, MA, 1990.

3. If a seal is provided, is it intact? (Sealing may be required by the management or by law in industrial and mercantile establishments and places of assembly.)

4. Is the discharge orifice unobstructed?

5. Is the shell of the extinguisher corroded, damaged, or dented in such a way as to suggest possible weakness?

6. Are connections between the hose and the shell and nozzle secure?

7. If the extinguisher is a pump-operated type, does the pump shaft operate freely?

8. Is the extinguisher readily accessible, plainly indicated, and visible from a distance?

9. If the extinguisher is a type that is subject to freezing, is it protected?

10. Is the hanger fastened solidly so that the extinguisher is well supported?

11. Is the extinguisher located too close to the hazard that it is intended to protect, so that it could not be reached in case of fire?

Bibliography

Carson, W. G. and Klinker, R. L., *Fire Protection Systems: Inspection, Test and Maintenance Manual,* 2nd edition, NFPA, Quincy, MA, 1992.

Cote, A. E., ed., *Fire Protection Handbook,* 17th edition, National Fire Protection Association, Quincy, MA, 1991.

"Rating and Fire Testing of Fire Extinguishers," *Fire Protection Equipment Directory,* 3rd edition, UL/ANSI 711, Underwriters Laboratories/American National Standards Institute, New York.

NFPA Codes, Standards, and Recommended Practices

NFPA 10, *Standard for Portable Fire Extinguishers.* Criteria for the selection, installation, inspection, maintenance, and hydrostatic testing of portable fire extinguishers.

NFPA 10L, *Model Enabling Act for the Sale or Leasing and Servicing of Portable Fire Extinguishers (Including Recommended Rules and Regulations for the Administration of the Act).* Regulations that govern selling, leasing, and servicing portable fire extinguishers.

NFPA 18, *Standard on Wetting Agents.* Covers uses, limitations, specifications, and test standards.

NFPA 408, *Standard for Aircraft Hand Fire Extinguishers.* Specifies requirements for the type, capacity, rating, number, location, installation, and maintenance of aircraft hand fire extinguishers.

CHAPTER 15

Life Safety Considerations

*I*nspections are necessary not only for property conservation purposes, but to help ensure that required life safety features are present and properly maintained, as well. As an inspector, you will need thorough understanding of the concepts and requirements of NFPA *101, Life Safety Code,* to conduct a meaningful inspection. This chapter summarizes some of those concepts in an attempt to interest you in delving into the subject in greater depth through a detailed review of the applicable requirements of the *Life Safety Code* and the corresponding commentary contained in the *Life Safety Code Handbook.*

The initial life safety inspections of a building occur during its construction and are closely tied to the original plan review. Such inspections are made to ensure that all the components and systems of the required means of egress, as detailed on the approved plans, have been installed properly and are capable of functioning. As the inspector at this stage, you do not need this manual to complete your task because you already are intimately familiar with the approved plans. Rather, it is the inspector who conducts subsequent inspections over the life of the building who can draw guidance from the following materials.

Section 1-6 of the *Life Safety Code* discusses equivalency concepts. These concepts are not only being accepted more these days by local officials, but they are actively being integrated by those officials into new buildings in their communities. The "equivalency" one most often sees is the installation of a sprinkler system in lieu of construction requirements. However, additional dead-end lengths, square footages, and so on also are allowed. It is important that you, as the inspector, talk with the fire marshal or building official, or both, to determine if any equivalencies were used or accepted for the buildings you are inspecting.

Arrangement of Means of Egress

Proper life safety features within a structure involve more than exits. In a building, the exit access portion of the means of egress system generally comprises the majority of the floor area. The actual exit portion makes up the relatively small remaining part of the floor area. The means of egress also includes an exit discharge portion that usually is located outside the building. In any inspection, you should spend most of your time and effort on exit access considerations; spend less effort and time on exit and exit discharge considerations.

Exit access includes all portions of a building through which an individual has to travel to reach an exit from any occupied spot in the building. In a single-story building with grade-level exit doors in the exterior walls, all the usable space within the building constitutes exit access. From an upper story of a multistory building, an exit typically is reached as one opens a door and steps into a properly enclosed exit stairwell; thus, all usable space on that floor except the exit stair enclosure is deemed to be exit access.

Because exit access is that portion of the building designed and occupied for the purpose for which the building was constructed, it is particularly subject to compromise by changes in the use of the building space. If furniture and partitions are introduced into what was formerly a large open office area containing desks, for example, the direction of travel to an exit could become less evident. In addition, the corresponding travel distance to a required exit and the portion of travel distance termed "common path of travel" could increase beyond that permitted by the *Life Safety Code.*

Understanding the *Life Safety Code* requirements that apply to the arrangement of the means of egress will help you recognize that you must question changes in the use of the floor area to determine their effect on the adequacy of the means of egress system.

Common Path of Travel

Common path of travel is the portion of the initial exit access travel for which a building occupant can travel in only one direction. It ends where the occupant reaches a point at which a choice of independent paths to remote exits becomes available. In any room with a single exit door or single exit access door, all possible travel paths converge at the door, so all travel within the room is deemed to be common path. If, from that room door, occupants can travel in only one direction along any portion of the remaining exit access, such as along a dead-end corridor, that incremental part of the common path of travel must be added to the path in the room to establish the total common path of travel. The total common path of travel measured in any portion of the exit access is then compared to that permitted by the *Life Safety Code* for the occupancy under consideration. As part of an inspection, you should note any common paths that exceed code allowances so you may consider later how the deficiency affects the overall level of life safety within the building.

In Figure 15-1(a), the exit access arrangement of an office area in an existing nonsprinklered business occupancy complies with the maximum 75-foot common path of travel the code permits for that occupancy. In Figure 15-1(b), the introduction of less-than-ceiling-height office partitions results in an increased common path of travel that exceeds the allowable 75-foot criterion. Although there appear to be two directions of travel within the partitioned room, the paths actually converge at the single door from the room so all travel within the room is considered to be common path of travel. The experienced inspector, equipped with an understanding of the concept of common path of travel and a copy of the *Life Safety Code* from which to draw the applicable common path limitation, can correctly determine that the introduction of the partitions since the last inspection has created a deficiency.

Travel Distance

The distance a building occupant must travel to reach his or her nearest exit is termed "travel distance." The maximum travel distance allowed in any given occupancy is specified in the chapter of the *Life Safety Code* that applies to that occupancy. For example, Chapters 26 and 27 of the code, which apply to new and existing business occupancies, respectively, limit travel distance to 300 feet in a sprinklered building and 200 feet in an unsprinklered building.

Figure 15-2(a) shows an existing nonsprinklered, single-story building used as a business occupancy. Its exits and exit access are arranged such that each occupant can reach his or her nearest exit within the 200-foot allowance specified by the code. In Figure 15-2(b), the same building has expanded its floor area with the addition at the left of the figure. The occupants of the new addition can reach their nearest exit well within the

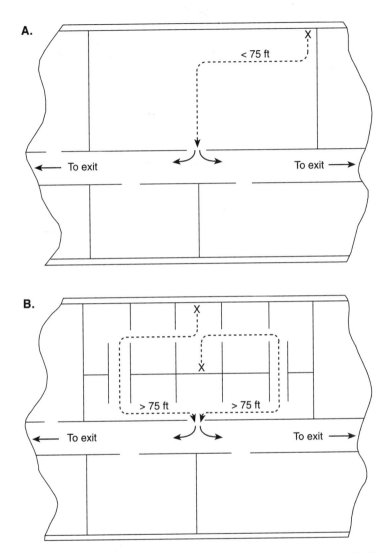

Figure 15-1(A). Exit access arrangement in an existing nonsprinklered office area with common path of travel within the 75-foot allowance for that occupancy, as specified by the **Life Safety Code.**
Figure 15-1(B). Following the introduction of new partitions, the arrangement of the exit access in the office has changed to include a common path of travel in excess of code allowance.

LIFE SAFETY CONSIDERATIONS   199

200 feet allowed as travel distance. However, the former exit door, which discharged directly to the outside from the left end of the original building, has been lost, and a person reaching that point finds that he or she is still within the exit access of the original building. Some of the occupants of the original building thus find that they have to travel further than the allowable 200 feet to reach their nearest exit. Using your understanding of the concept of travel distance, you note that, although the new addition meets code criteria, its arrangement has degraded that of the existing portion of the building to a level below what is permitted.

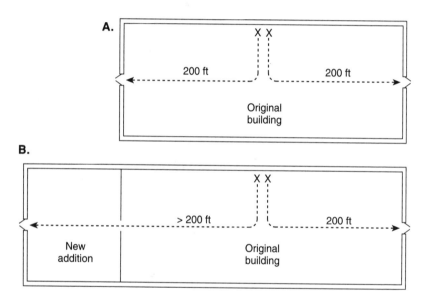

Figure 15-2(A). The exits and exit access in this existing non- sprinklered, single-story building, which is used as a business occupancy, are arranged such that each occupant can reach his or her nearest exit within the 200-foot travel distance allowance specified by the **Life Safety Code.**
Figure 15-2(B). The new addition at the left of the figure forces occupants of some portions of the original building to travel further than before to reach their nearest exit, thus degrading the arrangement of the means of egress within a portion of the building to a level below that permitted by the **Life Safety Code.**

Other Issues Related to Arrangement of Means of Egress

The above explanations of the concepts of common path of travel and travel distance do not fully detail all the issues related to the arrangement of the means of egress. Rather than relying on explanations of those additional concepts, which would unreasonably lengthen this chapter, you are advised to consult the *Life Safety Code* and the *Life Safety Code Handbook* on the subjects of capacity of means of egress, number of means of egress, remoteness of means of egress, and discharge of exits.

Means of Egress Components

Chapter 5, "Means of Egress," of the *Life Safety Code* provides detailed criteria for a variety of means of egress components. It describes doors, stairs, smokeproof enclosures, horizontal exits, ramps, exit passageways, escalators and moving walks, fire escape stairs, fire escape ladders, slide escapes, alternating tread devices, and areas of refuge. However, any of those components can be used within the required means of egress for a specific occupancy only if the code chapter applicable to that occupancy specifically recognizes the component. For example, slide escapes are recognized for use within the required means of egress only in high-hazard industrial occupancies and existing storage occupancies.

The following guidelines address features related to means of egress components that you can address readily as part of your inspection. Again, check the requirements of the *Life Safety Code* and the commentary of the *Life Safety Code Handbook* for additional details.

Doors

Doors in an exit enclosure, such as those opening into an enclosed exit stair, and doors within a fire barrier comprising a horizontal exit must swing in the direction of egress travel. Doors serving an area with an occupant load of at least 50 persons and those serving a high-hazard area also must swing in the direction of egress travel. Doors that do not swing in the direction of egress travel could delay or prevent egress if the persons trying to leave a room crowd against the doors so as to keep them from swinging back into the room from which egress is being attempted.

Holding doors open, such as fire-rated door assemblies, that normally are expected to remain closed when not in use with devices other than approved smoke-actuated, automatic-releasing hold-open devices reduces the effectiveness of the fire barrier or smoke barrier in which the doors are installed. Look for illicit use of wedges or hooks to hold doors open.

Life Safety Code requirements severely restrict door locking, as opposed to door latching with a readily usable means of release. Areas with occupant loads of 100 or more persons in assembly and educational occupancies are permitted to latch doors only if the latches are controlled by panic hardware or fire exit hardware. Familiarize yourself with those requirements before an inspection so that you will easily be able to identify problem areas and deficiencies.

During an inspection, note any deviations from the requirements described above.

Stairs

Although stairs built since the early 1980s have been restricted to a maximum riser height of 7 inches and a minimum tread depth of 11 inches, the *Life Safety Code* continues to recognize existing stairs with risers as high as 8 inches and treads as shallow as 9 inches. You can easily measure stair size during an inspection.

Handrails must be present on at least one side of existing stairs and on both sides of new stairs. Such handrails must be graspable, which generally means the cross-sectional dimension must be between 1.25 and 2.0 inches. For new handrails, there must be a clearance of at least 1.5 inches between the handrail and the wall to which it is fastened. New handrails also must be mounted between 34 and 38 inches above the stair tread; existing handrails may be mounted between 30 and 38 inches above the stair tread.

In addition to handrails, there must be guards at least 42 inches high on the open sides of stairs from which there is the potential of falling 30 inches or more. These guards also may serve as the required handrails if they meet the graspability criteria described above for handrails.

Signs indicating the floor level and the terminus of the top and bottom of the stair enclosure must be provided in new stair enclosures serving four or more stories. These signs also must identify the stair and the floor level of, and direction to, the exit discharge.

Stair enclosures cannot be occupied for any purpose other than occupant movement. Even if stair landings are larger than needed to satisfy the means of egress requirements, they cannot be used for storage. Building furnishings cannot be placed in such landings, and building service equipment, such as electrical panel boxes and conduit, cannot be installed in them. If the space below the last run of stairs at the base of the enclosure is to be used for any purpose, such as storage, it must be separated from the remainder of the stair enclosure by fire-rated construction with the same hourly rating as is required for the stair enclosure. Access to that space must be from outside the stair enclosure. In effect, such spaces must be wholly outside the stair enclosure so as not to adversely affect the use of the exit.

Again, note any deviations from the requirements described above during an inspection.

Exit Passageways

Although permitted within the required means of egress in all occupancies, exit passageways are used extensively in buildings with large floor areas, such as covered shopping malls. The protected corridor-like and tunnel-like exit passageway allows people to reach an exit without having to travel to an outside wall of the building and, thus, provides an acceptable solution to excessively long travel distance problems.

Because the exit passageway is an exit, it is subject to the same enclosure, penetration, and limited-use requirements that apply to an exit stair enclosure. The exit passageway can have no occupancy of its own, and it must be kept clear of furniture and stored materials. You should conduct a visual inspection of the entire length of all exit passageways as part of your building life safety features inspection.

Exit Discharge

One element of the means of egress that is often overlooked is that portion of the exit discharge on the exterior of the building. The means of egress is required to extend without interruption to a public way. Frequently, adequate interior exits lead only to a muddy yard or an obstructed walkway. This is particularly true of exits not normally used in the course of daily activities. Even where proper exterior exits are provided, they frequently become cluttered with trash storage or other combustible materials when they normally are not used as exits. Make sure that means of egress are kept clear, and see to it that every requirement applicable to the entire means of egress or to that portion designated as the exit discharge, including exit width, handrails, ramps, stairs, and lighting, extends from the building to the public way.

Awareness of the Means of Egress

To increase the effective use of the means of egress during a fire or any emergency requiring occupant evacuation or relocation, exits should be marked, and required illumination levels should be maintained. The subjects of illuminating and marking means of egress and of emergency lighting are addressed in detail in Chapter 5 of the *Life Safety Code*. Those features that can be checked easily as part of an inspection are summarized below.

Illumination of Means of Egress

The minimum required illumination level of 1 footcandle measured at floor level often is equated with the level of illumination provided by the full moon on a clear night. As part of any routine inspection, you should evaluate qualitatively—that is, without a lightmeter—the illumination level available in the designated aisles, corridors, ramps, and stairs comprising the exit access portion of the means of egress under normal, nonemergency lighting conditions. You also should make sure that the same minimum illumination level is available in exit enclosures, such as stairwells and exit passageways, and make the same check of the illumination level on any exterior walks, stairs, or similar components of the required exit discharge.

Emergency Lighting

Some occupancies require emergency lighting. Such lighting must become functional with no appreciable interruption of illumination following the loss of the normal electrical service. The maximum permitted changeover period to emergency lighting provided by an electric generator is 10 seconds. Test the emergency lighting capabilities during periodic inspections and make sure that illumination levels and durations meet the requirements specified by the code. Check the records to assure that emergency lighting is being tested for 1 1/2 hours once a year and for at least 10 seconds every month. Generators must be tested in accordance with the requirements of NFPA 110, *Standard for Emergency and Standby Power Systems*.

Marking of Means of Egress

Exit signs designate the location of an exit, and directional exit signs provide information on the direction of travel to an exit. In addition to noting whether signs are present over exit doors, you should make sure that such signs are visible from any direction of exit access travel. Determine whether additional signs have been provided wherever the way to reach an exit is not readily apparent, and make sure that no point within the exit access is more than 100 feet from the nearest visible sign. Required exit signs must be illuminated, either internally or externally, under normal lighting conditions. For those occupancies that require emergency lighting, exit signs also must be illuminated under emergency lighting conditions.

Bibliography

NFPA *101, Life Safety Code,* National Fire Protection Association, Quincy, MA, 1994. Covers requirements for establishing an acceptable minimum level of life safety incorporating a means of egress system and other fire protection and building services features for new and existing buildings. Requirements vary from occupancy to occupancy based on the needs and abilities of the occupants characteristic of a particular occupancy.

Life Safety Code Handbook, National Fire Protection Association, Quincy, MA, 1994. Reprints the complete text of the *Life Safety Code* and intersperses explanatory commentary, figures, and photographs in a contrasting color, thus more than tripling the quantity of the text contained in the code alone.

CHAPTER 16

Assembly Occupancies

*T*his chapter discusses items of special interest when inspecting an assembly occupancy. General inspection principles and items covered in other chapters apply, as well.

Assembly occupancies are defined by the *Life Safety Code* as buildings or portions of buildings in which 50 or more persons gather for such purposes as deliberation, worship, entertainment, dining, amusement, or awaiting transportation. They are divided into three basic groups: Class A, with occupant loads exceeding 1,000; Class B, with occupant loads between 301 and 1,000; and Class C, with occupant loads from 50 through 300. However, the character of a place of assembly should never be assumed to remain constant, and neither should the occupant load.

Because the many legal ways in which a place of assembly can be used are so diverse, you should thoroughly review the *Life Safety Code* before beginning an inspection to ensure that you understand the proper requirements for a particular place of assembly. Unlike most other occupancies, places of assembly encompass a wide range of uses, each of which necessitates different considerations.

Occupancy Characteristics

Changes of use, or the multi-use of assembly occupancies, could result in the application of provisions that normally might not be considered necessary. For example, a building used as a place of worship must meet certain, basic code requirements. Yet this same building also might be used for dining, dancing, or other purposes totally foreign to a place of worship, thus triggering the need to meet additional code requirements. Places of assembly in schools, such as multipurpose rooms, are rented or freely used for purposes other than education and often take on the character of exhibit halls. And the use of available space in hotels, banquet rooms, shopping malls, and exhibit halls can be very creative. When inspecting places of assembly, therefore, be sure to ascertain all intended or possible uses.

Inspecting the Premises

As when inspecting any other type of facility, it is important that you be seen by the owner of the place of assembly as providing a service to them by conducting your fire and life safety inspection. Always meet with the manager or owner of the establishment before beginning an inspection, and encourage him or her to accompany you on the inspection.

Inspecting assembly occupancies is no different from inspecting other occupancies. First you should do a general "once-over" inspection to spot any immediate concerns. You also should determine the square footage of the building by measuring it or by just "stepping it off." With this information, you can figure out the occupant load of the facility. Note any exterior violations, such as accumulations of trash, weeds, or obstructed fire lanes. Point out to the manager or owner any misuse of extension cords, sloppy maintenance practices, or other areas of concern so that they can be corrected before the facility is reinspected.

When completing an inspection, you should develop and file a sketch or drawing of the facility for future reference. This sketch should show the exterior and interior wall arrangements; the locations of all exit doors; the side yard, street, and property line clearances; and any other conditions of special hazard or consideration of special interest to assembly occupancies. The sketch also should identify any portable sliding or folding partitions used to divide rooms, as well as the occupant loads allowed for different room layouts, such as tables and chairs, theater-style seating, dancing, and so on. This sketch is essential for future use, not only as a reminder of existing conditions but, more importantly, as an easy reference to determine if any changes have occurred since the last inspection.

You also should keep a permanent checklist to indicate the construction of interior and exterior walls, floor and roof coverings, the flame-spread ratings, the type of heating, the lighting and electrical systems and their conditions, and the available fire protection devices and systems. You will find this checklist useful when you make future inspections.

Occupant Load

The intended use of the premises and the number of exits in excess of the minimum number required will influence the maximum allowable occupant load. If the use of the occupancy has changed since the last inspection, the maximum allowable occupant load probably has changed, too. If it is a multipurpose space, you should review any changes that would affect the variations described in the original sketches and change the sketches accordingly. The *Life Safety Code* contains guidance for calculating the occupant load. If the allowable load has changed in any way, you should ask the owner to provide a new "maximum occupant load" sign and display it as required.

Established occupant loads should be posted prominently to ensure that not only the owner, but also the manager, operator, and occupants, are aware of the limitations. Occupant loads for multipurpose rooms should be posted for each approved use, such as tables and chairs, theater seating, dancing, and so on. Posting load figures will also help you determine whether the occupancy is overcrowded.

Means of Egress

Exiting is the most critical of all requirements for any place of assembly. While the **probability** of a fire in a place of assembly might be low, the **potential** for loss of life once a fire occurs is extremely high. A fire of any magnitude easily can result in a large number of injuries and deaths. Therefore, it is essential that places of assembly have enough exits to accommodate the number of people likely to occupy the space and that they be properly located, easily accessible, and well maintained. The proper hardware (most often "panic" or "fire exit" hardware), handrails, guardrails, identification, and illumination also must be provided.

See that conditions altered since the last inspection have not compromised or blocked exit doors. If any alterations or renovations have been made since the last inspection, be sure that travel distances to exits have not been increased beyond the maximum allowed. Where exit paths merge, the path of travel must be wide enough to accommodate the combined occupant load that can be expected to use the individual paths of travel before they merge.

You must make sure that all exit doors open easily, with no more than 15 pounds of pressure necessary on the panic bar. See that exit doors are not chained or padlocked closed. Remember that life safety requirements, particularly those relating to exits, must be maintained at **all** times.

Do not allow registration booths, head tables, projection screens, ticket booths, turnstiles, revolving doors, guide ropes, and so on to obstruct any means of egress. When loose chairs are provided, setting up and maintaining proper aisles is a particularly difficult problem. Normally, loose chairs must be ganged—that is, connected to each other—when the number of chairs exceeds 200.

The allowable configuration of aisles will vary depending on the type of seating provided—that is, continental seating, banquet or conference-type tables, auditorium arrangements, bleachers, grandstands, and so on. Spaces between and around such seating must be adequate to provide access to aisles.

You also should make sure that the means of egress, as well as the exit and directional signs, are illuminated in both the normal and emergency modes.

Interior Finish

Another major issue is the flame-spread rating of interior finish materials and the flammability of decorative materials, curtains, drapes, and similar finishings. Interior finish in stairways always should be Class A. In corridors and lobbies, it may be Class A or B. In the general assembly area itself, it may be Class A or B; however, in Class C assembly occupancies Class C is permitted. Only rated material is allowed. See Chapter 6 for further information.

Combustible, decorative materials should be treated with a flame retardant. From a practical standpoint, flame-spread ratings are difficult to ascertain during a field inspection. If you are unable to see any markings on the products, ask if the original construction, any subsequent installations, or manufacturers' test data are available. Check your inspection file for acceptance of existing materials.

It might be possible to obtain a sample of the decorative material from an unobtrusive location—along an inside seam, for example—and test it in a relatively wind-free location outside the building. Place the sample in a vertical position and set a flame to the lower edge of the material. If charring does not occur beyond the flame and no flame or charring occurs after the flame has been removed, you may assume that the product is reasonably safe. If charring, dripping, or flaming continues, however, the product is suspect and should be removed, replaced, or subjected to a standard fire test.

Some products that carry a Class A rating will not pass the field flame test. This generally occurs when a product is tested and rated for an application that is different from the application found in the field. A good example is carpeting that has been tested and rated for horizontal applications but is applied vertically to a wall for aesthetic or acoustical purposes.

Building Services

The inherent sources of ignition in places of assembly also include air heating and refrigeration units or systems, electrical wiring, and electrical appliances, as well as conditions that exist in commercial kitchens. Frying and deep-fat cooking constitute the greatest single danger. Because hood and duct fires are very common, you should inspect the operating condition of the hood and vent extinguishing and exhaust systems carefully. Examine hoods and vents to determine if there has been a build-up of flammable material. These areas must be surveyed and cleaned continually, sometimes daily. Make sure that the exhaust damper opens when the exhaust fan is operated.

Determine the type of heating system used in the facility and the type of fuel used in the heating system. Must the heating unit be separated from the rest of the building? Are the walls, ceiling, and floor of proper construction? Are all openings, including duct openings, properly protected? Are there any smoke detectors on the downstream side of filters in the air supply or return system?

If the heating system fuel is LP-Gas, find out if the system has shut-off controls that activate automatically if the pilot light goes out. Is the system located where LP-Gas will pocket or become trapped in the building in the event of a gas leak? LP-Gas cylinders never should be stored or used inside except under very limited conditions. Where is the LP-Gas supply located? If supply tanks are used, make sure they are properly installed, secured, protected, and safeguarded against tampering or accidental damage. And make sure the cylinders are stamped and designed for use with LP-Gas.

If the fuel is a flammable or combustible liquid, determine whether the door opening is diked. On gravity feed systems, verify that there is an antisiphon device. And make sure there is a fusible shut-off device that will activate in the event of fire near the heating equipment.

When checking the electrical wiring and appliances, determine whether any permanent installations have been made using temporary equipment. Are the electric circuits large enough to handle the expected load? Are the noncurrent-carrying metal parts of portable and fixed electrically operated equipment properly grounded? Have any electrical extension cords been approved for their intended use, and are they being used properly? If you have any doubts about these items, you should have your community's electrical inspector make the determination.

Smoking

Smoking is not always prohibited in public assembly occupancies, with one exception: smoking is never allowed in theaters or assembly occupancies similar to theaters, such as facilities hosting stage shows and concerts. The prohibition of smoking in restaurants is becoming more popular, but this essentially is a health-related issue, not a fire-related issue.

Special Safeguards for Unique Occupancies

Stages and Projection Rooms

Stages and enclosed platforms present unique hazards associated only with assembly occupancies, and they require special safeguards, such as protection of the proscenium wall, including the proscenium curtain; automatic sprinklers above and below the stage; and automatic venting. Motion picture projection rooms require special supply and exhaust air, egress, and port openings, all of which must be protected. They also require room enclosure and proper working space. Projection machines require individual exhaust capabilities, which vary with the type of equipment. Projection rooms in which cellulose nitrate film is used must comply with NFPA 40, *Standard for the Storage and Handling of Cellulose Nitrate Motion Picture Film.*

Exhibits and Trade Shows

Because promoters and exhibitors often are very creative in what they want to do and the materials they want to use, exhibits and trade shows can be challenging to inspect. You should review the products that will be displayed, as well as the exhibits, and closely review special provisions in the *Life Safety Code* for help with this difficult assignment.

When inspecting exhibits and trade shows, make sure you have a plan that shows details of the area, the booth arrangement, the fire protection equipment, and so on. The exhibit booths' construction should be of noncombustible or limited combustible materials, and curtains, drapes, acoustical materials, decorations, and so on should be flame retardant. Multilevel booths and those over 300 square feet should be sprinklered when in sprinklered occupancies. Access must be plainly visible, and the travel distance inside a booth to an exit access aisle should not exceed 50 feet.

Cartons and crates should be stored in a room separated from other portions of the building with construction that has a 1-hour fire-resistance rating and sprinkler protection. Cooking devices should be limited in number and protected with sprinklers or some other form of extinguishing agent.

You also may have to deal with vehicles in this type of occupancy. The electrical system on vehicles should be disconnected to reduce ignition sources, and fuel tanks should be sealed. Fueling and defueling should not be allowed inside the structure.

Special Amusement Buildings

Special amusement buildings present yet another life safety problem because they generally entertain customers by confusing them. Nonetheless, the means of egress must be plainly visible and lighted during an emergency. Under certain conditions, smoke detection systems may be necessary. The *Life Safety Code* requires that every special amusement building be protected with automatic sprinklers. Moveable or portable special amusement buildings also must be protected, and the water supply must come from sources approved by the authority having jurisdiction.

Tents

Tents are becoming more and more popular as temporary buildings for many events, usually public assembly. To ensure that all conditions are met, you should refer to the *Life Safety Code* and to NFPA 102, *Standard for Assembly Seating, Tents and Membrane Structures,* in addition to the local building, zoning, and fire codes, before making your inspection.

Tents require special precautions due to their construction. All tents used for assembly purposes should already have been treated with a flame-retardant material, and a certificate attesting to that process should be sewn into the fabric at one corner of the tent. If there is no certificate indicating that the tent has been treated with a flame-retardant material, the tent in question should not be used.

Open-flame devices should be prohibited in tents. Portable heaters should be supplied by a fuel source that is outside and at some distance from the tent; it should not accessible to the public. Exiting must be adequate, and the aisles must be large enough to accommodate the occupant load. Lighting should be installed to illuminate the exits and the means of egress in an emergency.

You should check the location of the tent in relation to other structures, making sure that these other structures do not obstruct egress from the tent and do not present a potential fire exposure. A site plan showing the proposed tent and all the surrounding structures and noting the tent's intended use and the length of time it is to be used should be reviewed and authorized before the tent is set up. An inspection should be conducted before the tent is occupied to determine whether it complies with all applicable codes and ordinances.

Open Flames and Pyrotechnics

In addition to the sources of heat and open flame previously discussed, restaurant owners often use table candles to enhance atmosphere. This practice should be discouraged. When it is permitted, however, the candles should be placed in stable containers or holders of noncombustible construction that are designed to not tip over easily. You should test one of the typical candle holders to ensure that the flame does not come in contact with other combustible materials if it does tip over.

Table carts with open flames used as food warmers or for actual cooking are another potential source of ignition. In many cases, food on these tables is saturated with alcohol, which is then ignited. This activity generally is conducted very close to the restaurant patrons. There is no established means of protection against the obvious hazards of this practice, except prohibition. Most jurisdictions allow this practice only when the restaurant is fully sprinklered.

The *Life Safety Code* and NFPA 58, *Standard for the Storage and Handling of Liquefied Petroleum Gases,* both prohibit indoor use or storage of propane and butane containers. The practice of bringing these containers indoors is common in restaurants and presents an extreme life safety hazard.

In places of worship, the congregation occasionally holds lighted candles and sometimes marches in procession with them. While limited use of candles by designated officials can be permitted for religious purposes, the general assembly never should be allowed to hold any open flame devices.

Pyrotechnics traditionally have been used on the stages and platforms of places of assembly, particularly during magic acts or shows. With the advent of discos and rock concerts, however, there has been a dramatic increase in the use of pyrotechnic devices. This practice can create extremely hazardous conditions, depending on the type, volume, setting, and control exercised when they are used. See NFPA 1126, *Standard for the Use of Pyrotechnics before a Proximate Audience,* for more information on this subject. There also is the tendency to overcrowd such facilities beyond the occupant load allowed by permit. It is essential to minimum life safety that both of these conditions be limited; this must be enforced on a performance-by-performance basis.

Another type of stage production that is extremely hazardous involves performers who conduct ritual dances using flaming torches. This activity should also be prohibited inside any building.

Fire Protection Systems

On-site or built-in fire protection equipment includes portable fire extinguishers, interior standpipes and hose lines, automatic sprinkler systems, and fire alarm systems. Most new assembly occupancies are required to be fully sprinklered, either by the *Life Safety Code* or by local amendments to it. Other methods of on-site or built-in fire protection also may be used, and you should review each system or item to determine whether it is an approved method for the hazard protected. You also should review the general condition of fire protection systems and, where applicable, supervise performance tests.

When located in a building of mixed occupancy, the assembly occupancy might require separation from the remaining occupancies by fire-resistive assemblies of various ratings. Under these circumstances, openings in such assemblies also must be protected. In some instances, however, no separation is needed because the exposure hazard is low or nonexistent. In other instances, a 1-, 2-, 3-, or even a 4-hour fire-resistive separation will be necessary. The specifics of these requirements will depend on the applicable local building code.

Bibliography

NFPA 40, *Standard for the Storage and Handling of Cellulose Nitrate Motion Picture Film*
NFPA 58, *Standard for the Storage and Handling of Liquefied Petroleum Gases*
NFPA 96, *Standard for Ventilation, Control and Fire Protection of Commercial Cooking Operations*
NFPA *101, Life Safety Code*
NFPA 102, *Standard for Assembly Seating, Tents and Membrane Structures*
NFPA 1126, *Standard for the Use of Pyrotechnics before a Proximate Audience*

ASSEMBLY OCCUPANCY FIRE INSPECTION FORM

Property Name: Owner:

Address: Phone Number:

OCCUPANCY

Occupancy Subclassification: A☐ B☐ C☐ Change from Last Inspection: Yes☐ No☐

Occupant Load: Egress Capacity: Any Renovations: Yes☐ No☐

High Rise: Yes☐ No☐ Windowless: Yes☐ No☐ Underground: Yes☐ No☐

Smoke Protected: Yes☐ No☐ Occupancy Load Posted: Yes☐ No☐

Used for Shows or Exhibits: Yes☐ No☐ Tents: Yes☐ No☐

BUILDING SERVICES

Electricity☐ Gas☐ Water☐ Other☐ Are Utilities in Good Working Order: Yes☐ No☐

Elevators: Yes☐ No☐ Fire Service Control: Yes☐ No☐ Elevator Recall: Yes☐ No☐

Heat Type: Gas☐ Oil☐ Electric☐ Coal☐ Other☐ In Good Working Order: Yes☐ No☐

Emergency Generator: Yes☐ No☐ Size: Last Date Tested:

Date of Last Full Load Test: In Automatic Position: Yes☐ No☐

Fire Pump: Yes☐ No☐ GPM: Suction Pressure: System Pressure:

Date Last Tested: Date of Last Flow Test:

In Automatic Position: Yes☐ No☐   Jockey Pump: Yes☐ No☐

EMERGENCY LIGHTS

Operable: Yes☐ No☐ Tested Monthly: Yes☐ No☐

Properly Illuminate Egress Paths: Yes☐ No☐ In Good Condition: Yes☐ No☐

EXIT SIGNS

Illuminated: Internally☐ Externally☐ Emergency Power: Yes☐ No☐ Readily Visible: Yes☐ No☐

FIRE ALARM

Yes☐ No☐ Location of Panel:

Coverage: Building☐ Partial☐ Monitored: Yes☐ No☐ Method:

Fire Department Notification: Yes☐ No☐

Type of Initiation Devices: Smoke☐ Heat☐ Manual☐ Water Flow☐ Special Systems☐

Date of Last Test: Date of Last Inspection:

Notification Signal Adequate: Yes☐   No☐

FIRE EXTINGUISHERS

Proper Type for Hazard Protecting: Yes☐   No☐   Mounted Properly: Yes☐   No☐

Date of Last Inspection: Adequate Number: Yes☐   No☐

FIRE PROTECTION SYSTEMS

Type: Sprinkler☐   Halon☐   CO2☐   Standpipe☐   Water Spray☐   Foam☐   Dry Chemical☐

Wet Chemical☐   Other☐

Coverage: Building☐   Partial☐   Date of Last Inspection:

Cylinder or Gauge Pressure(s): 1   psi.,2   psi.,3   psi.,4   psi.,5   psi

Valves Supervised: Electrical☐   Lock☐   Seal☐   Other☐   Are Valves Accessible: Yes☐   No☐

System Operational: Yes☐   No☐   Sprinkler Heads 18" from Storage: Yes☐   No☐

FIRE RESISTIVE (FR) CONSTRUCTION

Stairway FR: Yes☐   No☐   Hourly Rating:

Corridors FR: Yes☐   No☐   Hourly Rating:

Elevator Shaft FR: Yes☐   Yes☐   No☐   Hourly Rating:

Major Structural Members FR: Yes☐   No☐   Hourly Rating:

Floor-Ceiling Assemblies FR: Yes☐   No☐   Hourly Rating:

All Openings Protected in FR Walls and Floor-Ceiling Assemblies: Yes☐   No☐

HAZARDOUS AREAS

Protected by: Fire-Rated Separation☐   Extinguishing System☐   Both☐

Door Self-Closures: Yes☐   No☐

Kitchen Exhaust Hoods Properly Protected: Yes☐   No☐   Clean: Yes☐   No☐   Date of Last Inspection

Not Located Under or Near Exits: Yes☐   No☐

Projection Room Properly Protected: Yes☐   No☐

HOUSEKEEPING

Areas Free of Excessive Combustibles: Yes☐   No☐

Smoking Regulated: Yes☐   No☐

INTERIOR FINISH

Walls and Ceilings Proper Rating: Yes☐   No☐   Floor Finish Proper Rating: Yes☐   No☐   Scenery

Flame Resistant: Yes☐   No☐   Decorations Flame Resistant: Yes☐   No☐

MEANS OF EGRESS

Readily Visible: Yes☐   No☐   Clear and Unobstructed: Yes☐   No☐

Two Remote Exits Available: Yes☐   No☐   Travel Distance within Limits: Yes☐   No☐

Common Path of Travel within Limits: Yes☐   No☐   Dead-Ends within Limits: Yes☐   No☐

50% Maximum through Level of Exit Discharge: Yes☐   No☐

Adequate Illumination: Yes☐   No☐

Proper Rating on All Components: Yes☐   No☐

All Exit Enclosures Free of Storage: Yes☐   No☐

Door Swing in the Direction of Egress Travel (when required): Yes☐   No☐

Panic/Fire Exit Hardware Where Required: Yes☐   No☐   Operable: Yes☐   No☐

Doors Open Easily: Yes☐   No☐   Self-Closures Operable: Yes☐   No☐

Doors Closed or Held Open With Automatic Closures: Yes☐   No☐

Corridors and Aisles of Sufficient Size: Yes☐   No☐

Stairwell Re-Entry: Yes☐   No☐

Mezzanines: Yes☐   No☐   Proper Exits: Yes☐   No☐

Seats and Tables Provided Proper Aisles: Yes☐   No☐

Layouts Approved by Authority Having Jurisdiction: Yes☐   No☐

Dwelling Units and Mercantile Occupancy Sole Exits Through Assembly Occupancy: Yes☐   No☐

SPECIAL AMUSEMENT BUILDING

Yes☐   No☐   Sprinklered: Yes☐   No☐   Smoke Detection System: Yes☐   No☐

Detection: Lighting Level Increased: Yes☐   No☐   Noised Stopped: Yes☐   No☐

Low Level Exit Signs: Yes☐   No☐   Directional Exit Marking: Yes☐   No ☐

STAGES

Legitimate☐   Regular☐   Thrust☐

Sprinklers: Yes☐   No☐   Venting: Yes☐   No☐   Standpipes: Yes☐   No☐

Deluge System: Yes☐   No☐

Proscenium Wall: Yes☐   No☐   Proscenium Curtain: Yes☐   No☐   Operable: Yes☐   No☐

In Good Condition: Yes☐   No☐

Candles used: Yes☐   No☐   Pyrotechnics Used: Yes☐   No☐

Open Flames Used: Yes☐   No☐

VERTICAL OPENINGS

Properly Protected: Yes☐   No☐

Atrium: Yes☐   No☐   Properly Protected: Yes☐   No☐

Are Fire Doors in Good Working Order: Yes☐   No☐

OPERATING FEATURES

Crowd Managers Class A: Yes☐   No☐

Drills Conducted: Yes☐   No☐   Employees Instructed in Use of Fire Extinguishers: Yes☐   No☐

Announcement Made Before Each Performance on Exit Location: Yes☐   No☐

Seats Connected in Group of 3-7: Yes☐   No ☐

CHAPTER 17

Educational Occupancies

*N*FPA *101, Life Safety Code,* defines educational occupancies as build
ings used for gatherings of six or more persons, for 4 or more hours a
day, or more than 12 hours a week, for the purpose of instruction through
the twelfth grade. They include schools, academies, kindergartens, and
nursery schools. Day-care facilities are not classified as educational
occupancies, but they must meet the requirements of Sections 10-7
through 10-9 or 11-7 through 11-9 of the *Life Safety Code.*

Schools for levels beyond twelfth grade are not classified as educational occupancies. They must comply with the requirements for business, assembly, or other appropriate occupancies.

The activities in educational occupancies can vary from education in a
classroom with contents of a low fire hazard to work in a laboratory or
shop area where the contents could pose a moderate or high fire hazard.
Those occupancies also typically contain assembly areas, such as auditoriums, cafeterias, and gymnasiums, where the fire hazard is low or
moderate, the concentration of occupants is high, and persons using such
assembly areas may not be familiar with the facility.

Day-care facilities usually house a varying number of children. The
children commonly take nap or rest periods during the day. It is important for you, the fire inspector, to fully understand the activities taking
place and the number and age of the occupants in the facility you are
inspecting, as they will affect the requirements for the facility.

You should review applicable codes and previous inspection reports
before conducting your inspection. Existing facilities must meet the
requirements of Chapter 11 of the *Life Safety Code.* New and renovated
buildings, and buildings whose occupancy classification have changed—
such as from residential to educational or day care—must meet the

requirements of Chapter 10 of the *Life Safety Code*. If only part of a building is renovated, or the occupancy changes, that portion and its means of egress must meet the requirements of Chapter 10 of the Life Safety Code and the rest of the building must meet the requirements of Chapter 11.

It is very important that you cite all code deficiencies, such as exit enclosure doors that are propped open, even if they are corrected in your presence. If they continue to appear on future inspections, legal action or suspension of the license might be required to fix them permanently.

You also should review drawings of the facility before conducting your inspection. If none are available, suggest that the owner get them from the architect for his or her own use in planning as well as for future inspections. In fact, this may be required by law, especially for public schools. Features such as means of egress sometimes are more obvious on a plan than when you see them in the facility. You should check that any conditions violating code have been permitted by the authority having jurisdiction under an "equivalency" agreement.

In some facilities, the corridors will be enclosed, with each room having a door directly to the corridor, or there may be no corridors, with each room having a door directly to the outside.

Occupant Load

Occupant load varies in educational occupancies. It is based on a minimum of one person for every 20 square feet in classroom areas and one person for every 50 square feet in shops, laboratories, and similar vocational rooms. In individual lecture rooms, gymnasiums, or cafeterias used for 50 or more persons, the occupant load is the same as that for assembly occupancies. The occupant load in such rooms not having fixed seating should be posted at the main exit. This posted maximum occupant load should be based on the available exit width and minimum aisle widths.

Means of Egress

Corridors in schools are a major component of the means of egress, and it is common for them to be lined on either side by classrooms and education support rooms. The corridors should lead directly to an exit or to other corridors that lead to an exit. Usually they must be enclosed by either 1-hour or 20-minute fire-rated walls. They must have self-closing latching doors. There are exceptions in the *Life Safety Code*, especially in sprinklered facilities. Transoms or other glass must be either wire glass or 20-minute rated glazing material encased in 20-minute frames.

The most important action to be taken when fire occurs in a school is evacuation, thus it is imperative that the means of egress be maintained.

Exit stairways and passageways must be unobstructed, and they cannot be used for any other purpose, especially storage. Combustible materials are often found stored under stairs or in stair enclosures.

Corridors, which should be at least 6 feet wide, cannot be restricted. Often, when a special function is being held in an assembly area such as an auditorium or gymnasium, tables are set up for purposes such as ticket sales and coat racks on wheels are found. They should not restrict the corridor and cannot be placed within the assembly area in such a way that they interfere with the means of egress. Athletic equipment stored along the walls of the gymnasium must not encroach on the means of egress.

If doors swinging into corridors are not recessed they must swing 180 degrees so that they stop against the wall and do not restrict the corridor. Corridor doors should not be wedged open; have any wedges that you find removed and cite them in your report.

The means of egress should be illuminated at all points from beginning to end. Emergency lighting should be provided in all interior stairs and corridors and in all normally occupied spaces and portions of the building that are interior or windowless, except administrative areas, general classrooms with windows, and mechanical or storage areas.

Be sure banners, signs, and similar materials are flame retardant and do not obstruct or cover exit doors, signs, or other egress components. Note whether exit signs delineating the exits and paths to exits are illuminated and visible from any point in a corridor. Spotlight-type emergency lighting should be located so that it illuminates the exit signs; it shouldn't shine in the eyes of those looking for exits.

Security gates or doors chained to secure an area used for events taking place after normal school hours from the remainder of the facility should not restrict the exit facilities needed for the in-use area.

Make sure that exit doors designed to be kept closed, such as for enclosed stairways or through firewalls, are self-closing or automatic closing by smoke detection. Check that they close and latch freely.

Observe that all exit doors are accessible, unobstructed, and cannot be locked except as allowed by the appropriate code requirements. Open each exit and exit access door to determine that it will open easily and that it opens on a landing as required and leads to a public way or area of refuge. Check the exit discharges from outside the building to be sure that they are not blocked in any way and that the paths to public ways are clear.

Smoke barriers should be installed to create smoke compartments no more than 30,000 square feet in size with no dimension exceeding 300 feet. Doors in the smoke partitions should not be wedged open. If they are, have the wedges removed and cite them in your report. If violations persist, you may require the installation of smoke detectors and magnetic hold-open devices. Smoke barriers shall be continuous from outside wall to outside wall and floor slab to floor or roof deck above.

Preschool, kindergarten, and first-grade students must not be located above or below the floor of exit discharge. Second-grade students must not be more than one story above the floor of exit discharge.

Fire drills must be conducted regularly.

If there are any signs of remodeling or renovation, check that all egress areas still meet requirements for capacity, travel distance, illumination, or marking. Travel distances to exits still must be within required limits and exits must not have been eliminated where they are required. If plans for renovations are required to be reviewed in your jurisdiction, require that they be submitted by a certain date. Be sure to enforce your deadline.

Windows

There must be a window or door for ventilation and rescue in each room occupied by students in buildings not protected by automatic sprinklers. This does not apply to toilet rooms and offices. The window or door must be at least 20 inches wide and 24 inches high and have an area of at least 5.7 square feet.

Hazardous Areas

Fire experience has shown that hazardous areas in schools include basements, boiler rooms, storerooms, and closets. Fires also have started in workshops, laboratories, classrooms, and auditoriums. In all educational occupancies good housekeeping is basic to safety to life from fire.

Housekeeping in basements must be of the highest order. Storage should be confined to sprinklered areas, or to storerooms of fire-resistive construction equipped with fire doors. Check that the doors are kept closed.

In boiler rooms, look for improper storage, such as odd pieces of furniture or equipment. The boiler or mechanical room should be used only for the heating plant and associated equipment. If your jurisdiction requires boilers to be tested, certified, and the certificate posted, check the posting and verify that it is current.

Laboratories in which hazardous chemicals and flammable liquids and gases are used also deserve your special attention. Their location and the amounts of materials stored in them should be noted, and this information should be passed on to the local fire department. Make certain that flammable materials are stored in reasonable quantities in appropriate containers and cabinets. Examine labels on containers of chemicals to determine whether any have exceeded their shelf life and whether any are unstable. In either case, the material should be removed from the laboratory. Watch for indications of chemicals that should be kept segregated from others to prevent hazardous situations in the event of fire or accidental spills. Check that chemicals are discarded properly. Check that laboratories are equipped with suitable fire extinguishers and fire blankets. Laboratories should comply with the requirements of NFPA 45, *Standard on Fire Protection for Laboratories Using Chemicals.*

Educational and building maintenance workshops are also potential hazardous areas, so you must pay particular attention to housekeeping in these areas. Oily waste should be kept in self-closing containers until it is removed from the building for disposal. Check sawdust removal equipment. Sawdust suspended in the air is an explosion hazard. Scrap material should be cleaned up after each class and safely stored until it is removed for disposal. Note whether equipment and machinery appear to be well maintained and in good condition.

If the occupancy has kitchen facilities, inspect them as you would a commercial or restaurant kitchen. Check for grease accumulations on and around fryers, ranges, hoods, and filters. Do the locations of cooking equipment and construction of the hood and ducts meet code requirements? Examine the fire protection equipment to see that it is in good condition, charged, and within acceptable limits. The extinguishing agents in the portable fire extinguisher near the hood and in the fire suppression system must be compatible. Check that any deficiencies found in the fire protection system in previous inspections have since been corrected.

Interior Finish

Interior finish should be Class A in exits such as enclosed stairways; it can be either Class A or B elsewhere in the building. Ascertain that draperies, curtains, and similar furnishings and decorations have been treated with a flame retardant.

Teaching materials and students' artwork should not cover more than 20 percent of the wall area. You should be especially concerned with seasonal decorations—such as those for halloween or Thanksgiving—and the props used for theatrical presentations. Items such as cardboard, paper, or cloth spook houses are often used for Halloween parties, and combustible materials such as corn stalks, straw, or paper are sometimes used for decoration. Special effects to be used in theatrical productions must meet the requirements of all applicable codes and ordinances. Intumescent paints and surface coatings can be used to reduce the surface flame spread on interior finish. However, some of these coatings have a short life and must be reapplied frequently.

Napped, tufted, looped, woven, nonwoven, or similar interior finish materials should not be applied to walls or ceilings unless it is at least Class A mounted on a rigid material. If this type of covering is used in a new or renovated building, the room must be sprinklered, or the material must be approved by the authority having jurisdiction. It is the responsibility of the owner or his or her agent—such as the architect—to prove that the material complies.

Fire Protection

In educational occupancies fire alarm systems are often disabled. Thus, you should locate the fire alarm control box. Is the system operational? Are any trouble lights on? Is the supervisory signal silenced? Are back up batteries in place and fully charged?

Check the condition of each pull station of the fire alarm system for signs of damage. Examine records to check that the fire drills meet requirements for evacuation time. Are there any recurring problems when the building is evacuated that might need to be corrected? Is the fire alarm signal distinct from the signal to change classes? When was the system last tested?

Flexible and Open-Plan Buildings

In addition to the features and conditions to be inspected in traditional school buildings, you must also check additional items in flexible or open-plan buildings. Flexible and open-plan buildings are designed to have multiple teaching stations. Flexible plan buildings may have movable corridor walls and partitions of full height.

The interior furnishings in open-plan schools may be arranged to designate the exits and paths of exit travel. The paths should be direct, not circuitous, and at least 6 feet wide. Determine that the layout has not been altered since the last inspection without the approval of the authority having jurisdiction.

Temporary Buildings

There appears to be an increase in the use of modular or portable structures, which present a unique problem. They are on the school grounds, but they are detached and sometimes are located great distances from the main school buildings and on surfaces that would not support fire fighting vehicles.

The school fire alarm system should be audible, visible, and capable of being activated from the modular structures. If the temporary buildings have two-way communication with the main school buildings and if they have a constantly attended receiving station from where an alarm can be sounded, they do not need manual pull stations unless required by the authority having jurisdiction.

Egress routes should have level landings. Steps, ramps, handrails, and guards should met code requirements. There should be room for maneuvering wheelchairs at doors, and switches and fire alarm pulls should be low enough for students in wheelchairs to reach.

Day-Care Facilities

Day-care facilities are divided into three classes: day-care centers, group day-care homes, and family day-care homes. They are not subject to the requirements for schools except where specifically referred to in the *Life Safety Code.*

Day-care centers are those facilities housing 12 or more clients, for less than 24 hours a day, with care provided by persons other than relatives or legal guardians. Group-day care homes are those providing care for 7 to 12 clients by persons other than relatives or legal guardians. Family day-care homes are those in which fewer than 7 clients receive care, maintenance, and supervision by persons other than relatives or legal guardians.

In all day-care facilities, you must check that door locks and latches on closets can be opened by a child from inside the closet. Door locks and latches on bathroom doors should be openable from outside the bathroom by staff members.

Flammable and combustible liquids should be stored in fire-separated areas accessible only by designated individuals. Waste baskets and waste containers should be constructed of noncombustible materials.

Check for protective covers on electrical receptacles in rooms children under 6 years of age will use.

Day-Care Centers

The occupant load in day-care centers is based on at least one person for each 35 square feet of area.

Each floor must have two remote exits. The exit doors should swing in the direction of egress when the room or area has an occupant load of 50 or more persons.

In buildings not protected by automatic sprinklers, each room used by clients—children or the elderly—must have a door or window leading directly to the outside. The size of the window opening must be at least 20 inches wide and 24 inches high, and it must have an area of at least 5.7 square feet.

Interior finish must be at least Class A in stairways, lobbies, and corridors and at least Class B in other areas. In sprinklered buildings the interior finish may be reduced one class, such as A to B or B to C, but C cannot be reduced. Interior floor finish must be at least Class II in corridors, lobbies, and exits. Unless you are inspecting a new building, find out if any alterations have been made since the last inspection and how they affected the class of interior finish. Find out if any plans need to be reviewed.

Determine the type of building construction and check that it meets minimum height and construction limits. If the facility is located on one floor of a building, however, you do not need to consider floors above the one on which the day-care facility is located. For example, in a 2-story Type II (000) building the first floor can be used for day care if the second story is not used for day care.

If the facility is in a mixed-occupancy building, the occupancies must be separated by 1-hour fire barriers, except in churches.

In facilities caring for more than 100 occupants, the fire alarm should automatically notify the fire department by the most practical method allowed. Smoke detectors must be connected to the building fire alarm system unless it is a single-room center or all clients are 6 years of age or older and there are no sleeping facilities. Note the general condition of the detectors, and review their service and maintenance records. Ensure that the report of the last monthly fire inspection, conducted by a senior staff member, is posted in a conspicuous place. Also check that the required monthly fire drills are being held.

Group Day Care and Family Day Care

If the facility is used after daylight hours, the means of egress must be artificially illuminated. There must be at least one operable flashlight for use in the event of power failure in family day-care homes and one for each staff member in group day-care homes.

Group Day-Care Homes: Each floor should have two remote means of escape, and the travel distance to the nearest exit must not exceed 150 feet. One alternate means of escape—not an exit—may be a window with an opening at least 20 inches wide and 24 inches high, and it must have an area of at least 5.7 square feet.

If the day-care facility is in an apartment building where both required means of egress enter the same corridor as the apartment occupancy, the exit accesses must be separated by a 1-hour fire-rated smoke barrier. Check the operation of the 20-minute smoke barrier doors. Spaces above the floor of exit discharge used for sleeping must have one accessible exit that leads directly to the outside.

The doorway between the floor of exit discharge and any floor below it must have at least a 20-minute self-closing and latching fire door. Make sure that these doors work properly.

Interior finish should be at least Class B in exits and at least Class C in other areas.

No facility can be located more than one floor below ground level.

Space heaters used in areas occupied by children should be separated by screens, partitions, or some other means.

Family Day-Care Homes: In one- and two-family dwellings of unprotected wood frame construction, two means of escape are required. At least one must be a door or stairway to the outside of the building at street or ground level. One means of escape may be a window with an opening as previously described. See that these means of egress are unobstructed. If the facility is located below the level of exit discharge at least one exit must discharge directly to the outside. Travel distance to the exits should not be more than 150 feet. Be sure that travel distance has not been increased by any additions or renovations. Doors in the means of egress must be at least 28 inches wide.

Interior finish must be Class A or B in the exits and Class A, B, or C in other areas.

Be sure that no unvented heaters are being used.

Bibliography

NFPA *101, Life Safety Code*

EDUCATIONAL OCCUPANCY FIRE INSPECTION FORM

Property Name: Owner:

Address: Phone Number:

OCCUPANCY

Change from Last Inspection: Yes☐ No☐

Occupant Load: Egress Capacity: Any Renovations: Yes☐ No☐

Students < 1st Grade on 1st Floor: Yes☐ No☐   Students 2nd Grade < 2nd Floor: Yes☐ No☐

High Rise: Yes☐ No☐   Windowless: Yes☐ No☐   Underground: Yes☐ No☐

BUILDING SERVICES

Electricity☐ Gas☐ Water☐ Other☐   Are Utilities in Good Working Order: Yes☐ No☐

Elevators: Yes☐ No☐   Fire Service Control: Yes☐ No☐   Elevator Recall: Yes☐ No☐

Heat Type: Gas☐ Oil☐ Electric☐ Coal☐ Other☐   In Good Working Order: Yes☐ No☐

Emergency Generator: Yes☐ No☐   Size: Last Date Tested:

Date of Last Full Load Test: In Automatic Position: Yes☐ No☐

Fire Pump: Yes☐ No☐   GPM: Suction Pressure: System Pressure:

Date Last Tested: Date of Last Flow Test:

In Automatic Position: Yes☐ No☐   Jockey Pump: Yes☐ No☐

EMERGENCY LIGHTS

Operable: Yes☐ No☐   Tested Monthly: Yes☐ No☐

Properly Illuminate Egress Paths: Yes☐ No☐   In Good Condition: Yes☐ No☐

EXIT SIGNS

Illuminated: Internally☐ Externally☐   Emergency Power: Yes☐ No☐ Readily Visible: Yes☐
No☐

FIRE ALARM

Yes☐ No☐   Location of Panel:

Coverage: Building☐ Partial☐   Monitored: Yes☐ No☐   Method:

Fire Department Notification: Yes☐ No☐

Type of Initiation Devices: Smoke☐ Heat☐ Manual☐ Water Flow☐ Special Systems☐

Date of Last Test: Date of Last Inspection:

Notification Signal Adequate: Yes☐ No☐

FIRE EXTINGUISHERS

Proper Type for Hazard Protecting: Yes☐ No☐   Mounted Properly: Yes☐ No☐

Date of Last Inspection: Adequate Number: Yes☐ No☐

FIRE PROTECTION SYSTEMS

Yes☐ No☐

Type: Sprinkler☐ Halon☐ CO_2☐ Standpipe☐ Water Spray☐ Foam☐ Dry Chemical☐
   Wet Chemical☐ Other☐

Coverage: Building☐ Partial☐   Date of Last Inspection:

Cylinder or Gauge Pressure(s): 1   psi.,2   psi.,3   psi.,4   psi., 5   psi.

Valves Supervised: Electrical☐ Lock☐ Seal☐ Other☐   Are Valves Accessible: Yes☐ No☐

System Operational: Yes☐ No☐   Sprinkler Heads 18" from Storage: Yes☐ No☐

FIRE RESISTIVE (FR) CONSTRUCTION

Stairway FR: Yes☐ No☐   Hourly Rating:

Corridors FR: Yes☐ No☐   Hourly Rating:

Elevator Shaft FR: Yes☐ Yes☐ No☐   Hourly Rating:

Major Structural Members FR: Yes□ No□ Hourly Rating:

Floor-Ceiling Assemblies FR: Yes□ No□ Hourly Rating:

All Openings Protected in FR Walls and Floor-Ceiling Assemblies: Yes□ No□

HAZARDOUS AREAS

Protected by: Fire-Rated Separation□ Extinguishing System□ Both□

Door Self-Closures: Yes□ No□ Janitors Closets Sprinklered: Yes□ No□

Laboratories Properly Protected: Yes□ No□ Chemicals Properly Inventoried: Yes□ No□

Chemicals in Approved Containers: Yes□ No□

Kitchen Exhaust Hoods Properly Protected: Yes□ No□ Clean: Yes□ No□

Date of Last Inspection:

HOUSEKEEPING

Areas Free of Excessive Combustibles: Yes□ No□ Smoking Regulated: Yes□ No□

Decorations on Walls < 20% of Wall Area: Yes□ No□

Clothing Stored in Corridor: Yes□ No□

INTERIOR FINISH

Walls and Ceilings Proper Rating: Yes□ No□ Floor Finish Proper Rating: Yes□ No□

Furniture and Decorations Fire Resistive: Yes□ No□

MEANS OF EGRESS

Readily Visible: Yes□ No□ Clear and Unobstructed: Yes□ No□

Two Remote Exits Available: Yes□ No□ Travel Distance within Limits: Yes□ No□

Common Path of Travel within Limits: Yes□ No□ Dead-Ends within Limits: Yes□ No□

50% Maximum through Level of Exit Discharge: Yes□ No□

Adequate Illumination: Yes□ No□

Proper Rating on All Components: Yes□ No□ All Exit Enclosures Free of Storage: Yes□ No□

Door Swing in the Direction of Egress Travel (when required): Yes□ No□

Panic/Fire Exit Hardware Where Required: Yes□ No□ Operable: Yes□ No□

Doors Open Easily: Yes□ No□ Self-Closures Operable: Yes□ No□

Doors Closed or Held Open With Automatic Closures: Yes□ No□

Corridors and Aisles of Sufficient Size: Yes□ No□

Stairwell Re-Entry: Yes□ No□

Mezzanines: Yes□ No□ Proper Exits: Yes□ No□

Rescue Windows in Each Classroom: Yes□ No□ 5.7 sq. ft.: Yes□ No□

Smoke Barriers Provided: Yes□ No□ Proper Size and Fire Resistance Rating: Yes□ No□

Occupied Rooms over 1,000 sq. ft. Two Means of Egress: Yes□ No□

VERTICAL OPENINGS

Properly Protected: Yes□ No□

Atrium: Yes□ No□ Properly Protected: Yes□ No□

Are Fire Doors in Good Working Order: Yes□ No□

OPERATING FEATURES

Fire Drills Conducted: Yes□ No□ Number to Date:

Meeting Places Established: Yes□ No□ Student Accountability: Yes□ No□

Fire Inspections Conducted Monthly by Staff: Yes□ No□ Date of Last Inspection:

CHAPTER 18

Health Care Facilities

*N*FPA *101, Life Safety Code,* defines a health care occupancy as a building, or any portion thereof, used on a 24-hour basis to house or treat four or more people who cannot escape from a fire without assistance. The reasons these people may not be able to escape include physical or mental illness, age, and security measures that the occupants cannot directly control. And the buildings or portions of buildings in question include hospitals or other medical institutions, nurseries, and nursing homes.

One occupancy subclassification recently added to the code is the limited care facility. This includes a building or part of a building that is used on a 24-hour basis to house four or more persons who are incapable of self-preservation because of age or physical limitation due to accident, illness, or mental limitations, such as mental retardation or developmental disability, mental illness, or chemical dependency but are not receiving medical or nursing care.

The code also addresses the ambulatory health care center. This is a building or any part of a building that provides services or treatment for four or more patients that would temporarily render them incapable of self-preservation during an emergency without assistance from others. These facilities include hemodialysis units, free-standing emergency medical units, and outpatient surgical areas in which general anesthesia is used. While ambulatory health care facilities do not provide overnight sleeping accommodations, the other categories of health care facilities do.

Throughout the fire protection profession, there remains a rather basic assumption that a fire of any consequence in any type of health care facility spells impending disaster to those inside. Health care facilities pose exceptional problems when it comes to moving and evacuating

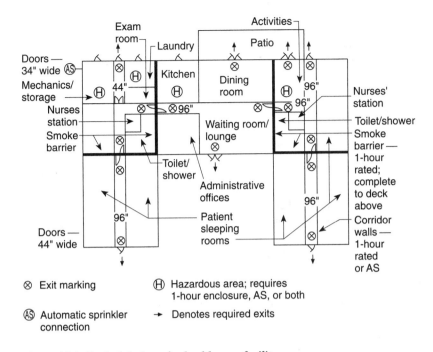

Figure 18-1. Typical design of a health care facility.

people, especially along great distances and down stairways from the upper floors of multistory buildings, to a safe area outdoors. It is for these reasons that the basic features of health care fire protection involve a limited amount of patient movement.

The residents of a health care facility can remain safe even when relatively close to a fire if the corridor walls have been constructed properly, if the appropriate smoke and fire barriers have been installed, if hazardous areas that are likely to sustain a well-developed fire are protected or enclosed, and if approved fire detection and suppression systems have been installed. In many cases, this protect-in-place theory is not only desirable, it is necessary, especially in hospital intensive care units, cardiac care units, and operating room suites, where moving a patient could result in major health complications or even death.

Installing automatic sprinkler protection throughout all new health care facilities also provides enhanced protection for patients and staff who may be intimately involved with fire ignition. These sprinklers include listed quick response and residential sprinklers installed throughout the smoke compartments containing patient sleeping rooms. The rapid activation of these specially designed sprinklers is intended to restrict the spread of fire and the associated products of combustion, thus reducing the need for extensive patient evacuation.

Protecting the Patient

The *Life Safety Code* emphasizes the protection and ultimate evacuation of persons from the immediate fire area to a safe area of refuge until the fire has been extinguished. The initial level of patient protection actually begins right in the patient's bedroom.

Draperies, curtains, furnishings, and decorations must be flame resistant. However, no restrictions currently apply to the actual clothing or bedding materials a patient may use.

If the fire is not contained within its immediate area of ignition, containment is attempted within the room. In new and fully sprinklered existing buildings, corridors must be separated from all other areas by partitions that form a barrier to limit the transfer of smoke. In existing unsprinklered structures, these partitions must have a fire-resistance rating of at least 20 minutes and must extend, through any concealed spaces, from the floor slab to the underside of the floor or roof slab above. In nonsprinklered existing buildings verifying the continuity of corridor walls to the floor deck above will be very difficult and time-consuming. Vision panels in these fire-rated walls are permitted only if they are made of approved, fixed fire window assemblies or of previously accepted wired glass construction, installed in steel or other approved metal frames, and limited in size to 1,296 square inches. Corridor walls or associated vision panels in new buildings need not be fire rated because recent requirements mandate that these facilities be protected with automatic sprinkler protection throughout.

Protection of Openings

Door openings in fire-rated corridor walls must be protected by approved assemblies that will resist the passage of fire for at least 20 minutes. These doors need not be fire-rated door assemblies, nor must they be equipped with self-closing devices. However, they must be equipped with approved positive latching hardware that will keep the door tightly closed. Vision panels for these doors can only be approved fixed fire window assemblies or previously accepted 1/4-inch-thick wired glass mounted in approved frames no larger than 1,296 square inches. As with corridor walls, corridor doors in fully sprinklered buildings need not resist the passage of fire, but they must be constructed so as to limit the transfer of smoke and be equipped with positive latches.

When other fire protection features are provided, fire ratings and, in some cases, the partitions themselves may be eliminated. Even in existing facilities, the installation of approved automatic sprinkler protection throughout the building permits corridor partitions and the door openings in them to be constructed of materials that only resist the passage of smoke; thus, they need not have a fire-resistance rating. In addition, each smoke compartment may contain treatment rooms, spaces that are not used for patient sleeping rooms, hazardous areas, lounges, or waiting areas that may open directly to the exit corridor, provided the size of these areas is limited, they are supervised directly by the facility staff or by an electrically supervised automatic smoke-detection system, and their furnishings are arranged so as not to obstruct access to the exits. However, devices that permit the passage of smoke, such as transfer grills or undercuts, can be installed only in small areas that are unlikely to contain flammable or combustible materials. Small miscellaneous openings, including mail slots and pass-through windows, also are permitted in corridor vision panels or doors in smoke compartments that do not contain sleeping rooms.

During your fire safety inspection, you should check the integrity of all the required fire-rated and smoke-resistant corridor wall and door assemblies and verify that all spaces open to the egress corridors are adequately arranged and protected.

Compartmentation

Because history has shown that smoke is the cause of most fire deaths, proper protection against smoke must be installed and properly maintained in a health care facility. All health care buildings must be subdivided into separate smoke compartments into which patients can be moved without having to leave the building or change floors. This requirement reduces the distance persons with limited mobility must be moved in order to be protected adequately.

It is important that smoke barriers in new buildings have at least a 1-hour fire-resistance rating; in existing buildings, they should have at least a 30-minute fire-resistance rating. Smoke barriers must extend uninterrupted from outside wall to outside wall and from floor slab to floor or roof slab above, passing through all concealed spaces. A major problem in many health care facility inspections is verifying that smoke barriers have not been violated with unsealed penetrations. They must be positioned to provide that at least 30 net square feet per nursing home or hospital patient or 15 net square feet per limited-care facility resident in a public access area. Each smoke compartment must be no larger than 22,500 square feet, and the travel distance from any point in the building to a smoke barrier door must be no farther than 200 feet.

Openings in smoke barriers must be protected by substantial doors that will resist fire for at least 20 minutes and are equipped with vision panels of approved fixed fire windows. Although these doors must be self-closing, they need not be a part of a rated fire door assembly and are not required to have positive latches. However, appropriate rabbets, bevels, or astragals are required along the edges where the doors meet to prevent smoke from crossing the barrier. In most cases, these doors are held open by electromagnetic devices, which must be arranged to release when any component of the fire alarm system, including an approved smoke detector located near the doorway opening, activates. You should check the construction, arrangement, and operation of all smoke-barrier doors and their associated release devices and automatic closers as part of each routine inspection.

In unsprinklered buildings and sprinklered buildings with unducted air supply systems, the air supply, return, or exhaust penetrating the smoke barrier must be protected by an approved smoke damper arranged to close when a smoke detector located within the duct or at the smoke barrier activates. You should visually examine the smoke damper installations, and, if possible, check their operation. Specific requirements for these smoke barriers may be modified when an engineering smoke-control system is installed in accordance with NFPA 90A, *Standard for the Installation of Air Conditioning and Ventilating Systems.*

In some cases, it is necessary to subdivide a building into separate fire, as well as smoke, zones. This is particularly true when buildings are of differing construction types, when existing portions of a building must be segregated from new additions, and when a building is more than one story high. These separations basically are the same as, and can be incorporated in, the smoke barrier, although the fire wall must be constructed to prevent the passage of fire, as well as smoke. This requires the use of approved, labeled fire door and damper assemblies and is particularly important for vertical openings, such as stairways and service shafts; in some cases, they also are used to enclose hazardous areas. You must inspect the construction of horizontal and vertical opening protection and make sure that doors are equipped with self-closers and positive latching hardware. You also should make sure that doors are indeed closed, not wedged open.

The actual construction type of a building—that is, the combustibility and the fire resistance of the structure—plays a very important role in ensuring building integrity during a fire and allowing time to move and evacuate patients. The two major aspects of such construction involve the enclosure of hazardous areas and means of egress and the protection of building structural elements. Because actual construction specifications are developed when a building is designed, it is your duty as an inspector to ensure adherence to the design features and to ensure that the specified construction types are maintained. Make sure that any alterations or modifications have not compromised any of the fire protection features, including construction type, fire-rated and smoke-resistant walls, partitions, and door assemblies. In each inspection, you also should check for the proper certification of all new interior finish materials, such as wall coverings and carpet, to ensure that they comply with the appropriate flame-spread ratings and smoke-development numbers based on the area of installation and other fire protection features.

Means of Egress

Although the objective of *Life Safety Code* requirements for health care facilities is basically to protect patients in place, the importance of required exits cannot be ignored. Each floor or fire section of the building must have at least two exits. Travel distances and exit capacities are contained in Sections 5-6 and 5-3 of the code; increases are allowed for travel distance and exit capacities in fully sprinklered buildings.

Make sure that exits throughout the building are accessible so that persons with impaired mobility can be moved in the event of a fire. Are the corridors clear and wide enough to evacuate patients? Corridors may have to be widened to allow for necessary health care functions such as the movement of wheelchairs and beds; the delivery of food, medicine, and laundry; and temporary storage. In addition, the discharges of such exits must remain unobstructed. The use of exterior stairways and ramps and the operation of exterior doors must not be compromised by accumulations of snow or ice.

Any locks installed on exit doors must be of an approved type, and the staff must be able to open them quickly and easily for the rapid removal of occupants, either with the keys they carry at all times or by remote-control. Thus, you must make sure that keys or some other means of unlocking secured egress doors are available to an appropriate number of on-duty staff to permit unimpeded evacuation.

Fire Protection

Besides building construction features that serve to protect occupants from fire, all health care facilities must have a combination of systems to warn occupants, detect fires, and aid in fire control and extinguishment. Appropriate exit illumination, emergency lighting, and exit markings must be provided along all means of egress, and an approved manual fire alarm system must be installed. A special exception to the fire alarm requirements for health care facilities permits the installation of manual fire alarm pull stations at nurses' control stations or other continuously attended staff locations, as long as such pull stations are visible, are continuously accessible, and meet all travel distance requirements. Although zoned and coded systems can be used, the operation of any fire alarm device must automatically provide a general alarm, perform all the control functions the device requires, and transmit an alarm automatically to the fire department by the most direct and reliable method approved by local regulations. In addition, areas in new nursing homes and limited care facilities that are not equipped with quick response sprinklers must be equipped with either a complete corridor or sleeping room smoke detector system. During your inspection, you should make an operational check of these systems or, at the very least, review their maintenance and test records.

Complete automatic sprinkler protection is required for all new facilities. Listed quick response or residential sprinklers should be installed throughout the smoke compartments containing patient sleeping rooms. Sprinkler protection also is required in all existing facilities except those of Type I or single-story buildings of Type II (111) construction. Construction types are described in NFPA 220, *Standard on Types of Building Construction.* Partial systems can be installed in place of the fire-rated enclosures of hazardous areas in existing facilities. However, areas housing severe hazards in new and existing buildings must be separated by 1-hour construction and must be sprinklered. In existing unsprinklered facilities that are being renovated, altered, or modernized, complete sprinkler protection need only extend to the smoke compartments in which the work is being done.

Because so much depends on sprinkler operation, it is vital to install and maintain these systems correctly. Essentially, they must be installed in accordance with NFPA 13, *Standard for the Installation of Sprinkler Systems,* for light-hazard systems; special installation specifications are needed for systems with six sprinklers or less. All components, including the supervision of the main sprinkler control valves, must be interconnected electrically to the proper components of the fire alarm system.

To ensure an adequate means of first-aid fire fighting, portable fire extinguishers of an appropriate size and type should be provided at locations that are accessible to staff at all times. All building fire protection equipment, including fixed fire extinguishing systems for particular hazards such as kitchen hoods, cooking equipment, and specialized computer equipment must be marked to indicate that it has been inspected, tested, and maintained in accordance with fire code requirements and accepted engineering practices.

Health care fire safety depends on proper maintenance of all exits and fire protection equipment and on proper staff preparation. All utility, HVAC, and other service equipment should be installed and maintained in accordance with the applicable standards of the National Fire Codes. Smoking regulations and evacuation plans must be adopted, implemented, and prominently posted throughout the facility. Fire exit drills must be conducted quarterly on each shift to familiarize facility personnel with the signals and the emergency actions required under varied conditions.

Health care facilities may contain several other occupancies. For example, auditoriums and cafeterias are considered assembly occupancies, while laundries, boiler rooms, and maintenance shops are categorized as industrial occupancies. Other occupancies that are a section of, or are contiguous to, health care facilities may be classified as other occupancy types provided they are not meant to house, treat, or be customarily accessible to health care patients and are adequately separated from the health care occupancies by construction with a fire-resistance rating of at least 2 hours. Consult the appropriate chapters in this book for help in inspecting these and the business occupancies—office areas—of any health care facility. Because of the number and nature of the occupants, health care fire protection features must be maintained stringently to protect those who are unable to protect themselves.

Bibliography

NFPA 90A, *Standard for the Installation of Air Conditioning and Ventilating Systems*
NFPA 96, *Standard for Ventilation Control and Fire Protection of Commercial Cooking Operations*
NFPA 99, *Standard for Health Care Facilities*
NFPA *101, Life Safety Code*

HEALTH CARE OCCUPANCY FIRE INSPECTION FORM

Property Name: Owner:
Address: Phone Number:
OCCUPANCY
Change from Last Inspection: Yes☐ No☐
Occupant Load: Egress Capacity: Any Renovations: Yes☐ No☐
Hospital☐   Nursing Home☐   Ambulatory Health Care☐   Limited Care Facility☐
High Rise: Yes☐ No☐   Windowless: Yes☐ No☐   Underground: Yes☐ No☐
BUILDING SERVICES
Electricity☐ Gas☐ Water☐ Other☐   Are Utilities in Good Working Order: Yes☐ No☐
Elevators: Yes☐ No☐   Fire Service Control: Yes☐ No☐   Elevator Recall: Yes☐ No☐
Heat Type: Gas☐ Oil☐ Electric☐ Coal☐ Other☐   In Good Working Order: Yes☐ No☐
Emergency Generator: Yes☐ No☐   Size: Last Date Tested:
Date of Last Full Load Test: In Automatic Position: Yes☐ No☐
Fire Pump: Yes☐ No☐   GPM: Suction Pressure: System Pressure:
Date Last Tested: Date of Last Flow Test:
In Automatic Position: Yes☐ No☐   Jockey Pump: Yes☐ No☐
EMERGENCY LIGHTS
Operable: Yes☐ No☐   Tested Monthly: Yes☐ No☐
Properly Illuminate Egress Paths: Yes☐ No☐   In Good Condition: Yes☐ No☐
EXIT SIGNS
Illuminated: Internally☐ Externally☐   Emergency Power: Yes☐ No☐ Readily Visible: Yes☐
  No☐

FIRE ALARM

Yes☐ No☐ Location of Panel:

Coverage: Building☐ Partial☐ Monitored: Yes☐ No☐ Method:

Fire Department Notification: Yes☐ No☐

Type of Initiation Devices: Smoke☐ Heat☐ Manual☐ Water Flow☐ Special Systems☐

Date of Last Test: Date of Last Inspection:

Notification Signal Adequate: Yes☐ No☐

FIRE EXTINGUISHERS

Proper Type for Hazard Protecting: Yes☐ No☐ Mounted Properly: Yes☐ No☐

Date of Last Inspection: Adequate Number: Yes☐ No☐

FIRE PROTECTION SYSTEMS

Type: Sprinkler☐ Halon☐ CO2☐ Standpipe☐ Water Spray☐ Foam☐ Dry Chemical☐
Wet Chemical☐

Other☐ Coverage: Building☐ Partial☐ Date of Last Inspection:

Cylinder or Gauge Pressure(s): 1 psi.,2 psi.,3 psi.,4 psi.,5 psi

Valves Supervised: Electrical☐ Lock☐ Seal☐ Other☐ Are Valves Accessible: Yes☐ No☐

System Operational: Yes☐ No☐ Sprinkler Heads 18" from Storage: Yes☐ No☐

FIRE RESISTIVE (FR) CONSTRUCTION

Stairway FR: Yes☐ No☐ Hourly Rating:

Corridors FR: Yes☐ No☐ Hourly Rating:

Elevator Shaft FR: Yes☐ Yes☐ No☐ Hourly Rating:

Major Structural Members FR: Yes☐ No☐ Hourly Rating:

Floor-Ceiling Assemblies FR: Yes☐ No☐ Hourly Rating:

All Openings Protected in FR Walls and Floor-Ceiling Assemblies: Yes☐ No☐

HAZARDOUS AREAS

Protected by: Fire-Rated Separation☐ Extinguishing System☐ Both☐

Door Self-Closures: Yes☐ No☐

Kitchen Exhaust Hoods Properly Protected: Yes☐ No☐ Clean: Yes☐ No☐ Date of Last
Inspection:

Laboratories Properly Protected: Yes☐ No☐

Anesthesia Areas Properly Protected: Yes☐ No☐

Medical Gases Stored Properly: Yes☐ No☐

Gift Shops Properly Protected: Yes☐ No☐

Other Occupancies Separated by 2-hour Construction: Yes☐ No☐

HOUSEKEEPING

Areas Free of Excessive Combustibles: Yes☐ No☐

Smoking Regulated: Yes☐ No☐ Items Stored in Corridors: Yes☐ No☐

INTERIOR FINISH

Walls and Ceilings Proper Rating: Yes☐ No☐ Floor Finish Proper Rating: Yes☐ No☐

Furniture/Draperies Flame Resistive: Yes☐ No☐

Wastebasket/Containers Non-Combustible: Yes☐ No☐

MEANS OF EGRESS

Readily Visible: Yes☐ No☐ Clear and Unobstructed: Yes☐ No☐

Two☐ Remote Exits Available: Yes☐ No☐ Travel Distance within Limits: Yes☐ No☐

Dead-Ends within Limits: Yes☐ No☐

50% Maximum through Level of Exit Discharge: Yes☐ No☐

Patient Sleeping Rooms > 1000 sq. ft. Tw☐   Means of Egress: Yes☐   No☐
Other Rooms > 2500 sq. ft. Tw☐   Means of Egress: Yes☐   No☐
Suite Sleeping Rooms < 5000 sq. ft.: Yes☐   No☐
Other than Sleeping Suites < 10000 sq. ft.: Yes☐   No☐
Adequate Illumination: Yes☐   No☐
Proper Rating on All Components: Yes☐   No☐
All Exit Enclosures Free of Storage: Yes☐   No☐
Door Swing in the Direction of Egress Travel (when required): Yes☐   No☐
Panic/Fire Exit Hardware Operable: Yes☐   No☐
Doors Open Easily: Yes☐   No☐   Self-Closures Operable: Yes☐   No☐
Patient Room Doors Latch: Yes☐   No☐   Locked: Yes☐   No☐   Staff have Keys: Yes☐   No☐
Corridors and Aisles of Sufficient Size: Yes☐   No☐
Stairwell Re-Entry: Yes☐   No☐
Mezzanines: Yes☐   No☐   Proper Exits: Yes☐   No☐
Smoke Barriers Proper Size and Rating: Yes☐   No☐
Doors Closed or Held Open With Automatic Closures: Yes☐   No☐
Patient Rooms Outside Window: Yes☐   No☐
VERTICAL OPENINGS
Properly Protected: Yes☐   No☐
Atrium: Yes☐   No☐   Properly Protected: Yes☐   No☐
Are Fire Doors in Good Working Order: Yes☐   No☐
OPERATING FEATURES
Written Fire Emergency Plan: Yes☐   No☐   Date of Last Update:
Available t☐   Employees: Yes☐   No☐   Employees Trained: Yes☐   No☐
Fire Drills Conducted: Yes☐   No☐   Date and Time of Last Drill:

CHAPTER 19

Detention and Correctional Occupancies

*D*etention and correctional occupancies are facilities in which occupants are confined or housed under some degree of restraint or security. These occupancies provide sleeping facilities for four or more residents who are prevented from taking action for self preservation—that is, leaving the building—because of security measures that are not under their control. These occupancies include jails, detention centers, correctional institutions, reformatories, houses of correction, prerelease centers, work camps, training schools, and other residential-restrained care facilities.

As an inspector, you should recognize that detention and correctional occupancies present unique fire safety concerns by their very nature. Supervisory and operating personnel are substantially responsible for maintaining security within the facility in order to protect both the occupants and the general public. As a result, the personnel may be reluctant to initiate evacuation procedures or to take any other action that could compromise security, even in the case of a fire. It is, therefore, critical that detention and correctional facilities be designed, constructed, operated, and maintained so as to minimize the possibility of a fire.

Detention and correctional facilities may be a complex of buildings that serve a variety of purposes. The facility may include assembly occupancies, such as gymnasiums and auditoriums; business office areas; industrial shop areas; and storage occupancies. There also may be an infirmary or similar patient care areas that are classified as health care occupancies. Chapters 14 and 15 of the *Life Safety Code* primarily address the residential housing areas of the facility; other areas should meet the applicable *Life Safety Code* requirements for the appropriate occupancy classification. Where security measures require that the egress doors in those other occupancies be locked, however, a remote system for releasing the locks should be provided, or a sufficient number of attendants with keys must be available to promptly unlock the egress doors. Supervision in these areas must be continuous when the spaces are occupied.

Areas of a facility in which the egress doors are not locked are not classified as detention and correctional occupancies. An example of such an area is a halfway house or a prerelease area located in a larger detention complex. Facilities in which occupants are supervised but are not locked in are classified as residential occupancies and must comply with the appropriate residential occupancy requirements.

Classifying the Occupancy

When conducting your inspection, first you should determine the proper user category or use condition of the occupancy. The requirements for protecting the occupants increase as the degree of restraint increases. Remember, the primary difference between a detention and correctional occupancy and a residential occupancy is the presence of locks on the required means of egress, which are not under the occupants' control. Therefore, you must understand the arrangement and management of the locking system.

Five use conditions have been established that correspond to five degrees of restraint.

Use Condition I—Free Egress

The occupants of such areas are permitted to move freely to the exterior. In other words, there are no locks that the occupants cannot control. Such an area is not considered a detention and correctional occupancy and is subject to the requirements of some other occupancy.

Use Condition II—Zoned Egress

Free movement is allowed from sleeping areas from any occupied smoke compartment to other smoke compartments, but the doors to the the exterior are locked.

Use Condition III—Zoned Impeded Egress

The occupants are allowed to move freely within any smoke compartment, but the doors to the outside are locked and the doors providing access to other smoke compartments are remotely unlocked.

Use Condition IV—Impeded Egress

Occupants are locked in their rooms or cells, but the room doors can be remotely unlocked. The doors providing access to other smoke compartments also are remotely unlocked.

Use Condition V—Contained

Occupants are locked in their rooms or cells by manually operated locks, and the staff must go physically to the room door to release them. The doors providing access to other smoke compartments also are manually locked.

"Remote control release" means that the locking mechanism can be released mechanically, electrically, pneumatically, or by some other means that is not located in the immediate area where the residents are housed. It does not mean that the door has to be opened, but only that the lock can be released. The remote location need not be in another fire area, although this could be beneficial from a fire safety standpoint. You should be reasonably sure that the remote locking system will function as intended and that the staff can promptly gain access to the controls in an emergency.

An exception to the remote control release requirement does permit the use of some manual locks in Use Condition IV facilities. Not more than ten manual unlocking operations using no more than two separate keys are permitted to move the occupants promptly to some other smoke compartment. This allows small areas within a facility to have manual locks but still permits the entire facility to be classified as having remote control locks. You should establish that keys are immediately available to staff and that the locks can be released promptly in an emergency.

The code requires that emergency power be provided for electrically operated doors and locks. You should verify that the emergency power system is connected to all necessary devices and assess the system's reliability by reviewing its maintenance and testing. A manual mechanical redundant means also may be required to release the occupants should the emergency power system fail.

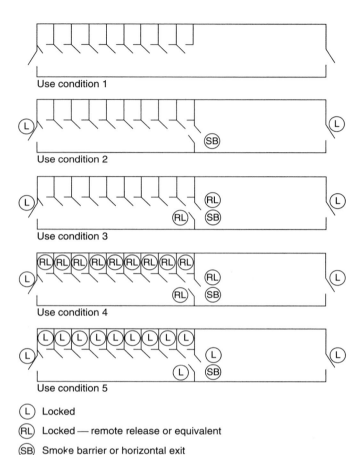

Use condition 1

Use condition 2

Use condition 3

Use condition 4

Use condition 5

(L) Locked

(RL) Locked — remote release or equivalent

(SB) Smoke barrier or horizontal exit

Figure 19-1. Use condition diagram. Source: Figure A-14-1.4.1, NFPA, 101, Life Safety Code, NFPA, Quincy, MA, 1994.

To determine a facility's appropriate use condition, you must fully understand its operation. For example, if the residents are free to move about the facility during the day when you are conducting the inspection but are locked down for eight hours at night, you must apply the use condition that reflects the more restricted movement. Each occupied area should be under continuous supervision, and the supervising personnel must be able to promptly release the occupants.

You also should recognize that staffing levels may be much higher during the day when an inspection typically is made. Large numbers of administrative, supervisory, educational, and maintenance personnel probably will not be present at night, and security staffing levels also may be reduced at night. The administration should be required to demonstrate that there are enough operating personnel present on each shift to properly supervise all occupied areas and to perform effectively during a fire.

Occupancy Characteristics

Construction Type

Building construction type is classified in accordance with NFPA 220, *Standard on Types of Building Construction.* Larger detention and correctional occupancies generally are of Type I construction, due to security considerations. Smaller facilities can be of Type II construction, and road or field camps often are of a combustible construction classification. Existing buildings can be of any construction type. Automatic sprinkler protection may be required, depending on the type of building construction, the height of the building, and its use condition. Consult the applicable codes for specific construction requirements.

Occupant Load

Generally, occupant load versus exit capacity is not a major consideration in detention and correctional occupancies. As noted in the *Life Safety Code,* the occupant load factor is 120 square feet per person, reflecting a sparse population density. (This occupant load factor is not related to the minimum square footage requirements per resident in a room or cell specified by correctional standards.) The most appropriate way to determine the occupant load is to count the number of beds in a given housing area.

Means of Egress

Detention and correctional occupancies allow various exceptions to standard egress requirements.

Horizontal Exits: Far greater attention is paid to horizontal exits in detention and correctional occupancies than in the other occupancy classifications. In fact, the code allows up to 100% of the required exits from a fire or smoke compartment to be horizontal exits. This reflects the philosophy that management generally will choose to move the residents within the facility rather than take them outside and possibly compromise security. When horizontal exits compose 100% of the required exits of a fire compartment, an exit other than a horizontal exit must be accessible in some other, though not necessarily adjacent, compartment, without requiring that the occupants return through the compartment where the fire originated. Figure 19-2 clarifies the intent of the code.

Sliding Doors: Sliding doors are permitted in detention and correctional facilities. The force required to slide the door to its fully open position must not exceed 50 pounds with a perpendicular force of 50 pounds against the door.

Exit Discharge: The exit may discharge into a fenced yard or court that is either outside or inside the facility. The outside area of refuge must provide at least 15 square feet of space per person at least 50 feet from the building. If the area of refuge is an interior courtyard that is used as a smoke barrier, the lock on the door must comply with the locking provisions required on other smoke-barrier doors.

Day Rooms: Occupants may exit sleeping rooms through a day room or group activity space. In other words, one intervening room is permitted between the sleeping room and the exit access corridor.

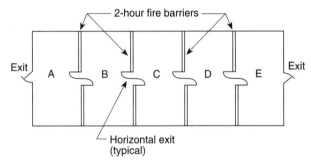

Figure 19-2. A horizontal exit system. One hundred percent of the required exits of fire Compartments B, C, and D are horizontal exits. The arrangement is in compliance as long as Compartments A and E have an approved exit other than a horizontal exit.

City and county jails often are housed in the same building as county or city offices or court facilities, or both. Where this is the case, the detention and correctional area must be separated from the other occupancies by construction with a minimum 2-hour fire-resistance rating. Horizontal exits are permitted into other contiguous occupancies, provided the other occupancies conform tto the code requirements for detention and correctional facilities. If no high-hazard contents are present, however, the other occupancies may conform to the requirements of their appropriate occupancy classification.

Sally ports often are used in means of egress from detention areas for security purposes. The two doors usually are interlocked to that only one of them can be opened at a time. This arrangement can obstruct the flow of persons out of the area and prevent a hose line from being stretched into the detention area. The *Life Safety Code* requires that an emergency override feature be provided so that both doors of a sally port can be opened at the same time in order to permit continuous and unobstructed passage in an emergency. The override feature should be tested to ensure that it operates properly.

As will frequently be the case for security purposes, all exits may discharge through the level of exit discharge. Where this occurs, the level of exit discharge must be subdivided so that not more than 50% of the exits discharge into a single fire compartment. In existing buildings, a smoke barrier may be used to subdivide the level of exit discharge if the level of discharge has approved automatic sprinkler protection.

Dead-end corridors are permitted up to a limit of 50 feet. In Use Condition V facilities (manual locks on all doors), however, this limit is reduced to 20 feet. No limits are specified for existing buildings, although dead-end corridors should be corrected whenever possible.

The use of exit signs in detention and correctional facilities is a contradiction because residents generally cannot use the exits until they are released. For this and other reasons, exits signs may be omitted from resident sleeping areas. However, emergency lighting is required through throughout the means of egress.

Hazardous Areas

Hazardous areas such as boiler rooms, kitchens, laundries, commissaries, storage rooms, trash rooms, and similar spaces require 1-hour rated enclosures with self-closing 3/4-hour labeled fire door assemblies or automatic sprinkler protection, or both. Hazardous areas that are not considered incidental to the resident housing area must be separated by a 2-hour fire barrier and be provided with automatic sprinkler protection.

Protecting Openings

Vertical openings, such as stairways, ramps, elevators, chutes, and HVAC shafts, must be enclosed with fire barriers, including fire-rated door assemblies. The required fire-resistance rating of the enclosure depends on a number of factors. For example, how high is the building? Is it new or existing construction? Does the vertical opening serve as a required exit?

Various exceptions are permitted, some of which are unique to detention and correctional occupancies. Multilevel housing areas need not be enclosed if the distance between the lowest and highest floor level does not exceed 13 feet. With complete automatic sprinkler protection, unprotected openings are permitted in residential housing areas if the distance between the lowest and highest floor levels is no more than 23 feet. In neither instance is the actual number of levels restricted. The code is even more flexible for existing buildings, particularly where automatic sprinkler protection or an approved smoke control system is provided.

Interior Finish

In an effort to create a more habitable environment, facility designers may introduce finish materials that permit fires to develop rapidly. This is particularly true in correctional facilities that encourage self-help programs where the residents install paneling or other finish materials. Such areas require regular and thorough inspections to make sure that they comply with applicable code requirements for interior finish.

Interior finish also has proven to be a serious fire problem in padded cells. Some foam padding can develop extremely rapid and intense fires, and fire development is accentuated by the cell's small area and the insulating qualities of the foam. While undesirable, padded cells are not prohibited. However, they are considered hazardous areas and require both a 1-hour rated enclosure with a self-closing 3/4-hour fire door assembly and automatic sprinkler protection.

Contents

Because contents are the major fuel problem in detention and correctional facilities, the quantity and flammability of furnishings and decorations must be strictly limited, particularly in the residential housing areas. The rates of fire development, smoke generation, and heat release are directly related to the quantity and nature of the interior furnishings. Since the time needed to release and move residents during a fire can be a major problem, it is essential to effectively control the fuel loading in order to slow fire development. You should review management policies to ensure that supervisory personnel understand the importance of this limitation and are practicing effective fuel control.

Requirements for the control of flammable contents can be found in Chapter 31 of the *Life Safety Code*. Combustible personal property allowed in sleeping rooms must be stored in closable metal lockers or fire-resistant containers. Furnishings such as mattresses and upholstered furniture must not be highly flammable. Specific flammability standards apply in spaces that are not protected by automatic sprinklers. Curtains and draperies must be flame-resistant, and wastebaskets must be of noncombustible or other approved materials. Combustible decorations are prohibited unless they are flame-retardant. The facility administration also must control the use of heat-producing appliances, such as hot plates.

Fire Protection

Detention and correctional facilities must be equipped with an approved fire alarm system. Manual fire alarm stations are required in the normal path of travel near each exit, but the code does allow fire alarm activation stations to be placed within staff locations. Manual fire alarm stations also may be locked. In all instances, you need to verify that staff locations are occupied continuously and that keys are readily available to operating personnel so that the fire alarm system can be activated promptly if a fire is discovered. It is important that you evaluate the staffing levels and key distribution policies on all shifts.

Activation of the building fire alarm system must automatically, without delay, activate an audible alarm signal to alert the building occupants. Presignal systems are specifically prohibited. In addition, activation of the building fire alarm system must automatically transmit an alarm to notify the fire department by an approved means.

The residential housing areas of detention and correctional facilities must be equipped with an approved smoke detection system. However, the required extent of smoke detector coverage varies, depending on the facility's use condition and the presence or absence of automatic sprinkler protection. Automatic smoke detectors can be arranged to sound at a constantly attended location, and they need not sound the building fire alarm or transmit an alarm to the fire department. Smoke detectors also may be located in exhaust ducts from cells or behind grills to prevent them from being damaged or tampered with, as long as the design achieves the speed of detection prescribed by the code.

Sprinkler and Standpipe Protection

Automatic sprinkler protection may be required in detention and correctional facilities, depending on the building's construction type and height. Automatic sprinkler protection also may be provided to allow greater design flexibility, including the use of multilevel housing areas and atriums, and to reduce the required fire-resistance ratings of room and corridor separations. In addition, automatic sprinkler protection may be installed in existing nonconforming facilities to give them an acceptable level of safety. New high-rise detention and correctional facilities must be fully sprinklered.

Class I standpipe systems are required in all detention and correctional facilities over two stories high. Class III standpipe systems, which are combined Class I and Class II systems, are required in facilities over two stories high that are not protected with automatic sprinklers. Portable fire extinguishers also are required. They may be located in staff areas or in locked cabinets if there is reasonable evidence that operating personnel will have prompt access to them when needed.

It is essential that you verify that fire protection equipment is operational and will function as designed when needed. You should review documentation to verify that the equipment is being serviced, inspected, and tested by qualified personnel. You also should witness operational tests of fire protection equipment during the course of your inspection and check the fire alarm control panels and sprinkler control valves to verify that the systems have not been shut off.

Subdividing the Building

One of the major protection features of the *Life Safety Code* is the requirement to subdivide the building into smoke compartments using approved smoke barriers. The smoke barriers provide areas of refuge into which the residents will be moved.

You should determine the location of the smoke barriers to ensure that they do, in fact, subdivide the building as required. You can do this by reviewing a floor plan. Then you should make a field check to ensure that the smoke barriers are of adequate construction and are continuous from slab to slab; that the doors are of adequate construction and are equipped with closers and the necessary hardware; and that HVAC ducts that penetrate the smoke barrier have dampers that will resist the passage of smoke. You also should make sure that cross corridor doors in smoke barriers have the required vision panels.

The *Life Safety Code* requires further subdivisions of the residential housing areas. These requirements, which can be found in Table 19-1 and also in Chapters 14 and 15 of the *Life Safety Code,* relate to the separation walls of the cell or room and the day space. If the facility has to be sprinklered because of its construction type, the sprinkler option can be used. If the code does not require a sprinkler system, management may choose whether or not to use sprinklers. This should be taken seriously because it can have a major impact on the construction and operation of the detention and correctional facility.

You should inspect each of the enclosing walls of the room or cell for completeness and for the required fire resistance. Note that minimum 45-minute fire-rated glazing is now permitted in vision panels where the code previously specified 1/4-inch wired glass.

Building Services

During your inspection, you should review the building services, including the heating, ventilating, and air conditioning (HVAC) systems. The *Life Safety Code* prohibits space heaters, and conducting inspections during cold weather will provide you with an opportunity to check for their use. In addition, you should review management policies for any discussion of portable heaters.

Make sure that you inspect all elevators, dumbwaiters, vertical conveyors, rubbish chutes, incinerators, and laundry chutes for compliance with applicable codes. All chute doors should be self-closing, and the fire-resistive enclosures of vertical openings should be equipped with well-fitted, self-closing doors.

Emergency Planning

Each detention and correctional occupancy must have a written fire emergency plan that is given to supervisory personnel and reviewed

Table 19-1. Use conditions and required fire protection features in detention and correctional occupancies.

Use condition	II		III		IV		V	
Feature	NS	AS	NS	AS	NS	AS	NS	AS
Room to room separation	NR	NR	NR	NR	ST	NR	FR(1/2)	ST
Room face to corridor separation	ST	NR	ST	NR	ST	NR	FR	ST
Room face to common space separation	NR	NR	NR <50 ft / ST >50 ft		NR <50 ft / ST >50 ft	ST	NR <50 ft / ST >50 ft	FR	ST
Common space to corridor separation	FR	NR	FR	NR	FR	NR	FR	ST
Total openings in solid room face	120 sq in.		120 sq in.		120 sq in.		120 sq in.*	

AS, protected by automatic sprinklers; NS, not protected by automatic sprinklers; NR, no requirement; ST, smoketight; FR, fire rated (1 hour); FR(1/2), fire rated (1/2 hour); *closable from inside or 120 sq in. with smoke control.

periodically with all operating personnel. This plan should establish specific procedures for discovering and isolating a fire, using alarm systems, responding to fire alarms, extinguishing fires, evacuating residents in immediate danger, notifying the fire department, and conducting zone evacuations. The plan should clearly establish authority and designate responsibilities, giving special consideration to procedures for night shifts, weekends, and holidays. The *Life Safety Code* requires that the facility review and coordinate the emergency plan with the fire department that is legally committed to serve the facility.

Realistic fire drills should be conducted periodically on each shift. These drills should include training on the use and location of the alarm systems, portable fire extinguishers, and related fire protection equipment. Fire emergency procedures should be reviewed with all new employees, and refresher training should be provided for all employees at least annually. Fire drills and employee training should be documented and available for your review.

Bibliography

NFPA 90A, *Standard for the Installation of Air Conditioning and Ventilating Systems*
NFPA *101, Life Safety Code*

DETENTION OCCUPANCY FIRE INSPECTION FORM

Property Name: Owner:

Address: Phone Number:

OCCUPANCY

Change from Last Inspection: Yes☐ No☐

Occupant Load: Egress Capacity: Any Renovations: Yes☐ No☐

Condition I☐ Condition II☐ Condition III☐ Condition IV☐ Condition V☐ High Rise: Yes☐

No☐ Windowless: Yes☐ No☐ Underground: Yes☐ No☐

BUILDING SERVICES

Electricity☐ Gas☐ Water☐ Other☐ Are Utilities in Good Working Order: Yes☐ No☐

Elevators: Yes☐ No☐ Fire Service Control: Yes☐ No☐ Elevator Recall: Yes☐ No☐

Heat Type: Gas☐ Oil☐ Electric☐ Coal☐ Other☐ In Good Working Order: Yes☐ No☐

Emergency Generator: Yes☐ No☐ Size: Last Date Tested:

Date of Last Full Load Test: In Automatic Position: Yes☐ No☐

Fire Pump: Yes☐ No☐ GPM: Suction Pressure: System Pressure:

Date Last Tested: Date of Last Flow Test:

In Automatic Position: Yes☐ No☐ Jockey Pump: Yes☐ No☐

EMERGENCY LIGHTS

Operable: Yes☐ No☐ Tested Monthly: Yes☐ No☐

Properly Illuminate Egress Paths: Yes☐ No☐ In Good Condition: Yes☐ No☐

EXIT SIGNS

Illuminated: Internally☐ Externally☐ Emergency Power: Yes☐ No☐ Readily Visible: Yes☐ No☐

FIRE ALARM

Yes☐ No☐ Location of Panel:

Coverage: Building☐ Partial☐ Monitored: Yes☐ No☐ Method:

Fire Department Notification: Yes☐ No☐

Type of Initiation Devices: Smoke☐ Heat☐ Manual☐ Water Flow☐ Special Systems☐

Date of Last Test: Date of Last Inspection:

Notification Signal Adequate: Yes☐ No☐

FIRE EXTINGUISHERS

Proper Type for Hazard Protecting: Yes☐ No☐ Mounted Properly: Yes☐ No☐

Date of Last Inspection: Adequate Number: Yes☐ No☐

FIRE PROTECTION SYSTEMS

Type: Sprinkler☐ Halon☐ CO2☐ Standpipe☐ Water Spray☐ Foam☐ Dry Chemical☐

Wet Chemical☐ Other☐ Coverage: Building☐ Partial☐   Date of Last Inspection:

Cylinder or Gauge Pressure(s): 1   psi.,2   psi.,3   psi.,4   psi.,5   psi.

Valves Supervised: Electrical☐ Lock☐ Seal☐ Other☐ Are Valves Accessible: Yes☐ No☐

System Operational: Yes☐ No☐   Sprinkler Heads 18" from Storage: Yes☐ No☐

FIRE RESISTIVE (FR) CONSTRUCTION

Stairway FR: Yes☐ No☐   Hourly Rating:

Corridors FR: Yes☐ No☐   Hourly Rating:

Elevator Shaft FR: Yes☐ Yes☐ No☐   Hourly Rating:

Major Structural Members FR: Yes☐ No☐   Hourly Rating:

Floor-Ceiling Assemblies FR: Yes☐ No☐   Hourly Rating:

All Openings Protected in FR Walls and Floor-Ceiling Assemblies: Yes☐ No☐

HAZARDOUS AREAS

Protected by: Fire-Rated Separation☐ Extinguishing System☐ Both☐

Door Self-Closures: Yes☐ No☐

Kitchen Exhaust Hoods Properly Protected: Yes☐ No☐   Clean: Yes☐ No☐

Date of Last Inspection: Other Occupancies Separated by 2-hour Construction:☐ No☐

Padded Cells 1-hour Fire Resistance Rated and Sprinklers: Yes☐ No☐

HOUSEKEEPING

Areas Free of Excessive Combustibles: Yes☐ No☐   Smoking Regulated: Yes☐ No☐

INTERIOR FINISH

Walls and Ceilings Proper Rating: Yes☐ No☐   Floor Finish Proper Rating: Yes☐ No☐

Furniture/Draperies Flame Resistive: Yes☐ No☐

Wastebasket/Containers Non-Combustible: Yes☐ No☐

Inmate Belongings in Metal Locker: Yes☐ No☐

MEANS OF EGRESS

Readily Visible: Yes☐ No☐   Clear and Unobstructed: Yes☐ No☐

Two☐ Remote Exits Available: Yes☐ No☐   Travel Distance within Limits: Yes☐ No☐

Common Path of Travel within Limits: Yes☐ No☐

Dead-Ends within Limits: Yes☐ No☐

50% Maximum through Level of Exit Discharge: Yes☐ No☐

Adequate Illumination: Yes☐ No☐   Proper Rating on All Components: Yes☐ No☐

All Exit Enclosures Free of Storage: Yes☐ No☐

Door Swing in the Direction of Egress Travel (when required): Yes☐ No☐

Panic/Fire Exit Hardware Operable: Yes☐ No☐   Doors Open Easily: Yes☐ No☐

Self-Closures Operable: Yes☐ No☐   Doors that are Locked Tested: Yes☐ No☐

Staff have Keys: Yes☐ No☐   Doors Closed or Held Open With Automatic Closures: Yes☐ No☐

Corridors and Aisles of Sufficient Size: Yes☐ No☐

Mezzanines: Yes☐ No☐   Proper Exits: Yes☐ No☐

Smoke Barriers Proper Size and Rating: Yes☐ No☐

VERTICAL OPENINGS

Properly Protected: Yes☐ No☐ Atrium: Yes☐ No☐   Properly Protected: Yes☐ No☐

Are Fire Doors In Good Working Order: Yes☐ No☐

OPERATING FEATURES

Written Fire Emergency Plan: Yes☐ No☐   Date of Last Update:

Available t☐ Employees: Yes☐ No☐   Employees Trained: Yes☐ No☐

Fire Drills Conducted: Yes☐ No☐   Date and Time of Last Drill:

Keys ☐ Unlock Doors Identifiable by Feel and Sight: Yes☐ No☐

CHAPTER 20

Hotels

*T*he term "hotel" is not specifically reserved for the modern fire-resistive high-rise building. Indeed, it may apply to any motel, inn, or club that provides sleeping accommodations for more than 16 people. As a result, hotels generally present a wide range of life safety and fire protection problems.

Inspecting hotels poses a special challenge because, in addition to providing sleeping accommodations for transient guests, hotels may house facilities such as meeting rooms, ballrooms, theatrical stages, kitchens, restaurants, storage rooms, maintenance shops, garages, offices, and retail shops, each of which may be classified as a different type of occupancy. For example, guest rooms are classified as residential occupancies, while ballrooms, theaters, and restaurants are assembly occupancies. Offices are business occupancies, garages and storage areas are storage occupancies, maintenance shops are industrial occupancies, and retail shops are mercantile occupancies.

If these different occupancies are separated and have their own means of egress, they can be considered separate occupancies, according to the *Life Safety Code.* If they share the same means of egress, however, egress and fire protection requirements should comply with the most restrictive requirements of the occupancies involved.

Inspection Observations

Before inspecting a hotel, you should familiarize yourself with NFPA *101, Life Safety Code,* which contains requirements for means of egress and fire protection for new and existing hotels, as well as dormitories. The *Life Safety Code* also provides requirements for operating features, such as fire drills and employee training.

Means of Egress

Occupants must be able to evacuate quickly and safely from a hotel to reduce the potential for loss of life. The guest room corridors should have a minimum clear width of 44 inches and be free of obstructions. Exit signs should be readily visible and should clearly identify the path of travel to each exit. The *Life Safety Code* requires emergency lighting in any hotel with more than 25 rooms.

Each floor should have two separate and remote exits. At least half the exits, in number and capacity, should discharge directly to the outside at a public way or an open space that leads to a public way. Parked vehicles, trash containers, fencing, or landscaping that could impede travel from the exit discharge should not be permitted.

The doors to the exit stairs should be self-closing, latching, fire-rated doors. They should have a 1-hour fire-resistance rating if the stairs connect three stories or fewer and a 2-hour rating if they connect four stories or more. All stair doors should open easily and, when released, should close completely and latch. Stair landings and the area under the last flight of stairs must not be used for storage. There should be nothing inside the stair enclosure that would interfere with its use as an exit.

You should inspect all fire escapes or outside stairs, if provided, from top to bottom. The fire escape must be attached securely to the outside of the building, and all handrails and guardrails should be secure. Counter-weights on fire escapes should be free to swing when necessary to lower the stairs. Observe the general condition of the structure and the quality of maintenance. There should be no accumulated trash beneath the outside stairways and fire escapes.

Interior

You can start your interior inspection at the top or bottom of the hotel, but beginning at the roof will give you a "birds-eye" view of the building.

Restaurants and meeting rooms may be located on the top floors of hotels, particularly in high-rise hotels. These are assembly occupancies and should comply with the requirements of the *Life Safety Code* for new or existing assembly occupancies (see also Chapter 16 in this book). The occupant load of these occupancies should not exceed the available exit capacity. You should keep in mind that the occupant load may have changed due to renovations.

Generally, the guest room floors consist of guest rooms opening into a corridor. It is critical that these corridors be protected from smoke and fire. Corridor walls should have a half-hour fire-resistance rating with 20-minute fire-rated, self-closing room doors, and any door that opens into the corridor should be self-closing. If a fire occurs in a guest room and the guest evacuates the room, the guest room door must close to protect the corridor from heat and smoke at least for the time it takes the guests to evacuate. Thus, it is critical that the doors' self-closers work properly.

Transoms over the doors in corridor walls should be permanently fixed in the closed position. There should be no louvers in corridor walls, although the *Life Safety Code* does permit them if automatic sprinklers are installed or if smoke detectors in the corridors are arranged to shut down the fans that draw air into the corridor from the guest rooms. Transfer grilles must be located in the lower third of the corridor wall.

During your inspection, you should examine a few guest rooms to ensure that their room doors are self-closing and that they close completely and latch. Each room should be equipped with a working smoke detector, and fire safety information should be posted in each room.

The guest room smoke detector is intended to set off an alarm in the room to alert the occupant. It is not intended to sound the alarm throughout the building. Because of the high incidence of false alarms, these smoke detectors should not be connected to the building alarm system.

Rooms that contain trash chutes, laundry chutes, or trash collection areas should be enclosed in 1-hour fire-rated walls or be protected with automatic sprinklers. If there are sprinklers, the enclosing walls need not have a fire-resistance rating, but they should be smoke-resistant. Doors should be self-closing.

The corridor interior finish should be Class A or B. Floor coverings should be Class I or II. New curtains, draperies, and similar furnishings should be flame-retardant. These materials should be tested in accordance with NFPA 701, *Standard Methods of Fire Tests for Flame-Resistant Textiles and Films.*

The front desk and its associated offices, restaurants, meeting rooms, and possibly ballroom usually are located on the ground floor. The occupant load of each of these assembly rooms should be posted conspicuously.

Meeting rooms and ballrooms generally have back-of-house service corridors, which the hotel staff uses to gain access to the rooms. They also may be used to store extra chairs, tables, and food carts. Some of these corridors are designed to be extra wide to accommodate these items, but the minimum required corridor width of 44 inches still must be maintained even if they are not. Because this information on the required corridor width need not be posted, you may have to calculate the occupant load/egress capacity.

Remember to check the general housekeeping and maintenance of the building. Chances are the areas used by the public will be in fairly good condition, but the back-of-house service areas might not be.

You also should remember that renovations or additions to the hotel may block exits, increase travel distance, decrease exit width, or disable exit signs or fire alarm equipment. Note any changes that have been made to the structure or its arrangements since the last inspection.

Fire-rated floor/ceiling assemblies are an important part of the building's fire-resistance features. An unprotected opening in the ceiling may compromise the assembly's integrity. All the panels or tiles of the suspended ceilings that are part of a floor/ceiling or roof/ceiling assembly must be in place. If the details of construction are not noted on the previous inspection report, you should check the building plans; the floor and roof design usually can be found on the architectural plans. Check the condition of electrical fixtures and wiring throughout the building, and make sure that flexible cords are used properly.

Storage rooms, building service equipment rooms, maintenance shops, shipping and receiving areas, the employees' locker room, the employees' cafeteria, and a garage might be located in the basement. Some common hazards you can expect to find in these occupancies include ordinary combustibles, such as paper and wood, which may be found in large quantities in storage rooms and in shipping and receiving areas, as well as paints and flammable solvents, which may be found in maintenance shops. Heat-producing equipment also presents hazards.

Good housekeeping practices are essential in service areas. Combustible trash should not be allowed to accumulate, and hazardous materials should be stored properly. Hand trucks and service carts should not be left in corridors and hallways because they can impede emergency evacuation. And building service equipment rooms should not be used as storage areas.

In building service equipment rooms and maintenance shops, you should check machinery and appliances for frayed wiring, evidence of leaks, and signs of general deterioration. Be sure that the clearances between heat-producing equipment and combustible materials are adequate.

Inspect all the kitchens, including employee cafeteria kitchens. Check the hood exhaust filters and exhaust ducts for grease accumulations, and examine the nozzles and valves on the range hood extinguishing system to make sure they are not blocked, are properly aligned over the cooking surfaces, and are not clogged with grease. Make sure that the nozzles for the kitchen hood systems are covered, something most manufacturers require. Note the date the system was last inspected and serviced.

Stairwell doors often are locked from the inside for security reasons. The *Life Safety Code* permits this, as long as the doors unlock automatically when the building fire alarm system operates or when the power goes out. You should examine the hardware arrangement of all stair doors.

Fire Protection

The *Life Safety Code* requires that hotels over three stories high with guest rooms that open into corridors have a fire alarm system. Buildings that are seven stories or higher also must have an annunciator to indicate the floor or area from which the alarm was transmitted. Manual fire alarm stations should be located adjacent to each exit, and there should be a manual station at the hotel desk or some other convenient location. Responsible hotel staff should continuously supervise this station. The fire alarm system must activate automatically, without delay, and sound the building's internal audible alarms. Presignal systems are permitted only with express permission of the authority having jurisdiction.

You should have the fire alarm system tested to ensure that it operates properly and that it can be heard in the guest rooms when their doors are closed. If it is impractical to conduct a test during your inspection, you should review the system's maintenance and test records. There should be smoke detectors in the corridors in nonsprinklered hotels in accordance with the requirements of the *Life Safety Code*, and they should be connected to the building fire alarm system.

If the building is sprinklered, check the sprinklers' general condition. This includes, but is not limited to, ensuring that floor-control valves are open and that sprinklers are neither painted nor obstructed. There should be a clear space of 18 inches below each sprinkler. Painted sprinklers should be replaced.

There should be portable fire extinguishers in hazardous areas. During your inspection, check the inspection tags on the extinguishers for the most recent inspection date. See that they are properly mounted, fully charged, and undamaged. Look for dents in the containers or cylinders and cracks in hoses and nozzles.

Check each hose station in any building equipped with a standpipe system. If the station consists of a valve and an outlet, examine the hose connection threads for damage and look for signs of leakage. If the station is equipped with hose for occupant use, see that the hose is properly hung in the rack and that the nozzle is attached.

Planning and Training

Do not forget to review the fire plan for the hotel, which should detail the duties of the staff in the event of a fire and spell out the procedures for immediately calling the fire department and for notifying and keeping the guests informed. You also should review the fire drill records and ask employees randomly if they have actually been trained and practice the fire plan. See Chapter 31 of the *Life Safety Code* for guidance on fire drills and plans.

Bibliography

NFPA 90A, *Standard for the Installation of Air Conditioning and Ventilating Systems*
NFPA 96, *Standard for Ventilation Control and Fire Protection of Commercial Cooking*
NFPA *101, Life Safety Code*

HOTEL OCCUPANCY FIRE INSPECTION FORM

Property Name: Owner:
Address: Phone Number:

OCCUPANCY

Change from Last Inspection: Yes☐   No☐

Occupant Load: Egress Capacity: Any Renovations: Yes☐   No☐

High Rise: Yes☐   No☐   Windowless: Yes☐   No☐   Underground: Yes☐   No☐

BUILDING SERVICES

Electricity☐   Gas☐   Water☐   Other☐   Are Utilities in Good Working Order: Yes☐
No☐

Elevators: Yes☐   No☐   Fire Service Control: Yes☐   No☐   Elevator Recall: Yes☐
No☐

Heat Type: Gas☐   Oil☐   Electric☐   Coal☐   Other☐   In Good Working Order: Yes☐
No☐

Emergency Generator: Yes☐   No☐   Size: Last Date Tested:

Date of Last Full Load Test: In Automatic Position: Yes☐   No☐

Fire Pump: Yes☐   No☐   GPM: Suction Pressure: System Pressure:

Date Last Tested: Date of Last Flow Test:

In Automatic Position: Yes☐   No☐   Jockey Pump: Yes☐   No☐

EMERGENCY LIGHTS

Operable: Yes☐   No☐   Tested Monthly: Yes☐   No☐

Properly Illuminate Egress Paths: Yes☐   No☐   In Good Condition: Yes☐   No☐

EXIT SIGNS

Illuminated: Internally☐   Externally☐   Emergency Power: Yes☐   No☐   Readily Visible:
Yes☐   No☐

FIRE ALARM

Yes☐   No☐   Location of Panel:

Coverage: Building☐   Partial☐   Monitored: Yes☐   No☐   Method:

Fire Department Notification: Yes☐   No☐

Type of Initiation Devices: Smoke☐   Heat☐   Manual☐   Water Flow☐   Special Systems☐

Date of Last Test: Date of Last Inspection:

Notification Signal Adequate: Yes☐   No☐

Room Smoke Detectors Operable: Yes☐   No☐

FIRE EXTINGUISHERS

Proper Type for Hazard Protecting: Yes☐   No☐   Mounted Properly: Yes☐   No☐

Date of Last Inspection: Adequate Number: Yes☐   No☐

FIRE PROTECTION SYSTEMS

Type: Sprinkler☐   Halon☐   CO2☐   Standpipe☐   Water Spray☐   Foam☐
Dry Chemical☐   Wet Chemical☐   Other☐

Coverage: Building☐   Partial☐   Date of Last Inspection:

Cylinder or Gauge Pressure(s): 1   psi.,2   psi.,3   psi.,4   psi.,5   psi.

Valves Supervised: Electrical☐   Lock☐   Seal☐   Other☐   Are Valves Accessible: Yes☐
No☐   System Operational: Yes☐   No☐   Sprinklers 18" from Storage: Yes☐   No☐

FIRE RESISTIVE (FR) CONSTRUCTION

Stairway FR: Yes☐   No☐   Hourly Rating:

Corridors FR: Yes☐   No☐   Hourly Rating:

Elevator Shaft FR: Yes☐   Yes☐   No☐   Hourly Rating:

Major Structural Members FR: Yes☐   No☐   Hourly Rating:

Floor-Ceiling Assemblies FR: Yes☐   No☐   Hourly Rating:

All Openings Protected in FR Walls and Floor-Ceiling Assemblies: Yes☐   No☐

HAZARDOUS AREAS

Protected by: Fire-Rated Separation☐   Extinguishing System☐   Both☐

Door Self-Closures: Yes☐   No☐

Kitchen Exhaust Hoods Properly Protected: Yes☐   No☐   Clean: Yes☐   No☐   Date of Last
  Inspection:

HOUSEKEEPING

Areas Free of Excessive Combustibles: Yes☐   No☐

Smoking Regulated: Yes☐   No☐

INTERIOR FINISH

Walls and Ceilings Proper Rating: Yes☐   No☐   Floor Finish Proper Rating: Yes☐   No☐

Furniture and Decorations Flame Retardant: Yes☐   No☐

MEANS OF EGRESS

Readily Visible: Yes☐   No☐   Clear and Unobstructed: Yes☐   No☐

Two Remote Exits Available: Yes☐   No☐   Travel Distance within Limits: Yes☐   No☐

Common Path of Travel within Limits: Yes☐   No☐   Dead-Ends within Limits: Yes☐   No☐

50% through Level of Exit Discharge: Yes☐   No☐

Adequate Illumination: Yes☐   No☐

Proper Rating on All Components: Yes☐   No☐

All Exit Enclosures Free of Storage: Yes☐   No☐

Door Swing in the Direction of Egress Travel (when required): Yes☐   No☐

Panic/Fire Exit Hardware Operable: Yes☐   No☐

Doors Open Easily: Yes☐   No☐   Self-Closures Operable: Yes☐   No☐

Number of Latches:

Doors Closed or Held Open With Automatic Closures: Yes☐   No☐

Corridors and Aisles of Sufficient Size: Yes☐   No☐

Stairwell Re-Entry: Yes☐   No☐

Mezzanines: Yes☐   No☐   Proper Exits: Yes☐   No☐

Rescue Windows in Each Room: Yes☐   No☐   5.7 sq. ft.: Yes☐   No☐

Smoke Barriers Provided: Yes☐   No☐   Proper Size and Fire Resistance Rating: Yes☐   No☐

Rooms > 2000 sq. ft. Two Means of Egress: Yes☐   No☐

VERTICAL OPENINGS

Properly Protected: Yes☐   No☐   Atrium: Yes☐   No☐   Properly Protected: Yes☐   No☐

Are Fire Doors in Good Working Order: Yes☐   No☐

OPERATING FEATURES

Employees Instructed in Emergency Duties: Yes☐   No☐   Drills Held Monthly: Yes☐   No☐

Floor Diagram and Emergency Instructions Posted on Each Guest Room Door: Yes☐   No ☐

CHAPTER 21

Apartment Buildings

*A*partment buildings are among the most difficult occupancies to inspect for many different reasons. The nature and character of the occupancy may vary considerably from building to building because of design, geographic location, and occupant age and social status. Another factor that must be considered is the edition of NFPA *101, Life Safety Code* that was in force when the building was constructed. These factors, among many others, require you to identify the particular issues and features of the fire protection system in a given building and conduct the inspection with knowledge of the various code requirements.

Chapters 18 and 19 of the *Life Safety Code* address the code requirements for new and existing apartment buildings. You should become familiar with these requirements before you conduct an inspection so that you can identify specific issues, such as adequacy of means of egress and amount of fire protection.

Most fire codes are maintenance codes and are only in force after a building has been completed. However, the *Life Safety Code* is written for both **new** and **existing** properties.

Previous editions of the *Life Safety Code* list four options for basic fire protection that could be applied to all new and existing apartment buildings, and you should be familiar with them. They are:

1. Buildings without fire suppression or detection systems.
2. Buildings with a complete automatic fire detection and notification systems.
3. Buildings with automatic sprinkler protection in selected areas.
4. Buildings protected throughout by an approved automatic sprinkler system.

In addition to the above, the 1981 edition of the *Life Safety Code* had requirements for apartment buildings that are used as housing for the elderly. These were adopted by HUD and used as a code for the construction of most of the federally subsidized housing for the elderly. However, times have changed. The 1991 edition of the *Life Safety Code* no longer recognizes those options in new construction. **All new apartment buildings are required to be sprinklered.** There are three exceptions to this rule and they are listed as exceptions to 18-3.5.2; you should be familiar with these provisions.

Inspecting New Apartment Buildings

If you, the inspector, are reviewing plans for new construction, you should know the definition of an apartment building. An apartment building is defined as any building containing three or more living units with independent cooking facilities. The building can be anything from a garden-type apartment to a high rise building.

A sprinkler system meeting the requirements of NFPA 13R, *Standard for the Installation of Sprinkler Systems in Residential Occupancies* Up to and Including Four Stories in Height, is permitted in buildings up to four stories in height. As the inspector, you should be aware of the exceptions for closets and bathrooms. You also must be aware of the differences between a system complying with the requirements of NFPA 13, *Standard for the Installation of Sprinkler Systems,* and a system complying with the requirements of NFPA 13R.

You should be able to inspect the sprinkler system to determine if the installation complies with code requirements. You should witness a test of the operation of the sprinkler system or have the owner provide acceptable documentation of tests.

Smoke detectors powered by the building electrical system are required within the apartments of all buildings.

You should be aware that in 16-2.1.1 of the *Life Safety Code* a distinction is made between a means of egress and a means of escape. You will need to study Section 21-2 to be familiar with this provision.

Hazardous areas must be enclosed by a smoke-tight enclosure even if they are sprinklered. Laundries outside of living units are the only exception.

All new high rise apartment buildings must comply with Section 30-8, which requires automatic sprinklers, a voice alarm system, standby power and light system, and a central control room. All existing high rise apartment buildings must be sprinklered or protected with an "engineered life safety system" approved by the authority having jurisdiction.

While there are no special construction requirements for apartment buildings, knowledge of the building's construction can be of great value to the fire department. For example, fire fighters should be notified if there is truss construction in either the roof or lightweight floor trusses.

Inspecting Existing Apartment Buildings

You must see all official records and previous inspections if you want to make a thorough inspection. Official records should indicate the option that was selected for protecting the occupants of the building when it was built or renovated. As subsequent inspections are made, a file of the reports will be provided for the new inspector. If you have this information you will be in a better position to understand the level of protection that was originally provided and evaluate any changes that may have been made.

If there are no official records that identify a specific option or if the building was built before the code was established, you should record sufficient information during the inspection to evaluate which option the building presently represents.

Tables 21-1 and 21-2 summarize the requirements for existing apartments based on the protection that is provided. The following are some general guidelines that may be helpful in inspecting apartment buildings with particular attention paid to what the *Life Safety Code* classifies as existing apartment buildings.

Inspection Observations

Your new inspection actually starts as you approach the building. Check to see if the distance to the nearest fire hydrant is acceptable. Is the hydrant on a public main, or is it a private water system? If it is a private hydrant, has it been inspected to ensure the proper flow and pressure? Was it installed according to NFPA 24, *Standard for the Installation of Private Fire Service Mains and Their Appurtenances?* What is the water supply? Many garden-type apartments have private water supplies.

Are there obstructions to fire hydrants such as trees, shrubs, trash collectors, or new construction? Is access to the building blocked by signs, marquees, or overhangs that could inhibit rescues?

Table 21-1. Alternate requirements for new apartment buildings according to protection provided.

	No suppression or detection system Option no. 1	Total automatic detection Option no. 2	Sprink. prot. in select areas Option no. 3	Auto ext. NFPA 13 (with exceptions) Option no. 4
Max. gross area per story between horizontal exits				
1–3 stories	NR	NR	NR	NR
≥4 stories <HR	20,000 sq ft	20,000 sq ft	NR	NR
HR	NP	NP	NP	NR
Exit access				
Travel distance	100 ft	100 ft	100 ft	200 ft
Smoke barrier req.	Req.	Req.	Req.	NR
Max. common path of travel	35 ft	35 ft	35 ft	50 ft
Max. dead end	35 ft	35 ft	35 ft	50 ft
Fire resistance				
Walls	1 hr	1 hr	3/4 hr	1/2 hr
Doors (fire protection rating)	20 min	20 min	20 min	20 min
Flame spread				
Walls and ceilings	A or B	A or B	A or B	A, B, or C
Floors	I or II	I or II	NR	NR
Exits—vertical				
Fire resistance walls				
1–3 stories	1 hr	1 hr	1 hr	1 hr
>3 stories	2 hr	2 hr	2 hr	1 hr
Smokeproof enclosures				
≥1 story <HR	NR	NR	NR	NR
HR	NP	NP	NP	NR
Doors				
1–3 stories	1 hr	1 hr	1 hr	1 hr
>3 stories	1-1/2 hr	1-1/2 hr	1-1/2 hr	1 hr
Flame spread				
Walls and ceilings	A	A	A	A or B
Floors	I or II	I or II	NR	NR
Exits—horizontal				
Fire resistance				
Walls	2 hr	2 hr	2 hr	NA
Doors	1-1/2 hr	1-1/2 hr	1-1/2 hr	NA

(Continued)

Table 21-1. *(Continued)*

	No suppression or detection system Option no. 1	Total automatic detection Option no. 2	Sprink. prot. in select areas Option no. 3	Auto ext. NFPA 13 (with exceptions) Option no. 4
Habitable spaces				
Max. distance—door to corridor	75 ft	75 ft	75 ft	125 ft
Flame spread—walls and ceilings	A, B, or C	A, B, or C	A, B, or C	A, B, or C
Smoke detector in unit	Req.	Req.	Req.	Req.
Door to corridor self closing	Req.	Req.	Req.	Req.
Bedroom windows	Req.	Req.	Req.	NR
Alarm system				
>3 stories or >11 units	manual	manual and auto	manual and auto	manual and auto
>2 stories or >50 units	annunciator panel	annunciator panel	annunciator panel	annunciator panel
HR	NP	NP	NP	NR
HVAC				
HR; pressurized corridor, 0.01 in. Water (2.5 Pa), min.	NP	NP	NP	NR
Elevator				
ANSI	A17.1	A17.1	A17.1	A17.1

NR, no requirements; NA, not applicable; NP, option not permitted for high-rise buildings; HR, high-rise buildings; Req., required.

Older buildings could have old fire escapes in need of repair. Examine them closely or have the owner document that they have been approved by a qualified person. Do not confuse old fire escapes with the safer, more substantial outside exit stairs that could have been added to remedy exit deficiencies where it was not practical to install new interior stairs. The *Life Safety Code* gives requirements for acceptable construction of outside stairs. Make certain that materials posing a fire hazard are not stored under the outside stairs.

At the beginning of the inspection, make sure that the use of the building has not changed. Has another occupancy been added? If the

Table 21-2. Alternative requirements for existing apartment buildings according to protection provided.

	No suppression or detection system Option no. 1	*Total automatic detection* Option no. 2	*Sprink. prot. in select areas* Option no. 3	*Auto. ext. NFPA 13 (with exceptions)* Option no. 4
Max. gross area per story between horizontal exits				
1–3 stories	NR	NR	NR	NR
≥4 stories <HR	NR	NR	NR	NR
HR	NR	NR	NR	NR
Exit access				
Travel distance	100 ft	150 ft	150 ft	200 ft
Smoke barrier req.	Req.	Req.	Req.	NR
Max. common path of travel (mod)	35 ft	35 ft	35 ft	50 ft
Max. dead end	50 ft	50 ft	50 ft	50 ft
Fire resistance				
Walls	1/2 hr	1/2 hr	1/2 hr	1/2 hr
Doors (fire protection rating)	20 min	20 min	NA	NA
Flame spread				
Walls and ceilings	A or B	A or B	A or B	A, B, or C
Floors	I or II	I or II	NR	NR
Exits—vertical				
Fire resistance walls				
1–3 stories	1 hr	1 hr	1 hr	3/4 hr
>3 stories	2 hr	2 hr	2 hr	1 hr
Smokeproof enclosures				
≥1 story <HR	NR	NR	NR	NR
HR	Req.	Req.	Req.	NR
Doors				
1–3 stories	1 hr	1 hr	1 hr	3/4 hr
>3 stories	1-1/2 hr	1-1/2 hr	1-1/2 hr	1 hr
Flame spread				
Walls and ceilings	A or B	A or B	A or B	A, B, or C
Floors	I or II	I or II	NR	NR
Exits-horizontal				
Fire resistance				
Walls	2 hr	2 hr	2 hr	NA
Doors	1-1/2 hr	1-1/2 hr	1-1/2 hr	NA

(Continued)

Table 21-2. *(Continued)*

	No suppression or detection system Option no. 1	Total automatic detection Option no. 2	Sprink. prot. in select areas Option no. 3	Auto ext. NFPA 13 (with exceptions) Option no. 4
Habitable spaces				
Max. distance—door to corridor	75 ft	125 ft	75 ft	125 ft
Flame spread—walls and ceilings	A, B, or C	A, B, or C	A, B, or C	A, B, or C
Smoke detector in unit	Req.	Req.	Req.	Req.
Door to corridor self closing	Req.	Req.	Req.	Req.
Bedroom windows	Req.	Req.	Req.	NR
Alarm system				
>3 stories or >11 units	manual	manual and auto	manual and auto	manual and auto
>2 stories or >50 units	annunciator panel	annunciator panel	annunciator panel	annunciator panel
HVAC				
HR; pressurized corridor, 0.01 in. Water (2.5 Pa), min.	NR	NR	NR	NR
Elevator				
ANSI	A17.1	A17.1	A17.1	A17.1

NR, no requirements; NA, not applicable; HR, high-rise buildings; Req., required.

building is no longer solely an apartment building but shares the premises with another type of occupancy, such as stores or offices, then it is possible that new safety hazards have been introduced. The *Life Safety Code* requires that in mixed occupancies the most restrictive life safety requirements of the occupancies involved be applied if they are so intermingled that separate safeguards are impractical. Separate safeguards usually mean separation by fire-rated construction or automatic protection in the more hazardous occupancy. For example, if there is a drug store (mercantile occupancy) on the premises that was not there at the last inspection, separation between the store and the apartments must be by construction having a fire-resistance rating of at least 1 hour, or automatic sprinkler protection must be provided for the store area.

Occupant Load

Although the occupant load is not required to be posted in a conspicuous place in apartment buildings, it is nevertheless an important consideration in the number of exits. The occupancy load for apartment buildings is one person for every 200 square feet of gross floor area. Some apartments could have dormitory-type sleeping arrangements, such as several or many bunk beds in apartments occupied by students, that would appear to increase the occupant load well beyond 200 square feet per person. If the occupancy is found to exceed this limit, then you must assess the adequacy of the exits.

Exits

Check to make sure that all exit doors operate properly. Be certain that the means of egress are not blocked in any manner and are not hazardous in any other way. One of the greatest problems in existing apartment buildings is that through age or lack of maintenance, those life safety features originally constructed into the building have deteriorated to the point where they no longer function. In many apartment buildings it is quite common for tenants to put wedges under the doors that lead into stairwells to keep the doors open. Unapproved devices must not be allowed to hold the doors open. Check that self-closing devices function properly and completely close the door. Check the latching devices on all fire-rated doors.

The accumulation of household goods and trash in corridors and stairwells is a common problem. Trash should be removed immediately so that egress out of the building can be safe and quick if a fire should occur. Many apartment buildings provide the tenants with storage areas, but even when not provided, some areas seem to evolve into storage spaces. Inspect these areas closely. Almost anything, including outboard motors, flammable and combustible liquids, old tires, mattresses, and all kinds of furniture, will be found. These materials may have accumulated over many years and might cause the fuel load to exceed that which the building was designed to handle. Many times these spaces communicate with the means of egress, vertical plumbing stacks, and there is almost always a lack of proper separation from the floor above. The code requires that they be protected by 1-hour construction or automatic sprinkler protection. In extreme cases both may be required.

Dwelling Units

Most of the time you will not be able to enter the individual dwelling units. But you should inspect public areas, such as corridors, stairs, storage areas, utility areas, the building exterior, and exit doors. If central air conditioning is a part of the building, you should check carefully for the accumulation of stored materials in the fan rooms. If renovations have been made, check to ensure the distance to exits has not been violated.

The *Life Safety Code* requires that each unit in an apartment building be equipped with single station or multiple station smoke detectors that are continuously powered by the house electrical service. They may not be battery operated. This requirement is in addition to any sprinkler system or other detection system installed in the building. The 1991 code also mandates single station detectors in the sleeping rooms of all nonsprinklered apartments (most new apartment buildings must be sprinklered). Installation of single station and multiple station smoke detectors must comply with NFPA 72, *National Fire Alarm Code.* NFPA 72 requires that in addition to a detector located outside of each sleeping area, a smoke detector installed on a story without a separate sleeping area must be located in close proximity to the stairway leading to the floor above. If possible, arrange with the building manager to look at the detectors in a vacant apartment or take a random sample of one in every 10 apartments, which should be representative of detector installations throughout the building; also ask to witness a test of the representative detector(s). This will at least show you the manager knows how to conduct a test following the manufacturer's instructions. If the manager is not able to do this, you could surmise that the information is not being passed on to the tenants.

You also should check individual apartments to be sure the entrance doors are self closing. The *Life Safety Code* requires that doors between living units and apartments be self closing; transfer grills are not permitted in the doors or walls. A fire occurring in the apartment could easily generate sufficient smoke, heat, and toxic gases to create untenable conditions in the corridor if air transfer grills were permitted.

Protection of Openings

In most instances vertical openings in apartment buildings are required to be enclosed or protected, but there are exceptions to this requirement. Where enclosure is required, it must be complete and continuous. Vertical openings are not just stairways; they include openings for rubbish chutes, building services and passages for pipes, conduits, ductwork, elevator shafts, to name a few. Take some time to search for these openings. Doors to stairways and other vertical openings must be fire-rated, self-closing, and positive-latching.

The most common unprotected vertical openings are plumbing stacks and chases found in bathrooms and kitchens. Many times these shafts communicate from the boiler rooms, laundry rooms, and storage rooms up to the attic or roof. Chapter 6 of the *Life Safety Code* gives guidance on protection of all types of floor openings via fire-resistive shafts or fire stopping.

Check elevator doors carefully to see if they would permit the spread of fire. Any openings found in elevator shafts should be repaired at once. Where horizontal exits or smoke barriers are required, check the cross-corridor doors for operation. Check the wall above the ceiling for unprotected penetrations. If there are suspended ceilings, note whether all the ceiling tiles are in place. The ceiling could be part of a fire-rated floor/ceiling assembly, and missing tiles can badly compromise the effectiveness of the fire barrier.

If the building is of type III, IV, or V construction, it is likely that concealed combustible spaces will exist. Such spaces must be fire stopped in accordance with Chapter 6 of the *Life Safety Code*. In addition in existing buildings, if Option 4 was used, these spaces will most likely require sprinkler protection. Check these spaces for fire stopping and sprinkler protection. Make sure they are not connected with unprotected vertical communications such as pipe chases, stacks, wire runs, and so on.

Waste Chutes

In older apartment buildings, refuse chutes may be present and have access openings in the corridors. The fire hazard is seriously increased and the fire integrity of the building is reduced with the continued use of these chutes. The refuse chute can become an avenue to transmit fire from floor to floor and from chute to floor. Nevertheless, these chute openings into corridors can be made relatively safe if the chute is properly enclosed and the service openings are properly maintained. Make sure that all openings are equipped with fire-rated hopper-type doors that are self-closing and positive-latching. Gravity-type metal chutes are required to have automatic sprinkler protection in the terminal room, at the top, and at alternate floor levels. NFPA 82, *Standard on Incinerators, Waste, and Linen Handling Systems and Equipment,* gives requirements for the construction and maintenance of waste chutes.

The code now requires service openings in waste chutes in newer buildings to be located in a room or compartment separated from other parts of the building by 1-hour fire-rated enclosures with a 45-minute fire door with closer and latch. Be sure that you understand the method of handling household waste in the building. Inquire if chute clogging has been a recurring problem. It could be that the chute, as originally designed, is too small to handle the type of trash that it must now accept, which could include compressed packages from kitchen compactors.

Interior Finish

Interior finish, or the exposed surface of walls and ceilings in exit enclosures, must be Class A in exits and Class A or B in corridors and lobbies. Class A, B, or C interior finish is allowed in living units and in lobbies and corridors that do not provide access to exits. Review Section 6-5 of the *Life Safety Code* before making decisions on interior finish. Note especially multiple layers of vinyl wall covering and wallpaper. Require verification of the product if carpet is found on wall or ceiling surfaces.

Hazardous Areas

Pay particular attention to hazardous areas of the building, such as boiler and heater rooms, laundries, repair shops, refuse storage rooms, and general storage areas set aside for occupants' personal belongings, which usually are found in basements. If the hazardous area is not sprinklered it must be separated from other parts of the building by walls and floor-ceiling construction having at least a 1-hour fire-resistance rating and with openings protected by 45-minute rated fire doors with closers and latches. If the building is sprinklered, enclosures around the hazardous area can be of any reasonably smoke-resistant construction with or without a fire rating.

Note the general level of housekeeping in the service areas. Determine if flammable liquids in the amounts allowed by the local fire prevention code are stored in approved containers in approved cabinets. If the building is equipped with a sprinkler system, make sure that access to the main control valves is not blocked.

Fire Protection

The best protected apartments have complete automatic sprinkler systems. Use NFPA 13, 13R, and NFPA 25, *Standard for the Inspection, Testing, and Maintenance of Water-Based Fire Protection Systems,* for guidance when inspecting sprinkler systems. In those areas to which you have access, examine the sprinklers to make sure they have not been painted over or tampered with in ways that make their operation questionable. Painted sprinkler heads must be replaced. In basement areas, make sure there is at least 18 inches of clearance between stored materials and sprinkler heads. Look for any other obstruction to sprinklers. Sometimes partitions are put up without consideration of the effects on the sprinklers; partitions can create areas that are no longer reached by sprinkler discharge, thus seriously affecting the fire protection for the whole building.

Portable fire extinguishers are required by the *Life Safety Code* for hazardous areas in apartment buildings. Make sure that access to the extinguishers is not blocked and that the extinguishers are clearly visible and properly hung. Note the date (usually noted on an attached tag) when each extinguisher was last given a maintenance inspection. Refer to NFPA 10, *Standard for Portable Fire Extinguishers,* for details on maintenance and placement of extinguishers.

Alarm Systems

In most cases the *Life Safety Code* requires that apartment buildings four or more stories in height or with 11 or more apartment units have a manual alarm system. Buildings that are more than three stories high and buildings that contain more than 50 dwelling units are required to have annunciating panels. The requirements for the particular type of alarm system are established by the fire protection option selected for a particular apartment building. What is important to you as an inspector is that the alarm system that you observe be compatible with the present use of the building; thus you should become familiar with requirements of the *Life Safety Code* for alarm systems in new and existing apartments.

Once you have determined if the system is adequate for the building, inquire about the testing and maintenance schedule that is followed for the system. (See the applicable NFPA standards for details). If you have concerns about the readiness of the system, you should arrange to witness the next scheduled test.

Visual examination of detector units from the floor could indicate some points of maintenance. Paint on the unit might indicate obstructed ports in the unit housing. Close examination also could reveal accumulations of dust or insects that might impede operation.

Lighting

The *Life Safety Code* requires that sufficient illumination be provided for the safe egress of occupants. Emergency lighting is required in apartment buildings with more than 12 living units or over three stories in height. Exit signs are to be provided in all apartment buildings, unless the living units have direct access to the outside. You should become familiar with Chapter 5 of the code for details of all the above requirements. You also should be aware of the requirements of 31-6.5 of the *Life Safety Code* regarding requirements for emergency instructions for apartment buildings.

Apartments for the Elderly

The 1981 edition of the *Life Safety Code* had requirements for apartments for the elderly. If you are inspecting an apartment building that was designed for the elderly, you need to check the special requirements generated in that edition. Section 21-4 of the 1988 edition of NFPA *101* addresses the requirements for housing a residential board and care occupancy in an apartment building. You should pay special attention to travel distances to exits, smoke partitions in exit access corridors, adequate exits, alarm systems, and protection of vertical openings in apartments for the elderly.

When you are inspecting apartment buildings, remember that residential buildings are required to have a higher level of protection than other occupancies that do not provide sleeping accommodations. Because residential buildings represent the greatest exposure to life loss today, your inspection will have a direct impact on the level of safety provided in that building.

Bibliography

NFPA 13, *Standard for the Installation of Sprinkler Systems*
NFPA 13R, *Standard for the Installation of Sprinkler Systems in Residential Occupancies Up to and Including Four Stories in Height*
NFPA 82, *Standard on Incinerators, Waste, and Linen Handling Systems and Equipment*
NFPA 90A, *Standard for the Installation of Air Conditioning and Ventilating Systems*
NFPA 101, *Life Safety Code*

APARTMENT OCCUPANCY FIRE INSPECTION FORM

Property Name: Owner:

Address: Phone Number:

OCCUPANCY

Change from Last Inspection: Yes□　No□

Occupant Load:　　　　　　　　　　　Egress Capacity: Any Renovations: Yes□　No□

High Rise: Yes□　No□　Windowless: Yes□　No□　Underground: Yes□　No□

BUILDING SERVICES

Electricity□　Gas□　Water□　Other□　Are Utilities in Good Working Order: Yes□　No□

Elevators: Yes□　No□　Fire Service Control: Yes□　No□　Elevator Recall: Yes□　No□

Heat Type: Gas□　Oil□　Electric□　Coal□　Other□　In Good Working Order: Yes□　No□

Emergency Generator: Yes□　No□　Size:　Last Date Tested:

Date of Last Full Load Test:　　　　　In Automatic Position: Yes□　No□

Fire Pump: Yes□　No□　GPM:　　　　Suction Pressure: System Pressure:

Date Last Tested:　　　　　　　　　　Date of Last Flow Test:

In Automatic Position: Yes□　No□　　Jockey Pump: Yes□　No□

EMERGENCY LIGHTS

Operable: Yes□　No□　Tested Monthly: Yes□　No□

Properly Illuminate Egress Paths: Yes□　No□　In Good Condition: Yes□　No□

EXIT SIGNS

Illuminated: Internally□　Externally□　Emergency Power: Yes□　No□　Readily Visible: Yes□　No□

FIRE ALARM

Yes□　No□　Location of Panel:

Coverage: Building□　Partial□　Location of Annunciator:

Monitored: Yes□　No□　Method:

Type of Initiation Devices: Smoke□　Heat□　Manual□　Water Flow□　Special Systems□

Date of Last Test:　　　　　　　　　Date of Last Inspection:

Notification Signal Adequate: Yes□　No□　Fire Department Notification: Yes□　No□

Single Station Room Smoke Detectors: Yes□　No□　Power Source:

FIRE EXTINGUISHERS

Proper Type for Hazard Protecting: Yes□　No□　Mounted Properly: Yes□　No□

Date of Last Inspection:　　　　　　　Adequate Number: Yes□　No□

FIRE PROTECTION SYSTEMS

Type: Sprinkler□　Halon□　CO2□　Standpipe□　Water Spray□　Foam□　Dry Chemical□

Wet Chemical☐   Other☐

Coverage: Building☐ Partial☐   Date of Last Inspection:

Cylinder or Gauge Pressure(s): 1 psi.,2 psi.,3 psi.,4 psi.,5 psi

Valves Supervised: Electrical☐ Lock☐ Seal☐ Other☐   Are Valves Accessible: Yes☐ No☐

System Operational: Yes☐ No☐   Sprinkler Heads 18" from Storage: Yes☐ No☐

FIRE RESISTIVE (FR) CONSTRUCTION

Stairway FR: Yes☐ No☐   Hourly Rating:

Corridors FR: Yes☐ No☐   Hourly Rating:

Elevator Shaft FR: Yes☐ Yes☐ No☐   Hourly Rating:

Major Structural Members FR: Yes☐ No☐   Hourly Rating:

Floor-Ceiling Assemblies FR: Yes☐ No☐   Hourly Rating:

All Openings Protected in FR Walls and Floor-Ceiling Assemblies: Yes☐ No☐

HAZARDOUS AREAS

Protected by: Fire-Rated Separation☐ Extinguishing System☐ Both☐

Door Self-Closures: Yes☐ No☐ Fire Extinguishers Provided in Hazardous Areas: Yes☐ No☐

HOUSEKEEPING

Areas Free of Excessive Combustibles: Yes☐ No☐

Smoking Regulated in Common Areas: Yes☐ No☐

INTERIOR FINISH

Walls and Ceilings Proper Rating: Yes☐ No☐   Floor Finish Proper Rating: Yes☐ No☐

MEANS OF EGRESS

Readily Visible: Yes☐ No☐   Clear and Unobstructed: Yes☐ No☐

Two Remote Exits Available: Yes☐ No☐   Travel Distance within Limits: Yes☐ No☐

Common Path of Travel within Limits: Yes☐ No☐   Dead-Ends within Limits: Yes☐ No☐

50% Maximum through Level of Exit Discharge: Yes☐ No☐

Adequate Illumination: Yes☐ No☐

Proper Rating on All Components: Yes☐ No☐

All Exit Enclosures Free of Storage: Yes☐ No☐

Door Swing in the Direction of Egress Travel (when required): Yes☐ No☐

Panic/Fire Exit Hardware Operable: Yes☐ No☐

Doors Open Easily: Yes☐ No☐   Self-Closures Operable: Yes☐ No☐

Doors Closed or Held Open With Automatic Closures: Yes☐ No☐

Corridors and Aisles of Sufficient Size: Yes☐ No☐

Stairwell Re-Entry: Yes☐ No☐

Mezzanines: Yes☐ No☐   Proper Exits: Yes☐ No☐

Second Means of Escape Provided: Yes☐ No☐   Window 5.7 sq.ft.: Yes☐ No☐

VERTICAL OPENINGS

Properly Protected: Yes☐ No☐

Atrium: Yes☐ No☐   Properly Protected: Yes☐ No☐

Fireplaces: Yes☐ No☐   Properly Installed: Yes☐ No☐

Are Fire Doors in Good Working Order: Yes☐ No☐

OPERATING FEATURES

Emergency Instructions Provided to Occupants Yearly: Yes☐ No☐

CHAPTER 22

Lodging or Rooming Houses

General Description of Use and Applicable Requirements

Lodging or rooming houses, as defined in NFPA *101, Life Safety Code,* include buildings with sleeping rooms that provide sleeping accommodations for a total of 16 or fewer persons on either a transient or permanent basis. Meals might or might not be available, but separate cooking facilities for individual occupants are not part of the arrangement. Examples of occupancies classified as lodging or rooming houses might include guest houses, bed and breakfasts, small inns or motels, and foster homes. It also can include small sleeping accommodations in other occupancies such as fire stations, coast guard stations, etc. One- and two-family dwellings can accommodate up to three "outsiders" in rented rooms, which effectively narrows the scope of code requirements for lodging or rooming houses to only those facilities accommodating from 4 to 16 persons. The requirements for lodging or rooming houses apply to both new buildings and to existing or modified buildings.

Lodging or rooming houses generally are distinct occupancies, often located in a converted one- or two-family dwelling. Unfortunately, past experience has shown that these conversions may occur without proper review and approval, resulting in facilities that do not meet applicable code requirements. All too often, remodeling creates combustible voids and concealed spaces. This hazard is increased in older buildings if the remodeling process covers walls and ceilings that lack the proper firestopping features.

If a lodging or rooming house shares a building with another type of occupancy and the facilities are so intermingled that separate safeguards are impractical, the occupancies are considered to be mixed, and the most restrictive requirements of each of the occupancies involved are applicable throughout the entire facility. If the occupancies can be adequately separated, however, the requirements of each occupancy are to be separately applied.

As is true with all multiple-dwelling residential occupancies, lodging or rooming houses cannot be located above a mercantile, business, or assembly occupancy unless the dwelling occupancy and the exits from it are separated from the mercantile, business, or assembly occupancy by 1-hour fire-rated construction, or the mercantile, business, or assembly occupancy is protected throughout by an approved automatic sprinkler system. No dwelling unit can have its sole means of egress through any mercantile, business, or assembly occupancy that is housed in the same building.

Several common problems are associated with lodging or rooming houses. One is the tendency to increase accommodations by altering the building's interior layout to create additional guest quarters. If you suspect that this is the case, make sure that a required exit has not been eliminated and that there are sleeping accommodations for no more than 16 persons. Another problem is a tendency to accept as residents individuals who may not be able to care adequately for themselves or to evacuate on their own in the event of a fire. Thus, occupants will have to be evaluated periodically to assess whether they are mentally capable of self-preservation and have the appropriate escape capabilities. In either case, if the facility no longer meets the definition of a lodging or rooming house, it should be reclassified immediately to its applicable use. Refer to Chapters 12 and 22 of the *Life Safety Code* for additional information.

Interior Finish

Interior finish has been proven to be a significant factor in fires involving lodging or rooming houses. This is particularly true in older buildings that were renovated or remodeled with extensive use of unrated paneling and combustible ceiling tile.

Interior finish in lodging and rooming houses is limited to Class A, B, or C in all areas. The *Life Safety Code* permits the use of fire-retardant paints to achieve required flame-spread ratings. However, you should study the code thoroughly to understand the limitations of this process. You also might want to require proof of application and assurances that the manufacturer's guidelines have been followed strictly. Items that do not meet the required flame-spread and smoke-generation limitations pose an extremely serious problem.

If you see a combustible interior finish, you should ask to see all the information necessary to verify that the flame-spread and smoke-generation ratings of the materials used meet the requirements for acceptable interior finish. The classification—if there is one—of wall paneling will be stamped on the back of each sheet. Be advised that, in most instances, the paneling classification is only valid if the paneling is attached to a noncombustible substrate, such as gypsum board or plaster.

Suspended ceiling tiles will not have such a stamp, but they may have a sticker indicating their classification. If they do not, you will have to see the original packing paper for information pertaining to flame spread and smoke generation. Verifying that the ceiling tiles are acceptable might not be a problem in new construction, but identifying various interior finish materials in existing buildings may be virtually impossible. If this is the case, you should insist that the material in question be tested by an approved testing laboratory or be protected with a fire-retardant coating.

Protection of Exits

Before conducting your inspection, it is important that you understand that exit requirements for lodging or rooming houses and single-family dwellings are different from those of other occupancies. Most notably, exit requirements are referred to as means of escape rather than means of egress. Two means of escape are required from every story of every **new** lodging or rooming house that exceeds 2,000 square feet in area or where the travel distance to the primary means of escape is more than 75 feet, unless the facility is protected throughout by an approved supervised automatic sprinkler system.

Vertical openings of lodging or rooming houses must be protected because occupants may be sleeping, thus unaware of a rapidly developing fire, and they may not be familiar with their means of escape due to their potentially transient nature. Generally, this is done by providing the vertical openings along the primary exit route with 20-minute-rated enclosures. An exception is permitted in buildings of three or fewer stories if they are equipped with an approved automatic sprinkler system.

In such a case, however, there still must be one primary means of escape from each sleeping area that does not pass through any open area in the lower levels.

Remember, the exit requirements for lodging and rooming houses are intended to provide for a level of safety that is higher than that found in single-family dwellings. Thus, your inspection of the lodging or rooming house exit system should verify that every sleeping room has access to a primary means of escape that provides a safe path of travel to the outside without traversing any corridor or space exposed to an unprotected vertical opening. Every sleeping room in a nonsprinklered facility also should have a second means of escape that meets the requirements of the *Life Safety Code*. Note that the code exempts the requirement of a secondary escape if the building is equipped with an approved sprinkler system.

All sleeping rooms should be separated from the escape route corridors by smoke-resistant walls and doors. The doors must latch, and no louvers are permitted. The doors also must have self closers or close automatically upon detection of smoke, unless the building has an automatic sprinkler system.

During your inspection, you should make sure that the exits are not blocked or equipped with locks that do not meet code requirements. Delay releasing locks should only be used in facilities with a complete automatic sprinkler system or a complete fire detection system.

Check to be sure that the safe path of travel does not pass through an area or room that might be locked or blocked and that the entire path of travel, including exterior stairs and walks, is adequately illuminated. All doors and paths of travel to a means of egress should be at least 28 inches wide.

Finally, determine whether closet door latches can be opened easily from the inside and bathroom doors can be opened from the outside with an unlocking device.

Building Services

There are four basic items relating to building services that you should check while you are inspecting any facility: housekeeping, electrical installations, heating appliances, and cooking operations.

Housekeeping

Housekeeping is a general barometer from which a great deal can be learned. Poor housekeeping generally reflects a lack of concern on the part of the owner or tenant. Storage areas in particular inevitably contain a large amount of combustible materials. Inspect these areas thoroughly for combustibles and for any unusual hazards, such as oil-based paints, thinners, and flammable liquids, which must be removed.

Electrical Installations

Improper or damaged electrical installations always present a fire hazard in buildings of any occupancy classification. Deficiencies you should look for include overloaded circuits, open junction boxes, frayed wiring, overloaded extension cords and outlets, and improperly maintained appliances, fixtures, and heating appliances.

In many cases, the problems and corrective actions are clear. When in doubt about a condition involving an electrical installation, however, request that it be inspected and approved by a local electrical inspector, a licensed electrician, or a reputable electrical inspection agency.

Heating Appliances

There is a wide range of heating appliances. With fixed permanent heater installations and portable heaters, you should be concerned primarily with proper maintenance and clearance to combustibles. You also should make sure that any extension cords used for electrical heaters are of the proper size, that only UL-listed heating devices are used, and that gas unit heaters are installed properly. In addition, verify that kerosene heaters are operated safely taking into account their location with respect to means of egress, venting for combustion air, fuel storage, refueling, and use of the correct fuel. Unvented fuel-fired heaters are prohibited.

Cooking Operations

Cooking operations in lodging and rooming houses generally are limited in nature. However, control of individual hot plates or similar appliances is very important, considering the frequency of fires caused by these devices.

In the case of larger cooking operations using appliances not typically found in a person's home that produce grease-laden vapors, the installation must comply with the requirements of NFPA 96, *Standard on Ventilation Control and Fire Protection of Commercial Cooking Operations.*

Key among the items to inspect is the fixed extinguishing-system protecting the cooking surfaces, plenum, and duct. Ask for proof that the extinguishing system is inspected and serviced semiannually. The hood and duct should meet the minimum construction requirements, with liquid-tight continuous external weld seams and joints, and a clearance of at least 18 inches must be maintained between all hoods and ducts and any combustibles. Deep-fat fryers should have secondary high-limit controls, hoods, and ducts. Grease-removal devices should be cleaned frequently to prevent grease from accumulating.

Fire Protection Systems

Detection and Alarm Systems

Detection and alarm systems in residential occupancies play an extremely important role in warning residents of a fire in time to evacuate safely. A fire alarm system complying with NFPA 72, *National Fire Alarm Code,* is required in lodging or rooming houses. However, it is up to the authority having jurisdiction to approve or reject the use of existing battery-powered smoke detectors, based on demonstrated testing, maintenance, and battery replacement programs. NFPA analysis of reported fires indicates that about one-third of all smoke detectors installed in homes are inoperative, usually because the batteries are dead or missing. It is extremely important that facility operators maintain a written log of periodic battery replacement and conscientiously conduct a testing program.

During your inspection, you should locate and test the manual pull stations, which should be installed at the main exit or at the entrance to enclosed stairs on each floor. Make sure that these alarms are audible in all occupiable areas. Then you should verify the presence of approved smoke detectors in each living unit and make sure that they are mounted properly and are located in accordance with manufacturers' guidelines. Finally, perform a functional test of the alarm/detection system and document that such tests are conducted periodically.

Sprinkler Systems

Sprinkler systems are required in all new lodging and rooming houses in which a door from each sleeping room does not open directly to the outside at street or ground level or to an exterior stairway that leads to the ground. Existing lodging or rooming houses often do not have automatic sprinkler systems, even though current code alternatives and residential sprinkler systems make sprinklers a worthwhile and affordable investment.

If an automatic sprinkler system is to be used in the facility to compensate for otherwise deficient construction features, the proper classification of the sprinkler design is "light hazard," even though the classification of the occupancy itself is "ordinary hazard." This classification makes the design and installation of automatic sprinklers an affordable consideration for many facilities and should be encouraged whenever possible.

If a sprinkler system is present, you should verify that it is in service and that all control valves are open. Sprinkler systems that are required or that are used as an alternative method of protection, either for total or partial building coverage, must actuate the fire alarm system upon activation. This includes systems complying with the requirements of NFPA 13D, *Standard for the Installation of Sprinkler Systems in One- and Two-Family Dwellings and Mobile Homes.* You should verify that all areas to be protected have adequate coverage and that there is adequate clearance between the heads and any obstructions. You also should make sure that the piping is properly protected against freezing.

Bibliography

NFPA 96, *Standard on Ventilation Control and Fire Protection of Commercial Cooking Operations*
NFPA *101, Life Safety Code*

LODGING & ROOMING HOUSE OCCUPANCY
FIRE INSPECTION FORM

Property Name: Owner:

Address: Phone Number:

OCCUPANCY

Number of Sleeping Accommodations:

Change from Last Inspection: Yes☐ No☐   Any Renovations: Yes☐ No☐

Windowless: Yes☐ No☐   Underground: Yes☐ No☐

BUILDING SERVICES

Electricity☐ Gas☐ Water☐ Other☐   Are Utilities in Good Working Order: Yes☐ No☐

Heat Type: Gas☐ Oil☐ Electric☐ Other☐   In Good Working Order: Yes☐ No☐

FIRE ALARM

Fire Alarm: Yes☐ No☐   Location of Panel:

Coverage: Building☐ Partial☐   Monitored: Yes☐ No☐   Method:

Type of Initiating Devices: Smoke☐ Heat☐ Manual☐ Water Flow☐ Special Systems☐

Date of Last Test: Date of Last Inspection:

Notification Signal Adequate: Yes☐ No☐   Fire Department Notification: Yes☐ No☐

Single Station Smoke Detectors: Yes☐ No☐   In Each Living Unit: Yes☐ No☐

In Each Bedroom: Yes☐ No☐   Audible in All Areas: Yes☐ No☐   Power Source:

FIRE EXTINGUISHERS

Proper Type for Hazard Protecting: Yes☐ No☐   Mounted Properly: Yes☐ No☐

Date of Last Inspection: Adequate Number: Yes☐ No☐

FIRE PROTECTION SYSTEMS

Sprinkler System: Yes☐ No☐   Dry Chemical: Yes☐ No   Wet Chemical: Yes☐ No☐

Coverage: Building☐ Partial☐   Date of Last Inspection:

Cylinder or Gauge Pressure(s): 1   psi.,2   psi.,3   psi.,4   psi.,5   psi.

Valve Supervised: Electrical☐ Lock☐ Seal☐ Other☐   Are Valves Accessible: Yes☐ No☐

System Operational: Yes☐ No☐

FIRE RESISTIVE (FR) CONSTRUCTION

Stairway FR: Yes☐ No☐   Hourly Rating:

Corridors FR: Yes☐ No☐   Hourly Rating:

Elevator Shaft FR: Yes☐ Yes☐ No☐   Hourly Rating:

Major Structural Members FR: Yes☐ No☐   Hourly Rating:

Floor-Ceiling Assemblies FR: Yes☐ No☐   Hourly Rating:

All Openings Protected in FR Walls and Floor-Ceiling Assemblies: Yes☐ No☐

HAZARDOUS AREAS

Not Located to Block Escape: Yes☐ No☐   Separated from Other Occupancies: Yes☐ No☐

Kitchens Properly Protected: Yes☐ No☐

Flammable and Combustible Liquids Stored Properly: Yes☐ No☐

HOUSEKEEPING

Areas Free of Excessive Combustibles: Yes☐ No☐   Smoking Regulated: Yes☐ No☐

INTERIOR FINISH

Walls and Ceilings Proper Rating: Yes☐ No☐

MEANS OF ESCAPE

Readily Visible: Yes☐ No☐   Clear and Unobstructed: Yes☐ No☐

Two Remote Means of Escape Available: Yes☐　No☐

Every Story > 2,000 sq. ft. Two Primary Means of Escape Provided: Yes☐　No☐

Doors Open Easily: Yes☐　No☐　　Corridors and Aisles of Sufficient Size: Yes☐　No☐

Secondary Means of Escape from Every Sleeping Rooms and Living Area: Yes☐　No☐

Window 5.7 sq. ft.: Yes☐　No☐　　Minimum Height and Width: Yes☐　No☐

Operable: Yes☐　No☐

Doors of Closets and Bathroom Operable from the Inside and Outside: Yes☐　No☐

Doors not Locked to Impede Escape: Yes☐　No☐

VERTICAL OPENINGS

Properly Protected: Yes☐　No☐

Are Fire Doors in Good Working Order: Yes☐　No☐

OPERATING FEATURES

Escape Plan Posted: Yes☐　No☐

CHAPTER 23

Residential Board
and Care Occupancies

*R*esidential board and care occupancies provide lodging, boarding, and personal care services for four or more residents who are unrelated by blood or marriage to the owner or operator of the facility. Residential board and care occupancies also can be called residential care or personal care homes as well as group homes. These occupancies are distinguished from lodging houses because personal care services are provided to the residents. If nursing care is provided, the facility would be more appropriately considered a health care occupancy.

The concept of personal care is critical in distinguishing a residential board and care occupancy from other occupancies. Personal care is intended to indicate that the owner or operator has responsibility for the safety and welfare of the residents. Personal care might include a daily awareness of the residents' whereabouts, the arrangement of appointments for residents, supervision of the residents' nutrition and medication, and the provision of transient medical care. For example, a residential board and care occupancy often will employ staff who will ensure that the residents eat properly and take their medication. The staff also might make doctor appointments for residents and notify a physician if a resident experiences some medical difficulty. However, unlike a health care occupancy, the staff will not actually administer or prescribe medication or treatment.

Examples of facilities that might be residential board and care occupancies include: group homes for the physically or mentally disabled; rest homes for the aged; shelters for battered persons, unwed mothers, or runaways; and halfway houses for rehabilitated alcoholics, drug abusers, or prison parolees. In determining the appropriate occupancy classification, you should be more concerned with the level of care provided, if any, than the name under which the facility operates. Additional guidance can be obtained from the license under which the facility is operating, if such a license is required. The license might indicate whether the staff is permitted or expected to provide medical care, personal care, or no care. In NFPA *101, Life Safety Code*, board and care occupancies are covered in Chapter 22 for new construction (including renovations and changes of occupancy) and in Chapter 23 for existing facilities.

Residential board and care occupancies exist in a variety of configurations and sizes. Some facilities house a limited number of residents in a homelike arrangement. Many of these facilities are located in buildings that originally were single-family dwellings or small apartment buildings. Other facilities are located in larger facilities or multiple-building complexes, which appear and operate similar to an apartment building or hotel. Because certain protection features, such as smoke barriers, are not as functional in small buildings and because larger buildings usually are more difficult to evacuate, chapters 22 and 23 of the *Life Safety Code* distinguish between small and large facilities. Small facilities are defined as board and care occupancies that provide sleeping accommodations for not more than 16 residents. This limit does not include staff members. Large facilities are defined as those providing sleeping accommodations for more than 16 residents.

Evacuation Capability

When evaluating a residential board and care occupancy you must first evaluate the residents' capabilities to evacuate. For most occupancy classifications it is assumed that the occupants will have similar capabilities from one facility to another. However, as the list of typical residential board and care occupancies indicates, the ability of the residents to evacuate can vary significantly. Prison parolees in a halfway house might have the ability to evacuate the building as quickly as the general population; however, residents in a group home for the mentally retarded might require assistance from staff or other residents.

The *Life Safety Code* defines three levels of evacuation capabilities for residential board and care occupancies. *Prompt* evacuation capability is considered to be equivalent to the general population. If realistic fire drills are used to determine evacuation capability, the residents should be able to evacuate to a point of safety within 3 minutes. *Slow* evacuation capability indicates that the residents can move to a point of safety in a timely manner with some residents requiring assistance from the staff. If realistic fire drills are used, the residents should be capable of evacuating to a point of safety within 13 minutes. *Impractical* evacuation capability is when the residents cannot move reliably to a point of safety in a timely manner, even with assistance. As with the other levels, if fire drills are used, impractical evacuation capability would indicate that the residents cannot evacuate to a point of safety within 13 minutes.

Unless an acceptable methodology has been used to evaluate the evacuation capability of the residents, you might assume they have a slow evacuation capability provided they all are capable of traveling to a centralized dining room without staff assistance and the facility is staffed continuously. If the above two conditions are not met, you should assume that the facility houses residents who have an impractical ability to evacuate unless the staff can demonstrate otherwise. One method that can be used to evaluate the residents is contained in Chapter 5 of NFPA 101M, *Alternative Approaches to Life Safety.*

It should be noted that the above discussion on evacuation capability refers to a "point of safety" and not necessarily evacuation to the exterior of the building. A point of safety is a location that meets one of the following criteria:

1. A point of safety can be exterior to and away from the building. As such, if the means of egress system complies with the criteria for exit discharge to a public way, the exit discharge can be considered as the point of safety.
2. If the building is protected with an approved automatic sprinkler system, a point of safety can be a code-complying exit enclosure or the other side of a smoke barrier, which has a fire-resistance rating of at least 20 minutes. The area also must have access to a means of escape or an exit, as permitted by the code, that does not require the residents to travel back through the smoke barrier to the area from which they were evacuated.
3. If the building is of a construction type that has at least a 1-hour fire-resistance rating [Type I, Type II (222), Type II (111), Type III (211), Type IV, or Type V (111)], a point of safety can be a code-complying exit enclosure or the other side of a smoke barrier that

has a fire-resistance rating of at least 20 minutes. The area also must have access to a means of escape or exit, as permitted by the code, that does not require the residents to travel back through the smoke barrier to the area from which they were evacuated.

Occupancy Characteristics

Residential board and care occupancies are similar in nature to other residential occupancies. The fire load within individual sleeping rooms is similar to that in sleeping rooms within dwellings. Many facilities provide some furnishings, but permit the resident to bring personal furnishings such as chairs and tables into the rooms. The facilities also may include common living areas and lounges as well as a common dining area. Cooking usually is done at one central location, although residents might have access to a stove for personal use. Some residents might be responsible for their own laundry, although items such as bed linen might be laundered at a central location.

Facilities usually are staffed with personnel who supervise the residents and who might make appointments or plan activities for the residents. In some facilities, the staff live in a separate area or apartment within the facility. As such, the staff might not always be awake, alert, or directly supervising the residents.

Buildings that house occupancies other than residential board and care occupancies (mixed occupancies) must comply with the more restrictive provisions of the occupancies involved. As an alternative, the other occupancies can be separated from the residential board and care facility and its exit system by construction having a fire-resistance rating of at least 2 hours. Also, Sections 22-4 and 23-4 of the *Life Safety Code* contain requirements that apply specifically to residential board and care facilities that are located within an apartment building.

Residential board and care facilities can be of virtually any type of construction. Because the vast majority of facilities, especially small ones, are located in single-family dwellings, it is reasonable to expect the construction type to be Type III or Type V. Construction types permitted by NFPA *101* depend on the size of the facility, the evacuation capability of the residents, the height of the facility, and the provision of automatic sprinkler protection.

Occupant Load

The occupant load factor for residential board and care occupancies is 200 square feet per person. However, depending on the amount of common living and dining areas, the actual occupant load might be well in excess of that figure. In facilities in which the occupant load factor does not truly represent the anticipated occupancy, the maximum probable population of the room, space, or facility should be considered, and the maximum probable population must include residents, staff, and visitors.

Means of Egress

Small Facilities

In small facilities the means of egress is more appropriately referred to as the means of escape because there are numerous deviations from the standard means of egress arrangements. You must evaluate both the means of escape from sleeping rooms as well as from the facility in general. The means of escape requirements vary depending on the evacuation capability of the residents.

Each sleeping room and living area must have a primary means of escape that should lead to the exterior of the building without being exposed to any unprotected vertical openings. In facilities where residents are considered to have slow or impractical evacuation capabilities, the primary means of escape cannot be exposed to common living spaces such as living rooms or kitchens. By "exposed to," the code is referring to unprotected openings into such spaces. If the building is protected throughout with quick response or residential sprinklers, there is no restriction on the primary means of escape being exposed to common living spaces. (See vertical openings.)

Each sleeping room also must have access to a secondary means of escape. The most common arrangements involve either a window to the outside or a path of travel that is remote from the primary means of escape. The window must be operable from the inside without the use of tools and must provide a clear opening not less than 20 inches in width, 24 inches in height, and 5.7 square feet in area. The bottom of the opening cannot be more than 44 inches above the floor. Other alternatives include passage through an adjacent space to which the residents have free access or the enclosure of the room with construction having a fire-resistance rating of at least 20 minutes. Secondary means of escape are not required in rooms that have a door leading directly to the outside or if the facility is protected with an automatic sprinkler system.

In addition to two means of escape from each room, the facility also should have two means of escape from each normally occupied story. Windows can only serve as one means of escape from the facility and only if the residents are considered to have prompt evacuation capabilities. In buildings that are protected with an automatic sprinkler system, a second means of escape is not required from each story as long as the entire facility still has two means of escape. This exception cannot be used in conjunction with the sprinkler exception for two means of escape from each sleeping room. Exit signs and emergency lighting are not required in small facilities.

Large Facilities

The means of egress from large facilities should be similar to the more traditional egress arrangement involving exit access doors to corridors that lead to standard exits. While dead-end corridors are not limited by the 1991 edition of the *Life Safety Code,* the code does restrict the permitted travel distance from a room door in a corridor with exit access in one direction only to a maximum of 35 feet. This restriction is a modified common path of travel because it is measured from the room door instead of from a remote point in the room.

Travel within a room, suite, or living area to a corridor must be limited to 75 feet unless the building is protected with an automatic sprinkler system, in which case the limit is 125 feet. The travel distance from the exit access door to an exit is limited to 100 feet. This travel distance can be increased to 200 feet for exterior ways of exit access such as exterior balconies. Also, the *Life Safety Code* permits an increase in the travel distance to 200 feet between room doors and exits if automatic sprinkler protection is provided.

Exit signs must be provided when the exit or the path of travel to an exit is not immediately visible to the occupants. Emergency lighting is required in facilities with more than 25 sleeping rooms. However, if each sleeping room has a direct exit to the outside of the building at ground level, no emergency lighting is required. In addition to the standard means of egress, sleeping rooms in large facilities must contain an operable window not less than 20 inches wide, 24 inches high, 5.7 square feet in area, and not more than 44 inches above the floor. The specified windows are not required if the room has a door directly to the outside, the building is protected with an automatic sprinkler system or an engineered smoke-control system, or the building is considered to be an existing building. Also, on floors more than six stories above grade, the window need only be openable to a dimension necessary for ventilation.

Protection of Vertical Openings

Small Facilities

In general, vertical openings must be enclosed with construction having a fire-resistance rating of at least 20 minutes. In facilities where residents have prompt or slow capabilities to evacuate that are three stories or less in height, unprotected vertical openings are permitted only if the facility is protected with an automatic sprinkler system. However, the primary means of escape must still be separated from all unprotected vertical openings. Therefore, if the opening is part of or is adjacent to the primary means of escape, a 20-minute fire-resistant cutoff must be provided. If the facility is protected throughout by quick response or residential sprinklers, this three-story opening can be completely unprotected as long as it is not used for the primary means of escape.

Large Facilities

In general, vertical openings are required to be enclosed with construction having a fire-resistance rating of 1 or 2 hours, depending on the number of stories connected by the vertical shaft. In existing buildings 1/2-hour rated enclosure walls are still permitted. In addition to the permitted use of atriums, other unprotected openings can be permitted depending on the number of stories connected, the openness of the area, and the provision of automatic sprinkler protection.

Compartmentation

Small Facilities

In general, corridor walls must have a fire-resistance rating of at least 20 minutes with corridor doors of at least 1 3/4-inch solid, bonded, wood-core construction. In facilities where residents can evacuate promptly or in facilities that are protected by automatic sprinkler systems, the corridor walls and doors must resist the passage of smoke. Corridor doors must be self-latching with latches that will keep the door closed. Corridor doors must be self-closing or automatic-closing unless the building is protected with an automatic sprinkler system.

Large Facilities

In general, corridor walls must have a fire-resistance rating of at least 1 hour in new construction and 20 minutes in existing buildings and converted buildings. The *Life Safety Code* contains several exceptions to the general requirement, one of which is the provision of an automatic sprinkler system. If an automatic sprinkler system is provided, corridor walls can have a fire-resistance rating of 30 minutes in new construction and no minimum fire-resistance rating in existing buildings. The walls and the doors also must resist the passage of smoke. Corridor doors must have a fire-resistance rating of at least 20 minutes unless the corridor wall is only required to resist the passage of smoke. Existing 1 3/4-inch solid, bonded, wood-core doors also should be considered acceptable.

Corridor doors to sleeping rooms must be automatic closing by smoke detection because the operation of the facility could be such that the doors normally are open. However, if the doors have occupant-control locks such that the doors normally are closed for security or privacy purposes, the door can be self closing. Corridor doors to other rooms must be self closing or automatic closing. In buildings protected with an automatic sprinkler system, the corridor doors need not be self closing or automatic closing unless required for another purpose such as for an exit enclosure door or a door to a hazardous area.

Smoke barriers are required in large facilities with an aggregate corridor length of more than 150 feet on the floor. Smoke barriers that have a fire-resistance rating of at least 20 minutes also can serve as a point of safety as discussed previously. Smoke barriers are not required in buildings protected with an automatic sprinkler system or if each sleeping room is provided with exterior ways of exit access.

Hazardous Areas

Small Facilities

In small facilities, a hazardous area is considered to be one in which the fire threat is greater than that which is commonly found in one- and two-family dwellings (see Chapter 24). Therefore, a typical kitchen arrangement would not necessarily constitute a hazardous area. However, rooms used for central storage of residents' belongings would most likely be considered a hazardous area. These areas must either be enclosed or protected by automatic sprinklers. If the hazardous area is on the same floor as and abuts or is in the primary means of escape, the enclosure must have a fire-resistance rating of at least 1 hour, or if automatic sprinklers are provided in the enclosure, the enclosure must be smoke resistant. All other hazardous areas, such as basement storage areas, must be enclosed with construction having a fire-resistance rating of 20 minutes unless automatic sprinklers are provided.

Large Facilities

Large facilities typically will contain more hazardous areas because of the increased centralization of services such as cooking, laundry, and storage. Boiler or heater rooms and repair areas also might pose a greater fire threat than those commonly found in one- and two-family dwellings. Such hazardous areas must be separated from all other parts of the building by construction having a fire-resistance rating of at least 1 hour, or the area must be protected by automatic sprinklers.

Detection and Alarm Systems

Small Facilities

A means should be provided by which the staff and residents can be alerted to a fire emergency. Although a standard fire alarm system can serve this function, the *Life Safety Code* permits other alternatives due to the size and arrangement of many small facilities. For example, if smoke detectors are interconnected, a manual fire alarm station can be provided on each floor, which can be activated to continuously sound the smoke detector alarms. Although not specified in the code, the stations should be located in a conveniently accessible location that is in the normal path of escape. You also might accept a "system" consisting of alarms and manual switches, which can serve to notify the occupants and staff. The size and arrangement of the facility should dictate what constitutes an acceptable alternate system. In accepting a system, you must consider issues such as audibility, activation, power, secondary power, supervision, maintenance, and testing.

In order to minimize the impact of a fire on the means of escape, smoke detectors must be provided in all living rooms, day rooms, dens, and so on, as well as one detector per floor excluding crawl spaces and attics. The detectors should be powered by the house electrical service. It must be verified that the source of power is not subject to control by a wall switch. If plug-in type detectors are used, a restraining mechanism must be used to secure the plug. Additional guidance on smoke detector installation can be found in NFPA 72, *National Fire Alarm Code,* which contains minimum requirements for the selection, installation, operation, and maintenance of the detectors. The detectors can be omitted in buildings protected by an automatic quick response or residential sprinklers system. In addition, single-station house-powered smoke detectors must be installed in all sleeping rooms unless the rooms are protected by quick response or residential sprinklers. However, sprinklers cannot be used as a substitute for both the sleeping room smoke detectors and the corridor and common space smoke detectors. In existing buildings, existing sleeping room smoke detectors can be battery powered. Also, sleeping room smoke detectors do not have to be added if corridor and common space detectors are in place in existing buildings.

Large Facilities

In general, a fire alarm system must be installed in large facilities to permit the quick notification of staff, residents, and visitors of a fire emergency. The *Life Safety Code* contains some exceptions and variations, which can be permitted in certain facilities. In new high rise buildings a means also must be provided by which the occupants can be notified of the fire emergency by voice communication. The system should be arranged so that the proper evacuation or emergency instructions can be given to the buildings' occupants.

Corridors and common spaces must be provided with automatic smoke detectors that are connected to the fire alarm system. Detectors are not required in common spaces if the entire facility is protected with an automatic sprinkler system. In addition, single-station smoke detectors must be provided within sleeping rooms. The room detectors must be powered by the building's electrical service unless the detectors were installed before adoption of the *Life Safety Code,* in which case battery-powered detectors are permitted. However, battery-powered detectors should be permitted only if you believe that the facility's testing, maintenance, and battery-replacement programs will ensure the reliability of the detectors. In existing buildings that have an existing corridor smoke detection system, sleeping rooms are not required to have smoke detectors.

You also should ensure that a reliable means exists by which both staff and residents can notify the fire department. Public telephones are the most commonly used device to satisfy this criteria. Access to outside lines and the awareness of the correct telephone number all should be evaluated. You also should evaluate the location of the fire alarm annunciator panel to ensure that it is in a location that is convenient and accessible to fire department personnel when they are arriving at the scene of a fire emergency.

Fire Suppression Equipment

Using Chapters 22 and 23 of the *Life Safety Code,* you need to carefully ascertain whether automatic sprinklers are required for partial protection of the facility, total facility protection, or complete building protection. For example, protection of hazardous areas can be accomplished with sprinklers serving the hazardous area only. Other code sections might apply to facilities protected throughout with an automatic sprinkler system. Finally, requirements such as allowable construction types depend on whether the entire building, which may contain other occupancies, is protected with an automatic sprinkler system.

Small Facilities

In new construction, which includes converted buildings, automatic sprinkler protection using quick response or residential sprinklers is required throughout a new board and care facility by the 1991 edition of the *Life Safety Code.* In existing facilities, with the exception of facilities where residents' evacuation capabilities are considered impractical, automatic sprinkler protection is not required unless one or more of the exceptions related to sprinkler protection are contained within the facility. The code permits the use of NFPA 13D, *Standard for the Installation of Sprinkler Systems in One- and Two-Family Dwellings and Mobile Homes;* NFPA 13, *Standard for the Installation of Sprinkler Systems;* or NFPA 13R, *Standard for the Installation of Sprinkler Systems in Residential Occupancies Up to and Including Four Stories in Height,* in such facilities. However, in facilities in which the resident have impractical evacuation capabilities, the minimum water supply allowed for an NFPA 13D system is 30 minutes, and there must be sprinklers in all habitable areas and closets except small bathrooms (55 square feet). Activation of the sprinkler system must activate the building fire alarm system. Although portable fire extinguishers are not required, you might recommend that extinguishers be provided in certain areas if trained personnel are available to operate them.

Large Facilities

Automatic sprinkler protection using quick response or residential sprinklers is required throughout new board and care facilities, which includes converted buildings, by the 1991 edition of the *Life Safety Code.* In existing facilities automatic sprinkler protection is not required unless one or more of the exceptions related to sprinkler protection are contained within the facility. You might recommend that consideration be given to sprinkler protection if code requirements such as door closers present a problem or concern to the facility owner or operator. If installed, the sprinkler system must comply with the requirements of NFPA 13 or NFPA 13R, except that sprinklers can be omitted from small closets (24 square feet) and small bathrooms (55 square feet). Portable fire extinguishers must be provided near hazardous areas.

Operating Features

Smoking should be restricted to areas where it is safe. The smoking policy, as a minimum, should discourage smoking in bed. In many facilities a smoking lounge is designated in order to minimize the potential for fires originating in sleeping rooms. Wherever smoking is permitted, proper noncombustible ashtrays or receptacles must be provided. Care must be exercised in the location of smoke detectors in such spaces.

Every facility should have a fire emergency plan that identifies the proper procedures to be followed by staff, residents, and visitors upon discovery or notification of a fire emergency. The plan should be evaluated at least six times a year by conducting fire exit drills. The drills must include the use of all designated means of escape or egress. If the means of escape involves windows, the residents need not actually climb out the windows. However, they should be required to go to the windows and open them. Staff personnel should participate in all fire exit drills. Experience with fires in board and care facilities has demonstrated that the lack of staff and resident training as well as the failure to familiarize the residents with egress routes other than the primary path have resulted in additional fatalities.

Bibliography

NFPA 90A, *Standard for the Installation of Air Conditioning and Ventilating Systems*
NFPA *101, Life Safety Code*
NFPA 101M, *Manual on Alternative Approaches to Life Safety*

RESIDENTIAL BOARD AND CARE OCCUPANCY
FIRE INSPECTION FORM

Property Name: Owner:

Address: Phone Number:

OCCUPANCY

Change from Last Inspection: Yes☐   No☐

Occupant Load: Egress Capacity: Any Renovations: Yes☐   No☐

Prompt☐   Slow☐   Impractical☐   Small☐   Large☐   Apartment Building☐

High Rise: Yes☐   No☐   Windowless: Yes☐   No☐   Underground: Yes☐   No☐

BUILDING SERVICES

Electricity☐   Gas☐   Water☐   Other☐   Are Utilities in Good Working Order: Yes☐   No☐

Elevators: Yes☐   No☐   Fire Service Control: Yes☐   No☐   Elevator Recall: Yes☐   No☐

Heat Type: Gas☐   Oil☐   Electric☐   Coal☐   Other☐   In Good Working Order: Yes☐   No☐

Emergency Generator: Yes☐   No☐   Size: Last Date Tested:

Date of Last Full Load Test: In Automatic Position: Yes☐   No☐

Fire Pump: Yes☐   No☐   GPM: Suction Pressure: System Pressure:

Date Last Tested: Date of Last Flow Test:

In Automatic Position: Yes☐   No☐   Jockey Pump: Yes☐   No

EMERGENCY LIGHTS

Operable: Yes☐   No☐   Tested Monthly: Yes☐   No☐

Properly Illuminate Egress Paths: Yes☐   No☐   In Good Condition: Yes☐   No☐

EXIT SIGNS

Illuminated: Internally☐   Externally☐   Emergency Power: Yes☐   No☐   Readily Visible: Yes☐
No☐

FIRE ALARM

Yes☐   No☐   Location of Panel:

Coverage: Building☐   Partial☐   Monitored: Yes☐   No☐   Method:

Type of Initiation Devices: Smoke☐   Heat☐   Manual☐   Water Flow☐   Special Systems☐

Date of Last Test: Date of Last Inspection:

Notification Signal Adequate: Yes☐   No☐   Fire Department Notification: Yes☐   No☐

Single Station Smoke Detectors in Sleeping Room: Yes☐   No☐   Audible in All Areas: Yes☐   No☐

FIRE EXTINGUISHERS

Proper Type for Hazard Protecting: Yes☐   No☐   Mounted Properly: Yes☐   No☐

Date of Last Inspection: Adequate Number: Yes☐   No☐

FIRE PROTECTION SYSTEMS

Type: Sprinkler☐   Standpipe☐   Dry Chemical☐   Wet Chemical☐   Other☐

Coverage: Building☐   Partial☐   Date of Last Inspection:

Cylinder or Gauge Pressure(s): 1   psi.,2   psi.,3   psi.,4   psi.,5   psi.

Valves Supervised: Electrical☐   Lock☐   Seal☐   Other☐   Are Valves Accessible: Yes☐   No☐

System Operational: Yes☐   No☐   Sprinkler Heads 18" from Storage: Yes☐   No☐

FIRE RESISTIVE (FR) CONSTRUCTION

Stairway FR: Yes☐   No☐   Hourly Rating:

Corridors FR: Yes☐   No☐   Hourly Rating:

Elevator Shaft FR: Yes☐   Yes☐   No☐   Hourly Rating:

Major Structural Members FR: Yes☐   No☐   Hourly Rating:

Floor-Ceiling Assemblies FR: Yes☐   No☐   Hourly Rating:

All Openings Protected in FR Walls and Floor-Ceiling Assemblies: Yes☐ No☐

HAZARDOUS AREAS

Protected by: Fire-Rated Separation☐ Extinguishing System☐ Both☐

Door Self-Closures: Yes☐ No☐

Kitchens Properly Protected: Yes☐ No☐

Other Occupancies Separated: Yes☐ No☐

HOUSEKEEPING

Areas Free of Excessive Combustibles: Yes☐ No☐

Smoking Regulated: Yes☐ No☐

INTERIOR FINISH

Walls and Ceilings Proper Rating: Yes☐ No☐ Floor Finish Proper Rating: Yes☐ No☐

Furniture and Draperies Flame Resistive: Yes☐ No☐

MEANS OF EGRESS

Readily Visible: Yes☐ No☐ Clear and Unobstructed: Yes☐ No☐

Two Remote Exits Available: Yes☐ No☐ Travel Distance within Limits: Yes☐ No☐

Common Path of Travel within Limits: Yes☐ No☐ Dead-Ends within Limits: Yes☐ No☐

50% Maximum through Level of Exit Discharge: Yes☐ No☐

Second Means of Escape Provided: Yes☐ No☐

Window 5.7 sq. ft.: Yes☐ No☐ Operable: Yes☐ No☐

Adequate Illumination: Yes☐ No☐

Proper Rating on All Components: Yes☐ No☐

All Exit Enclosures Free of Storage: Yes☐ No☐

Door Swing in the Direction of Egress Travel (when required): Yes☐ No☐

Panic/Fire Exit Hardware Operable: Yes☐ No☐

Doors Open Easily: Yes☐ No☐ Self-Closures Operable: Yes☐ No☐

Doors Closed or Held Open With Automatic Closures: Yes☐ No☐

Corridors and Aisles of Sufficient Size: Yes☐ No☐

Stairwell Re-Entry: Yes☐ No☐

Mezzanines: Yes☐ No☐ Proper Exits: Yes☐ No☐

Smoke Barriers Provided: Yes☐ No☐ Proper Fire Resistance Rating and Size: Yes☐ No☐

VERTICAL OPENINGS

Properly Protected: Yes☐ No☐

Atrium: Yes☐ No☐ Properly Protected: Yes☐ No☐

Are Fire Doors in Good Working Order: Yes☐ No☐

OPERATING FEATURES

Emergency Plan: Yes☐ No☐ Date of Last Update:

Staff and Residents Trained in Plan: Yes☐ No☐

Fire Drills Conducted: Yes☐ No☐ Date of Last Drill:

CHAPTER 24

One- and Two-Family Dwellings

*N*FPA *101*, *Life Safety Code*, defines one- and two-family dwellings as buildings containing not more than two dwelling units in which each living unit is occupied by members of a single family with no more than three outsiders, if any, accommodated in rented rooms. The manner in which living units are separated from one another can determine their occupancy classification. For example, a row of six townhouses with complete vertical fire wall separations between each unit, including the attic spaces, and with independent means of egress from each unit can be considered as six individual units.

In most jurisdictions existing one- and two-family dwellings are not required to be inspected. New dwellings usually are inspected by the enforcement official having jurisdiction before they are occupied, but routine inspections are not performed after they have been occupied. However, homeowners frequently ask fire inspectors to conduct voluntary fire prevention inspections. And some states mandate inspections, especially of smoke detectors, at the time a one- or two-family dwelling is sold.

Occupancy Characteristics

When a dwelling unit is located within a mixed-use occupancy, the most restrictive life safety requirements apply. The *Life Safety Code* lists specific requirements for mixed residential and mercantile, business, or assembly occupancies. Dwelling units may not have their sole means of egress through any mercantile, business, or assembly occupancy in the same building. Multiple-dwelling occupancies may not be located above mercantile, business, or assembly occupancies unless the dwelling occupancy and its exits are separated from the occupancy below by construction having a fire-resistance rating of at least 1 hour, or the occupancy below is protected by automatic sprinklers. In an existing mixed-occupancy arrangement, a building with not more than two dwelling units above another occupancy is permitted if the occupancy below is protected by an automatic fire detection system.

Means of Escape

Means of escape should not be confused with means of egress; the requirements for each are different. Any dwelling unit with more than two rooms must have at least two means of escape from every bedroom and living area. Within the dwelling unit at least one means of escape must be a door or stairway with an unobstructed path of travel to the outside. Bedroom and living areas should be accessible by means other than ladders, folding stairs, or trap doors.

Most residential occupancies must have a second means of escape. It can be a door or stairway with an unobstructed path of travel to the outside, or window that can be opened from the inside without the use of tools. The window should provide a clear opening at least 20 inches wide, 24 inches high, and 5.7 square feet in area. The bottom of the opening cannot be more than 44 inches above the floor.

However, a second means of escape is not required if the room has a door leading directly outside of the building to grade level, or if the building is protected throughout by an approved automatic sprinkler system installed in accordance with NFPA 13D, *Standard for the Installation of Sprinkler Systems in One- and Two-Family Dwellings and Mobile Homes.*

The means of escape from any room must not pass through another room or apartment not under the immediate control of the occupant or family of the first room, nor through a bathroom or other space subject to locking. For example, the second means of escape from a windowless living area could be through a bedroom and out the bedroom window as long as the bedroom door cannot be locked and the use of the bedroom is under the control of the occupant.

Doors in the path of travel of a means of escape must be at least 28 inches wide, but bathroom doors can be 24 inches wide. Exterior exit doors must swing or slide open; they are not required to swing in the direction of exit travel.

Children must be able to open closet door latches from inside the closet, and locks on bathroom doors must be operable from the outside. Stairs in the path of travel in the means of escape must be at least 36 inches wide. Winders and spiral stairs are permitted within a single living unit.

When the building is occupied, doors in any means of egress cannot be locked with double cylinder or dead-bolt locks that can only be unlocked with a key from the inside.

Interior Finish

Interior finish on walls and ceilings of occupied spaces must be Class A, B, or C.

The flame-spread and smoke-development characteristics of a material usually cannot be determined by visual inspection, so documentation certifying the characteristics of the interior finish must be provided by the installer or owner. Some times this information is printed on the backside of materials or on their packages.

Fire Protection

In new construction at least one approved smoke detector powered by the house electric service must be installed in an approved manner in every dwelling unit. In existing construction, approved battery-powered smoke detectors can be used. When activated, the detector must initiate an alarm that is audible in the sleeping rooms. Refer to NFPA 72, *National Fire Alarm Code,* for additional information.

Single-station smoke detectors located in the hallway near the bedrooms are the most common installations. If there is more than one story or it is a large single story, additional detectors will be needed. Single-station detectors often are interconnected so that when one detector is activated, the sounding devices in the others are also activated. This method is required by NFPA 72 in new construction.

Voluntary Inspections

Fire inspections conducted in one- and two-family dwellings most frequently are voluntary fire prevention inspections done at the request of a homeowner to help evaluate fire safety. The following recommendations will help the homeowner maintain a fire safe home.

Utilities

All gas, electric, and oil-fired utilities and appliances should be kept in good repair and serviced as needed. The homeowner should be instructed on the proper installation and use of electrical extension cords, portable heaters, and wood-burning stoves. Damaged light and appliance cords should be replaced. You should emphasize that all major electrical work should be done by a licensed electrician.

Coal and Wood Stoves

Coal and wood stoves warrant special attention because of their record as a cause of fires. Inspect stoves very carefully for the adequacy of the installation and the clearance of the stove and its chimney connector from combustibles. Your jurisdiction might have specific requirements for the installation of stoves. If there are no specific local requirements, ask the homeowner if the stove was installed according to the manufacturer's instructions. There should be a minimum clearance of 36 inches between stoves and combustible walls and ceilings, and the stove should be positioned on a base of noncombustible material, such as metal or brick, extending at least 18 inches beyond the stove in all directions. The stove pipe, or connector, between the stove and chimney should be as short and straight as possible, and there should be at least 18 inches of clearance between the pipe and combustible surfaces.

Remind occupants that creosote accumulations, which form very quickly in airtight chimneys that are not used properly, in the connector and the chimney are a very dangerous fire hazard. Suggest that the chimney be inspected frequently and cleared when necessary to prevent chimney fires.

See NFPA 211, *Standard for Chimneys, Fireplaces, Vents, and Solid Fuel-Burning Appliances,* for requirements for proper clearances, and modifications that might be permitted, for heating appliances. The *Fire Protection Handbook* also has information on hazards and protection of coal- and wood-burning stoves.

Storage

The storage of flammable and combustible materials within the home should be controlled. Check the way in which paint, solvents, gasoline, and other materials are stored in the workshop areas. Explain that these materials must be stored away from ignition sources and preferably outside the home. Many homeowners do not understand that flammable liquids produce vapors that can be ignited by the furnace or other devices. There is no substitute for good housekeeping. Check storage areas for accumulations of trash and large amounts of combustibles and bring them to the attention of the occupant.

Detection Equipment

Smoke detectors should be installed in all one- and two-family dwellings, and you can recommend which type to install and where they should be placed. Ionization and photoelectric smoke detectors are comparable and either type can be used in residential occupancies. The detectors should be located near the sleeping areas of the house, with at least one detector located on each floor, and they should be audible throughout the house.

If the detectors are plugged into a wall receptacle, make sure there is a restraining means for the plug and that the receptacle is not controlled by a wall switch that could shut off the power.

Because single-station battery detectors are so easy to install and are allowed in one- and two-family dwellings, they are the most common. Emphasize that the detectors should be tested on a regular basis to ensure the batteries are working. The batteries should be replaced on a regular schedule, as well.

Fire Extinguishers

Homeowners will most likely have questions about type, size, location, and number of fire extinguishers. For your own information, refer to NFPA 10, *Standard for Portable Fire Extinguishers,* but assist the occupants by summarizing the different types, such as carbon dioxide, dry chemical, and multipurpose dry powder. The weight of the extinguisher should be a consideration when deciding which size to buy. Explain to the occupants that they should be familiar with the operation of the extinguishers and should practice using them. Refer occupants to NFPA 10 and the manufacturer's recommendations for inspection, testing, and servicing the extinguishers.

Residential Sprinklers

The use of residential sprinklers in one- and two-family dwellings is an increasing trend in some jurisdictions. All sprinklers should be inspected visually to ensure they are not painted over and that their spray is unobstructed. All water-flow devices, alarms, pumps, water tanks, and other components of the system should be in proper operating condition. Inspect all valves to ensure that they are open. You should point out that, according to NFPA 13D, proper maintenance of a sprinkler system is the responsibility of the owner or manager, who should understand how the system operates.

Fire Escape Plan

Help the homeowner establish a fire escape plan from each room of the house. Emphasize that once the plan is made, it should be practiced. The NFPA pamphlet, "E.D.I.T.H. Exit Drills In the Home," is a good reference. The principles of E.D.I.T.H. are simple and sound: Have smoke detectors on each level of the house, and make sure they work. Know two routes to the outside from all rooms, especially bedrooms. Have everyone in the house memorize the fire department telephone number, and put the number on the telephones in the house. Choose a place outdoors for everyone to meet for roll call. Locate the closest telephone or emergency call box from which to report a fire in your home. Never go back into a burning building. Practice escape routines— testing closed doors for fire on the other side, crawling low under smoke, and getting out of bedroom windows—and know what to do if occupants become trapped.

You can help the family make an escape plan by reviewing potential escape routes from sleeping areas, pointing out alternatives that might be available, and demonstrating the proper techniques for testing doors for fire and exiting through windows. Your interest might help to convince a family that E.D.I.T.H. is serious business.

Bibliography

NFPA 13D, *Standard for the Installation of Sprinkler Systems in One- and Two-Family Dwellings and Mobile Homes*
NFPA *101, Life Safety Code*

ONE & TWO FAMILY DWELLING OCCUPANCY
FIRE INSPECTION FORM

Property Name: Owner:

Address: Phone Number:

OCCUPANCY

Number of Families: Change from Last Inspection: Yes☐ No☐

Any Renovations: Yes☐ No☐

Windowless: Yes☐ No☐   Underground: Yes☐ No☐

BUILDING SERVICES

Electricity☐ Gas☐ Water☐ Other☐   Are Utilities in Good Working Order: Yes☐ No☐

Heat Type: Gas☐ Oil☐ Electric☐ Other☐   In Good Working Order: Yes☐ No☐

Wood or Coal Stove: Yes☐ No☐   Properly Installed: Yes☐ No☐

Properly Maintained: Yes☐ No☐   Fuel Stored Properly: Yes☐ No☐

Combustible Materials; Adequate Distance from Stove: Yes☐ No☐

Proper Clearances of Stove and Pipes: Yes☐ No☐

FIRE ALARM

Single Station Smoke Detectors: Yes☐ No☐   In Each Living Unit: Yes☐ No☐

In Each Bedroom: Yes☐ No☐   Audible in All Areas: Yes☐ No☐   Power Source:

FIRE EXTINGUISHERS

Proper Type for Hazard Protecting: Yes☐ No☐   Mounted Properly: Yes☐ No☐

Date of Last Inspection: Adequate Number: Yes☐ No☐

FIRE PROTECTION SYSTEMS

Sprinkler System: Yes☐ No☐   Water Source:

 Coverage: Building☐ Partial☐   Date of Last Inspection:

Valve Supervised: Electrical☐ Lock☐ Seal☐ Other☐   Are Valves Accessible: Yes☐ No☐

System Operational: Yes☐ No☐

FIRE RESISTIVE (FR) CONSTRUCTION

Stairway FR: Yes☐ No☐   Hourly Rating:

Corridors FR: Yes☐ No☐   Hourly Rating:

Elevator Shaft FR: Yes☐ Yes☐ No☐   Hourly Rating:

Major Structural Members FR: Yes☐ No☐   Hourly Rating:

Floor-Ceiling Assemblies FR: Yes☐ No☐   Hourly Rating:

All Openings Protected in FR Walls and Floor-Ceiling Assemblies: Yes☐ No☐

HAZARDOUS AREAS

Not Located to Block Escape: Yes☐ No☐   Separated from Other Occupancies: Yes☐ No☐

Flammable and Combustible Liquids Stored Properly: Yes☐ No☐

HOUSEKEEPING

Areas Free of Excessive Combustibles: Yes☐ No☐

INTERIOR FINISH

Walls and Ceilings Proper Rating: Yes☐ No☐

MEANS OF ESCAPE

Readily Visible: Yes☐ No☐   Clear and Unobstructed: Yes☐ No☐

Two Remote Means of Escape Available: Yes☐ No☐

Every Story > 2,000 sq. ft. Two Primary Means of Escape Provided: Yes☐ No☐

Doors Open Easily: Yes☐ No☐   Corridors and Aisles of Sufficient Size: Yes☐ No☐

Secondary Means of Escape from Every Sleeping Room and Living Area: Yes☐ No☐

Window 5.7 sq. ft.: Yes☐ No☐ Minimum Height and Width: Yes☐ No☐ Operable: Yes☐ No☐

Doors of Closets and Bathroom Operable from the Inside and Outside: Yes☐ No☐

Doors not Locked to Impede Escape: Yes☐ No☐

OPERATING FEATURES

Do Occupants have an Escape Plan: Yes☐ No☐ Do They Practice the Plan: Yes☐ No☐

Do Occupants Know Emergency Numbers: Yes☐ No☐

Are They Located Near the Phone: Yes☐ No☐

Do Occupants Have a Meeting Place: Yes☐ No☐

CHAPTER 25

Mercantile
Occupancies

*M*ercantile occupancies perhaps require more thorough inspections than any other occupancy. They include shopping centers, department stores, drugstores, supermarkets, auction rooms, and any occupancy (or portion thereof) that is used for the display and sale of merchandise.

The term "mercantile" encompasses many different types of materials and operations. As an inspector, you are just as apt to inspect a store dealing in glassware as you are one that sells a large number of paper products. Large department stores have a wide variety of products that react differently in a fire situation. In the past, the great majority of combustible material found within any mercantile occupancy has been Class A, which are products made of wood, paper, or cloth. These days, though, there are more plastic items or plastic materials that were designed and manufactured to look like something else, such as a plastic baby crib that looks, and even smells, like wood. Plastics in their various forms are introducing much higher than expected fuel loads into sales and storage areas, and this should be considered when determining the overall fuel load because when plastics burn they spread fire rapidly and also produce heavy, thick, black, toxic smoke. Presently there is no restriction on the use of plastics in furniture or other industries, nor is there a restriction on the overall amount of the material one can have in a mercantile occupancy.

The separation and treatment of other occupancies found within or attached to a mercantile occupancy is another factor you will have to be concerned with. In large shopping malls, a variety of different mercantile occupancies often will, in one way or another, connect to several assembly occupancies. In this case, you must consider the different occupant load factors. Remember that as you inspect the premises, you should use the same walk-through process to thoroughly familiarize yourself with the building; after all, you may have to visit the building under fire conditions someday. And with this approach, you will be able to make educated decisions as to the probable occupant load when a fire alarm does sound.

The *Life Safety Code* separates mercantile occupancies into three categories. A Class A mercantile occupancy is any store having an aggregate **gross** sales area larger than 30,000 square feet, or a store utilizing more than three floor levels for sales purposes. For example, a single-story store with 32,650 square feet of gross sales area is a Class A mercantile occupancy; a four-story sporting goods store with 20,000 square feet of gross sales area is also a Class A mercantile occupancy. Remember also to measure the total square footage (gross) instead of only the floor area not covered with stock of some sort (net).

A Class B mercantile occupancy is any store with less than 30,000 square feet, but greater than 3,000 square feet, of aggregate gross sales area, or one that utilizes any balconies, mezzanines, or floors above or below the street floor for sales purposes. The exception to this is one of the examples used above for Class A mercantiles: a four-story, 20,000-square-feet space that is Class A regardless of the size. A Class B mercantile then is the two-story, 25,000-square-feet department store or the 4,000-square-feet drugstore.

Class C mercantile occupancies are all stores with 3,000 square feet or less of gross sales area that are **located on the street floor only.** If they are less than 3,000 square feet but above or below the street floor, they are Class B. Thus, a 850 square-feet tobacco store is a Class C occupancy if it is located on the street floor. If it is located below the street floor, it is a Class B occupancy. Being located above the street floor also would make it Class B, regardless of gross square footage.

As you begin your inspection of any mercantile occupancy to determine compliance with the *Life Safety Code* and other pertinent *National Fire Codes,* as well as the building codes and ordinances of your local jurisdiction, you should get an immediate and general idea of what level of maintenance is carried out by the store staff. If the area is somewhat cluttered, with questionable aisles and unswept floors, the chances are good that the entire store will look that way or worse. This will indicate to you what general level of conscious fire safety behavior is practiced in that particular store and further indicate how much of a task you have ahead of you.

Occupant Load

The occupant load for mercantile occupancies is covered in paragraphs 24-1.7 and 25-1.7 of the *Life Safety Code:* 30 square feet of gross square footage of sales space per person on the street floor or sales floors below the street floor; 60 square feet of gross floor area of sales space per person on upper floors used for sales; 100 square feet per person on floors or portions of floors used only for offices; and 300 square feet of gross floor area per person for those floors or portions thereof not open to the general public but used for storage, shipping, or receiving. The *Life Safety Code* has special provisions for malls. Although the occupant load is not specifically required to be posted in a conspicuous place within the business, it is a good idea to suggest doing so to the manager. That same occupant load should be recorded on your inspection sheet when conducting prefire planning in the building so that you will know what occupant load to expect in the event of a fire.

Various types of exits are allowed from any mercantile occupancy, such as stairways, smokeproof towers, doors, ramps, and, in some cases, escalators. Still others require the approval of the authority having jurisdiction or very special applications, such as revolving doors or fire escape stairs. For the exact application of each type of exit, you should refer to paragraphs 24-2.2 and 25-2.2 of the *Life Safety Code.*

Means of Egress

Generally speaking, at least two exits must be provided and be accessible from every part of every floor, and especially from floors below the street-level floor. The few exceptions to this requirement can be found in 24-2.4 and 25-2.4 of the *Life Safety Code.* Dead-end corridors should be avoided, and none are allowed to be more than 20 feet long. However, they can be up to 50 feet long if the building is completely sprinklered. Exits should be located as far apart as practical, but generally not closer to one another than one-half the longest diagonal distance of the space served. In a grocery, discount, or variety store where checkout stands and turnstiles are provided to restrict exiting, at least one-half of the required exits in both number and capacity must be provided in such a manner that they can be reached **without** having to go through the turnstiles and checkout stands. This, you will find, is commonly violated, although its purpose is clear. In a fire or other emergency, persons within the space must be able to exit quickly and easily, without any obstructions to that exit travel.

Generally speaking, all exit doors are required to swing in the direction of exit travel, particularly 1) when used in an exit enclosure (e.g., stairway), 2) when serving a high hazard area, or 3) when serving an occupant load of 50 or more.

Although special locking features are allowed in some configurations, the general rule is that all locking devices on exit doors must be operable without the use of a key or special knowledge, and the method of operation must be obvious even in darkness.

No occupants of any mercantile occupancy should have to travel more than 100 feet to find the exit nearest them. This distance can be increased to 150 feet in those buildings protected throughout by an approved automatic sprinkler system. In some instances exit access can pass through the storerooms of mercantile occupancies, but only 1) if at least one other means of egress is provided, 2) the storeroom is not subject to locking, 3) the main aisle through the storeroom is not less than 44 inches wide and in the clear, and 4) the main path of travel through the storeroom is obvious, with fixed barriers, and completely unobstructed.

All required exits from a mercantile occupancy must have illuminated exit signs above them. These signs, if in a Class A or B mercantile occupancy, must be connected to the emergency lighting system or have backup battery power.

Emergency lighting is required in all Class A and Class B occupancies. Class C stores, due to their small size and occupant load, are not required to have such installations. Emergency lighting should provide not less than 1 footcandle of light at the floor for 90 minutes, throughout the means of egress, in the event of failure of the normal lighting. For more specific details concerning emergency lighting, you should refer to Section 5-9 in the *Life Safety Code.*

Protection of Openings

Vertical openings in all mercantile occupancies are required to be enclosed or protected in some manner, but the exceptions to this are numerous; you should refer to paragraphs 24-3.1 and 25-3.1 of the *Life Safety Code* for each specific application.

Protection of Hazards

Any area of the space creating a greater hazard than other portions of the occupancy is required to be separated from those other portions by construction having no less than a 1-hour fire-resistance rating, or it must be protected by automatic sprinklers. Some areas requiring this special protection include maintenance closets, fuel storage areas, maintenance shops, general storage areas, boiler or furnace rooms, and kitchens.

Any areas with contents considered to be highly hazardous, that is liable to burn with extreme rapidity or result in an explosion, are required to be both separated by construction with at least a 1-hour fire-resistance rating **and** must have complete automatic sprinkler protection. It is up to the authority having jurisdiction to determine what degree of hazard the contents represent, and then to make a case for that decision.

Interior Finish

Interior finish is required to be either Class A or Class B, except that **existing** Class C interior finishes are allowed on walls only (not ceilings) and in existing Class C stores (see Chapter 6 for further discussion and flame-spread ratings). You should use reasonable discretion when determining what the existing finish is and, if it is illegal according to code, what reasonable methods should be required to correct the violation.

There are no specific prohibitions concerning floor finishes. However, if you find a floor finish that is of an unusual hazard, 6-5.2.2 of the *Life Safety Code* gives the authority having jurisdiction power to regulate it.

Fire Protection

While you are walking through the complex, determine which type of portable extinguishers are available, if they are fully serviced and operational, and if the number provided is sufficient for the space. The general rule is that at least one hand extinguisher of at least a 2A:10BC rating be available within a travel distance not exceeding 75 feet, and that at least one should be provided for every 3,000 square feet of floor space. You should refer to the pertinent sections of NFPA 10, *Standard for Portable Fire Extinguishers,* for further information.

Alarm Systems

All Class A stores are required to have a manual fire alarm system throughout the building. However, buildings protected throughout by an approved automatic fire detection and alarm initiation system, or protected throughout by an approved automatic sprinkler system that provides alarm initiation, are not required to also have a manual fire alarm system.

An alarm system, if present, should have pull stations at each exit, and should also provide for a local alarm in the event one of the pull stations is activated. Whether required or not, the system should be maintained in an operational condition. If people see an alarm pull station, they naturally assume that it will work when needed.

Sprinkler Systems

Approved automatic sprinkler protection is required 1) in all mercantile buildings having a story over 15,000 square feet in area, 2) in all mercantile buildings exceeding 30,000 square feet in gross area, and 3) throughout all stories of the occupancy below the level of exit discharge having an area exceeding 2,500 square feet that are used for sales, storage, or handling of combustible goods or merchandise. Generally, any large store is required to be sprinklered not only by applicable codes, but also by the company that insures the property. This is not always the case, however, and you should rely on paragraphs 24-3.5 and 25-3.5 of the Life Safety Code to ensure that the spaces meeting those areas listed above are provided with full sprinkler protection. The requirements for new construction are more stringent.

Covered malls require special considerations when it comes to inspections and code compliance. For the most part, a covered mall and all the shops that open into it are required to be fully sprinklered. There also are numerous requirements for exit widths and distances to exits, which are given in 24-4.4 and 25-4.4 of the *Life Safety Code*. A fire alarm system that is activated by the building's smoke detectors or automatic sprinkler system is required within a covered mall. Manual pull stations are not required, however. Smoke venting and a smoke control system also must be provided in covered malls.

If an area is required by code to have sprinkler protection and there is none, you should require that it be installed. If sprinkler protection is in place, check to see that no heads are obstructed, that they are not painted, and that there is no sales stock hanging from the piping. All areas of the store should be covered by sprinkler protection, and the control valves and inspector's test pipes should be easily accessible by engine crews and test personnel. You should perform the necessary tests to verify that the flow alarm and outside horn and light are operational. Be sure to let the monitoring company know you will be testing the system because the tests could result in fire department response, panic among patrons, or interruption of business.

You should check the design densities under which the sprinkler system was installed. If the densities are not now sufficient for the products being protected, those densities should be upgraded to ensure that the system will do what it is being counted on to do; which is to control (or extinguish) a fire. If the sprinkler system was designed as an ordinary group 1 system but is now protecting large amounts of plastic material, or a much greater load of Class A material, or perhaps a storage area with flammable or combustible liquids, that system will not perform as expected, and it should be upgraded to meet the new demands. If you are not sure if the sprinkler system will perform as it was designed to, your fire department plans reviewer, the fire marshal, fire chief, or building official should be consulted to ensure the protection is still adequate.

If some other form of extinguishing system is present in the facility (such as a dry chemical system inside a cooking hood), that system should be fully operational and serviced within the last 6 months. All nozzles must be unobstructed, and cooking should only be done under the hood.

The store area must be neat, with aisles organized as required by the *Life Safety Code.* Storage height should not obstruct the sprinkler protection. Any stored flammable liquids should be in a separate area, and the total amount of allowed flammable liquids should be kept to about 50 gallons.

Bibliography

NFPA 30, *Flammable and Combustible Liquids Code*
NFPA *101, Life Safety Code*

MERCANTILE OCCUPANCY FIRE INSPECTION FORM

Property Name: Owner:

Address: Phone Number:

OCCUPANCY

Occupancy Subclassification: A☐   B☐   C☐   Change from Last Inspection: Yes☐   No☐

Occupant Load: Egress Capacity: Any Renovations: Yes☐   No☐

Covered Mall: Yes☐   No☐   Anchor Store: Yes☐   No☐

High Rise: Yes☐   No☐   Windowless: Yes☐   No☐   Underground: Yes☐   No☐

BUILDING SERVICES

Electricity☐   Gas☐   Water☐   Other☐   Are Utilities in Good Working Order: Yes☐   No☐

Elevators: Yes☐   No☐   Fire Service Control: Yes☐   No☐   Elevator Recall: Yes☐   No☐

Heat Type: Gas☐   Oil☐   Electric☐   Coal☐   Other☐   In Good Working Order: Yes☐   No☐

Emergency Generator: Yes☐   No☐   Size: Last Date Tested:

Date of Last Full Load Test: In Automatic Position: Yes☐   No☐

Fire Pump: Yes☐   No☐   GPM: Suction Pressure: System Pressure:

Date Last Tested: Date of Last Flow Test:

In Automatic Position: Yes☐   No☐   Jockey Pump: Yes☐   No☐

EMERGENCY LIGHTS

Operable: Yes☐   No☐   Tested Monthly: Yes☐   No☐

Properly Illuminate Egress Paths: Yes☐   No☐   In Good Condition: Yes☐   No☐

EXIT SIGNS

Illuminated: Internally☐   Externally☐   Readily Visible: Yes☐   No☐

FIRE ALARM

Yes☐   No☐   Location of Panel:

Coverage: Building☐   Partial☐   Monitored: Yes☐   No☐   Method:

Type of Initiation Devices: Smoke☐   Heat☐   Manual☐   Water Flow☐   Special Systems☐

Date of Last Test: Date of Last Inspection:

Notification Signal Adequate: Yes☐   No☐   Fire Department Notification: Yes☐   No☐

FIRE EXTINGUISHERS

Proper Type for Hazard Protecting: Yes☐   No☐   Mounted Properly: Yes☐   No☐

Date of Last Inspection: Adequate Number: Yes☐   No☐

FIRE PROTECTION SYSTEMS

Type: Sprinkler☐   Halon☐   CO2☐   Standpipe☐   Water Spray☐   Foam☐   Dry Chemical☐   Wet Chemical☐   Other☐

Coverage: Building☐   Partial☐   Date of Last Inspection:

Cylinder or Gauge Pressure(s): 1   psi.,2   psi.,3   psi.,4   psi.,5   psi.

Valves Supervised: Electrical☐   Lock☐   Seal☐   Other☐   Are Valves Accessible: Yes☐   No☐

System Operational: Yes☐   No☐   Sprinkler Heads 18" from Storage: Yes☐   No☐

Smoke Removal System: Yes☐   No☐   In Good Working Order: Yes☐   No☐

Date of Last Test:

FIRE RESISTIVE (FR) CONSTRUCTION

Stairway FR: Yes☐   No☐   Hourly Rating:

Corridors FR: Yes☐   No☐   Hourly Rating:

Elevator Shaft FR: Yes☐   Yes☐   No☐   Hourly Rating:

Major Structural Members FR: Yes☐   No☐   Hourly Rating:

Floor-Ceiling Assemblies FR: Yes□ No□   Hourly Rating:

All Openings Protected in FR Walls and Floor-Ceiling Assemblies: Yes□ No□

HAZARDOUS AREAS

Protected by: Fire-Rated Separation□   Extinguishing System□   Both n

Door Self-Closures: Yes□ No□

Residential Separated: Yes□ No□   1-Hour Fire Resistive Rating□   Sprinklers□

Parking Structure Separated: Yes□ No□

HOUSEKEEPING

Areas Free of Excessive Combustibles: Yes□   No□

Smoking Regulated: Yes□   No□   Stock Properly Stored: Yes□   No□

Trash Removed on a Regular Basis: Yes□ No□

INTERIOR FINISH

Walls and Ceilings Proper Rating: Yes□   No□   Floor Finish Proper Rating: Yes□   No□

MEANS OF EGRESS

Readily Visible: Yes□ No□   Clear and Unobstructed: Yes□   No□

Two Remote Exits Available: Yes□   No□   Travel Distance within Limits: Yes□   No□

Common Path of Travel within Limits: Yes□   No□   Dead-Ends within Limits: Yes□   No□

50% Maximum through Level of Exit Discharge: Yes□   No□

50% Maximum through Checkout Stands: Yes□   No□

Exit through Stockroom: Yes□   No□   Not Capable of Locking: Yes□   No□

Aisle 44˝: Yes□   No□   Aisles Marked and have Physical Barriers: Yes□   No□

Adequate Illumination: Yes□   No□

Proper Rating on All Components: Yes□   No□

All Exit Enclosures Free of Storage: Yes□   No□

Door Swing in the Direction of Egress Travel (when required): Yes□   No□

Panic/Fire Exit Hardware Operable: Yes□   No□

Doors Open Easily: Yes□   No□   Self-Closures Operable: Yes□   No□

Doors Closed or Held Open With Automatic Closures: Yes□   No□

Corridors and Aisles of Sufficient Size: Yes□   No□

Stairwell Re-Entry: Yes□   No□

Mezzanines: Yes□   No□   Proper Exits: Yes□   No□

VERTICAL OPENINGS

Properly Protected: Yes□   No□

Atrium: Yes□   No□   Properly Protected: Yes□   No□

Are Fire Doors in Good Working Order: Yes□   No□

OPERATING FEATURES

Employees Trained in Fire Exit Procedures: Yes□   No□

Employees Trained in Fire Extinguisher Use: Yes□   No□

CHAPTER 26

Business Occupancies

*N*FPA *101, Life Safety Code,* defines business occupancies as those used for the transaction of business, for the keeping of accounts and records, and similar purposes. They include general offices, doctors' offices, government offices, city halls, municipal office buildings, courthouses, outpatient medical clinics where patients are ambulatory, college and university classroom buildings, and instructional laboratories. Business occupancies typically have large numbers of occupants during normal business hours and very few occupants during nonworking hours.

Occupancy Characteristics

Business occupancies can be in buildings of any construction type permitted by local building codes; the *Life Safety Code* does not specify construction requirements for business occupancies. Many fire-resistive high rise buildings are classified as business occupancies.

With the exception of apartments, the *Life Safety Code* does not require business occupancies to be separated from other occupancies. However, where business occupancies are mixed with other occupancies, local building codes might require occupancy separation, usually with at least 1-hour fire-resistant construction.

In mixed occupancies, the *Life Safety Code* requirements for both occupancies must be satisfied. In other words, the *Life Safety Code* requirements for both occupancies are applied simultaneously. Where there are conflicting requirements, the requirements affording the highest level of safety must be applied. As the inspector, you must understand the potential for loss in the event of a fire caused by the conditions in the building, and you must make enforcement decisions that affect fire safety.

Business occupancies traditionally have been subdivided into many small office cubicles. While done for other reasons, these subdivisions compartmentalized an otherwise large floor area. The advent of open plan office space, however, has, for the most part, taken away these natural fire barriers. In an open-plan design, large floor areas are subdivided into cubicles using office furniture and partitions that do not extend from the floor to ceiling. Fire can spread more quickly from one work station to another because of the exposed combustibles. One advantage of the open plan arrangement, however, is that occupants usually are able to detect a fire quickly because they have an open view of the floor area.

Business occupancies generally are thought to have a light hazard fuel load. Although the fuel load in office space from wood furniture and trim has declined since the 1940s, it has increased due to the use of more paper in office operations, and the use of more plastics and other synthetic materials in furnishings and equipment. Because of the increase in the use of synthetic material, mostly plastics, the concept of fuel load should be used carefully as a predictor of fire severity. Synthetic products often have high heat release rates, which causes fires of these materials to be more severe than those of an equal volume of wood.

In addition, business occupancies often have significant fuel loads that are not fixed or constant. They include delivered materials and furniture, and trash that is removed from the buildings. These fuels usually are found in aisles and corridors, which increases their threat to life safety. A fire load analysis cannot be considered complete without an estimate of the transient fuel loads expected in the building.

The atrium has become an extremely popular design characteristic in both large and small office buildings. An atrium can be a problem or a benefit, depending on its size and location in the building. An atrium can present a fire safety problem because heat and smoke can spread through its opening from floor to floor, especially in smaller atria. On the other hand, an atrium can provide a place for the heat and smoke to go. It can also help dilute smoke, which typical features of conventional designs do not. The *Life Safety Code* now contains special requirements for atria, which include automatic sprinklers. Engineered smoke control systems are required for atria more than three stories in height. You should evaluate atrium designs carefully because older ones do not incorporate these concepts and may pose a risk to life or property.

Although building occupancies typically have light fuel loads, large life loss fires can occur in them during normal working hours because occupant load can be up to one person for each 100 square feet of gross floor area. The significant transient fuel loads also contribute to this potential problem.

Business occupancy floor plans change often, and these renovations can cause a properly designed means of egress to be disturbed, obstructed, or blocked. These renovations also can be a source of ignition, increasing the chance of fire. One of your first tasks during your inspection is to determine if there will be or have been any recent changes or renovations to the building or changes to floor plans.

Means of Egress

The basic requirements of means of egress for other occupancies apply to business occupancies, as well. There should be two remote exits from every floor, and egress travel paths should be illuminated. The exits must be located in a way that will reasonably reduce the possibility of both exits being blocked by a single fire incident. In some instances, there can only be one exit. Those circumstances are described in Chapters 26 and 27 of the *Life Safety Code.*

When two exits are required, they must be remotely located, and they must have separate paths of travel. The entrances to the exits as well as their discharges also must be located so that a single fire would not block both exits. Two exits discharging through a common lobby do not meet this requirement. One of the most prevalent problems in business occupancies is excessive common paths of travel. See Chapter 15 for a discussion on common path of travel.

If occupants must walk through corridors to reach exits, the walls separating the corridors from spaces must be of 1-hour fire-resistant construction. Exceptions to this requirement are permitted for single-tenant spaces and in spaces protected by automatic sprinklers. Corridor walls primarily are required to control smoke; therefore, even when a 1-hour rated wall is not used, it should be smoke resistant. The *Life Safety Code* gives requirements for permissible corridor penetrations and required protection of openings.

The exit discharge probably is the most overlooked portion of the means of egress. All the requirements pertaining to an unobstructed path of travel and illumination apply to the exit discharge even though the exit discharge is outside the building. When emergency lighting is required, the exit discharge also must have some degree of emergency lighting. The exit discharge must be kept free of obstructions, and there must be a reliable method for preventing ice and snow from accumulating in areas subject to such weather conditions. Check the areas around the exit doors to determine if there is anything unusual that could cause problems in an emergency.

To be useful, exit doors must be accessible. Many times, in attempting to lay out an office for best space utilization, little consideration is given to maintaining clear access to exits. In open plan office spaces, be alert for furniture arrangements that obstruct direct access to exit doors.

Exit doors must be capable of being opened from the occupied side at all times. In multiple tenant offices, doors sometimes are locked for security reasons with little thought given to life safety. Only locking devices capable of being opened by the person seeking egress are permitted. Special locking arrangements, including time-delay locks and locks operated by motion sensors, are permitted and usually can be arranged to solve security concerns.

The exit itself must be accessible and unobstructed. Locking of stair doors is a common problem that you must look for. You should walk the stairs from top to bottom to ensure the path of travel is unobstructed. Doors at the termination of exits must be obvious and openable. Stair doors should not be locked from the stair side so that people using them won't get trapped if there is a fire in the stairway. If stair doors are locked from the stair side, there must be some method of unlocking them, or some floors should be designated to remain unlocked.

The *Life Safety Code* permits two methods for reentry in business occupancies. The first is electric locking devices that automatically unlock (but not unlatch) doors, allowing reentry upon the activation of the building fire alarm system. These devices must unlock if the device or power fails. The second method requires that at least two doors for reentry be provided in each stair, one of which must be at the top or next-to-top floor. In tall buildings, reentry doors must be provided so that there are no more than four intervening floors between unlocked doors.

When emergency lighting is required, the coverage must be adequate to maintain the minimum 1 footcandle illumination. Emergency lighting is required at the exit discharge, both inside and outside the building, and this is often overlooked.

Travel distance to an exit, which is a measurement of the time people have to react and escape from a fire, must not exceed 200 feet in unsprinklered buildings, or 300 feet in sprinklered buildings. Travel distance is an important life safety requirement, but care must be taken to ensure that the travel distance requirement is met in a reasonable way. Some open floor plans can be arranged in such a way that the furniture creates a maze, which greatly hinders occupants who are trying to escape. Travel distance is important, but you must use flexibility when enforcing its requirements.

Exits must be marked in business occupancies, and exit signs should be placed to properly mark exits and paths to exits that otherwise are not readily apparent. The *Life Safety Code* requires exit signs to be placed in corridors so that a person is not more than 100 feet from an exit sign at any point in the corridor. In buildings with open floor plans, the exit signs must properly mark the path to the exit. In occupancies with floor plans using low height partitions, the signs might be visible from a great distance, but the floor plan might prohibit direct travel to the exit. Thus it might be necessary to place some signs on the partitions.

Although internally illuminated exit signs are not required, all exit signs must be illuminated in some way. If emergency lighting is required, then the exit signs also must be illuminated by the emergency lighting source. Often, a placard-type sign lit by emergency lights will meet this requirement.

Protection of Openings

Openings in fire-rated walls should be protected with doors or other approved protective devices. Check the doors to ensure that they close and latch properly. Closing devices are required on fire doors, and they should function properly. A labeled door leaf, door frame, closer, and latch are required. Have any wedges used to hold doors open removed immediately. Automatic hold-open-and-release devices should be used on fire doors that, for functional purposes, need to remain open daily.

Windows in rated walls and doors must be of fire-resistant glass (usually wired) or an approved material in steel frames. There are also transparent materials that provide a fire-resistive barrier but do not have wires that obstruct the view. Review information available on such material carefully. Windows of plain glass, or wooden or aluminum frames, in rated walls should be replaced with proper assemblies. Tempered glass protected by a water curtain in an atrium does not have to be wired.

Hazardous Areas

General storage rooms, boiler rooms, fuel storage rooms, janitor closets, and maintenance shops are considered hazardous areas and should be separated from the rest of the building by 1-hour fire-resistant construction; openings should be protected by 3/4-hour, C-labeled fire doors. If hazardous areas are protected by sprinklers, they only need to be enclosed by smoke-resistant walls, and the openings should be protected by self-closing, smoke-resistant doors.

Computer Rooms

Electronic data processing equipment has become both vital and commonplace in many businesses. This equipment can be highly sophisticated and extremely valuable; in fact, both equipment and data can be so unique that they can't be replaced. If there are computers in the building, you will have to inspect them. With the advent of office automation, practically any office can look like a computer room, but there are significant differences that you cannot determine solely by visual inspection. Discuss the operation with the occupants to determine what impact a fire would have on the equipment. A business can be destroyed if it loses its computers, associated software, or data. And even a small fire can produce enough smoke to wreak havoc with the computers.

Computer rooms should be of fire-resistive construction with noncombustible interior finish. They should be located away from hazardous areas. The floor should be raised to house electrical and signal wiring, and to function as a plenum for air conditioning systems.

Computers use considerable quantities of paper and other combustible support media, such as magnetic tape. It is good practice to restrict paper materials in the computer room to the absolute minimum necessary for efficient operations. Check that there are enclosed metal cabinets for storing combustibles in the computer room. Extra paper and other combustible supplies should be stored in an orderly fashion in proper areas outside the computer room, but they should not be stored in halls or corridors.

Computer rooms require reliable fire protection because the machines and the magnetic tapes, flexible discs, and similar materials used with them can be damaged by heat as low as 100°F-200°F, or by small amounts of smoke. The room should be protected by automatic sprinklers if there is a significant amount of combustible materials.

Computer rooms also can be protected by total flooding halon 1301 systems with automatic and manual controls. However, the effectiveness of such systems on ordinary combustibles such as paper, is questionable, because halon is more effective on flaming combustion but less effective on surface combustion. In addition, once the extinguishing agent is released, it must be held in the room to work; if the room has leaks, the system cannot be considered reliable. You also should make the users of such systems aware that production of halon is gradually being phased out, and its users will be significantly taxed, because of its ozone depletion potential.

Portable fire extinguishers should be provided, and occupants should be trained to use them to extinguish small fires in the computer room. Carbon dioxide extinguishers should be used for extinguishing electrical fires, and pressurized water extinguishers should be provided for extinguishing fires of ordinary combustibles.

If there is a raised floor, check that smoke detectors are installed in the under-floor area. Find out how audible and visual alarms are activated. Ensure that there are ways to disconnect all electronic equipment in and the air conditioning system for the computer room in the event of an emergency, such as fire. The means of disconnecting should be located near the operator's console and next to the main entrance door and all exits. Employees should have and know a well defined emergency plan describing proper action in a fire emergency.

NFPA 75, *Standard for the Protection of Electronic Computer/Data Processing Equipment,* contains more detailed requirements for fire protection for computer installations.

Protection of Records

Records are important to businesses, and you should find out what provisions have been made to protect them. Inquire if vital records—those records that are irreplaceable and absolutely essential to sustain the business—are protected properly. Important records—records that can be reproduced from original sources—also require protection, but not, perhaps, at the level required for vital records.

Small quantities of valuable records can be stored in factory-built record protection equipment, such as insulated record containers, fire-resistant safes, and insulated fire devices, all of which can have varying degrees of resistance to fire, heat, and impact. Containers providing special production are rated by tests conducted under fire conditions and bear labels indicating they have been listed or labeled for the degree of protection stated. Containers intended to provide protection for magnetic tapes and disc packs associated with electronic computers must meet more stringent requirements than must containers for paper records.

Vaults usually are used when the volume of valuable records is large. For many years it was considered impractical and dangerous to penetrate the walls of vaults with piping and electrical wiring because it was thought that such penetrations would provide paths for heat and fire to enter the vault. In reality, though, the internal contents of some vaults are more hazardous than any external exposure. Consequently, vault standards have been revised to permit sprinkler systems, lighting, and circuits for fire detection systems. You may find older vaults that have no internal protective devices; if so, it might be appropriate to recommend internal protection.

Specially protected file rooms, which permit lighting, heating, ventilation, filing cabinets, and furniture, are practical if there is a comparatively large volume of important records. Less important records can be stored in a variety of uninsulated record containers and shelf storage ranging from open shelves to mobile shelving consisting of open shelves on tracks.

Evaluating the worth of records, no matter what kind they are, is a management responsibility in which your only responsibility as an inspector is to provide information on possible exposure to loss; therefore, you should be prepared to tell management what different levels of protection are available for records of different value and volume.

You can find more specific information and requirements for the protection of records in the *Fire Protection Handbook,* and in NFPA 232, *Standard for the Protection of Records.*

Building Services

Waste Disposal

Business occupancies can generate large amounts of waste paper. Usually this waste is removed at the end of the day. This can create a significant fuel load in corridors and freight elevator lobbies as the occupants of the building are leaving or have left. In areas containing computers or other very valuable contents, trash containers with special tops that limit air supply, which thus smothers a fire in the can, should be used.

The principal concern is how waste material is handled after it is collected from the various offices and work stations. Smoking materials improperly discarded into trash collection containers have ignited other trash in the containers, and these fires have spread to other areas. Thus, special precautions to prevent this should be taken. These include using specially designed container tops and discarding smoking materials into noncombustible cans and allowing them to cool before they are disposed of.

All waste should be removed from the building quickly. If it's stored within the building for short periods of time, the waste should be in proper containers or stored in specially designed rooms. The practice of piling up waste in plastic bags in elevator lobbies or corridors while awaiting removal can have disastrous results. Once waste is removed from the building, it is commonly held in outside storage bins (dumpsters) for frequent removal from the premises. If that is the case, observe the general condition of the outside storage area. It should be far enough away from the building so that it does not present a fire exposure to the building. Sturdy enclosures around trash storage areas can discourage vandalism and unauthorized dumping, both of which can lead to dumpster fires.

Some buildings have waste chutes running from upper floors to a collection bin or room. These chutes should be protected by sprinklers. The walls, ceiling, and floor of the room must have a fire-resistance rating equal to that of the chute. Chutes, which are floor openings, must have fire-rated hopper-type doors that are self closing and positive latching. Check that the doors work well, which may not be the case in older buildings. Newer buildings might have pneumatic waste-chute services, which require electrical interlocks between the inner and outer doors at the chute openings.

NFPA 82, *Standard on Incinerators, Waste, and Linen Handling Systems and Equipment,* contains more specific requirements for trash chutes and rooms.

Cafeterias

Many large business occupancy buildings have their own cafeteria facilities and kitchens. Examine the kitchen equipment for evidence of grease accumulations in hoods and exhaust ducts; good duct installations will have cleaning and inspection openings. Ducts and their interior must be 18 inches from any combustible material.

Hoods, exhaust ducts, and grease removal devices must be protected by approved extinguishing systems, which usually consist of fixed-pipe carbon dioxide, dry chemical, or foam sprinkler or spray systems. If there are no special extinguishing systems, the cooking equipment might be served by a listed or labeled grease retractor, which may provide sufficient protection. The cooking surface of fat fryers, ranges, griddles, and broilers, which can be a source of ignition, also need to be protected by appropriate extinguishing systems.

Make sure that instructions for manually operating the fire extinguishing systems are posted conspicuously. Asking kitchen employees how the systems operate should give you an indication of how familiar they are with the systems. Check the log to determine when the special systems were last serviced and inspected; they should be inspected and serviced every six months.

Make sure there are enough portable fire extinguishers suitable for Class B and Class C fires near the cooking equipment. If the fixed extinguisher uses a dry chemical extinguishing agent, make sure that the portable fire extinguishers in the area are compatible with it. For example, if the fixed system uses a BC dry chemical, the portable extinguisher should also be BC, not ABC. Note when portable extinguishers were last inspected and serviced.

Cleaning ducts is a messy business and is frequently neglected, but it must be done. Commercial firms are available to do it, but you can suggest to management that cleaning the ducts with a powder consisting of one part calcium hydroxide and two parts calcium carbonate has worked well, if they want in-house staff to clean the ducts. The compound saponifies the grease or oily sludge, thus making it easier to remove and clean.

See Chapter 47, "Venting Systems for Commercial Cooking Equipment" of this Manual and NFPA 96, *Standard on Ventilation Control and Fire Protection of Commercial Cooking Operations,* for more complete discussion of and specific requirements for kitchen cooking equipment installations.

Shafts and Chases

The integrity of shafts and chases is as important in business occupancies as in any other occupancy. When new buildings are constructed, utility risers usually are enclosed in fire-resistive construction, or floor penetrations are sealed with appropriate fire-resistive materials. As buildings are used, often new cable, conduit, or piping is run between floors, and the new penetrations may not be sealed.

Check telephone and electric closets and mechanical shafts and risers to determine if there are unprotected floor openings or penetrations through fire-resistive walls. Such openings can be sealed with lightweight concrete or other suitable materials, such as silicon foam.

Fire Protection

Automatic Sprinklers

Automatic sprinklers are required in business occupancies that are in buildings higher than 75 feet when measured from the lowest level of fire department access to the highest occupiable floor. The sprinkler system must be electrically supervised. In lieu of sprinklers, existing buildings can be equipped with an alternative equivalent system approved by the authority having jurisdiction.

The adequacy of sprinklers, or an equivalent system, depends on several basic conditions. The hazard severity must be analyzed to ensure that the protective system is sufficient to control a fire. The impact of the expected fire must be judged to determine its effect on the occupants and the rest of the building. And the occupants' response, both first aid fire fighting and ability to escape, must be determined as part of the incident impact. You can use this information to determine whether adequate protection is provided.

Sprinkler systems, although highly reliable, require regular testing and maintenance. Ensure that all sprinkler valves, including water supply, are open and locked or supervised in that position. Closed water supply valves are the most common cause of sprinkler system failures. Find out if there is a procedure for ensuring that sprinkler valves are closed only when properly authorized and turned on again following any maintenance or modification. Check records of sprinkler system testing and maintenance.

Because of legal liability issues, you should have a policy regarding testing systems: In general the building owner, or representative, should do all testing; you should witness any tests required to be performed as part of an inspection.

Alarm Systems

A manual fire alarm system and an emergency lighting system, are required when a business occupancy is two or more stories above the level of exit discharge, when the occupant load above or below the level of exit discharge is 100 or more, or when the occupant load of the building is 1,000 or more. When the building is fully sprinklered or totally protected by an automatic fire alarm system, manual pull stations are not required if the sprinklers or automatic system cause the evacuation alarm to sound.

Because of poor maintenance in many business occupancies, you must test all fire protection systems. Special attention should be paid to alarm annunciation and control sequence for smoke control fans. As with sprinkler systems, you should witness tests, with the building owner, or representative, doing the actual testing.

Portable Fire Extinguishers

Portable fire extinguishers are required in business occupancies. They should be used, placed, and maintained in accordance with NFPA 10, *Standard on Portable Fire Extinguishers,* and state and local laws. Examine testing and maintenance records to ensure that they are being properly tested and maintained.

Operating Features

Chapter 31 of the *Life Safety Code* contains requirements on operating features for all occupancies. Check Section 31-1 for general operating requirements. Specific requirements for business occupancies include having a written fire exit procedure, and all occupants must be trained in that procedure. In addition, fire drills must be held on a schedule acceptable to the local authorities. Employees of the building, usually the operating staff, must be trained in the proper use of portable fire extinguishers in the building.

Bibliography

NFPA 75, *Standard for the Protection of Electronic Computer/Data Processing Equipment*
NFPA 86, *Standard for Ovens and Furnaces*
NFPA 96, *Standard on Ventilation Control and Fire Protection of Commercial Cooking Operations*
NFPA *101, Life Safety Code*
NFPA 232, *Standard for the Protection of Records*

BUSINESS OCCUPANCY FIRE INSPECTION FORM

Property Name: Owner:

Address: Phone Number:

OCCUPANCY

Change from Last Inspection: Yes☐ No☐

Occupant Load: Egress Capacity: Any Renovations: Yes☐ No☐

High Rise: Yes☐ No☐   Windowless: Yes☐ No☐   Underground: Yes☐ No☐

BUILDING SERVICES

Electricity☐ Gas☐ Water☐ Other☐   Are Utilities in Good Working Order: Yes☐ No☐

Elevators: Yes☐ No☐   Fire Service Control: Yes☐ No☐   Elevator Recall: Yes☐ No☐

Heat Type: Gas☐ Oil☐ Electric☐ Coal☐ Other☐   In Good Working Order: Yes☐ No☐

Emergency Generator: Yes☐ No☐   Size: Last Date Tested:

Date of Last Full Load Test: In Automatic Position: Yes☐ No☐

Fire Pump: Yes☐ No☐   GPM: Suction Pressure: System Pressure:

Date Last Tested: Date of Last Flow Test:

In Automatic Position: Yes☐ No☐   Jockey Pump: Yes☐ No☐

EMERGENCY LIGHTS

Operable: Yes☐ No☐   Tested Monthly: Yes☐ No☐

Properly Illuminate Egress Paths: Yes☐ No☐   In Good Condition: Yes☐ No☐

EXIT SIGNS

Illuminated: Internally☐ Externally☐   Readily Visible: Yes☐ No☐

FIRE ALARM

Yes☐ No☐   Location of Panel:

Coverage: Building☐ Partial☐   Monitored: Yes☐ No☐   Method:

Type of Initiation Devices: Smoke☐ Heat☐ Manual☐ Water Flow☐ Special Systems☐

Date of Last Test: Date of Last Inspection:

Notification Signal Adequate: Yes☐ No☐   Fire Department Notification: Yes☐ No☐

FIRE EXTINGUISHERS

Proper Type for Hazard Protecting: Yes☐ No☐   Mounted Properly: Yes☐ No☐
Date of Last Inspection: Adequate Number: Yes☐ No☐

FIRE PROTECTION SYSTEMS

Type: Sprinkler☐ Halon☐ CO2☐ Standpipe☐ Water Spray☐ Foam☐ Dry Chemical☐
   Wet Chemical☐ Other☐
Coverage: Building☐ Partial☐   Date of Last Inspection
Cylinder or Gauge Pressure(s): 1   psi.,2   psi.,3   psi.,4   psi.,5   psi.
Valves Supervised: Electrical☐ Lock☐ Seal☐ Other☐   Are Valves Accessible: Yes☐ No☐
System Operational: Yes☐ No☐   Sprinkler Heads 18" from Storage: Yes☐ No☐

FIRE RESISTIVE (FR) CONSTRUCTION

Stairway FR: Yes☐ No☐   Hourly Rating:
Corridors FR: Yes☐ No☐   Hourly Rating:
Elevator Shaft FR: Yes☐ Yes☐ No☐   Hourly Rating:
Major Structural Members FR: Yes☐ No☐   Hourly Rating:
Floor-Ceiling Assemblies FR: Yes☐ No☐   Hourly Rating:
All Openings Protected in FR Walls and Floor-Ceiling Assemblies: Yes☐ No☐

HAZARDOUS AREAS

Protected by: Fire-Rated Separation☐ Extinguishing System☐ Both☐
Door Self-Closures: Yes☐ No☐
Residential Separated: Yes☐ No☐   1-Hour Fire Resistance Rating☐ Sprinklers☐
Parking Structure Separated: Yes☐ No☐
Kitchen Exhaust Hoods Properly Protected: Yes☐ No☐   Clean: Yes☐ No☐
Date of Last Inspection:

HOUSEKEEPING

Areas Free of Excessive Combustibles: Yes☐ No☐
Smoking Regulated: Yes☐ No☐

INTERIOR FINISH

Walls and Ceilings Proper Rating: Yes☐ No☐   Floor Finish Proper Rating: Yes☐ No☐

MEANS OF EGRESS

Readily Visible: Yes☐ No☐   Clear and Unobstructed: Yes☐ No☐
Two Remote Exits Available: Yes☐ No☐   Travel Distance within Limits: Yes☐ No☐
Common Path of Travel within Limits: Yes☐ No☐   Dead-Ends within Limits: Yes☐ No☐
50% Maximum through Level of Exit Discharge: Yes☐ No☐
Adequate Illumination: Yes☐ No☐
Proper Rating on All Components: Yes☐ No☐
All Exit Enclosures Free of Storage: Yes☐ No☐
Door Swing in the Direction of Egress Travel (when required): Yes☐ No☐
Panic/Fire Exit Hardware Operable: Yes☐ No☐
Doors Open Easily: Yes☐ No☐   Self-Closures Operable: Yes☐ No☐
Doors Closed or Held Open With Automatic Closures: Yes☐ No☐
Corridors and Aisles of Sufficient Size: Yes☐ No☐
Stairwell Re-Entry: Yes☐ No☐
Mezzanines: Yes☐ No☐   Proper Exits: Yes☐ No☐

VERTICAL OPENINGS

Properly Protected: Yes☐   No☐

Atrium: Yes☐   No☐   Properly Protected: Yes☐   No☐

Are Fire Doors in Good Working Order: Yes☐   No☐

OPERATING FEATURES

Employees Instructed in Fire Extinguisher Use: Yes☐   No☐

Fire Drills Performed: Yes☐   No☐   Date of Last Fire Drill:

Are Records Protected: Yes☐   No☐

. . . .

CHAPTER 27

Industrial Occupancies

*A*n industrial occupancy is any building, portion of a building, or group of buildings used for the manufacture, assembly, service, mixing, packaging, finishing, repair, treatment, or other processing of goods or commodities by a variety of operations or processes. Industrial occupancies include, but are not limited to, the following:

Chemical plants
Factories of all kinds
Food processing plants
Furniture manufacturers
Hangars (for servicing/maintenance)
Laboratories involving hazardous chemicals
Laundry and dry cleaning plants
Metalworking
Plastics manufacture and molding
Power plants
Refineries
Semiconductor manufacturing
Telephone exchanges
Woodworking

Each building or separated portion of an industrial building should be inspected in accordance with the requirements of its principal use, for example: warehouses as storage occupancies; offices as business occupancies; and auditoriums, cafeterias, and lunchrooms as assembly occupancies. Because of the complexity of industrial occupancies, the inspections can be time consuming.

Classification of Occupancy

Industrial occupancies are subclassified in the *Life Safety Code* into three types of usage: general, special purpose, and high hazard.

General Industrial Occupancy: This subclassification involves ordinary and low hazard manufacturing operations conducted in buildings of conventional design suitable for various types of manufacture. Included are buildings suitable for such occupancy, or multistory buildings where floors are occupied by different tenants and, therefore, subject to possible use for types of manufacturing with a high density of employees.

Special Purpose Industrial Occupancy: This subclassification includes low and ordinary hazard manufacturing operations in buildings that were designed for and suitable only for particular types of operations. This subclassification is characterized by a relatively low density of employees, with much of the area occupied by machinery or equipment.

High Hazard Industrial Occupancy: Buildings in this subclassification include those having high hazard materials, processes, or contents. Incidental high hazard operations in low or ordinary hazard occupancies that are protected with automatic extinguishing systems or other protection (such as explosion suppression or venting) appropriate to a particular hazard are not considered high hazard occupancies overall.

Some of the common problems encountered in industrial occupancies include overcrowding, poor housekeeping, poor maintenance of electrical equipment and wiring, inadequate exit facilities, locked or blocked exits, misuse of flammable liquids and heat-producing appliances, and poor maintenance of fire protection systems and appliances. Code enforcement must be rigid and inspection thorough, with some emphasis on fire safety education and pre-fire planning.

Occupant Load

The occupant load in industrial occupancies is one person for each 100 square feet (9.3 square meters) of gross floor area, and exit facilities must be provided for them. In most plants, the space occupied by work benches, machinery, and equipment generally tends to keep the population well within the ratio. "Sweat shops," however, tend to be the exception.

An increased ratio is permitted if a floor plan showing that proper aisles and adequate exits are available to safely accommodate the increased load is submitted to the official having jurisdiction. In most instances, overcrowding will be fairly obvious to you when you make your inspection. In a special purpose industrial occupancy, the occupant load is the maximum number of persons to occupy the area under any probable conditions.

Means of Egress

Requirements for exits in industrial occupancies are found in Chapter 28 of the *Life Safety Code*. You should be aware of the requirements because you are responsible for seeing that all portions of a means of egress are maintained in a safe condition.

All exits must discharge to a clear and unobstructed path of travel on a public way. Where there is evidence of parked vehicles or other obstructions, signs or barriers should be erected to discourage the practice. Barriers should not obstruct the flow of persons exiting the building.

Exits must be clearly illuminated, identified, and accessible. You should establish the habit of opening every exit door to be sure it is unlocked, works freely, latches properly, is labeled when required, swings in the direction of egress travel when so required, and that self-closing or automatic-closing devices and mechanisms function properly.

Where pilferage might be a problem, means other than locking are available to prevent unauthorized use of exits. The *Life Safety Code* permits the use of approved, listed, special locking devices on exterior doors in industrial occupancies. All conditions set forth for their use must be followed. Special locking devices do not prevent the door from opening; they merely delay opening and sound an alarm. Special locking arrangements cannot be used in high hazard areas.

Where exit stairs are required to be enclosed, the enclosure and its protected openings must be of the proper fire-resistance ratings. Handrails must be secure, and stair treads and landings should be slip-resistant. Stairways cannot be used for storage or any other purpose, and they must be illuminated.

Every worker must have access to not less than two remotely located exits. The path of travel must be clear, illuminated, unobstructed, and as direct as possible without exceeding maximum travel distances. Where the exit and path of travel are not clearly visible, signs must be provided to indicate the direction. A short common path of travel to two otherwise remote exits is permitted, except from an area of high hazard. Exitway access must not pass through areas of high hazard. When evacuation must be delayed because of the need to safely shut down an operation, or for any other reason, special provisions to protect the workers might be required.

You must ensure that all elements composing the means of egress remain in compliance with the requirements during periods of renovation and construction. This is especially important when partitions are erected to separate construction areas from work or production areas. Large loss fires have occurred in all types of occupancies during periods of construction, and industrial occupancies are particularly vulnerable due to their complexity and the work processes performed in them.

Emergency lighting is required in all facilities except those occupied only during daylight hours in which skylights or windows are arranged to provide, during those hours, the required level of illumination for all portions of the means of egress. You should check the type of lighting used and review records of servicing and testing. If battery packs are used for an emergency power supply, there should be an indicator light to show full-charge condition and a test button to check its operability.

Protection of Openings

When inspecting industrial occupancies, you must check on the integrity of fire-rated wall, floor/ceiling, and roof/ceiling assemblies. With changing technology, changing operations and processes, and new tenants, industrial plants undergo revisions that create openings and holes through fire-rated assemblies. Pipes, electrical conduits, cable trays, and other penetrating items must be properly sealed and firestopped. Penetration seals must be made of approved or listed materials and be installed such that they maintain the fire rating of the wall or floor assembly in which they are installed.

Ductwork going through rated assemblies must be equipped with fire doors or fire dampers unless specifically exempted by code. Where dampers are prohibited, such as for exhaust systems for cooking appliances, such ductwork must not pass through rated assemblies.

Check to see that fire doors are of the proper rating for the enclosure in which they are installed and that they are self-closing. Check that automatic closure devices and mechanisms operate properly. Any obstructions that could interfere with the fire door closing completely must be removed (e.g., wooden wedges or the door being tied open). Check the tracks of vertical sliding and roll-up doors for mechanical damage, especially when the openings are used by industrial trucks. Consideration should be given to installing guards to prevent stock from being piled up against the door or vehicles from striking it. Check that all doors get closed at the end of the business day. Inspect each door for evidence of excessive wear and tear, modifications to the door, or other defects that make its continued use suspect.

Check all vertical openings, such as conveyors, elevators, stairs, dumbwaiters, and refuse chutes, for proper enclosure and to be sure that all openings are properly protected and of the proper fire rating. Check that pipe chases and other vertical recesses are firestopped.

Fire shutters should be checked to ensure that they have proper automatic closing devices and that such mechanisms are operable. On building exteriors facing fire exposure hazards, check doors and windows for rating and glazing. Check the glazing of all fire doors that are permitted to have glass to ensure that the wired glass is of the proper size and thickness.

Hazardous Materials

As the inspector, you must determine the properties of all of the materials used in industrial plants and see that they are stored and handled safely. In order to do this, especially with chemicals, you must have good reference sources. Because inspection is not an emergency activity, you can record what is found, how it is stored and handled, and then do research back at your desk. If the research indicates that special precautions are required, you will need to perform a follow-up inspection to ensure that such precautions are being taken.

Once a material has been identified, classified, and categorized by the degree of its physical and chemical properties, half the work has been done. You must then determine if there are excessive amounts of materials for the fire area and for the provided level of protection. You also must determine the requirements for and the adequacy of the venting, if provided; if electrical equipment has been classified properly; if electrical wiring is in good condition and properly maintained; and if there are ignition sources.

Production and process areas should contain only those amounts of hazardous materials that are necessary to the immediate process or operation. The maximum amount should be limited to the needs of one day or one shift, and then only when relatively small amounts are used. Be sure to inspect the methods used to transfer hazardous materials from the shipping container or bulk storage area into the process or operation area. You also should look for possible ignition sources.

Many hazardous industrial processes have been fully evaluated, and standards have been established for their safe operation. The *National Fire Codes* (see Appendix) contain all of the standards for safe operation of the most common industrial processes and many that are not common. In addition, the NFPA *Industrial Fire Hazards Handbook* covers a broad range of fire hazards that are found in major industrial occupancies. You should use this material when evaluating hazardous industrial processes and also when conducting your inspection. It is desirable for the *Life Safety Code* (NFPA 101), the *Fire Prevention Code* (NFPA 1), and the *National Fire Codes* to be adopted by your jurisdiction so that compliance becomes mandatory, thereby making it easier to enforce their requirements.

In those situations where there is no established standard to follow, you must use judgment in identifying the process or operational hazards and determining if they are being controlled properly. The protection afforded must be appropriate to the hazard or hazards, and ignition sources must be controlled. A relatively small hazardous process incidental to the main operations, such as a small paint spray booth, should not change the classification of the entire area to one of high hazard. You should look for the installation of a special extinguishing system, such as carbon dioxide or dry chemical, because very often it is required by the codes. You also may find the installation of draft curtains or special venting arrangements.

In the chemical and allied industries, there are hundreds of different processes and thousands of variations that are well beyond your ability to evaluate. This is not to say that you should skip inspecting these properties or only give them a superficial inspection. You should identify all of the chemicals used and their hazardous properties, and they should then be placed in broad classifications, such as corrosive, flammable, combustible, unstable, or reactive, based on their degrees of hazard. Ask to see a copy of the Material Safety Data Sheet (MSDS). An MSDS is provided by the manufacturer or compounder, or blender, of the chemical and contains information about the chemical composition, physical and chemical properties, health and safety hazards, emergency response, and waste disposal of the material. Evaluating storage, transfer method, compatibility, and so on can give you a good indication of whether or not safe practices are being followed.

Some general questions concerning the various processes can be asked. Is there an operator's manual? Is the operator trained? Does the manual cover the hazards of the materials, the safe and critical temperatures and pressures, the proper sequence for adding materials, the consequences for failure to follow a formula exactly? Does the process have fail-safe automatic controls? Asking many additional questions can help you make a limited evaluation.

If you are to obtain meaningful information, you must gain the confidence of management and show that you can be trusted with trade secrets and confidential information. Because there are trade secrets in every phase of industry, you should not be insulted if you are asked to sign a pledge of confidentiality.

Storage

Outdoor Storage

The storage of materials outdoors usually is limited to those used in large quantities and those that are not susceptible to damage by weather. Storage practices should follow recommended safe practices.

All outdoor storage should be arranged so that it will not interfere with fire fighting access to and around buildings. Where the materials stored are combustible or flammable, or both, they should be far enough away from other buildings so that, if on fire, one will not be an exposure hazard to another. There should be sufficient fire hydrants and hose houses with fire lanes to make outdoor combustible storage accessible on all sides. Areas must be free of vegetation and other loose combustibles.

Indoor General Storage

Preferably, storage areas should be in separate buildings or in cutoff sections of buildings used for no other purpose.

Where storage is incidental to the main use of the building, you still should follow the general rules for storage occupancies as much as possible, but you also must make additional judgments as to safe practices. Hazardous materials in relatively small amounts should be stored with due regard for their hazardous properties: flammable liquids should be stored inside storage rooms or cabinets; loose, highly combustible fibers should be stored in metal or metal-lined bins with automatic-closing covers; and pyroxylin plastics should be stored in vaults and tote boxes.

Be certain that piles are stable and separated by adequate aisles, that clearance to sprinklers is maintained, and that materials being stored are compatible.

Stock piled over 12 feet in height and rack storage of materials require special consideration. See NFPA 231C, *Standard for Rack Storage of Materials,* for proper methods of storage and protection.

Idle pallets awaiting reuse, repair, or disposal can be a constant problem. They never should be stored in unsprinklered areas. When they are stored in sprinklered areas, the piles should cover a small area and be less than 8 feet high. Preferably they should be stored outdoors, well away from buildings and other storage areas.

Building Services

Housekeeping and Maintenance

Poor housekeeping and maintenance practices can be the most frustrating problem you will encounter and are probably the principal reasons for follow-up inspections. Improper housekeeping is not only a fire hazard, but it also indicates a lack of management commitment. Improper storage of materials and poor maintenance on pumps, piping, and exhaust systems can make floors slippery, atmospheres dusty, and interfere with the proper operation of fire protection equipment.

Industrial occupancies with good housekeeping and maintenance practices are relatively easy to inspect. As a general rule, where housekeeping and maintenance are a priority, most items of fire safety and protection also will be good, and less time probably will be needed to make a thorough inspection.

You should see that waste is removed properly and disposed of safely. Where waste has value as salvage, a safe collection area should be set apart and maintained in an orderly way. Chemical wastes must be disposed of in a manner that is safe for the environment and in accordance with state and federal regulations.

Fire Protection

When inspecting industrial plants you must be certain that existing fire protection systems and equipment are properly maintained. Check that portable fire extinguishers are properly located and are accessible. The locking pin should be in place and sealed, free from damage. There should be no foreign materials in hoses and nozzles that would interfere with their operation. Pressure gauges on extinguishers should indicate they are ready for use. Examine the tag for the last inspection and hydrostatic test dates. Extinguishers should be in cabinets or have covers when they are located in dusty or corrosive atmospheres. Their location should be marked clearly.

Water Supplies and Fire Pumps

You will have to rely on records and reports when inspecting water supplies because much of the piping and valves are buried. Industrial occupancies often have more than one source of water supply (e.g., tanks, ponds, city connections), and you will have to check each one. Check aboveground portions for proper maintenance. Make sure that all supply valves are open, gravity tanks work, fire hydrants are maintained, and so on. Review records of water-flow tests, pump tests, valve-operating records for underground valves, and hydrant inspection reports. Signs of neglected maintenance usually will be obvious.

Check pump rooms to determine if fire pumps and fire booster pumps are ready for operation if needed. The power should be on at the controller of electrically driven pumps, no trouble lights should be on, and the jockey pump should not run excessively or kick on too often. The fuel tanks of internal combustion drivers should be full or nearly so, and batteries should be fully charged with a trickle charger to keep them charged. Review records of pump testing and maintenance.

Sprinkler Systems

If sprinkler systems are to perform as they were intended to, periodic inspection and maintenance are essential. You should inspect them visually and witness periodic tests. In general, "hands-on" testing should be the responsibility of the building owner or an authorized maintenance company.

Special Extinguishing Systems

Special extinguishing systems consist of halon 1301 (or approved replacement agents), carbon dioxide, dry chemical, and foam systems. You must have a good idea of how the various systems operate. Your inspection must be visual; you should not test or manipulate valves. Check that the extinguishing agent used is proper for the hazard(s) being protected and that a reserve supply is available, if required. Check actuating devices and alarms, see that nozzles are clear and free of foreign matter, and that nozzle caps, where used, are free. Nozzles should be properly aimed and protected from damage.

When systems are of the total flooding type, all openings required to be closed on system actuation should be checked for proper operation. It is important that the hazard enclosure be properly sealed before system discharge. Check piping, cable assemblies, valves, and manifolds for damage. Examine records of inspection, testing, and recharging to see if maintenance has been proper. Specific information on these systems can be found in the appropriate *National Fire Codes* (see Appendix).

Standpipe Hose Systems

In industrial occupancies, standpipes and hose stations are more often supplied from the sprinkler system than from a separate system. Therefore, you should inspect these systems as you would sprinkler systems. Check that all valves on the water supply are open and that the fire department connection is accessible. Threads should not be damaged and should be properly capped. Swivels should work freely, and threads should be compatible with those of the local fire department.

Check hose cabinets or reels for proper installation, location, and accessibility. Check the hose for signs of deterioration, need for reracking, and be sure that the attached nozzle works freely. Hoses and outlets should have the same threads as those of the local fire department, or there should be an adaptor in the cabinet or at the reel.

Alarm Systems

Your inspection of an alarm system should be visual. Testing should be the responsibility of thoroughly trained employees or an outside alarm service company. However, you should review these test records as part of your inspection. Observe alarm-initiating devices for proper location, mechanical or electrical damage, painting, loading, or damage due to a corrosive atmosphere. Wiring should be in good condition and solidly fastened. Control panels should be in a safe location and readily accessible. The "power on" light should be lit, and all trouble lights and signals should be off. Service and test records should be in the panel enclosure. When emergency power is required, batteries should be fully charged. Equipment should be free from dirt or grit that can find its way into delicate parts and contacts.

Manual alarm stations also should be inspected for signs of any problems. Wiring should be secure and in good condition, and there should be no tape, wire, string, or other encumbrance to the effective use of the system. The stations should be located along natural egress paths, near exits.

Check alarm bells or gongs to see if they have been tampered with, painted, or damaged. Check all records to determine that required servicing and testing has been done. Review records of all supervisory signal systems and alarm signal systems. Detection systems for actuating special extinguishing systems usually are serviced by an outside service company under contract.

Bibliography

NFPA 30, *Flammable and Combustible Liquids Code*
NFPA 30B, *Code for the Manufacture and Storage of Aerosol Products*
NFPA 32, *Standard for Drycleaning Plants*
NFPA 35, *Standard for the Manufacture of Organic Coatings*
NFPA 36, *Standard for Solvent Extraction Plants*
NFPA 61B, *Standard for the Prevention of Fires and Explosions in Grain Elevators and Facilities Handling Bulk Raw Agricultural Commodities*
NFPA 61C, *Standard for the Prevention of Fire and Dust Explosions in Feed Mills*
NFPA 61D, *Standard for the Prevention of Fire and Dust Explosions in the Milling of Agricultural Commodities for Human Consumption*
NFPA 65, *Standard for the Processing and Finishing of Aluminum*
NFPA 81, *Standard for Fur Storage, Fumigation and Cleaning*
NFPA 88B, *Standard for Repair Garages*

NFPA *101*, *Life Safety Code*

NFPA 120, *Standard for Coal Preparation Plants*

NFPA 480, *Standard for the Storage, Handling and Processing of Magnesium Solids and Powders*

NFPA 481, *Standard for the Production, Processing, Handling, and Storage of Titanium*

NFPA 482, *Standard for the Production, Processing, Handling, and Storage of Zirconium*

NFPA 505, *Fire Safety Standard for Powered Industrial Trucks Including Type Designations, Areas of Use, Maintenance, and Operation*

NFPA 513, *Standard for Motor Freight Terminals*

NFPA 651, *Standard for the Manufacture of Aluminum Powder*

NFPA 654, *Standard for the Prevention of Fire and Dust Explosions in the Chemical, Dye, Pharmaceutical, and Plastics Industries*

NFPA 664, *Standard for the Prevention of Fires and Explosions in Wood Processing and Woodworking Facilities*

NFPA 1124, *Code for the Manufacture, Transportation, and Storage of Fireworks*

INDUSTRIAL OCCUPANCY FIRE INSPECTION FORM

Property Name: Owner:

Address: Phone Number:

OCCUPANCY

Change from Last Inspection: Yes☐ No☐

Occupant Load: Egress Capacity: Any Renovations: Yes☐ No☐

General Industrial☐   Special Purpose Industrial☐   High Hazard☐

High Rise: Yes☐ No☐   Windowless: Yes☐ No☐   Underground: Yes☐ No☐

BUILDING SERVICES

Electricity☐ Gas☐ Water☐ Other☐   Are Utilities in Good Working Order: Yes☐ No☐

Elevators: Yes☐ No☐   Fire Service Control: Yes☐ No☐   Elevator Recall: Yes☐ No☐

Heat Type: Gas☐ Oil☐ Electric☐ Coal☐ Other☐   In Good Working Order: Yes☐ No☐

Emergency Generator: Yes☐ No☐   Size: Last Date Tested:

Date of Last Full Load Test: In Automatic Position: Yes☐ No☐

Fire Pump: Yes☐ No☐   GPM: Suction Pressure: System Pressure:

Date Last Tested: Date of Last Flow Test:

In Automatic Position: Yes☐ No☐   Jockey Pump: Yes☐ No☐

EMERGENCY LIGHTS

Operable: Yes☐ No☐   Tested Monthly: Yes☐ No☐

Properly Illuminate Egress Paths: Yes☐ No☐   In Good Condition: Yes☐ No☐

EXIT SIGNS

Illuminated: Internally☐ Externally☐   Emergency Power: Yes☐ No☐   Readily Visible: Yes☐ No☐

FIRE ALARM

Yes☐ No☐   Location of Panel:

Coverage: Building☐ Partial☐   Monitored: Yes☐ No☐   Method:

Type of Initiation Devices: Smoke☐ Heat☐ Manual☐ Water Flow☐ Special Systems☐

Date of Last Test: Date of Last Inspection:

Notification Signal Adequate: Yes☐ No☐   Fire Department Notification: Yes☐ No☐

FIRE EXTINGUISHERS

Proper Type for Hazard Protecting: Yes☐ No☐   Mounted Properly: Yes☐ No☐

Date of Last Inspection: Adequate Number: Yes☐ No☐

FIRE PROTECTION SYSTEMS

Type: Sprinkler☐ Halon☐ CO2☐ Standpipe☐ Water Spray☐ Foam☐ Dry Chemical☐ Wet Chemical☐ Other☐

Coverage: Building☐ Partial☐   Date of Last Inspection:

Cylinder or Gauge Pressure(s): 1   psi.,2   psi.,3   psi.,4   psi.,5   psi.

Valves Supervised: Electrical☐ Lock☐ Seal☐ Other☐   Are Valves Accessible: Yes☐ No☐

System Operational: Yes☐ No☐   Sprinkler Heads 18˝ from Storage: Yes☐ No☐

FIRE RESISTIVE (FR) CONSTRUCTION

Stairway FR: Yes☐ No☐   Hourly Rating:

Corridors FR: Yes☐ No☐   Hourly Rating:

Elevator Shaft FR: Yes☐ Yes☐ No☐   Hourly Rating:

Major Structural Members FR: Yes☐ No☐   Hourly Rating:

Floor-Ceiling Assemblies FR: Yes☐ No☐   Hourly Rating:

All Openings Protected in FR Walls and Floor-Ceiling Assemblies: Yes☐ No☐

HAZARDOUS AREAS

Protected by: Fire-Rated Separation☐   Extinguishing System☐   Both☐

Door Self-Closures: Yes☐ No☐

Hazardous Materials: Yes☐ No☐   Properly Stored and Handled: Yes☐ No☐

Properly Protected: Yes☐ No☐

Are Lift Trucks Properly Stored: Yes☐ No☐   Is the Fuel Properly Stored: Yes☐ No☐

Is Fueling Done Properly: Yes☐ No☐   Are Extinguishers Provided: Yes☐ No☐

Hazardous Processes: Yes☐ No☐   Properly Protected: Yes☐ No☐

HOUSEKEEPING

Areas Free of Excessive Combustibles: Yes☐ No☐

Smoking Regulated: Yes☐ No☐

Is Stock Stored Properly: Yes☐ No☐

Are Incompatible Materials Separated: Yes☐ No☐

Is Trash Removed on Regular Basis: Yes☐ No☐

INTERIOR FINISH

Walls and Ceilings Proper Rating: Yes☐ No☐   Floor Finish Proper Rating: Yes☐ No☐

MEANS OF EGRESS

Readily Visible: Yes☐ No☐   Clear and Unobstructed: Yes☐ No☐

Two Remote Exits Available: Yes☐ No☐   Travel Distance within Limits: Yes☐ No☐

Common Path of Travel within Limits: Yes☐ No☐   Dead-Ends within Limits: Yes☐ No☐

50% Maximum through Level of Exit Discharge: Yes☐ No☐

Adequate Illumination: Yes☐ No☐

Proper Rating on All Components: Yes☐ No☐

All Exit Enclosures Free of Storage: Yes☐ No☐

Door Swing in the Direction of Egress Travel (when required): Yes☐ No☐

Panic/Fire Exit Hardware Operable: Yes☐ No☐

Doors Open Easily: Yes☐ No☐   Self-Closures Operable: Yes☐ No☐

Doors Closed or Held Open With Automatic Closures: Yes☐ No☐

Corridors and Aisles of Sufficient Size: Yes☐ No☐

Stairwell Re-Entry: Yes☐ No☐

Mezzanines: Yes☐ No☐   Proper Exits: Yes☐ No☐

VERTICAL OPENINGS

Properly Protected: Yes☐ No☐

Atrium: Yes☐ No☐   Properly Protected: Yes☐ No☐

Are Fire Doors in Good Working Order: Yes☐ No☐

OPERATING FEATURES

Fire Drills Held: Yes☐ No☐   Employees Trained in Emergency Procedures: Yes☐ No☐

CHAPTER 28

Storage Occupancies

S torage occupancies are buildings or structures used to store or shelter goods, merchandise, products, vehicles, or animals. Examples are warehouses, freight terminals, parking garages, aircraft storage hangars, grain elevators, barns, and stables. These facilities may be separate and distinct facilities or part of a multiple-use occupancy. When storage is incidental to the main use of the structure, it should be classified as part of the main occupancy when determining life safety requirements.

Considerable judgment must be exercised when determining whether storage is incidental to the main use of the building. One consideration is the hazard classification of the contents stored in the area. If they are classified as high hazard, the room or space must be separated from the rest of the occupancy by fire-resistive construction that meets the requirements of the local code or, where no code has been adopted, NFPA 220, *Standard on Types of Building Construction*. In cases where the hazard is severe, both fire-resistive construction and automatic fire suppression might be required.

As an inspector, you should be aware that storage occupancies or areas of storage occupancies that are used for packaging, labeling, sorting, special handling, or other operations that require an occupant load greater than that normally contemplated for storage must be classified as industrial occupancies when determining life safety requirements.

Parking garages, whether closed or open, aboveground or below, also must be classified as industrial occupancies if they contain an area in which repair operations are conducted. If the parking and repair sections are separated by 1-hour fire-rated construction, they can be treated separately. If separation is not provided, however, the entire building must comply with the industrial occupancy requirements. You should be aware of the special requirements for underground and windowless structures, which are covered in Chapter 30 of NFPA *101, Life Safety Code.*

Occupancy Characteristics

Storage occupancies can be classified as low, ordinary, or high hazard or a combination of these where mixed commodities are stored together. Where different degrees of hazard exist in the same structure and cannot be separated effectively, the requirements for the most hazardous classification govern. The authority having jurisdiction must use sound judgment when applying this principle of hazard classification. The *Life Safety Code* uses the ordinary hazard classification as the basis for general requirements. Most storage occupancies fall into this classification, although an increasing percentage are being classified as high hazard due to the rapid fire and smoke development that can be expected in some situations.

When looking at the overall fire hazard, building construction also should be considered. Combustible building materials can affect the spread and development of fire, especially if there are combustible concealed spaces. Combustible insulation is a particular problem in certain storage facilities and represents a serious fire problem. You must specifically determine the type of any insulation present.

Modern developments in material handling have brought rapid changes to storage occupancies, including high-rack storage areas that can reach heights of 50 to 100 feet. Computer-controlled stacker cranes and robot-controlled material handlers are now being used to move materials. Regional distribution centers that cover several acres, which might contain two- or three-level mezzanines, are now being developed. Mini-storage complexes that consist of rental spaces ranging from 40 to 400 square feet in size also are being developed. These complexes, which consist of as many as 50 to 100 rental spaces in one building, often contain varying types and amounts of hazardous storage in one or more of the rental areas.

Storage occupancies can house raw materials, finished products, or goods in an intermediate stage of production, and these materials can be in bulk form, solid piles, palletized piles, or storage racks. Therefore, you should remember that the storage arrangement can greatly affect fire behavior.

Contents

In determining life safety features and requirements in a storage occupancy, you must first determine the hazard classification of the contents. Fire behavior will depend on the ease of ignition, rate of fire spread, and rate of heat release of the product itself. But products are often complex items whose fuel content, arrangement, shape, and form affect their performance in a fire. A packaged product must be considered as a whole because that is the way it burns, so in classifying the contents, you must examine the product, product container, and packaging material used.

Increasing amounts of plastics are now being used as part of the product and as part of the packaging. Bicycles traditionally have been all metal except for the tires, but now the frame and wheels of a bicycle may contain 50% or more plastic. Electrical and plumbing supplies traditionally have been metal, but now many of these supplies, including pipe, conduit, fittings, and junction boxes, are made of plastic. Washing machines typically have a limited amount of combustible parts in the machine assembly; however, today's typical packaging arrangement, the machine packed in a cardboard box surrounded with plastic foam, has made this commodity more hazardous even though the base commodity has not changed.

NFPA 231, *Standard for General Storage,* classifies commodities by general burning hazard based on the fire behavior of typical items. A comparison of the life safety hazard classifications can be made with the classifications found in NFPA 231 to aid you in determining the proper hazard classification of the storage area you will be inspecting. It is not uncommon to find items of mixed hazard levels spread throughout a storage area, and this would affect the hazard classification.

There are NFPA standards detailing requirements for the proper storage arrangement and level of protection for storage of specific items including flammable and combustible liquids, hanging garments, rolled paper, tires, and aerosol containers.

Occupant Load

A small number of people in relation to the total floor area usually will occupy a storage occupancy at any one time. Work patterns usually require employees to move throughout the structure using industrial trucks. In totally computerized warehouses an even smaller number of occupants are present, which reduces the likelihood of early fire detection as well as available personnel to begin fire fighting operations. Because of this, the *Life Safety Code* has no occupant load requirements for storage facilities. When establishing the occupant load for new and existing storage structures, the authority having jurisdiction will have to obtain in writing (from the building owner or occupant) the actual number of occupants allowed in each occupied space, floor, or building. The authority having jurisdiction must then designate the number of occupants to be accommodated on every floor and in each room or space. Special attention needs to be given to parking garages, which, at given times, could be occupied by many people, such as at the end of a work day or when an entertainment event is over. It should be noted that due to the typical low density of a storage occupancy, egress capacity is rarely a problem if the minimum number and size of exits along with maximum travel distance limitations are met.

Means of Egress

At least two separate means of egress, as remote from each other as possible, must be available from every floor in a storage structure. In smaller buildings a single exit is permitted as long as the common path of travel limitations are not exceeded. You should inspect the **exit access** from within the building; the **exit** locations; and the arrangement of the **exit discharge** from the exit to a public way or street.

Periodically the storage arrangements in storage occupancies are modified to keep up with new technology and operations, and these modifications can significantly affect the components of the building's means of egress. Without proper planning, exits can become blocked by storage, travel distances significantly increased, dead end corridors created, and even exit discharge adversely affected by building additions, altered security measures, or changes to property lines.

Exit Access and Travel Distances

All paths of travel from any part of the building must allow the occupants to travel safely without obstructions to the exits. Corridors and passageways must be at least 44 inches wide and completely clear of obstructions.

Travel distances to the exit locations must be as follows:

	Nonsprinklered	Sprinklered
A Low-hazard occupancies	no limit	no limit
Ordinary-hazard occupancies	200 ft	400 ft
High-hazard occupancies	75 ft	100 ft
B. Aircraft hangars and grain or bulk storage elevators	Special requirements are noted in the *Life Safety Code*	
C. Parking garages (mechanical or exclusively parked by attendants)	*See distances listed in A above*	
Parking garages (customers park own cars)		
Below ground or closed structure	150 ft	200 ft
Open-air structure	200 ft	300 ft

When repair operations are conducted within a parking garage, travel distances must meet the requirements for the industrial section, Chapter 28, of the *Life Safety Code*. If the repair operation area is separated by 1-hour fire-resistive construction, then the industrial requirements will only apply to the part that is used for repair operations.

Any rearrangement of the storage aisles or additions or changes to the rack systems made since the occupancy's last inspection can greatly affect travel distances to exits. When new mezzanine levels are added for additional storage space, you must check that travel distances to exits are correct and that the appropriate number of sprinklers have been added to the new area.

When determining exit access, you should look for areas where dead ends or common paths of travel are created by the storage arrangement. There is no limit to either in occupancies with a low hazard classification and in existing buildings with an ordinary hazard classification. In new storage occupancies with an ordinary hazard classification, a dead end or common path of travel of up to 50 feet is allowed, and up to 100 feet is allowed if the building is protected by an automatic sprinkler system. No dead-end conditions are allowed in areas that are classified as high hazard. In public parking garages a dead end or common path of travel of up to 50 feet is allowed.

Exits and Locations

At least two exit locations are required from all floors and areas of the building in storage occupancies classified as ordinary and high hazard, and they must be located so that a person can reach an exit location within the allowable travel distances.

In any enclosed parking garage in which there are gasoline pumps, there are several exit requirements. Travel away from the pumps in any direction should lead to an exit, and there must be no dead ends where people could be trapped by a fire originating at the pumps. The exits must lead to the outside of the building at the same level as the pumps, or they must lead to stairs. Any story below the one housing the pumps must have exits directly to the outside by means of outside stairs or doors at ground level.

In aircraft storage and servicing areas, there must be exits at intervals of every 150 feet on exterior walls of the hangar and every 100 feet along interior fire walls when serving as horizontal exits. The travel distance to reach the nearest exit from any point from a mezzanine floor located in an aircraft storage or servicing area must not exceed 75 feet. Such exits must lead directly to an enclosed stairwell discharging directly to the exterior, to a suitable cutoff area, or to outside stairs.

In grain or other bulk storage elevators, there should be two means of egress from all working levels of the head house. One must be stairs to the ground that are enclosed by a dust-resistant 1-hour fire-resistant enclosure. The second means of egress can be exterior stairs or a basket ladder-type fire escape that is accessible from all working levels of the head house and provides access either to ground level or to the top of an adjoining structure that provides a continuous path to another exterior stairway or basket ladder-type fire escape leading to the ground level. The underground spaces of an elevator must have at least two means of egress, one of which can be a ladder.

You should check all doors that serve as a required means of egress and are identified as exits for free and unobstructed operation to ensure that these doors are kept unlocked when the building is occupied. If locks requiring use of a key for operation from the inside of the building are used, make sure that a readily visible sign is posted next to the door on the egress side of the door stating, "This door to remain unlocked when the building is occupied." The locking device should be readily distinguishable if locked.

Make sure that exit doors located in a high hazard area swing out with exit travel. In areas where flammable vapors or gases are present, or the possibility of an explosion exists, see that exit doors are equipped with panic hardware.

In low and ordinary hazard areas that are protected throughout by an approved, supervised, automatic fire alarm or automatic sprinkler system, exit doors can be equipped with approved, listed, special locking devices that meet the requirements of Chapter 5 of the *Life Safety Code.*

The *Life Safety Code* permits horizontal sliding doors to be part of a means of egress. It also permits the use of a horizontal exit or smoke barrier. There are, however, special requirements in Chapter 5 of the *Life Safety Code.* It is quite common to find horizontal exits in storage occupancies due to the use of fire walls or barriers for compartmentation purposes. When the horizontal exit doorway is protected by a fire door on each side of the wall, one door must be swinging and the other can be an automatic-sliding fire door that must be kept open when the building is occupied.

In parking garages the opening for the passage of automobiles can serve as an exit from the street floor, provided that no door or shutter is installed in the opening.

In storage areas that contain low or ordinary hazard contents and have an occupant load of not more than 10 people, exit doors that are not side-hinged swinging are permitted.

Exit Discharge

You must determine that there is a path of travel from the building exit to a public way. Check that there is nothing in front of the exit door that would prevent it from working. Make sure the path of travel from exits opening into an alley leads to the public way, is well marked, and is illuminated.

Identification of Exits

All required exits and paths of travel to an exit must be identified properly by signs that are readily visible from any direction of exit access. Where the exit or the way to reach it is not visible to the occupants, the path of travel should be marked so that no point in the route is more than 100 feet from the nearest visible sign.

In large warehouses with high storage, exit identification can be a problem. Thus you might want to suggest that exit signs have large letters or that the travel paths to exits be painted on the floor. You should check that exit access routes are illuminated to allow the occupants to safely exit the building. If natural light is not available, the illumination must be continuous when the building is occupied. Emergency lighting is required in storage occupancies that are occupied at night or do not have exterior openings that would provide the required illumination during daylight hours. You should check that emergency lighting operates when the normal lighting circuits for the affected area are turned off. When a generator is used to power emergency lighting, check that the generator transfers automatic operation of the power and operates emergency lighting within 10 seconds. Check records and, if possible, run the generator to be sure it runs correctly. When checking battery-powered lighting units, check for acid corrosion, water level of wet-cell batteries, and that the unit is fully charged.

Protection of Openings

During your inspection, check that fire doors operate correctly, that they close tightly, and that the self-closing devices work. Check the general condition of the doors for obvious damage. Nothing that would prevent counter-balance closing hardware from operating freely should be stored around the fire doors, and nothing should block the doors open. Check that all door hardware and closing devices are lubricated and move freely. Examine all fusible links associated with the closing hardware to see that they are positioned properly and have not been painted or wired together.

You carefully must check materials-handling conveyor systems that pass through fire walls. Is there any air-handling ductwork passing through fire walls? NFPA 90A, *Standard for the Installation of Air Conditioning and Ventilating Systems,* requires any ductwork passing through a fire wall to be protected on each side of the wall by an approved self-closing fire door. Check that all openings from penetrations through the walls made for electrical cables or conduits are tightly sealed with a material that affords the same fire-resistance rating as the wall. Where storage buildings are susceptible to exterior exposure problems, check that fire shutters and wired-glass windows work and are properly placed. All wired glass that is missing or cracked should be replaced.

Verify that installed roof vents are operating properly and that snow is not allowed to accumulate on the vent hatches during the winter.

General Storage Practices

Indoor

In NFPA 231, *Standard for General Storage*, commodity storage not in racks has been grouped into four classes for ordinary commodities and three classes for plastics according to how easily automatic sprinklers will control a fire in them. Check this standard to determine the proper storage arrangement in buildings protected by automatic sprinkler systems.

Make sure that materials that could be hazardous in combination are stored so they cannot come in contact with each other. Verify that safe loads for floors are not exceeded. Floor loads for water-absorbent materials should be reduced to account for the added weight of water absorption during a fire. Check the clearance of stored material from sprinklers, heat ducts, unit heaters, duct furnaces, flues, radiant space heaters, and lighting fixtures. The wall aisle space should be at least 24 inches in storage areas where materials that will expand with absorption of water are stored. Verify that aisles are maintained to keep fire from spreading from one pile to another and to permit access for fire fighting, salvage, and removal or storage. Verify that all automatic sprinkler control valves, hose stations, and portable fire extinguishers are accessible and that there is free access to all fire protection equipment. All unused wood or plastic pallets should be kept outside or stored in stacks no higher than 6 feet. During your inspection, check to see if exterior access doors and windows are being blocked with storage that would affect fire fighting operations and prevent access into the building.

Outdoor

Make sure that storage piles are not stacked too high and are in stable condition and that aisles 10 feet wide are maintained between individual piles, between piles and buildings, and between piles and boundary lines of the storage site. Note whether the entire property is enclosed with a fence or some other means of keeping unauthorized persons from entering. There should be a gate to allow fire equipment to enter the area in the event of a fire. The storage yard should be free of unnecessary combustible materials, weeds, and grass, and any tarpaulins used to cover materials should be made of fire-retardant fabric.

Hazardous Materials

Many different materials with different hazards can be stored in a storage occupancy, or the entire occupancy can be used to store a specific hazardous material. Special requirements for the storage of hazardous materials are found in several *National Fire Codes* (see Appendix). As an inspector, you should be able to recognize out-of-the-ordinary storage and refer to the appropriate standard to determine special storage arrangements and protection requirements. Examples of hazardous materials include: rubber tires, plastic products, combustible fibers, paper and paper products, hanging garments, carpeting, pesticides, flammable liquids and gases, reactive chemicals, and flammable aerosol containers. Storage of aerosol containers should meet the requirements of NFPA 30B, *Code for the Manufacture and Storage of Aerosol Products.* All storage occupancies should be properly identified on the outside of the building using NFPA 704, *Standard System for the Identification of the Fire Hazards of Materials.*

Industrial Trucks

Determine that the industrial trucks being used are approved for use within the building for the hazard of the materials being stored. NFPA 505, *Fire Safety Standard for Powered Industrial Trucks Including Type Designations, Areas of Use, Maintenance and Operation,* designates the types of trucks that can be used in hazardous areas. A fire extinguisher that can be used on flammable liquid and electrical fires should be mounted on each truck. Check to see that the trucks are being maintained and that all refueling operations are conducted outside the building. Is fuel for the trucks properly stored? Examine the area where batteries are recharged for electrical trucks. Areas used for the repair of trucks should be separated from the storage area.

Hazardous Processes

Check the precautions management takes when a welding or cutting operation takes place in the storage area. In some cases, these operations should not be allowed at all until the hazardous materials are removed from the area. During welding operations, all combustible materials located below the operation should be removed or covered with a fire-retardant cover. Portable fire extinguishers and small hose lines should be laid out ready for operation. A fire watch should be present at all times during the operation and at least 30 minutes after the welding or cutting is completed.

If fuel pumps are located in a parking garage, check that the dispensing unit and nozzle are approved and that no ignition sources are located within 20 feet of the dispensing area. When the dispensing units are located below grade inside the building, the entire dispensing area must be protected with approved automatic sprinkler systems. Make sure there is mechanical ventilation for the dispensing area to remove flammable vapors. Is the mechanical ventilation system electrically interlocked with the dispensing unit so that no dispensing can be conducted without the ventilation system being in operation?

Building Services

Housekeeping

During your inspection look for debris and trash accumulated in out-of-the-way places and neglected corners. The level of fire safety is greatly improved when areas are kept clean and neat. Make sure that all waste generated daily is removed from the building and disposed of in a safe manner outside the building. Check for the accumulation of dust and lint on sprinklers, on fire door self-closing hardware, and around electrical motors and compressors. All containers used for the disposal of waste material must be made of noncombustible materials and have lids.

In grain storage buildings, the single most important fire prevention practice is effective daily removal of dust, which will collect everywhere. Housekeeping in this type of occupancy should be done consistently and carefully.

Fire Protection

Sprinkler Systems

A major factor in large fire losses in storage buildings has been the overtaxing of the automatic sprinkler system or associated water supply, which was or became improperly designed for the type of material stored and the storage arrangement. Fire losses also have occurred because the sprinkler system water supply has been shut off. Check sprinkler plans to determine the hazard for which the system was designed. During the inspection, check if the material being stored or the storage arrangement has changed in a way that would require redesign of the sprinkler system. Detailed inspection records should be kept indicating the type of material stored, pile arrangement, aisle width, storage methods, and height of storage materials. You should pay special attention to buildings protected by older sprinkler systems designed for Class III or lower commodities that now store more hazardous materials or have more hazardous storage arrangements.

During your inspection, verify that the sprinkler control valves are accessible, not blocked by storage, and in the open position. Verify that the system has been maintained properly, is in working order, and that all alarms operate when tested, properly identifying the alarm/supervisory condition. The outside fire department sprinkler connection must not be blocked by storage. Check for any areas unprotected by sprinklers such as small office enclosures with ceilings, mezzanines, or blind combustible spaces.

Standpipe Hose Systems

All hose stations and standpipe connections must not be blocked by storage materials. There should be adequate hose stations so that all areas of the storage buildings can be reached by the hose stream. All hose stations should be identified properly. Check the condition of the hose and nozzles. Find out if employees are expected to use this equipment and, if so, if they are trained properly for using the standpipe hose system.

Fire Extinguishers

Determine that fire extinguishers are accessible, the correct type for the hazard, and that their locations are identified. All extinguishers should be fully charged and inspected at least annually. Employees should be trained to use the extinguisher correctly.

Fire Pumps

Examine fire pumps to determine if the pump is being properly maintained and tested. Determine if the pump is being run weekly and tested by a competent contractor at least annually. Verify that all alarms operate when tested, and properly identify the alarm/supervisory condition. Determine if the pump is set for automatic or manual operation, and check that all controls are working. Determine that proper documentation of testing and maintenance is being maintained.

Alarm System

Because storage buildings usually are large open-floor areas that are occupied by only a few employees who are working in many different parts of the building, they should have a fire alarm system that, when operated, will sound an alarm at a continuously attended location so that some type of emergency action can be initiated. If the occupancy has a trained fire brigade or an emergency prefire plan, there should be a means of notifying people in all areas of the building so that the brigade or action plan can be initiated.

The *Life Safety Code* requires a fire alarm system in storage buildings when they contain either ordinary or high hazard contents and have an aggregate floor area of more than 100,000 square feet. This requirement would not apply if the occupancy is protected by an automatic extinguishing system.

A fire alarm system also is required in public parking garages except when the parking structure is classified as an open-air structure. When inspecting this type of alarm system, you should make sure that the entire system and all functions are in operating order. Check that all initiating devices, such as manual pull stations, are identified and not blocked by storage. Also check that the notification alarm or signal is adequate to notify all employees that are part of a fire brigade or to begin the established, emergency prefire plan.

Bibliography

NFPA 30, *Flammable and Combustible Liquids Code*
NFPA 30B, *Code for the Manufacture and Storage of Aerosol Products*
NFPA 40E, *Code for the Storage of Pyroxylin Plastic*
NFPA 43A, *Code for the Storage of Liquid and Solid Oxidizers*
NFPA 43B, *Code for the Storage of Organic Peroxide Formulations*
NFPA 43D, *Code for the Storage of Pesticides in Portable Containers*
NFPA 46, *Recommended Safe Practice for Storage of Forest Products*

NFPA 61A, *Standard for Prevention of Fire and Dust Explosions in Facilities Manufacturing and Handling Starch*

NFPA 61B, *Standard for the Prevention of Fires and Explosions in Grain Elevators and Facilities Handling Bulk Raw Agricultural Commodities*

NFPA 81, *Standard for Fur Storage, Fumigation and Cleaning*

NFPA 88A, *Standard for Parking Structures*

NFPA *101, Life Safety Code*

NFPA 231, *Standard for General Storage*

NFPA 231C, *Standard for Rack Storage of Materials*

NFPA 231D, *Standard for Storage of Rubber Tires*

NFPA 231E, *Recommended Practice for the Storage of Baled Cotton*

NFPA 231F, *Standard for the Storage of Roll Paper*

NFPA 480, *Standard for the Storage, Handling and Processing of Magnesium Solids and Powders*

NFPA 481, *Standard for the Production, Processing, Handling, and Storage of Titanium*

NFPA 482, *Standard for the Production, Processing, Handling, and Storage of Zirconium*

NFPA 490, *Code for the Storage of Ammonium Nitrate*

NFPA 505, *Fire Safety Standard for Powered Industrial Trucks Including Type Designations, Areas of Use, Maintenance, and Operation*

NFPA 513, *Standard for Motor Freight Terminals*

NFPA 704, *Standard System for the Identification of the Fire Hazards of Materials*

NFPA 1124, *Code for the Manufacture, Transportation, and Storage of Fireworks*

STORAGE OCCUPANCY FIRE INSPECTION FORM

Property Name: Owner:

Address: Phone Number:

OCCUPANCY

Change from Last Inspection: Yes☐   No☐

Occupant Load: Egress Capacity: Any Renovations: Yes☐   No☐

High Rise: Yes☐ No☐   Windowless: Yes☐ No☐   Underground: Yes☐ No☐

BUILDING SERVICES

Electricity☐ Gas☐ Water☐ Other☐   Are Utilities in Good Working Order: Yes☐ No☐

Elevators: Yes☐ No☐   Fire Service Control: Yes☐ No☐   Elevator Recall: Yes☐ No☐

Heat Type: Gas☐ Oil☐ Electric☐ Coal☐ Other☐   In Good Working Order: Yes☐ No☐

Emergency Generator: Yes☐ No☐   Size: Last Date Tested:

Date of Last Full Load Test: In Automatic Position: Yes☐ No☐

Fire Pump: Yes☐ No☐   GPM: Suction Pressure: System Pressure:

Date Last Tested: Date of Last Flow Test:

In Automatic Position: Yes☐ No☐   Jockey Pump: Yes☐ No☐

EMERGENCY LIGHTS

Operable: Yes☐ No☐   Tested Monthly: Yes☐ No☐

Properly Illuminate Egress Paths: Yes☐ No☐   In Good Condition: Yes☐ No☐

EXIT SIGNS

Illuminated: Internally☐ Externally☐   Emergency Power: Yes☐ No☐   Readily Visible: Yes☐ No☐

FIRE ALARM

Yes☐ No☐   Location of Panel:

Coverage: Building☐ Partial☐   Monitored: Yes☐ No☐   Method:

Type of Initiation Devices: Smoke☐ Heat☐ Manual☐ Water Flow☐ Special Systems☐

Date of Last Test: Date of Last Inspection:

Notification Signal Adequate: Yes☐ No☐   Fire Department Notification: Yes☐ No☐

FIRE EXTINGUISHERS

Proper Type for Hazard Protecting: Yes☐ No☐   Mounted Properly: Yes☐ No☐

Date of Last Inspection: Adequate Number: Yes☐ No☐

FIRE PROTECTION SYSTEMS

Type: Sprinkler☐ Halon☐ CO2☐ Standpipe☐ Water Spray☐ Foam☐ Dry Chemical☐ Wet
  Chemical☐ Other☐

Coverage: Building☐ Partial☐   Date of Last Inspection:

  Cylinder or Gauge Pressure(s): 1   psi.,2   psi.,3   psi.,4   psi.,5   psi.

Valves Supervised: Electrical☐ Lock☐ Seal☐ Other☐   Are Valves Accessible: Yes☐ No☐

System Operational: Yes☐ No☐   Sprinkler Heads 18´´ from Storage: Yes☐ No☐

In Rack Sprinklers: Yes☐ No☐

FIRE RESISTIVE (FR) CONSTRUCTION

Stairway FR: Yes☐ No☐   Hourly Rating:

Corridors FR: Yes☐ No☐   Hourly Rating:

Elevator Shaft FR: Yes☐ Yes☐ No☐   Hourly Rating:

Major Structural Members FR: Yes☐ No☐   Hourly Rating:

Floor-Ceiling Assemblies FR: Yes☐ No☐   Hourly Rating:

All Openings Protected in FR Walls and Floor-Ceiling Assemblies: Yes☐ No☐

HAZARDOUS AREAS

Protected by: Fire-Rated Separation☐ Extinguishing System☐ Both☐

Door Self-Closures: Yes☐ No☐

Hazardous Materials: Yes☐ No☐   Properly Stored and Handled: Yes☐ No☐

Properly Protected: Yes☐ No☐

Are Lift Trucks Properly Stored: Yes☐ No☐   Is the Fuel Properly Stored: Yes☐ No☐

Is Fueling Done Properly: Yes☐ No☐   Are Extinguishers Provided: Yes☐ No☐

HOUSEKEEPING

Areas Free of Excessive Combustibles: Yes☐ No☐

Smoking Regulated: Yes☐ No☐   Is Stock Stored Properly: Yes☐ No☐

Is Incompatible Materials Separated: Yes☐ No☐

Is Stock provided with Proper Aisles: Yes☐ No☐   Pallets Stored Properly: Yes☐ No☐

INTERIOR FINISH

Walls and Ceilings Proper Rating: Yes☐ No☐   Floor Finish Proper Rating: Yes☐ No☐

MEANS OF EGRESS

Readily Visible: Yes☐ No☐   Clear and Unobstructed: Yes☐ No☐

Two Remote Exits Available: Yes☐ No☐   Travel Distance within Limits: Yes☐ No☐

Common Path of Travel within Limits: Yes☐ No☐   Dead-Ends within Limits: Yes☐ No☐

50% Maximum through Level of Exit Discharge: Yes☐ No☐

Adequate Illumination: Yes☐ No☐

Proper Rating on All Components: Yes☐ No☐

All Exit Enclosures Free of Storage: Yes☐ No☐

Door Swing in the Direction of Egress Travel (when required): Yes☐ No☐

Panic/Fire Exit Hardware Operable: Yes☐ No☐

Doors Open Easily: Yes☐ No☐ Self-Closures Operable: Yes☐ No☐

Doors Closed or Held Open With Automatic Closures: Yes☐ No☐

Corridors and Aisles of Sufficient Size: Yes☐ No☐

Stairwell Re-Entry: Yes☐ No☐

Mezzanines: Yes☐ No☐ Proper Exits: Yes☐ No☐

VERTICAL OPENINGS

Properly Protected: Yes☐ No☐

Atrium: Yes☐ No☐ Properly Protected: Yes☐ No☐

Are Fire Doors in Good Working Order: Yes☐ No☐

OPERATING FEATURES

Fire Drills Held: Yes☐ No☐ Employees Trained in Emergency Procedures: Yes☐ No☐

CHAPTER 29

Occupancies in Special Structures

*O*ccupancies in special structures, as defined in Chapter 4 of NFPA *101, Life Safety Code,* include: open structures, towers, underground structures, vehicles, vessels, water-surrounded structures, and windowless buildings.

Open structures are those in which operations, and their necessary equipment, are conducted in open air and not enclosed within buildings, such as those used for oil refining and chemical processing plants. Roofs or canopies that provide shelter without enclosing walls can be provided and would not be considered an enclosure.

Towers are independent structures or portions of buildings occupied for observation, signaling, or similar limited use and not open to general use.

An underground structure is a structure or portions of a structure in which the story is below the level of exit discharge. (Exceptions for underground structures are discussed later in this chapter.)

Vehicles are any trailer, railroad car, street car, bus, or similar conveyance that is not mobile or is attached to a building or is permanently fixed to a foundation.

Vessels are any ship, barge, or other vessel permanently fixed to a foundation or mooring or unable to get under way under its own power and occupied for purposes other than navigation.

Water-surrounded structures are structures completely surrounded by water.

Windowless structures lack any means for direct access to the outside from the enclosing walls, or lack outside openings for ventilation or rescue through windows. (Exceptions for windowless structures are discussed later in this chapter.)

When an occupancy's use does not fit the other categories covered in the *Life Safety Code* because of the type of structure in which it is housed, it is classified under Chapter 30 of the code, "Special Structures and High Rise Buildings." Once this classification is determined, then the type of structure or building, such as towers, vehicles, or vessels, becomes a subclassification. In addition, the actual occupancy (i.e., assembly, mercantile, and so on) becomes a subclassification to the structure classification. One example of this is a restaurant with an occupant load of 350 located in a tower. Its occupancy classification is an assembly occupancy in a special structure, and its subclassifications are tower and Class B assembly occupancies.

Occupancy Characteristics

Occupancies in special structures are the most commonly overlooked occupancies because there seems to be a lack of awareness that this type of occupancy exists. And this occupancy group tends to be confusing just because it has been classified as a separate occupancy.

However, a typical occupancy in a special structure will fall under one of the occupancy classifications previously discussed. Thus, the means of egress and fire protection requirements for that occupancy apply as do the additional requirements for the special structure. Examples of typical occupancies in special structures include:

1. A restaurant located in a permanently fixed boat or ship. This is clearly a place of assembly (the occupancy classification), which is located in a ship (the special structure).
2. A souvenir shop in an earth bunker or cave. This is a mercantile facility (the occupancy classification) in an earth enclosure (the special structure).
3. A hotel supported on pilings along a waterfront that is connected to the mainland by access ramps. This is a hotel (the occupancy classification), which is housed on pilings (the special structure).

When inspecting a special structure, which can be difficult, you first must determine which general occupancy classification it falls under. Then it will be easier to determine the structure's special features and classify them correctly. If the special structure does not meet exactly all the criteria for a specific classification as specified in the *Life Safety Code,* you must use the fundamental provisions given in Chapter 2 of the *Life Safety Code* to evaluate the constraints the structure's special features place on the occupancy classification.

Special Structures

The information in this section will explain the unusual conditions you will see and the specific observations that you will have to make when inspecting special structures. You should use this information in conjunction with the information contained in chapters on specific, more typical, occupancies.

Open Structures

Open structures are common in industrial operations. Therefore, most of the time the structure will come under the guidelines of those for industrial occupancies. The primary problem for you, the inspector, will be determining whether the occupancy is a general, special purpose, or high hazard industrial occupancy. Typically, the high hazard industrial occupancy classification will be determined based on the hazard classification of the building's contents.

Open-air structures are classified more commonly as special purpose industrial occupancies, which are defined in Chapter 28 of the *Life Safety Code.* Special purpose industrial occupancies have a relatively low density of employees, and much of an open-air structure is occupied by machinery or equipment. Typically, the open structure facilitates access to the equipment with platforms, gratings, stairs, and ladders. The structure might even have a roof to provide some protection from the elements.

It is difficult to determine when a structure is open and when it is enclosed. Many open structures will have some walls that are intended to shield the operations from environmental conditions or to segregate operations. The authority having jurisdiction must determine whether or not the open-air structure truly meets the definition for open structures or if the facility is, in fact, a building.

To determine whether or not the structure really is an open structure, you must decide if it would react as an enclosed building in the event of a fire. Walls acting in conjunction with a roof enclose the combustion process and products of combustion, thereby allowing the fire to spread both horizontally and vertically to other unaffected areas within the building. However, an open structure allows the products of combustion to vent to the atmosphere instead of spreading to unaffected areas of the structure. Obviously, this is dependent on wind and climatic conditions, but the overall concept is valid. Could the walls cause the products of combustion during a fire to be directed or channeled to other unaffected portions of the structure, thus preventing them from venting to the atmosphere? If the answer to this question is yes or probably, then you might have to consider that portion of the structure as a building.

Once you have classified the structure, you should conduct the inspection based on the occupancy classification(s) and the special provisions provided in Chapter 30, "Special Structures and High Rise Buildings," of the *Life Safety Code*. There are no special provisions for open-air structures, but Chapter 30 contains several exceptions for this suboccupancy classification. One of them permits open structures to have a single means of egress when they are occupied by no more than three persons and have a travel distance of not more than 200 feet.

A fire that occurs in an open structure usually does not possess as serious a threat to life as does a fire in a building, unless the structure contains high hazard operations. When you are inspecting an open structure that houses a high hazard operation, you should refer to Chapter 28 of the *Life Safety Code* and carefully evaluate the life safety features of the open structure.

When high hazard operations are involved, the egress system usually becomes the biggest problem, especially on levels that are above grade. No simple generalizations can be made about this problem; therefore, each individual structure must be evaluated on its own merits and the level of protection being provided.

Piers

A pier, as defined by NFPA 307, *Standard for the Construction and Fire Protection of Marine Terminals, Piers, and Wharves,* is a structure, usually longer than it is wide that projects from land into a body of water. It can be either open deck or have a superstructure. Contrary to its exact definition, piers (sometimes called wharves) can be constructed over land. Occasionally, a designer will construct a pier of earth that pushes its way out from the main body of land into an area, which for grade purposes, might not be usable otherwise. A building that can be classified under one of the other categories covered in the *Life Safety Code* will be erected on this earthen pier. Although the pier is not made of traditional structural elements, it is still a pier. You must first determine the occupancy requirements for the building and then assess the affects the unusual structure, the pier, will have on them. Many times a structure is located within what first appears to be an unusual circumstance, but it still will probably have the typical fire protection problems.

Chapter 3 of NFPA 307 contains requirements for property conservation features of piers and wharves, and Chapter 30 of the *Life Safety Code* also discusses piers. An exception to the number of exits required is noted in Chapter 30 for "piers used exclusively to moor cargo vessels and to store materials, where provided with proper mean of egress from structures thereon to the pier and a single means of access to the mainland as appropriate with the pier's arrangement." Aside from this exception, the appropriate occupancy chapter and the rest of Chapter 30 would apply to piers.

Towers

It is difficult to determine when a tower is considered a tower for inspection purposes. A tower, as defined in Chapter 30 of the *Life Safety Code,* is an "independent structure or portion of a building occupied for observation, signaling, or similar limited use and not open to general use." An assembly occupancy or any other occupancy classification located on top of a tower must meet the requirements of the appropriate occupancy classification chapter of the *Life Safety Code,* not necessarily those of Chapter 30 of the *Life Safety Code.*

Chapter 30 of the *Life Safety Code* contains requirements for towers that typically are used for purposes such as forest fire observation, railroad signaling, industrial purposes, and aircraft control. Normally they are not occupied or are occupied by a specific number of persons who are capable of self preservation. Usually there are no provisions for living or sleeping in such towers. When inspecting towers that meet the requirements of Chapter 30 of the *Life Safety Code,* you must keep in mind the limited use and the nature and character of the specific occupancy involved. If the tower is used as an assembly occupancy or contains more than just a few occupants, it probably does not meet the requirements of Chapter 30 and should be reviewed under the requirements of the appropriate occupancy chapter.

The *Life Safety Code* does not require towers to have any special features for means of egress, but it does provide several exceptions to general requirements for means of egress in Chapter 30, some of which are described briefly here.

The code permits ladders to be used as a means of egress when the tower is occupied by three or fewer people.

The capacity and width of the means of egress have to provide only for the expected number of persons occupying the tower. (See Chapter 30 of the *Life Safety Code* for all of the exceptions.)

In the *Life Safety Code,* 30-2.4.1 requires there to be no less than two means of egress from every story or section, and the occupants must be able to reach one exit without traversing another story. However, towers are permitted to have a single exit if the following conditions are met:

(a) The tower is occupied by less than 25 persons.
(b) The tower is not used for living or sleeping purposes and is occupied by only able-bodied persons.
(c) The tower is of Type I, II, or IV construction.
(d) The tower interior finish is Class A or B.
(e) The tower has no combustible materials in, under, or in the immediate vicinity, except necessary furniture.
(f) There are no high hazard occupancies in the tower or immediate vicinity.

The average tower will meet these conditions, but some unusual towers, such as the Washington Monument and the Statue of Liberty, might not meet condition (a) and condition (b). Because of the special provisions made today for persons with mobility impairments, it would be reasonable for you to assume that the tower could be occupied by persons who might not be capable of self preservation in an emergency. When deciding if the exit exception applies, you must keep in mind the actual configuration of the tower, the fuel load, the exposure of the tower, and the protection it has. Usually the use of the exception can still be justified when an overall evaluation is completed.

During the inspection you must determine if the tower is exposed to any combustible materials that might be under or in the immediate vicinity of the structure. You or the authority having jurisdiction should not establish arbitrary requirements that would severely restrict the use of the tower; however, you should ensure that the tower could not be exposed to an exterior fire, which could affect the means of egress system before the occupants could evacuate.

You also should ensure that any high hazard occupancy located close to a tower will not threaten the integrity of the physical structure of the tower and the egress system. This not only includes hazards such as LP-Gas storage and explosive-prone occupancies, but should also include possible exposures to vehicles such as flammable liquid transport carriers.

Underground Structures

The *Life Safety Code* defines an underground structure as any structure or portions of a structure in which the story is below the level of exit discharge. At face value, any structure that has a floor level below the level at which the occupants exit is an underground structure. Since 1985, there virtually are no differences between an underground structure and a basement where, in both cases, the exit system requires the occupant to travel above the occupied floor to exit.

This change in definition recognizes that there is no real difference between the underground structure and a basement in regard to life safety, fire protection, and fire suppression problems within the underground levels. The code provides additional guidance by stating that a structure is not considered an underground structure if **all** of the following conditions exist:

1. The story (or each story that attempts to qualify for the exception) is provided on at least two sides with at least 20 square feet of opening entirely above the adjoining grade level in each 50 lineal feet of exterior enclosing wall area, *and*
2. The openings are at least 22 inches wide and 24 inches high, and they are unobstructed to allow for ventilation and rescue operations from the exterior, *and*
3. The bottom of the openings is not more than 44 inches above the floor, *and*
4. The openings are readily identifiable from inside and outside of the story, *and*
5. The openings are readily openable from both inside and outside of that floor level.

In summary, if there is a sufficient number of openings around the outside that are clearly identifiable and usable as rescue and ventilation openings, then that floor level is not required to meet the requirements of an underground structure. During your inspection keep in mind the following problems that arise in an underground structure: 1) safe egress, 2) accessibility for fire department and rescue operations, 3) ventilation and smoke control, and 4) control and suppression of fire. These issues will guide you in identifying problems and where the appropriate code issues apply.

When inspecting an underground structure, you should treat it as a typical structure erected on or above grade. The occupancy classifications, hazard levels of contents, occupant loads, exit systems, vertical openings, and other features of fire protection should be consistent with the appropriate occupancy chapter in the *Life Safety Code*.

Section 30-7 of the code gives additional special provisions for underground structures. Each exit from an underground structure with an occupant load over 50 (over 100 for existing) must have outside smoke-venting facilities or some other means of preventing the exits from becoming filled with smoke from any fire in the area served by the exits. Underground structures with an occupant load over 100 must have automatic smoke-venting facilities if areas in them have combustible contents, interior finish, or construction; however, there is an exception to this requirement for structures built before 1976 when this requirement was added to the code.

An underground structure with an occupant load over 50 (100 for existing) must be protected by an automatic sprinkler system installed in accordance with NFPA 13, *Standard for the Installation of Sprinkler Systems.* This system can be in conjunction with, but cannot be solely composed of, the smoke-exhaust system for the means of egress.

Because there is virtually no natural light in an underground structure, this type of structure must have an emergency lighting system that meets the requirements of appropriate sections of the *Life Safety Code.* Verify that the emergency lighting system operates and provides a level of light consistent with minimum code standards.

You also must check the emergency power supply to ensure that all air-handling and other electrically operated emergency mechanical support equipment will function if there is a power failure in the event of a fire. Test all smoke-venting systems in means of egress to ensure they are working properly. Ensure that all protection systems are being supervised.

Vehicles and Vessels

Occasionally you will have to inspect an occupancy that is located in a vehicle or vessel. The occupancy classification most commonly will be an assembly occupancy or a mercantile facility, but it could be another occupancy depending on the type of vehicle or vessel involved. An aircraft, boat, or ship could have been taken out of service, placed on a foundation, and turned into a restaurant. And one national restaurant chain places railroad cars on fake railroad tracks that are placed on foundations. The cars are then arranged and altered to accommodate a dining establishment.

Following are some specific points to cover when inspecting an occupancy in a vehicle or vessel.

Permanent Foundation or Mooring: The vehicle or vessel that is no longer mobile and is permanently fixed to a foundation or mooring will determine how the actual occupancy is regulated under the codes. In the case of a floating restaurant that is aboard a traditionally functional ship, the occupancy typically would not be under the regulation of a fire department or building department inspection agency but would most likely be regulated by the Coast Guard.

Unusual Nature and Character: Although the vehicle or vessel might house a traditional assembly occupancy such as a restaurant, many times the unusual configuration of the structure will cause the occupants to have to respond differently in the event of an emergency. In order to accommodate the occupancy in this vehicle or vessel and create a pleasant, attractive atmosphere, some renovations in direct contradiction to a more traditional design for the occupancy might be made. The changes, which make the structure marketable and attract customers, might compromise safety. And although you should try to accommodate the unique features of the occupancy, these features must not compromise any provisions for life safety.

Chapter 2 of the *Life Safety Code,* which contains the fundamental requirements of the code, and many times will be the only resource that you have to judge a certain configuration or condition. This chapter will help you to interpret the intent of the occupancy and determine that the required level of life safety is provided for the occupants.

Means of Egress: Because the vehicle or vessel was often not originally designed for the occupancy that it now contains, it will not comply with the *Life Safety Code* requirements for the means of egress.

Section 30-2 of the code details the specific types of exits that are allowed. Escape shoots, control-descent devices, ropes, and other nontraditional means of egress cannot be allowed as a substitute for the specific exit types required by this section. However, when a facility has been determined to be "existing" by the authority having jurisdiction certain allowances may be permitted for existing stairways, if approved by the authority having jurisdiction (see 1-5.4 of the *Life Safety Code*). There also are additional exceptions for structures fully surrounded by water, which are explained later in this chapter.

Emergency lighting must be provided in accordance with Section 5-9 of the code. However, if the structure is occupied in daylight hours only, emergency lighting might not be necessary to maintain the required level of illumination on all portions of the means of egress if approved by the authority having jurisdiction.

Special features such as spiral stairs might be allowed if they are permitted by the appropriate occupancy chapter and Section 5-2 of the code. There are also special provisions for stair winders in existing buildings (see Section 30-2 of the *Life Safety Code*).

Vertical Openings: Vertical openings must be protected in accordance with Chapter 5 and Section 6-2 of the *Life Safety Code*. If the structure cannot meet all the requirements for the protection of the vertical openings, the openings should at least be protected by a method that will provide equivalency under the provisions of Section 1-5 of the code, such as a supervised automatic sprinkler system.

Typical and/or Special Hazard Areas: Because of the character of special structures, Section 30-3 of the *Life Safety Code* allows the authority having jurisdiction to require whatever is necessary to ensure that egress systems work properly. This could include requiring automatic water suppression systems, fire alarm systems, modified sprinkler systems, or compartmentation. This methodology often will offset the design problems generated by a special structure's unique character and provide a reasonable level of life safety.

Look for any unusual approaches to or applications of a protection system intended to provide an equivalent level of life safety. Whatever method is used must be clearly documented, and properly installed and maintained to ensure it will be effective throughout the existence of the occupancy.

Interior Finish: Interior finish can be Class A, B, or C, in accordance with Section 6-5 of the *Life Safety Code,* but often the interior finish in special structures will not be any of these. You must clearly identify the structure's existing interior finish and determine the flame-spread rating(s). You can do this either by experience or by testing, but it must be consistent with the minimum provisions of the code.

Fire Alarm System: A ship or vessel used as a building must have a manual or automatic fire alarm installed in accordance with Section 7-6 of the code. You must determine the exact type of alarm system, if any, and ensure that it meets the requirements of the appropriate sections of the code.

In addition to those items specified in Chapter 30 of the *Life Safety Code,* you also must determine if the hazards that existed in the vehicle or vessel before its present occupancy use have been mitigated or adequately protected. Items such as fuel tanks, hydraulic machinery, and electrical equipment not relevant to the structure's present use must be removed or adequately protected. Any materials, hazardous or not, stored in preexisting compartments must be identified and their potential contribution to the fuel load assessed. You should check every area of the structure, looking carefully for any cosmetic feature that could conceal hazardous compartments or processes.

Because of the originally intended use of a vehicle or vessel, the designer of the present occupancy might not have considered how stable the structure would be in the event of a fire. Thus, the structure's supporting system might not perform as intended under fire conditions. Although a structure originally intended to be an assembly occupancy might be supported on a noncombustible foundation and fire-resistive supports, it would be unlikely to find a ship or vessel supported on a noncombustible foundation and structural supports.

Also, the structure's original foundations and supports may create concealed combustible spaces, and these spaces could contain emergency equipment and systems, which would adversely affect their integrity in a fire. When conducting your inspection you must determine that the structure's foundation meets code requirements, and you must assess its reaction in a fire and how this will affect the occupant's life safety.

Water-Surrounded Structures

Water-surrounded structures are completely surrounded by water, unlike piers where one side of the structure usually is attached to land. Typically, a water-surrounded structure can only be reached by a vehicle, but occasionally it might have a ramp that cannot qualify as a pier. Although Chapter 30 of the *Life Safety Code* does not contain any specific requirements for water-surrounded structures, it does have several exceptions that refer to U.S. Coast Guard regulations for water-surrounded structures.

Before inspecting a water-surrounded structure, you should first determine if your agency has jurisdiction over it; if it does, you should try to conduct a joint inspection with U.S. Coast Guard authorities. If this is not possible, then you should try to obtain previous inspection reports from the U.S. Coast Guard.

The traditional occupancy requirements and features of fire protection remain the same for water-surrounded structures. You should inspect the occupancy as if it were not surrounded by water, and then apply the special circumstances that are unique to the structure.

Windowless Buildings

The hazards of windowless buildings are very similar to those of underground structures. Therefore, the same concerns about underground structures would also relate to windowless structures. The significant difference from a code standpoint is that windowless structures are not required to have smoke-venting facilities. However, if the occupancy will have a high occupant load you might suggest that a smoke-control and smoke-venting system be installed, if feasible, because it will greatly improve the level of life safety.

Typically, it is not difficult to have a good exit system in a windowless building. This type of structure lends itself to the use of exterior access panels for fire department and emergency use; however, access panels not meeting the requirements of the means of egress cannot be considered as exits.

The most common problem with windowless buildings is determining whether or not the building is actually considered windowless.

The definition of a windowless building is actually in two parts—it addresses two considerations. The first part of the definition states that a windowless building is a structure, or portions of a structure, lacking means for direct access to the outside from the enclosing walls. This portion of the definition essentially involves determining the occupants' ability to exit the building. This is not typically a problem unless the designer intentionally deleted exits along the exterior of the building, which is commonly done for access control and security purposes. And as important as security and access control are, they cannot be allowed to interfere with a minimum level of life safety in the building.

The second portion of the definition addresses outside openings for ventilation or rescue through windows. The problem thus becomes determining how many windows a building can have before it is not considered a windowless structure.

The *Life Safety Code* contains two exceptions that will help you determine when a building can be considered windowless.

A building is not considered a windowless structure if it is a one-story structure with grade-level doors, access panels, or windows provided on two sides of the building spaced not more than 125 feet apart and:

1. The access panels or windows are at least 22 inches wide and 24 inches high to allow for ventilation or rescue
2. The bottoms of the openings are not more than 44 inches high
3. The openings are identified from the inside and the outside
4. The openings are openable from the inside and the outside

If a building has more than one story, the first story must meet the above requirements, and every story above the first story must have the following:

1. The access openings or windows on two sides must be spaced no more than 30 feet apart, *and*
2. The openings must be at least 22 inches wide by 24 inches high and must be unobstructed to allow for ventilation, and rescue, *and*
3. The bottoms of openings must be no more than 44 inches above the floor, *and*
4. The openings must be identifiable from the inside and the outside, and must be openable from both sides.

You should use judgment when determining whether or not the building is truly windowless. Your decision should also take into consideration the nature and character of the occupancy and the actual occupancy classification. It is not as imperative for the life safety requirements to be enforced in a windowless building in a storage occupancy as it is in a windowless building in an assembly occupancy.

Summary

Occupancies in special structures are not easy to inspect, but it is imperative that you inspect a special occupancy in a logical manner using the appropriate occupancy chapter, along with Chapter 30 of the *Life Safety Code,* and any other applicable NFPA standards (see Appendix). It is rare for only a single code to be applicable.

Even if the structure's building plans were processed through an appropriate plans review and approval process, it is very common for the structure and occupancy to change with time. This will mean that your inspection results might differ from those of the original requirements or observations. Every inspection is worthy of your best professional expertise and judgment. The objective is to identify, interpret, and record all aspects relative to life safety, property conservation, and the preservation of the public welfare. A fire inspector is one of the few professionals whose product, when produced with experience, sound judgment, and good technical skills, can literally save lives.

Bibliography

NFPA *101, Life Safety Code*
NFPA 307, *Standard for the Construction and Fire Protection of Marine Terminals, Wharves, and Piers*

SPECIAL STRUCTURE OCCUPANCY FIRE INSPECTION FORM

Property Name: Owner:

Address: Phone Number:

OCCUPANCY

Occupancy Classification: Change from Last Inspection: Yes☐ No☐

Occupant Load: Egress Capacity: Any Renovations: Yes☐ No☐

Vehicle or Vessel☐ Windowless☐ High Rise☐ Water Surrounded☐ Pier☐ Underground☐
  Other☐

BUILDING SERVICES

Electricity☐ Gas☐ Water☐ Other☐   Are Utilities in Good Working Order: Yes☐ No☐

Elevators: Yes☐ No☐   Fire Service Control: Yes☐ No☐   Elevator Recall: Yes☐ No☐

Heat Type: Gas☐ Oil☐ Electric☐ Coal☐ Other☐   In Good Working Order: Yes☐ No☐

Emergency Generator: Yes☐ No☐   Size: Last Date Tested:

Date of Last Full Load Test: In Automatic Position: Yes☐ No☐

Fire Pump: Yes☐ No☐ GPM: Suction Pressure: System Pressure:

Date Last Tested: Date of Last Flow Test:

In Automatic Position: Yes☐ No☐   Jockey Pump: Yes☐ No☐

EMERGENCY LIGHTS

Operable: Yes☐ No☐   Tested Monthly: Yes☐ No☐

Properly Illuminate Egress Paths: Yes☐ No☐   In Good Condition: Yes☐ No☐

EXIT SIGNS

Illuminated: Internally☐ Externally☐   Emergency Power: Yes☐ No☐ Readily Visible: Yes☐
  No☐

FIRE ALARM

Yes☐ No☐   Location of Panel:

Coverage: Building☐ Partial☐   Monitored: Yes☐ No☐   Method:

Type of Initiation Devices: Smoke☐ Heat☐ Manual☐ Water Flow☐ Special Systems☐

Date of Last Test: Date of Last Inspection:

Notification Signal Adequate: Yes☐ No☐   Fire Department Notification: Yes☐ No☐

FIRE EXTINGUISHERS

Proper Type for Hazard Protecting: Yes☐ No☐   Mounted Properly: Yes☐ No☐

Date of Last Inspection: Adequate Number: Yes☐ No☐

FIRE PROTECTION SYSTEMS

Type: Sprinkler☐ Halon☐ CO2☐ Standpipe☐ Water Spray☐ Foam☐ Dry Chemical☐ Wet
  Chemical☐ Other☐

Coverage: Building☐ Partial☐   Date of Last Inspection:

Cylinder or Gauge Pressure(s): 1   psi.,2   psi.,3   psi.,4   psi.,5   psi.

Valves Supervised: Electrical☐ Lock☐ Seal☐ Other☐   Are Valves Accessible: Yes☐ No☐

System Operational: Yes☐ No☐   Sprinkler Heads 18" from Storage: Yes☐ No☐

FIRE RESISTIVE (FR) CONSTRUCTION

Stairway FR: Yes☐ No☐   Hourly Rating:

Corridors FR: Yes☐ No☐   Hourly Rating:

Elevator Shaft FR: Yes☐ Yes☐ No☐   Hourly Rating:

Major Structural Members FR: Yes☐ No☐   Hourly Rating:

Floor-Ceiling Assemblies FR: Yes☐   No☐   Hourly Rating:

All Openings Protected in FR Walls and Floor-Ceiling Assemblies: Yes☐   No☐

HAZARDOUS AREAS

Protected by: Fire-Rated Separation☐   Extinguishing System☐   Both☐

Door Self-Closures: Yes☐   No☐

HOUSEKEEPING

Areas Free of Excessive Combustibles: Yes☐   No☐

Smoking Regulated: Yes☐   No☐

INTERIOR FINISH

Walls and Ceilings Proper Rating: Yes☐   No☐   Floor Finish Proper Rating: Yes☐   No☐

MEANS OF EGRESS

Readily Visible: Yes☐   No☐   Clear and Unobstructed: Yes☐   No☐

Two Remote Exits Available: Yes☐   No☐   Travel Distance within Limits: Yes☐   No☐

Common Path of Travel within Limits: Yes☐   No☐   Dead-Ends within Limits: Yes☐   No☐

50% Maximum through Level of Exit Discharge: Yes☐   No☐

Adequate Illumination: Yes☐   No☐

Proper Rating on All Components: Yes☐   No☐

All Exit Enclosures Free of Storage: Yes☐   No☐

Door Swing in the Direction of Egress Travel (when required): Yes☐   No☐

Panic/Fire Exit Hardware Where Required: Yes☐   No☐   Operable: Yes☐   No☐

Doors Open Easily: Yes☐   No☐   Self-Closures Operable: Yes☐   No☐

Doors Closed or Held Open With Automatic Closures: Yes☐   No☐

Corridors and Aisles of Sufficient Size: Yes☐   No☐

Stairwell Re-Entry: Yes☐   No☐

Mezzanines: Yes☐   No☐   Proper Exits: Yes☐   No☐

VERTICAL OPENINGS

Properly Protected: Yes☐   No☐

Atrium: Yes☐   No☐   Properly Protected: Yes☐   No☐

Are Fire Doors in Good Working Order: Yes☐   No☐

HIGH RISE

Central Control Station

Voice Fire Alarm Panel: Yes☐   No☐

Fire Department Two Way Telephone Communications: Yes☐   No☐

Fire Alarm System Annunciators: Yes☐   No☐

Elevator Floor and Control Annunciators: Yes☐   No☐

Emergency Generator Status Annunciator: Yes☐   No☐

Controls for Stairwell Unlocking: Yes☐   No☐   Fire Pump Status Annunciator: Yes☐   No☐

Telephone for Fire Department Use: Yes☐   No☐

Emergency Power

Emergency Lights: Yes☐   No☐   Fire Alarm System: Yes☐   No☐

Electric Fire Pump: Yes☐   No☐   Central Control Station Equipment and Lighting: Yes☐   No☐

At Least 1 Elevator Serving All Floors: Yes☐   No☐   Transferable: Yes☐   No☐

Mechanical Equipment for Smoke Control: Yes☐   No☐

OPERATING FEATURES

Fire Drills Conducted: Yes☐   No☐   Employees Trained: Yes☐   No☐

CHAPTER 30

Housekeeping Practices

*G*ood housekeeping is plain common sense. You do not need intensive training to recognize, almost intuitively at first glance, whether or not the housekeeping on the premises being inspected is satisfactory. Cleanliness and orderliness are basic to good fire safety. If you, as an inspector, feel uneasy about the quality of the housekeeping or the general care and management of the property, then more attention should be paid to hazard management in the facility.

Good housekeeping practices—both indoors and outdoors—are a good method of controlling the presence of unwanted fuels, obstructions, and sources of ignition. Although certain aspects of housekeeping are common to most properties, whatever their use, others are peculiar to a particular occupancy. Thus, it is neither practical nor possible to describe every feature of housekeeping for all occupancies. The alert inspector will visualize hazardous housekeeping situations peculiar to the occupancy being inspected and be prepared to offer recommendations to eliminate them.

Principles of Good Housekeeping

The basic requirements of good housekeeping fall into three categories: 1) proper layout and equipment, 2) correct materials handling and storage, and 3) cleanliness and orderliness. When proper attention is given to establishing the routines for these three factors, good housekeeping is almost a certainty.

Layout and Equipment

A close look at working areas, storage areas, and the equipment used to move materials around will highlight any housekeeping problems.

Aisles clogged with materials waiting to be processed, for example, can discourage effective overall cleanliness. Some simple rearrangements could improve the housekeeping considerably. At the least, suggest that management might look at its workflow procedures if haphazard arrangement adds to the cluttered appearance.

Materials Handling and Storage

Lack of facilities to store materials neatly and to move them about easily compounds the housekeeping problem. Exitways can become blocked; access to fire extinguishers, control valves for extinguishing systems, and small hose stations can be impaired; and other fire protection equipment, such as fire doors, can become inoperative. Disordered storage also attracts debris and trash in forgotten corners. The addition of storage areas or more efficient storage facilities might alleviate these problems.

Cleanliness and Orderliness

The level of fire safety is immeasurably improved when attention is paid to keeping all areas as clean and neat as possible. The principal defense against unsightly and dangerous accumulations of unwanted materials and trash is an efficient and timely waste-removal program, backed up by each individual's personal sense of responsibility and desire to keep his or her surroundings neat and clean.

Observe the adequacy of waste-removal devices. Are enough noncombustible wastebaskets, bins, cans, and other proper containers provided so that occupants will find tidiness convenient? Is there a regularly scheduled waste-removal program?

Control of Smoking

This is frequently a tough problem to solve. The urge to smoke often conflicts with the effect smoking will have on the level of fire safety and, in some cases, on manufacturing processes and equipment, such as computers. In some instances, complete prohibition of smoking is becoming more common due to health concerns related to secondary smoke. The following guidelines can help solve this problem:

1. Provide safe, supervised, and convenient smoking areas with independent ventilation, preferably equipped with sprinkler protection.

Figure 30-1. Waste containers designed to snuff out accidental fires in contents and to limit external surface temperatures of the container to no more than 175°F above room temperature. (Justrite Manufacturing Co.)

2. Equip smoking areas with ample smoking receptacles and fire extinguishers. Keep the area clean and free of combustibles.
3. Allow only safety matches or electrical or mechanical lighters to be used.
4. Implement a continual campaign against reckless smoking and careless use of matches.
5. Designate areas where smoking is prohibited and enforce the "no smoking" rules in restricted areas.
6. See that visitors are informed of the "no smoking" rules.
7. Make sure all outside contractors observe these regulations.

Areas in which smoking is permitted, as well as those in which it is limited or prohibited, must be marked clearly. Even though the premises are marked clearly as to permitted and prohibited smoking areas, do not be lulled into thinking the problem has been solved entirely. People often sneak smokes in remote and congested areas, such as warehouses. Keep an eye out for telltale evidence of crushed smoking materials underfoot. Tell management of your findings, and remind them what could happen if the practice is not stopped.

Process Housekeeping Problems

Different occupancies have special housekeeping problems depending on the nature of the processes performed in them. Some of the more common of these special problems are discussed below.

Flammable Liquid Spills

Spills can happen whenever flammable liquids are handled or used. Ask if there is a supply of suitable absorptive materials and tools on hand to contain spills. You can review with occupants ways they might eliminate sources of ignition, ventilate the area, and safely dissipate any flammable vapors from spills.

Figure 30-2. Examples of signs permitting (left) or forbidding (right) smoking in designated areas.

Flammable Liquid-Waste Disposal

Disposal is often a troublesome problem. Flammable liquid wastes should never be drained into sewers. Instead, they should be placed in metal drums until they can be disposed of safely. There are companies that specialize in collecting flammable liquid waste products. Review with management the procedures followed to dispose of flammable liquids.

Coatings and Lubricants

Paints, grease, and similar combustibles are sources of combustible residues. Spray booths, exhaust fan blades, and ducts must be cleaned frequently to avoid dangerous accumulations of these residues. Be particularly alert to the way sprinklers in spray booths are protected. A thin coating of oil placed on sprinklers and wiped off daily is one method of providing protection; another is to enclose each sprinkler in a light plastic or paper bag that is changed as needed to avoid heavy accumulations of combustible residues.

Clean Waste and Rags

Clean cotton waste or wiping rags are considered mildly hazardous, chiefly because there is always the possibility that dirty waste can become mixed with them. Dirty waste or small amounts of certain oils can lead to spontaneous heating. Clean waste is best stored in metal or metal-lined bins with covers, while local supplies of clean waste should be left in small waste cans.

Oily Waste

Oily wiping rags, sawdust, lint, clothing, and so on, are dangerous, especially if they contain oils that can spontaneously heat. Recommend that small amounts be stored in standard waste cans; large amounts should be stored in heavy barrels with covers. Cans containing oily waste should be emptied daily into an approved container.

Packing Materials

Most packing materials are combustible and extremely hazardous. Styrofoam pellets and shapes, excelsior, straw, and the like should be treated as clean waste. Large quantities, however, should be stored in special vaults or storerooms.

Figure 30-3. A portable metal waste can equipped with a self-closing cover for storage of oily waste. (Eagle Manufacturing Co.)

Notice whether there are provisions for removing waste or used packing crating and materials from shipping and receiving rooms. Large amounts of accumulated waste strewn over the floor around unpacking operations is an invitation to disaster. State your recommendations to clean up the premises and begin regularly scheduled waste removal as strongly as you deem necessary.

Lockers and Cupboards

Personal lockers, particularly in industrial plants, can be fire hazards. Lack of cleanliness and the general use of lockers for storing waste materials are the chief dangers. Unextinguished pipes and cigars are also dangerous if put in lockers or cupboards.

Obviously, you might not be able to open personal lockers to look for hazards, but observing the locker area will give you a good idea of the standards of cleanliness. If things look bad—doors open with oily clothes thrown haphazardly into the lockers, waste rags on the floor, and so on— you should report the condition to management.

Building Care and Maintenance

Certain maintenance procedures common to most occupancies are worthy of mention.

Cleaning and Treatment of Floors

Treating, cleaning, and refinishing floors can be hazardous if flammable solvents or finishes are used or if the procedures produce combustible residues in large quantities. In general, cleaning or finishing compounds that contain solvents with flash points below room temperature are too dangerous to use except in small quantities.

Ask about the solvents and compounds used in caring for floors. The labels on the containers probably will give you information on the flammability of the contents.

Floor Oils

Oils and low-flash-point compounds are a hazard, particularly when they are first applied. Some floor dressings can heat spontaneously. If you find that the floors on the premises are oiled, check that the oily mops and rags used are stored safely in metal or other noncombustible containers.

Flammable Cleaning Solvents

Use of hazardous flammable solvents is uncommon today because so many nonhazardous cleaning solvents that have high flash points, stability, and low toxity are available. However, flammable solvents could be present, so you should ask about the products used. If flammable cleaning solvents are being used, make sure that safety cans with tight-fitting caps for dispensing small quantities are also being used. Open pails, buckets, and dip tanks without self-closing lids are not acceptable.

Kitchen Exhaust Ducts and Equipment

Grease condensating in exhaust ducts from hoods over restaurant ranges is a serious problem. The grease can be ignited by sparks from the range or, more often, by a small fire in cooking oil or fat in pans or deep fryers.

The exhaust system should be inspected daily or weekly, depending on how often it is used. Hoods, grease-removal devices, fans, ducts, and associated equipment should all be cleaned at frequent intervals. Make sure flammable solvents or cleaning aids are not used in the cleaning process. If an automatic extinguishing system is present, precautions should be taken to ensure that the cleaning process does not cause a false actuation.

Be particularly certain to inspect the insides of the ducts. People often neglect to clean ducts because it is a nasty job, although there are commercial firms that do this type of work. In any case, never suggest burning the grease out, even though ducts installed according to NFPA standards are designed to withstand burnout.

If cleaning is done without commercial assistance, suggest using a powder compound consisting of one part calcium hydroxide to two parts calcium carbonate. This compound saponifies the grease or oily sludge (converts it to a soap), thus making it easier to remove. This process requires proper ventilation, however. Another method is to loosen the grease with steam and scrape the residue out of the duct. Spraying duct interiors with hydrated lime after they have been cleaned is a fire prevention measure. It tends to saponify the grease and make subsequent cleaning easier, but it does not provide permanent fire retardancy. For a complete discussion of the subject, see Chapter 47, "Venting Systems for Commercial Cooking Equipment."

Dust and Lint Removal

Combustible dust and lint accumulation on walls, ceilings, and exposed structural members is a problem in some occupancies. However, removing it can cause an explosion if it is not done correctly. Using vacuum-cleaning equipment with dust-ignition-proof motors is a safe method. In any event, occupants should take care not to dislodge into the atmosphere quantities of combustible dust or lint that could form an explosive mixture with air, ignite, and explode. Be sure to caution against blowing dust down with compressed air. This method can create dangerous dust clouds and should only be used as a last resort, after all possible sources of ignition have been eliminated.

Outdoor Housekeeping

Poor housekeeping outside a facility can threaten the fire security of exposed structures, goods stored in the yard, and the building itself.

Accumulations of rubbish, waste, tall grass, and weeds close to buildings and storage piles are probably the most common hazards. Before entering the premises, look around outside to get a general impression of the grounds and yard maintenance. You might want to spend considerable time outside later if your first observations make you suspect problems.

Weeds and Grass

Dry weeds and grass can be controlled by herbicides. Among the chemicals used as herbicides are chlorate compounds, particularly sodium chlorate. You should be aware that chlorate compounds are oxidizing agents and can contribute to fire conditions, particularly during long, hot periods in the summer when the dead weeds and grasses have dried out. Burning dry grass and weeds to remove them can lead to disaster unless the burning is controlled at the proper time of the year and supervised by the fire department.

Calcium chloride and agricultural borax, applied dry or in solution, are effective and nonhazardous weed killers. Other herbicides include ammonium sulfamate and other commercial chemical weed killers, which present little or no fire hazard, and sodium arsenite and other arsenic compounds, which are effective but toxic.

Refuse and Rubbish Disposal

Goods stored in piles outdoors must be separated by passageways that are kept clear of combustibles. Make sure that the aisles are kept clear and that separations are maintained between piles of combustibles in storage and between the piles and nearby combustible buildings. Do not let discarded crates, utility shacks, or other combustible materials clutter the clear spaces. And check that large receptacles are available for disposal of smoking materials before entering designated "no smoking" areas.

Combustible waste materials from industrial operations often are stored in the yard before being hauled away. Make sure the accumulations of waste are no closer than 20 feet from buildings, although 50 feet is preferable. Fences should surround the waste in storage, and ignition sources, such as incinerators, should be kept at a safe distance.

Bibliography

Cote, A. E., ed., *Fire Protection Handbook,* 17th edition, National Fire Protection Association, Quincy, MA, 1991. Section 2, Chapter 34, provides guidance on general housekeeping practices and control of housekeeping hazards.

"Good Housekeeping as a Means of Protection," *The Handbook of Property Conservation,* Factory Mutual System, Norwood, MA, 1983, pp. 169–172. Principles of good housekeeping are explained.

Linville, J. L., ed., *Industrial Fire Hazards Handbook,* 3rd edition, National Fire Protection Association, Quincy, MA, 1990. Chapter 50 contains information on housekeeping practices in industrial plants.

Overview Manual, 3rd edition, Industrial Risk Insurers, Hartford, CT, 1989. Section 14 covers housekeeping.

NFPA Codes, Standards, and Recommended Practices

NFPA 91, *Standard for Exhaust Systems for Air Conveying of Materials.* Covers safety requirements for fans, ducts, direct clearances, design, and dust-collecting systems for removing or conveying flammable vapors, corrosive fumes, dust stock, and refuse.

NFPA 96, *Standard for Ventilation Control and Fire Protection of Commercial Cooking Operations.* Contains guidance on the design, installation, and use of exhaust system hoods, grease-removal devices, ducts, dampers, air moving devices, and fire extinguishing equipment.

NFPA 231, *Standard for General Storage.* Recommended practices for storage of combustibles (Classes I through IV) and plastics (Groups A, B, and C).

CHAPTER 31

Waste-Handling Systems

A lthough the waste generated in the course of a normal day's activity is rarely a source of ignition, it can provide a significant source of fuel. And large accumulations of combustible waste represent a potentially serious fire hazard. Waste also may be contaminated with hazardous materials ranging from flammable solvents to highly toxic substances. Contaminated waste complicates the disposal process and further increases the possibility of unwanted fires.

Collecting and disposing of waste safely and efficiently dramatically reduces both the source of fuel and the fire hazard. Methods of handling and disposing of waste range from the simple to the sophisticated, from collecting it manually from waste baskets and disposing of it in small landfills to gathering it mechanically with pneumatic systems that service entire buildings and destroying it in huge, multistage incinerators.

Waste-Chute and Handling Systems

There are four basic types of waste-chute systems: general access gravity, limited access gravity, pneumatic, and gravity-pneumatic.

The general access gravity chute is an enclosed vertical passageway that leads to a building's storage or compacting room. The chute is accessible to all building occupants. The limited access gravity chute is similar, but its door is locked, and entry is limited to those who have a key.

Pneumatic waste-handling systems depend on airflow to move waste to a central collection point. This system often is used in hospitals and health care buildings to carry soiled linen, although it can be used for other types of waste. In pneumatic systems, fire dampers should be located wherever chutes penetrate fire-rated floor and ceiling assemblies, fire walls, and so on. The dampers should be inspected to ensure that they are in good operating condition.

The gravity-pneumatic waste system uses a conventional gravity system to feed a collecting chamber, which in turn feeds a pneumatic waste-handling system.

Waste Chutes

Waste chutes provide pathways along which flames and smoke may travel throughout a building. For this reason, they must be enclosed by a fire-rated barrier with rated fire doors and, depending on the type of chute, equipped with automatic sprinklers. Detailed guidance on protecting waste chutes can be found in NFPA 82, *Standard on Incinerators, Waste, and Linen Handling Systems and Equipment.*

Waste chutes often are considered storage areas because they can become clogged with combustibles, thus presenting a fire hazard. You should ask whether or not the chutes on the premises are frequently jammed with refuse. If they are, a thorough study of the volume and type of waste and the habits of chute users is warranted.

Gravity-type chutes are constructed of either masonry, refractory-lined steel, or stainless, galvanized, or aluminized steel. They must be enclosed by fire-rated construction to protect the building from a fire in the chute. Make sure the enclosing construction has not been damaged or penetrated in such a way that it is no longer a complete fire barrier.

Unlined metal chutes also should be protected by automatic sprinklers. These should be installed where they can be inspected and maintained yet remain out of the reach of vandals and falling objects.

Chute Terminal Enclosures

The chute room or bin where the waste from chutes is collected must have a fire-resistance rating at least equivalent to that required for the chute, and openings into the enclosure must be protected by fire doors suitable for Class B openings. The concentration of combustibles in such an area requires that it be equipped with automatic sprinklers.

Waste chutes should not discharge directly into incinerators because this increases the likelihood that they will serve as chimneys, spreading smoke and fire to other portions of the building.

Incinerators

Incineration significantly reduces the volume of wastes and, more importantly, the fire hazard associated with the accumulation of combustibles. Incinerators generally are of two types, either commercial-industrial or domestic.

Commercial-Industrial Incinerators

Most commercial-industrial waste incineration facilities use either a rotary kiln, multiple-chamber, or a controlled-air unit. each of which operates on a different principle. Multiple-chamber units use high quantities of excess air, while controlled-air incinerators operate under starved-air conditions in the primary chamber. The fire hazards associated with each are essentially the same.

Incineration Fire Safety

By their very nature, incineration operations are fraught with fire hazards. As a result, the following items require specific attention.

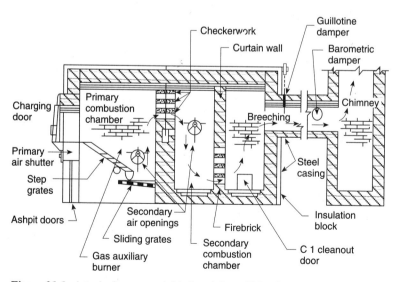

Figure 31-1. A typical commercial-industrial, multiple-chamber incinerator.

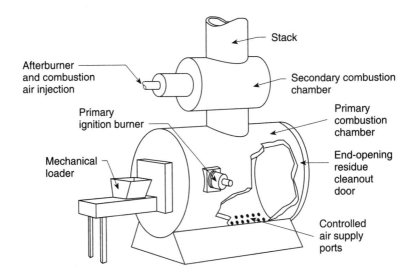

Figure 31-2. Cutaway of a controlled-air incinerator.

Incinerator and Waste-Handling Room: Incinerators and related waste collection and handling equipment must be enclosed in 2-hour fire-rated compartments equipped with self-closing fire doors suitable for Class B openings. These compartments should be used for no other purpose.

Equipment Design and Construction: Incinerators, breeching, stacks, and accessories that are subjected to high-temperature combustion reactions and gases should be able to resist cracking, erosion, warping, and distortion. Outside surface temperatures to which an operator may be exposed should be no higher than 70°F above ambient. The incinerator also should have some form of explosion relief, which may be the chimney.

Layout and Arrangement: The facility design should ensure that waste and residue containers and the like do not block charging and clean-out operations or access to work areas and that waste material can be charged in a smooth, efficient manner. All parts of the incinerator should be accessible for cleaning, repair, and service, and clearances above the charging door and between the top and sides of the incinerator and combustible materials should meet the requirements of applicable building codes and the specific requirements in NFPA 82.

Charging Systems

"Charging" is the feeding or loading of waste materials into the incinerator. An improperly designed or operated charging system could permit flames and combustion products to escape from the incinerator and ignite waste materials nearby.

There are basically two types of incineration charging systems: manual and mechanical.

Manual Systems: As the name implies, waste materials in a manual system are loaded into the incinerator by hand. Manual charging generally is used in small-capacity units. Fire prevention measures are directed primarily toward maintaining adequate clearances between the incinerator and combustible materials and minimizing the length of time the charging doors stay open. The door of the incinerator furnace is critical to confining the fire to the incinerator. This opening, normally sealed by a refractory-lined door, must be used frequently for feeding waste materials.

Mechanical Charging: Mechanical devices generally are used to load larger incinerators with small batches of waste at regular intervals. This protects the units against overcharging and provides for a continual and efficient combustion process.

One common mechanical charging system is the "hopper/ram assembly." Waste is loaded into a hopper, the hopper cover closes, a guillotine-type door opens, and a ram pushes the waste into the incinerator.

This particular mechanical system presents major fire and smoke problems against which you must guard. For example, waste can lodge under the fire door and prevent it from closing tightly. If this occurs, the lodged waste could ignite and spread fire back into the hopper, offering a path for fire spread. Thus, the fire door should be closed by power, not gravity, to seal the furnace opening as tightly as possible.

Another fire hazard associated with the hopper/ram assembly involves the ram itself. When the charging ram injects waste into the incinerator, its face is exposed to furnace heat. Eventually, this can cause the ram to heat up enough to ignite waste outside the incinerator. To avoid this problem, the charging ram should be cooled either by an internal water circulation system or a water spray system that quenches the ram face after every charging cycle.

The fire door on this type of mechanical charging system should be interlocked with the hopper cover, or outer door, to keep them from being opened at the same time while the incinerator is operating. There are a number of ways to protect against accidental ignition of waste materials in the hoppers. A fire detector with an audible alarm signal may be installed, or the system may be equipped with a high-temperature automatic sprinkler independent of the room sprinkler system. Another option is a manually activated water spray or quench valve or an emergency switch that would override the automatic charging cycle controls to inject the hopper contents immediately into the furnace.

Auxiliary Fuel Systems

Most incinerators have gas-fueled burners to help burn a greater variety of waste, as well preheating the incinerator, igniting the waste, and destroying odors and smoke. Burners must be equipped with an electronic flame safeguard system that automatically shuts off the burner fuel supply if the burner fails to ignite, its flame is extinguished, or the furnace draft is insufficient.

Domestic Incinerators

Domestic incinerators are classified as gas appliances. The greatest hazard domestic incinerators face is not "normal" garbage and waste, but large collections of highly combustible wastes, such as solvents, oils, plastics, remodeling debris, and so on. If materials with a high heat release rate are burned or excessive quantities of waste are loaded into the incinerator at one time, the resulting high temperatures in the fire box and chimney connector could ignite adjacent combustibles.

For these reasons, clearances to combustibles are especially important. The clearance above a charging door is 48 inches, while clearances from the sides, rear, and top are 36 inches. Clearance from the front is 48 inches. Side, rear, top, and front clearances may be reduced under special conditions (see NFPA 82).

Waste Compactors

Waste compactors use electro-mechanical-hydraulic means to reduce the volume of waste and to package it. Compactors may be either commercial-industrial or domestic.

Commercial-Industrial Compactors

There are four basic types of commercial-industrial compactor systems: the bulkhead compactor, the extruder, the carousel bag packer, and the container packer.

Bulkhead Compactor: In this type of compactor, waste is squeezed in a chamber against a bulkhead. When a block of waste is ready for removal, a bag is installed and filled with the compacted material.

Extruder: An extruder compacts waste by forcing it through a cylinder that has a restricted area and extruding it into a "slug," which is then broken off and bagged or placed in a container.

Carousel Bag Packer: In this compactor, waste is squeezed into a bagged container.

Container Packers: Container compactors compact waste directly into a bin, cart, or container. When it is full, the container can be either manually or mechanically removed from the compactor and taken out of the compaction area.

Chute Termination Bin

The waste chutes that serve compactors generally do not feed directly into the compactor but into a waste storage room, a chute connector, or an impact area. The potential fire hazard in the waste storage room can be minimized by installing sprinklers and a 2-hour fire-rated enclosure with Class B protection of the openings.

Compactor and Waste Storage Rooms

Because compacted material is combustible, it will burn if ignited, even though its density will affect the rate of burning. For this reason, only minimal amounts of compacted materials should be stored in buildings. Compactors larger than 2 cubic yards must be enclosed with 2-hour fire-rated wall, ceiling, and floor assemblies with fire doors suitable for Class B openings. These requirements also apply to waste storage rooms if their uncompacted capacity exceeds 3 cubic yards. These rooms should be equipped with automatic sprinklers unless the compactor is fed manually and is not used in conjunction with a chute.

Shredders

Shredders reduce waste to a uniform size. The major hazard associated with shredder operations is the possibility of explosion, which may result from the ignition of combustible dust in the vicinity of the shredder while it is operating. Ignition also may occur when ferrous materials, such as paper clips, are left in the material to be shredded; this makes magnetic separators desirable.

Methods of protecting shredder operations from fire include dust collection, explosion suppression in the shredder room, and explosion relief venting. Feed bins to the shredders and storage areas for the shredded and unshredded waste should be sprinklered, and all storage areas should be enclosed in fire-rated rooms with fire doors suitable for Class B openings.

Bibilography

Cote, A. E., ed., *Fire Protection Handbook*, 17th edition, National Fire Protection Association, Quincy, MA, 1991. Section 2, Chapter 33, and Section 9, Chapters 16 and 17, discuss the systems and equipment available for handling and disposing of waste to minimize the hazard potential.

NFPA Codes, Standards, and Recommended Practices

NFPA 13, *Standard for the Installation of Sprinkler Systems.* Illustrated installation and description of testing and procedures for all types of systems including wet pipe, dry pipe, deluge, and preaction systems.

NFPA 68, *Guide for Venting of Deflagrations.* Includes fundamentals of deflagration venting, vent design, and closures, and discusses interpreting test data.

NFPA 80, *Standard for Fire Doors and Fire Windows.* Covers the use, installation, and maintenance of fire doors, windows, glass blocks, and shutters.

NFPA 82, *Standard on Incinerators, Waste, and Linen Handling Systems and Equipment.* Contains requirements for reducing fire hazards associated with the installation and use of compactors, incinerators, waste-handling systems, linen-handling systems, and waste-storage rooms and containers.

NFPA 251, *Standard Methods of Fire Tests of Building Construction and Materials.* Specifies methods for determining the fire-resistive abilities of building members and assemblies.

CHAPTER 32

Radioactive
Materials

*R*adioactive materials are chemically identical to their nonradioactive counterparts and pose identical chemical hazards. However, they may pose an additional hazard because some types of radiation, in sufficient quantities, can damage living tissue. Since radiation can be measured more easily than almost any other hazard and the effects of accidental exposures calculated in advance, your main job as an inspector is to discover the nature, quantities, and locations of radioactive materials in a facility and determine the potential for them to be dispersed in an accidental fire.

Most types of radioactive materials that are handled or stored in quantities sufficient to pose a hazard during an accident are restricted to government facilities or facilities licensed by the Nuclear Regulatory Commission (NRC). Radioactive materials used in consumer products such as ionization smoke detectors and tritium-activated emergency lights pose such a small risk that the end-user needs no special permits to use, store, or dispose of them. They may be damaged in a fire, but the normal products of combustion of most fires will far exceed the hazard added by the dispersal of radioactivity from these limited-use consumer products.

NFPA standards recommend a safety analysis report, something major users and producers of radioactive materials, such as Department of Energy plants, power and research reactors licensed by the NRC, and fuel or waste handlers and processors, are required to have. This is a formal document that includes fire hazards analyses, failure analysis reviews, and descriptions of the most credible accidents, including fires, and the effects to be expected from each. These are openly available, and you should review them as part of an initial or pre-fire planning inspection.

Facilities that use radioactive materials typically are required to demonstrate that the most probable accident scenarios will not adversely affect the public. This means that most facilities have automatic fire extinguishing systems, generally ordinary wet-pipe systems.

Although nuclear facility managers sometimes express concern about water damage, the only real concern with water is that water is a neutron moderator. This means that a "criticality" accident may occur when some fissionable materials, such as enriched uranium or plutonium, are exposed to unlimited water. However, the hazard can be calculated in advance and protection, such as automatic sprinklers, provided.

Today, the overwhelming majority of all nuclear facilities are protected by automatic sprinkler systems, many precisely because the dispersion of possibly contaminated water is desired to be controlled. It is far easier to collect and store water from a few sprinkler heads that open directly over a fire than it is to deal with a much greater volume of water from one or more hose streams directed by fire fighters through smoke and obstructions from some distance away.

Your review will form the primary input to the facility's pre-fire plan. To ensure safe and adequate emergency operations, you should ascertain and discuss the types and quantities of materials present at the facility with knowledgeable people. The normal firefighter turnout gear will provide appreciable protection against a significant amount of alpha and beta radiation, and the consistent use of self-contained breathing apparatus is the principle protection against internal contamination. The remaining threat from high-level gamma or neutron radiation is readily measurable with the proper instrumentation. Where such hazards exist, you should review the radiation monitoring equipment available for both normal and emergency needs and determine whether trained people will be available to assist the fire department during emergencies at any hour. You also must ascertain the methods of containment available within the facility and the probable effectiveness of the containment during a fire.

Containment systems for radioactive materials include the usual fire doors and walls, ventilation enclosures and dampers, and sometimes special ventilation systems. In facilities from which contaminated air may be exhausted, the air commonly passes through a high-efficiency filter system. This may not have dampers in the ductwork in order to ensure that contamination will not back up into the plant. If this is the case, the filter system must be protected to ensure that fire will not damage the filters and allow contaminated air to escape. Filter systems typically consist of multiple banks of pre-filters and mesh screens, some of which are equipped with various combinations of automatic and manual water spray systems. You should make sure that these systems adequately cover the filters and are in service. The supervision, inspection, and maintenance of these systems should be at least as thorough as they are for any other fire protection system in the plant.

You should also review the disposition of water that has come in contact with a possibly contaminated filter. Contaminated water should be drained to a holding tank, or the room should be diked or curbed so that the low-volume water discharge from a protection system will not spread throughout the premises.

Since radioactive materials in bulk storage generally are quite valuable, as well as hazardous, they usually are stored in vaults or safes for security as well as safety. Thus, you must ascertain the integrity of all fire walls, doors, dampers, vaults, and ducts. The spread of contamination is not determined by the nature of the radiation but by the nature of the chemical form of the radioactive material and the way in which that chemical is affected by fire. Any opening through which smoke or hot gasses can spread is an opening through which radioactive contamination can spread. While hand-held meters make radiation detectable and the hazard more readily calculated, decontaminating a structure may require quite a bit of work; it may take much longer to remove radioactive contaminants than to remove smoke and soot.

The great importance of compartmentation and containment in nuclear facilities should not be underestimated. The 1969 Rocky Flats Plant fire resulted in a $26 million loss, of which $10 million alone was the cost of decontamination. This was the most costly contamination incident in the Atomic Energy Commission's history.

Machines, as well as radioactive materials, can pose radiation hazards. These machines may range from the small hospital x-ray machine to the multi-mile long particle accelerators used in nuclear research. All of them pose radiation hazards from the beam, but they all share a common characteristic: the radiation ceases when the beam is shut down. You should ascertain that adequate interlocks and manual shut-downs are provided to shut the machine off in an emergency and that the shielding is adequate to protect emergency forces engaged in activities in any supporting structures.

In particle accelerators, the beam is directed at a target, which may produce other beams to be directed at other targets and eventually at a "beam stop" of high-density materials. These materials may have residual levels of radioactivity resulting from the creation of new radioactive elements. You should determine the nature and extent of the target's radiation, as well as the protection afforded the target. In addition, you should check out the experimental area surrounding a target. This area is the most frequently changing area of the facility and often the most cluttered. Thus it may be the most difficult area in which to fight a fire. It may also contain one-of-a-kind electrical experimental or monitoring equipment that presents additional ignition potentials.

Containers used to ship radioactive material must be strong and constructed well enough to withstand credible accidents. To this end, containers for high-level materials must be tested to determine that they can withstand impact, fire, and water submersion, in sequence, without leaking. Strangely enough, the history of shipping and shipping accidents makes the transportation accident of little concern to the fire service. Rather, the potential problem lies in the facility in which shipping containers are stored or through which they pass. Why? Because a container designed to survive the maximum fuel spill fire may be inadequate when exposed to the maximum fire in a general shipping depot or warehouse.

When inspecting transportation facilities, you should always ascertain whether they are likely to be used to store high-level radioactive shipping containers, such as cobalt gamma ray machines. Unlike the electrical machine, these use a radioactive material as a power source. Thus, the unit is always highly radioactive and must be shielded. Since lead is a cheap material and is expensive to ship by virtue of its weight, it is often used to shield radioactive materials in storage. The presence of molten lead in the residue of a warehouse fire should be an immediate indicator of a possibly dangerous situation, and all overall operations should be suspended pending the completion of a thorough radiation survey. This also applies to any facility in which high-level radiation sources, protected by shielding, are used.

Hospitals are another occupancy in which the storage of radioactive materials—in this case radioisotopes—may present a hazard. Since radioisotopes are administered to patients in individual doses, the threat to a healthy fire fighter of exposure to radioactivity during a fire in a treatment area is minimal. Of greater concern are the areas in which these materials are stored and prepared. They may contain a considerable number of different isotopes and the quantity, as well as the combination of those with the highest activity and most volatility, may be very hazardous. Since patients cannot readily evacuate a hospital, separation and protection of storage areas is often more important for firesafety than it would be in an industrial or educational facility.

All other fire protection programs, procedures, and equipment applicable to a nonradiation facility are also applicable to the radiation facility. You should have no illusions that some fire protection practices may not apply because of the special "radioactive" nature of the facility. In fact, the provision of standard fire protection practices, particularly automatic protection, is a necessity in facilities in which radiation is a significant additional hazard.

All radioactive materials containers must be marked with appropriate warning signs. Samples of Department of Transportation shipping labels are shown in Figure 32-1. Containers used in facilities for interim storage should be labeled with the type of material they hold and the radiation levels measured at the surface of the container. These radiation levels can be readily translated into the maximum amount of time a person can remain adjacent to the container.

Figure 32-1. Examples of Department of Transportation shipping labels.

Considering the factors of time, distance, and shielding, it is generally unlikely that any reasonable fire fighting time can result in an exposure level of concern to a fire fighter. Again, this can be readily calculated, and such considerations should be included in any pre-fire plan. In most facilities, individual laboratories or process rooms will also be marked to indicate the type and level of hazard within. Considering that radiation exposure levels are proportional to time, a fire fighter who may be exposed to radiation for 2 or 3 hours at the most should not be overly concerned about his or her health. After all, the level at which a worker can be exposed without harm for an entire working year is some 2,000 hours.

Your primary concern as an inspector is whether a fire will be able to breach a facility's radioactive material containments. When a safety analysis report or an on-site analysis by knowledgeable radiation protection people cannot determine the likelihood of such an event, the fire department or whoever provides service during an emergency must resort to on-site monitoring.

Bibliography

Brannigan, F., *Living with Radiation: The Problems of the Nuclear Age for the Layman,* Energy Research & Development Administration, Division of Safety, Standards, & Compliance, Springfield, VA, 1976.

Cote, A. E., ed., *Fire Protection Handbook,* 17th edition, National Fire Protection Association, Quincy, MA, 1991.

Linville, J. L., ed., *Industrial Fire Hazards* Handbook, 3rd edition, National Fire Protection Association, Quincy, MA, 1990. See Chapters 7 and 40.

Purrington, Robert G. and Patterson, H. Wade, *Handling Radiation Emergencies,* National Fire Protection Association, Quincy, MA, 1977.

NFPA Codes, Standards, and Recommended Practices

NFPA 801, *Recommended Fire Protection Practice for Facilities Handling Radioactive Materials.*

NFPA 802, *Recommended Fire Protection Practice for Nuclear Research and Production Reactors.*

NFPA 803, *Standard for Fire Protection for Light Water Nuclear Power Plants.*

CHAPTER 33

Materials-Handling Systems

*A*s an inspector, you should be interested in the methods used to move materials from one place to another in manufacturing plants, warehouses, and other occupancies. Efficient handling of materials requires specialized equipment that can introduce serious fire and explosion hazards unless the equipment is properly selected, installed, protected, operated, and maintained. This equipment includes industrial trucks, mechanical stock conveyors, pneumatic conveyors, and cranes.

Industrial Trucks

The most common industrial trucks used to handle materials are lift trucks of the fork or squeeze-clamp type. They are powered by electric storage batteries, gasoline, LP-Gas, or diesel engines, which introduces an additional source of fuel into the plant and also provides a potentially serious ignition source. This is especially true if easily ignited fibers, dusts, vapors, or gases are present in the area in which the truck is to be used. Unless these vehicles are properly maintained and used, they can be extremely hazardous even if they are the appropriate type for the hazard.

Operation of Trucks

A system of easily recognized markings has been developed to help identify the different types of trucks and the areas in which they can be used safely. The appropriate markings are affixed to both sides of a truck so that its type can be readily identified.

Markers of corresponding shape should be posted at the entrances to hazardous areas. When a truck approaches a hazardous area, both the

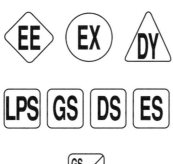

Figure 33-1. Markers for identifying industrial truck types and for posting in areas where various types of trucks would be permitted. The signs have black borders and lettering on a yellow background. See the text for definitions of the different types of trucks. Source: Figure 5-4.2.2.2, NFPA 505, **Fire Safety Standard for Powered Industrial Trucks Including Type Designations, Areas of Use, Maintenance, and Operation,** *NFPA, Quincy, MA, 1992.*

occupants of the facility and the driver will be able to see whether the truck can safely enter the area by comparing the markings affixed to the truck and those posted in the area.

NFPA 505, *Fire Safety Standard for Powered Industrial Trucks,* lists 13 different types of trucks and identifies the hazardous areas in which they may be used. As an inspector, you should be acquainted with the terms of NFPA 505 so that you can give advice as to when the different types of trucks can and cannot be used.

Battery-Powered Trucks

Four types of electric trucks are available, depending on the fire hazards present. These are the Type E, Type ES, Type EE, and Type EX.

The Type E has the minimum necessary safeguards for use in ordinary hazard areas, while Type ES has additional safeguards that prevent the ignition of fibers by controlling sparks emitted by the electrical system and limiting surface temperatures. In Type EE trucks, the electric motor and all other electrical equipment are completely enclosed so that they may be used in hazardous locations other than those that require Type EX trucks. Type EX trucks are explosion-proof (Class 1, Group D) or dust-tight (Class II, Group D) for use in areas in which explosive mixtures of flammable vapors or combustible dusts are likely during normal operations.

Gasoline-Powered Trucks

Two types of gasoline-fueled trucks are available, the Type G and the Type GS. The Type G truck has the minimum necessary safeguards for use in areas of ordinary fire hazard, and the Type GS truck has additional safeguards in the electrical, fuel, and exhaust systems for occupancies in which there are readily ignited combustible materials.

Diesel-Powered Trucks

Three types of diesel-fueled trucks currently are available. These are the Type D, which are comparable in hazard to Type G gasoline-powered trucks; the Type DS, which are comparable in hazard to Type GS gasoline-powered trucks; and the Type DY, which are equipped with additional safeguards to make them less hazardous than Type GS gasoline-powered trucks. The surface and exhaust gas temperatures of the Type DY trucks are limited, they have no electrical system, and they are equipped with other safeguards to minimize the fire hazard normally associated with internal combustion engines.

LP-Gas-Powered Trucks

Two types of LP-Gas-fueled trucks are manufactured, Type LP and Type LPS. They are considered comparable in fire hazard to Type G and Type GS gasoline-powered trucks, respectively.

Dual-Fuel Trucks

There are two types of dual-fuel trucks that may be operated with either gasoline or LP-Gas. They are designated either Type G/LP, which are comparable in fire hazard to Types G and LP, or Type GS/LPS, which require the same safeguards against the hazards of exhaust, fuel, and electrical systems that Types GS and LPS do.

The uniform marking system to identify the types of lift trucks and the areas in which they can be used is shown in Figure 33-1. Many of the fires caused by industrial trucks have been the result of using the wrong trucks in the wrong locations.

Fire Hazards of Industrial Trucks

The major potential fire hazard associated with gasoline-, diesel-, and LP-Gas-powered trucks are fuel leaks ignited by the hot engine, the hot muffler, the ignition system, other electrical equipment, or other external ignition sources. This danger is lower for diesel trucks because diesel fuel has a higher flash point. Particular care must be exercised when storing and dispensing fuels, as with any flammable liquid or gas.

Comparatively few fires have occurred in battery-powered trucks. Nevertheless, electrical short circuits, hot resistors, and exploding batteries have been known to ignite fires. Frayed wiring and loose battery terminals also indicate potential trouble.

Careless and uninformed operation of industrial trucks contributes to property loss. If you notice trucks being operated carelessly, recommend that the operators receive appropriate training and that the necessary rules be enforced strictly.

Also contributing to more serious fires are excessive material storage height; careless handling of loads, especially containers of flammable liquids; and collision with sprinkler piping, fire doors, and other fire protection equipment. The provision of adequate, clear passageways for truck travel and clear warning of overhead obstructions and exposed piping will help to reduce accidents. Make particularly sure that sprinkler piping is well marked if there is any possibility that elevated loads will damage sprinklers or sprinkler piping.

Maintenance

Proper maintenance of trucks is essential to good fire prevention. Observe the trucks carefully for signs of excessive wear and accumulations of lint, oil, and grease. A system of regularly scheduled maintenance based on engine-hour or motor-hour use can greatly reduce the danger of hazardous malfunctions. It is appropriate to ask for and to review maintenance records as part of an inspection.

Trucks—particularly their fuel and ignition systems—should be maintained and repaired only in specially designated areas. Repairs should never be attempted within a hazardous area. Some basic points of good maintenance include filling water mufflers daily or as frequently as necessary to keep the water supply at 75% of the fill capacity, keeping muffler filters clean, and making sure that LP-Gas fuel containers are mounted securely to prevent them from jarring loose, slipping, or rotating. Any trucks seen giving off sparks or flames from the exhaust system or found to be operating at excessive temperatures should be removed from service immediately. Do not permit them to return to service until the faults have been corrected. Each truck should be equipped with a portable extinguisher suitable for the fuel it uses.

Refueling and Recharging

Because almost half of the fires involving liquid-fueled trucks are caused by spillage during refueling, trucks should be refueled outdoors where there is minimal exposure to plant structures. Make sure the area is posted for "no smoking," that fuel-dispensing pumps are suitable for that use, and that scales for weighing the LP-Gas containers are accurately calibrated. LP containers should be stored outdoors, away from common fire exposures. Observe refueling operations.

Battery recharging operations also require special precautions. The corrosive chemical solutions (electrolytes) in the batteries present a chemical hazard to personnel. On charge, they give off hydrogen, which can accumulate to explosive concentrations if ventilation is inadequate. Note whether the recharging area includes some means for flushing and neutralizing spilled electrolytes and has a barrier for protecting charging apparatus. Most important, make sure that the ventilation is adequate to carry hydrogen away from gassing batteries.

During the charging operation, vent caps should be kept in place to avoid electrolyte spray. Check to be sure that the vent caps are functioning and that battery covers remain open during charging to dissipate heat.

Conveying Systems

Mechanical conveyors and elevators are among the most commonly used equipment in materials handling. There are many types of mechanical conveyors, including the common belt conveyor. The belt conveyor presents two principal fire hazards: the material being carried, if it is combustible, and the combustible belt itself. The belt conveyor also may communicate fire from one building or area to another.

Fire Causes in Conveyors

One common cause of fire in conveyors is friction between the moving conveyor belt and a stuck roller or other object. Conveyors should be inspected regularly to detect belt slippage or defective rollers, and their moving parts should be lubricated on a regular basis. The use of fire-retardant belt material significantly reduces the belt's ignition potential.

Careless cutting or welding operations on, or in the vicinity of, a conveyor or its housing is another leading cause of fire. Hot slag can ignite combustibles on the belt, debris around it, or the belt itself. If you see any cutting and welding being performed on conveyors, insist that safe practices be followed (see Chapter 45 of this book and NFPA 51B, *Standard for Fire Prevention in Use of Cutting and Welding Processes*).

Discharging excessively hot materials from kilns, ovens, or furnaces onto a conveyor belt is a fire hazard in some plants, as is the spontaneous combustion of the materials being handled, such as coal. Electrical short circuits, smoking, and incendiarism are other potential causes of conveyor fires.

One factor that occurs frequently in fires involving mechanical conveyors is the dust that is produced when loose combustible materials are being conveyed. If dust generation is not prevented by the process arrangement, dust collection systems are needed.

Static electricity is another hazard common to conveyors. Check to make sure all parts of the machines and conveyors are thoroughly bonded and grounded to minimize static discharges. Static electricity also can be controlled by the use of belts made of conductive material, the use of static collectors, or the application of conductive dressings to the belt surface (see NFPA 77, *Recommended Practice on Static Electricity*).

Loss experience shows that automatic sprinkler or water spray protection may be warranted for important belt conveyors.

Other Mechanical Conveyors

Chain conveyors equipped with hooks and roller conveyors commonly are used in assembly lines, while screw conveyors, pan conveyors, and bucket conveyors are used for handling loose, hot, or molten materials. Belt conveyors generally are not suitable for handling materials over 150°F.

Bucket elevators, which are found most often in bulk processing plants, convey loads vertically and are susceptible to the same fire hazards as other mechanical conveyors. These conveyors might need specialized fire protection if they handle combustible dust or materials.

Protection of Conveyor Openings

Protecting the openings in fire walls and floors through which conveyors pass is important in preventing the spread of fire. Many methods have been designed to protect openings for conveyors of different types, including water spray protection and fire doors with interlocks or counterweights to stop the flow of material. Some conveyors are even diverted through the roof. It should be noted that the use of passive protection might be preferable to the use of suppression alone based on the type of material present in the area.

You would be wise to consult the references at the end of this chapter for more information on protecting openings for conveyors. Examples of opening protection for conveyors are shown in Figures 33-2 and 33-3.

Pneumatic Conveyors

Pneumatic conveyor systems consist of enclosed tubing in which a material normally is transported by a stream of air with enough velocity

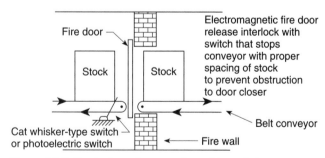

Figure 33-2. Protection of an opening where a belt conveyor can be interrupted at a wall opening. Source: Figure C-2, NFPA 80, Standard for Fire Doors and Fire Windows, NFPA, Quincy, MA, 1992.

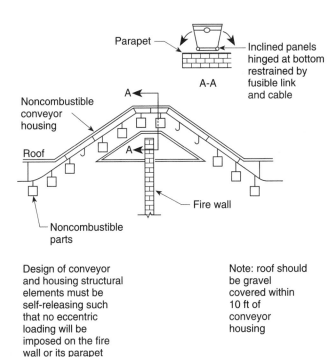

Parapet

A-A

Inclined panels hinged at bottom restrained by fusible link and cable

Noncombustible conveyor housing

Roof

Fire wall

Noncombustible parts

Design of conveyor and housing structural elements must be self-releasing such that no eccentric loading will be imposed on the fire wall or its parapet that could adversely affect the wall

Note: roof should be gravel covered within 10 ft of conveyor housing

Figure 33-3. Example of a conveyor carried over a fire wall.
Source: Figure C-1, NFPA 80, **Standard for Fire Doors and Fire Windows,** *NFPA, Quincy, MA 1992.*

to keep the conveyed material in motion. Where concentrations of powders and dusts are within the explosive range, noncombustible gases such as nitrogen sometimes are used in place of, or in addition to, air.

There are two principal types of pneumatic systems. The pressure type uses air at greater than atmospheric pressure, while the suction type transports materials using air at less than atmospheric pressure.

In an air-conveying system, any dry collector containing a dust-air mixture in the explosive range must be considered a potential explosion hazard (see Chapter 37). Look at the collector carefully to make sure it is in a safe location—preferably outdoors—to protect personnel. The collector should be constructed of conductive noncombustible materials and be completely bonded and grounded. Construction should be of nonferrous, nonsparking metal or nonmagnetic, nonsparking stainless steel.

Where conveying ducts are exposed to weather or moisture, examine them carefully to make sure they are moisture-tight. Moisture entering the system can react with dust, which generates heat and serves as a potential source of ignition. If the conveying gas-air mixture is relatively warm and the dust and collectors are relatively cold, the gas temperature could drop below the dew point, causing moisture to condense. If this is the case, it might be necessary to insulate the ducts and collectors or provide a heating system.

Explosion relief for ducts and collectors always should extend to the outside. They can be provided with antiflashback swing valves or rupture diaphragms. Fans and housings for fans that are used to move combustible solids or vapors should be constructed of conductive, nonferrous materials. It is important to note whether dust is drawn through the fan before it enters the final collector. You also should note whether the fan bearings are equipped with suitable temperature-indicating devices wired with an alarm to alert occupants to overheating. And remember: never attempt to inspect a fan while it is in operation.

Cranes

Cranes principally are used to move heavy materials. Some cranes move along rails, including overhead traveling, gantry, tower, and bridge cranes. Overhead traveling cranes may be used either indoors or out; gantry, tower, and bridge cranes are used mainly outdoors. Outdoor cranes may be damaged by high winds.

Large cranes that move along rails generally have automatic or manual rail clamps or some means of anchorage, such as crane traps, wedges, and cables. You should inquire into the method of anchorage.

Crane operators' cabs should be constructed of noncombustible materials. Check to make sure that they are left free of oily waste, rubbish, and other combustibles. Each cab should be equipped with portable fire extinguishers. In some large equipment, automatic fixed piping systems might be advisable.

Bibliography

Cote, A. E., ed., *Fire Protection Handbook,* 17th edition, National Fire Protection Association, Quincy, MA, 1991. Section 8, Chapter 31, provides basic information on industrial trucks, mechanical and pneumatic stock conveying systems, and cranes and discusses the fire and explosion hazards inherent with them as well as the protection of conveyor openings in walls.

Linville, J. L., ed., *Industrial Fire Hazards Handbook*, 3rd edition, National Fire Protection Association, Quincy, MA, 1990. Chapters 51 and 52 discuss in detail various materials-handling systems found in industrial plants.

Mitchell, D. W., et al., *Fire Hazard of Conveyor Belts,* Report of Investigations 7053, U.S. Bureau of Mines, Washington, D.C., 1967.

NFPA Codes, Standards, and Recommended Practices

NFPA 13, *Standard for the Installation of Sprinkler Systems.* Illustrated installation and description of testing and procedures for all types of systems, including wet pipe, dry pipe, deluge, and preaction.

NFPA 15, *Standard for Water Spray Fixed Systems for Fire Protection.* Covers the design, installation, maintenance, and test requirements based on sound engineering principles, test data, and field experience.

NFPA 51B, *Standard for Fire Prevention in Use of Cutting and Welding Processes.* Covers practices and precautions for cutting and welding processes involving the use of electric arcs and oxy-fuel gas flames.

NFPA 68, *Guide for Venting of Deflagrations.* Covers fundamentals of deflagration venting, important characteristics of vent design and vent closures, and interpreting test data.

NFPA 69, *Standard on Explosion Prevention Systems.* Covers requirements for explosion prevention systems based on reducing the concentration of combustible materials or oxidents; also includes requirements for inert gas systems, explosion-suppression systems, and deflagration pressure containment.

NFPA 77, *Recommended Practice on Static Electricity.* Explains the hazards of static accumulation and the means of minimizing or eliminating those hazards.

NFPA 80, *Standard for Fire Doors and Fire Windows.* Covers the use, installation, and maintenance of fire doors, windows, glass blocks, and shutters.

NFPA 498, *Standard for Explosives Motor Vehicle Terminals.* Discusses requirements for fire and explosion prevention and fire protection at interchange and parking facilities for vehicles transporting explosives.

NFPA 505, *Fire Safety Standard for Powered Industrial Trucks Including Type Designations, Areas of Use, Maintenance, and Operation.* Contains definitions of all types of industrial trucks and detailed descriptions of the different hazardous areas in which each type can be used.

NFPA 512, *Standard for Truck Fire Protection.* Specifies fire protection requirements for operating and maintaining property-carrying motor vehicles.

NFPA 513, *Standard for Motor Freight Terminals.* Requirements for fire protection in motor freight terminals, including transfer areas, offices, employee facilities, and vehicle service areas.

NFPA 650, *Standard for Pneumatic Conveying Systems for Handling Combustible Materials.* Covers requirements for pressure-type and suction-type systems and provides guidance on design safeguards of component parts.

CHAPTER 34

General
Storage

F ire hazards found in storage occupancies are as varied as the products
that are used in everyday life. The commodities being stored, the
storage arrangements used, and the height of the storage all have an
impact on the potential type of fire and on the criteria needed to protect
the storage area. Collectively, these items, viewed with the construction
of the storage building, will determine the type and level of protection
necessary to protect the stored commodity.

Commodity Classification

The most crucial and often most difficult task is correctly assessing the
fire potential of the commodity being stored. Many products are composed of a variety of materials, each having different burning characteristics. In addition, the performance of the commodity during a fire can be
influenced significantly by the materials in which it is packed and the
type of packaging enclosure being used. For example, a highly combustible product sealed inside a metal container might represent only a
minimal fire hazard. Conversely, a metal product enclosed in a thick
foamed polystyrene cocoon could be a serious fire challenge. In most
cases, the packaging container presents just as much of a threat to the
structure as the actual stored product.

To help the warehouse manager and the fire protection engineer assess
the fire hazards of stored materials, the various storage standards contain
classification categories with attendant definitions and examples (see the
Bibliography). These commodity classification systems must be studied
carefully because the lower numerical or alphabetical designations
indicate lesser hazards in some instances while they signify greater
hazards in others.

Most products found in a general-purpose warehouse can be categorized under the commodity classification system found in NFPA 231, *Standard for General Storage,* and NFPA 231C, *Standard for Rack Storage of Materials.* This basic system establishes four categories—Class I, II, III, and IV—with Class I representing a minimal hazard and Class IV the greatest hazard. A commodity defined as Class I presents a challenge to the fire protection system because of the packing container. Since the product in the container is a noncombustible material, the installed fire protection measures are based on the fire hazard associated with the storage container. A Class III commodity, on the other hand, involves the storage of a combustible product in a combustible container. Thus, the anticipated fire protection measures must consider the effect of the stored product, as well.

For those products that are mostly or totally composed of plastics, NFPA 231 and 231C contain a fifth classification system that places plastics in three groups. Group A plastics represent the greatest level of fire hazard and Group C the lowest level. Further, Group B plastics are equated with the general Class IV category, while Group C plastics are equated with the Class III category. Since the protection measures for Group A plastics are so different, the use of a term such as "Class V commodities" has been avoided.

When determining any of these classifications, and hence the fire protection for the warehouse, you must consider not only what is present on a given day but the potential for future changes in commodities or in the overall storage occupancy as well. The classic example in recent years has been the large-scale substitution of plastics for components that previously were made of metal, resulting in the need for major revisions or reinforcement in many warehouse sprinkler systems. This problem is further exacerbated by the tendency of some developers to build warehouses on speculation. No specific tenant or storage arrangement is considered at the time of construction; once the warehouse is completed, the owner hopes to find a tenant for the storage space.

Storage Arrangements

For the purpose of fire protection, storage can be divided into four main categories: bulk, solid piling, palletized, and rack. The chief difference between the four major categories as far as their effect on fire behavior and fire control is concerned is the nature of the horizontal and vertical air spaces, or "flues," that the storage configurations create.

Bulk Storage

Powders, granules, pellets, chips, and flakes, all unpackaged, are the principal forms of materials that are stored in bulk. Silos, bins, tanks, and large piles on the floor are the usual storage methods.

Fires that start on the surface of large piles tend to burrow into the pile, particularly in the case of coarse particles such as chips or pellets. In many instances, the overhead sprinklers will not operate promptly enough to intercept the spreading surface fire. For both reasons, it is advantageous to have small hand-hose stations installed around the perimeter of the pile for early fire control.

Certain materials, such as wood chips or pulverized coal, can spontaneously combust in the interior of large piles or when trapped for long periods of time in the corners or under the interior baffles of tanks or silos. Fires of this nature can be extremely difficult to extinguish; removing the burning material from the pile or storage vessel might be the only way to put out the fire. Pre-fire planning should encompass this possibility and provide for the needed handling and transporting equipment, hose streams, and disposal area. Supplemental agents added to the water, such as low- and high-expansion foam concentrates, can sometimes help control and extinguish fires in these environments. Low-expansion foams can enhance the penetrability of the water into the material, while high-expansion foams can be used to control dust while the product is being unloaded.

Conveyor equipment, such as belt conveyors, air fluidizing through ducts, and bucket conveyors, agitates materials as they move to and from bulk storage. If this agitation produces combustible dust clouds, particularly in grain storage facilities, an explosion hazard may result. Automatic sprinklers frequently are needed in the housings around conveyor equipment. Select NFPA standards, such as NFPA 61A, *Standard for Prevention of Fire and Dust Explosions in Facilities Manufacturing and Handling Starch,* will provide special requirements for minimizing dust production.

Solid Piling Storage

Cartons, boxes, bales, bags, and so on that are in direct contact with each other to the full dimension of each pile make solid piles. Air spaces, or flues, exist only where contact is imperfect or where a pile is close to, but not touching, another pile. Compared with palletized and rack storage, solid piling typically results in the slowest fire growth. However, if the outer surfaces possess rapid flame-spread properties—as do bales of fibers such as cotton, for example—high solid piles can still be a severe hazard.

Palletized Storage

Palletized storage consists of unit loads mounted on pallets that can be stacked on top of each other. Each pallet is about 4 inches high and usually is made of wood, although some are made of metal, plastic, expanded plastic, and cardboard. The height of palletized storage is limited by the "stackability" of a commodity—that is, its resistance to crushing at the lowest part of the pile—which usually is 30 feet at the most.

The increased hazard of palletized storage results from the horizontal air spaces formed by the pallets themselves within each layer of storage, as well as the vertical flues that exist between individual rows of palletized stacks.

Rack Storage

Rack storage consists of a structural framework supporting unit loads, generally on pallets. The height of storage racks is limited, potentially, only by the vertical reach of the materials-handling equipment which,

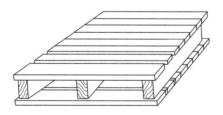

Figure 34-1. A conventional wood pallet. Source: Figure 1-2.2, NFPA 231C, **Standard for Rack Storage of Materials,** *NFPA, Quincy, MA, 1991.*

like the racks themselves, can be designed for great heights. In fully automatic warehouses, racks are sometimes as high as 100 feet; some have even exceeded that height. In some installations, the steel storage racks are part of the building framing. These are referred to as rack-supported structures.

Even more than they do in palletized storage, the vertical and horizontal flue spaces that surround each unit load in rack storage promote rapid fire development and efficient combustion. As a result, rack storage normally requires greater sprinkler protection than equal heights of equivalent material stored in palletized or solid pile arrays. In some, but not all, cases, this protection may include the installation of in-rack sprinklers. NFPA 231C uses decision tables to specify when in-rack sprinklers are necessary and what type of in-rack sprinklers, either longitudinal or face, are needed.

When rack storage is higher than 25 feet, special attention must be given to the problems that will exist in achieving fire overhaul and

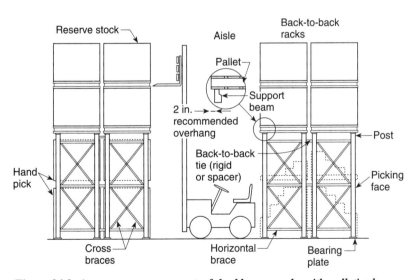

Figure 34-2. A common arrangement of double row racks with palletized storage atop. (Unarco Storage)

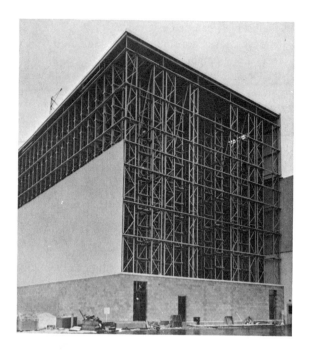

Figure 34-3. High steel storage racks as structural support for roofs and walls of a storage facility. (Clark Handling Systems Div.)

salvage. Although in-rack sprinkler protection can successfully control a fire that originates in, or spreads to, the upper reaches of high racks, full extinguishment cannot be expected. At some point, manual overhaul will be necessary, and there will be major logistical problems in elevating personnel and equipment safely and effectively from within the narrow aisles of automated high rack storage systems. Considerable pre-emergency planning and drills should be undertaken to determine the equipment needed and to simulate realistically the maneuvers to be undertaken in this work.

Fire Causes

Fires in storage arrangements are more likely to start with people than with any kind of equipment problems, although natural causes and exposure fires are important in this property class, too.

Arson is the leading cause, and any lack of security, such as outside storage of combustibles, can tempt anyone, from the juvenile firesetter to the profit-oriented arsonist. Warehouses with high values, desirable contents, and large concentrations of readily ignitable goods are natural targets, not only for arsonists, but also for thieves, some of whom may try to cover up their activities by setting fires when they leave. Among equipment-related causes, wiring, portable or other space heaters, and vehicles are worthy of attention.

As a result, areas and buildings devoted to storage should have high levels of security, tight access controls, and automatic fire protection systems where feasible. In the previously mentioned standards, NFPA 231 and NFPA 231C, approximately 90% of the protection criteria is centered on the installation of automatic sprinkler systems. Smoking should be limited to well defined, supervised, and safe locations and prohibited entirely in the storage sections. Cutting and welding operations must be handled only by means of a rigorous permit system that includes an authorized pre-inspection of the contemplated work area, removal of all combustibles to a safe distance, the use of flameproof tarpaulins, and the presence of an equipped firewatch during the work period and for at least 30 minutes after work ends. Forklift vehicles must be well maintained, and any combustion engine units must be refueled outside the storage areas.

Fire Protection for Goods in Storage

Automatic Sprinklers

The installation of automatic sprinkler systems is the primary means for protecting the various commodities found in a warehouse. The type of storage will govern the specific parameters for design of the system. Because of the variety of challenges posed by the different types of commodities and storage arrangements, warehouse sprinkler systems always must be designed hydraulically in order to ensure the proper level of protection.

For conventional sprinkler systems using 1/2- or 17/32-inch orifice sprinklers, the design consists of supplying a specific controlling density (gpm/ft^2 or l/min/m^2) over a prescribed area of operation (ft2 or m2). Methods for determining the appropriate density and area of application can be found in the applicable storage standards. Study these standards carefully so that you understand all the physical features that have an effect on fire development and the effectiveness of sprinkler protection. These would include items such as the height of the storage, encapsulation of the stored product, clearance to sprinklers, the size of flue spaces, and the presence of obstructions.

For palletized and solid pile storage of Group A plastics, a two-point design is necessary for combinations of storage. Two combinations of density and area of operation must be determined. In rack storage, in-rack sprinklers will reduce the amount of sprinkler protection otherwise needed at the ceiling. In-rack sprinklers are required in all storage racks over 25 feet high.

In recent years, two types of special sprinklers have been developed for the specific purpose of achieving greater effectiveness from overhead sprinkler protection. The first is the large-drop sprinkler with an orifice of 0.64 of an inch which produces a higher proportion of large droplets that can penetrate a fire plume more effectively. The other is the Early Suppression Fast Response (ESFR) sprinkler, which not only delivers a large quantity of water to the fire (100 gpm at 50 psi), but does so earlier in the development of the fire due to the use of a fast-response operating element.

Large-scale fire tests have demonstrated that this combination of heavy discharge and early response can protect up to 25 feet of racked or palletized storage of plastics, often with as few as four sprinklers operating. Special conditions apply when using both of these special sprinklers, one of which is the need for at least 3 feet of clearance above the top of stock instead of the usual 18 inches required for conventional sprinklers. Recent testing has shown that these devices can protect higher combinations of stored product when used at higher operating pressures. The advantage of using either one of these sprinklers is that it does away with the need to install in-rack sprinklers. In addition, the ESFR sprinkler can suppress a fire rather than control it. Translated, this means that less mass will be lost when the product is burning.

Hydrants, Hose Streams, and Extinguishers

Hydrants: Small storage facilities close to public hydrants present no special problem. In larger buildings, where the hydrants are not within 250 feet of the building, however, hose lays from public hydrants to the far side of the building often can be impractical and ineffective. In these instances, private hydrants are needed. These hydrants should be located near points of entrance to the building to reduce the amount of hose needed.

Small Hose: Stations for 1 1/2-inch hose should be located throughout the premises so that all areas can be reached. The hose can be supplied by adjacent wet-pipe sprinkler systems or by a separate piping system. These hose stations can be used for first-aid fire fighting or for overhaul operations by the fire department.

Portable Fire Extinguishers: Extinguishers are needed to fight Class B (flammable liquid) and Class C (electrical) fires and to protect in-plant vehicles. Portable extinguishers are of limited value on storage fires because of their short duration and limited reach. Often, piles have to be pulled apart manually to extinguish a fire within them and hose lines are needed to control the fire during these mop-up operations.

Storage of Specific Materials

Some commodities deserve special mention because of the nature of the fire hazards involved.

Idle Pallets

Piles of wood or plastic pallets are a severe fire hazard. After they have been used for a short time, pallets can dry out, and their edges can fray and splinter. They can ignite easily, and, even when sprinklers are operating, the underside of the pallets can provide a shielded area where fire can grow and expand. Normally, idle pallets in storage should be piled no more than 6 feet high to keep fire within limits manageable by automatic sprinklers discharging at ordinary densities (0.20 gpm/sq ft); higher piles require higher densities. If there is no sprinkler protection, unused pallets must be stored outdoors to reduce the threat of fire to the building.

Rubber Tires

Tires can be stored on their sides directly on the floor or on their tread or sides in fixed or portable racks. Tires in storage are a very high fire hazard. They burn readily, releasing much heat and smoke, and are extremely difficult to extinguish. NFPA 231D, *Standard for Storage of Rubber Tires,* provides detailed guidance on the selection of appropriate fire protection.

Automatic sprinklers with adequate discharge densities can control a fire, but they cannot be expected to extinguish it. Thus, it is essential that some means for manually venting the building to remove smoke are provided to allow fire suppression personnel to enter promptly and to allow overhaul to begin shortly after the sprinklers have brought the fire under control. Fire tests have shown that high-expansion foam will extinguish tire fires, but the tires must be inundated with the foam for several hours.

Roll Paper

Roll paper can be stored on its side, on end, on pallets, or in racks. Rolls stored on end as separate columns are the most hazardous configuration and present the greatest challenge to sprinkler protection. NFPA 231F, *Standard for the Storage of Roll Paper,* provides detailed guidance on selecting appropriate fire protection. This standard classifies the hazard of roll paper primarily according to the weight of the paper. The categories are heavyweight, mediumweight, and lightweight, with heavyweight paper representing the least hazard and lightweight, particularly tissue paper, the greatest. If mediumweight or lightweight papers are enclosed in a heavyweight paper wrapper on the sides and ends, however, the storage can be classified on the basis of the wrapper—that is, as heavyweight paper.

Fire protection of roll paper is best provided by automatic wet-pipe sprinkler systems. Hose streams must be managed carefully so that they do not rob the sprinklers of water, which might cause the loss of fire control. This is done by requiring the designer to reserve a given quantity of water in the hydraulic calculations for the use of the fire department.

Extreme caution is necessary when fighting a fire in the vertical storage of roll tissue paper, something that should be noted in prefire planning procedures. As rolls of tissue sitting on the floor absorb water, the vertical stacks become unstable and are prone to collapse, scattering the heavy rolls in all directions.

Aerosols/Flammable Liquids

Flammable aerosols or liquids present special hazards, and their introduction into a general purpose warehouse can spell disaster. The sprinkler protection probably will be inadequate for the hazard, and, as a result, any fire involving such storage will escalate so rapidly that it will be out of control before the fire brigade or fire department can mount an effective attack. The best protection measure is to store all flammable aerosols and liquids in separate cutoff areas and provide specialized protection to these areas.

Industry and insurance interests have established a classification system for aerosols which consists of three groups, Levels I, II, and III, with Level I representing the lowest hazard. NFPA 30B, Code for the Manufacture and Storage of Aerosol Products, governs the manufacturing, handling, and storage of aerosol products.

Flammable and combustible liquids are classified in NFPA 30, *Flammable and Combustible Liquids Code,* with Class IA representing the highest hazard and Class IIIB the lowest. Recent major fires and some test results have raised questions about the effect of storing flammable and combustible liquids in plastic containers. To examine these questions, the National Fire Protection Research Foundation organized a major research effort to investigate the overall fire implications of such a packaging approach. New criteria were included in NFPA 30 in 1990 to govern the storage of some liquids in plastic containers.

Refrigerated Storage

Temperatures in cold storage warehouses range from 40°F to 65°F for products, such as fruits, eggs, or nuts, that would be damaged by the lower temperatures of 0°F to –35°F needed for frozen foods. In other facilities, the temperature may be kept as low as –60°F.

Whether the building construction is combustible or not, its insulating materials, such as the widely used expanded plastics foamed polystyrene and polyurethane, generally are. Exposed foamed plastics on the walls and ceilings of warehouses are an unacceptable fire hazard because of the potential they present for rapid fire spread over the surface and for heavy smoke generation. In general, these insulations should be covered with a cementitious plaster or one of several proprietary coatings listed specifically for this purpose. Some low-flame-spread foamed isocyanate, isocyanurate, and phenolic plastics have been tested and listed for ceiling and wall applications when protected only by an adhered foil or sheet metal covering.

Combustible materials found in cold storage warehouses include wood dunnage, wood pallets, wood boxes, fiberboard containers, wood baskets, waxed paper, heavy paper wrappings, and cloth wrappings. There generally are enough of these combustibles in warehouses to produce a fire that requires sprinkler protection. Sprinkler systems for these occupancies can be either preaction or dry-pipe. In some facilities, double interlock preaction systems are used. Since these systems require a number of events to occur before they discharge water, they further reduce the likelihood of an inadvertent system trip.

Hanging Garments

Garments on hangers hung on pipe racks offer the opportunity for a fast developing, intense fire that could severely challenge sprinkler protection, particularly if the garments are stored more than two tiers high or if they are more than 10 feet from the overhead sprinklers. Garments can be hung with or without plastic dust covers, although these covers are not particularly effective in reducing loss from soot, water, or odor damage.

Carpets

Rolls of carpeting, commonly 12 to 15 feet long, are stored in deep shelving called racks, which are sometimes arranged back-to-back, so that the distances between aisles might total 30 feet. The rolls are stored individually in strong cardboard tubes on solid or slatted shelves or in racks arranged in cubicles. Each tier (shelf to shelf) is only about 2 to 3 feet high, and there are as many as 10 tiers in a rack. Racks frequently are 100 or more feet long.

This type of storage does not permit much water from ceiling sprinklers to penetrate the racks, so that in-rack sprinklers often are necessary. However, in-rack sprinkler protection at every tier usually is not economically feasible. As a result, fire may spread down the length of a rack in the unprotected tiers. This longitudinal fire spread is best curtailed by the use of vertical barriers at 24- to 30-foot intervals. Another solution is to maintain well-defined, transverse flue spaces at the vertical rack supports. Because it is difficult for sprinkler discharge to reach fire in all tiers, manual fire fighting must be relied upon for final control and extinguishment. Small hose stations should be available at intervals sufficient to reach all portions of the storage arrays, and provisions should be made to vent smoke to aid in overhaul efforts.

Outdoor Storage

Outdoor storage requires special protection. However, there are so many different elements to consider that no single set of rules can specify exactly what constitutes that protection. The best that can be done is to outline general principles and rely on the experience and judgment of those who apply them. Appendix C of NFPA 231 provides such guidance.

In general, outdoor storage sites should be level and firm underfoot with adequate clearances so that fire cannot spread to the site from other sources. Areas in which flooding and windstorms are problems should be avoided.

Some general principles also apply to site layout. Access to the yard and the piles in it must be made easy. Driveways should be at least 15 feet wide to permit fire apparatus to reach all portions of the yard. Aisles should be at least 10 feet wide, and main aisles or firebreaks can be used to subdivide the storage in unusually large storage areas or in moderate-sized yards with valuable commodities. The actual width of the aisles can be a matter of judgment, depending on the combustibility of the commodity, how it is stored, the height of piles, distance from buildings, wind conditions, available fire fighting forces, and so on. Particular emphasis should be placed on the control of potential ignition sources, such as refuse burners, overhead power lines, and acts of vandalism, as well as on the elimination of adverse factors, such as trash accumulations, weeds, and brush. Piles of materials that are stable under normal conditions can collapse during a fire and cause severe fire spread, particularly from flying brands. The fence surrounding the storage site should have an adequate number of gates. If public water flows are inadequate, private water storage facilities, pumps, or both might be needed.

Adequate public fire and police protection or the equivalent private fire brigade protection is a prime requirement for outside storage facilities. More recently, those agencies that enforce environmental regulation for the states have become involved in controlling some types of outdoor storage.

Monitor nozzles mounted on towers might be practical for adequate storage facilities, such as those in which lumber or wood chips are stored, and for facilities for which strong water supplies are available. Appropriate portable fire extinguishers placed at well-marked, strategic points throughout the storage area also are practical. If people usually are present, fully equipped hose houses can be provided, as long as personnel are trained to use hose lines.

Another important feature is the availability of some means of notifying the fire department. At the very least, a telephone should be available.

Identification of Materials

It is fairly easy to identify the fire hazards of materials commonly found in storage, such as wood, paper, fabrics, and LP-Gas cylinders. You know what to expect when one of these materials burns. However, there are literally thousands of combustible solids, flammable and combustible liquids, and liquefied and compressed gases for which the hazards are not so readily apparent. A system for identifying these hazards is needed so that the occupants can respond correctly in emergencies. One major approach is the NFPA 704 system.

The NFPA 704 System

NFPA 704, *Standard System for the Identification of the Fire Hazards of Materials,* provides usable and readily identifiable means of presenting information on the fire hazards of materials. The system only covers fixed installations such as storage tanks, storage rooms, warehouses, and so on. It does not cover materials that are being transported. However, it can be used (and often is used) to mark individual containers once they reach their destination.

The system identifies the fire hazards of a material in three areas: health, flammability, and reactivity or instability. It also indicates the relative severity of each hazard category with a numerical rating that ranges from four, indicating severe risk, to zero, indicating no risk. However, it is important to understand that the ratings are based on

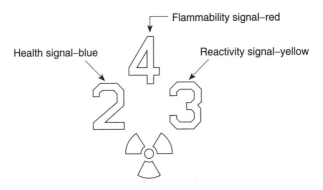

Flammability signal–red

Health signal–blue

Reactivity signal–yellow

Figure 34-4. The NFPA 704 identification system diamond.
Source: Figure 6-1, NFPA 704, **Standard System for the**
Identification of the Fire Hazards of Materials, *NFPA,*
Quincy, MA, 1990.

emergency situations, such as a fire or a spill. They do not provide
information on everyday hazards, which result from normal occupational
exposure. This is especially true for the health hazard rating. Although
many manufacturers include the NFPA 704 ratings on their material
safety data sheets, the ratings are not meant to be used to evaluate the
hazards presented by chronic exposure. The ratings are based on the
inherent hazards of the materials, but they also take into account changes
in behavior during a fire that could significantly exaggerate those
hazards.

The 704 system is presented as shown in Figure 34-4: the health
rating is always at the 9 o'clock position, the flammability rating is
always at the 12 o'clock position, and the reactivity rating is always at
the 3 o'clock position. Furthermore, each quadrant is identified by a
colored background: blue for health hazard, red for flammability hazard,
and yellow for reactivity hazard. Alternatively, the quadrant could be any
convenient contrasting color, and the numerals themselves could be
printed in the appropriate color described above for each hazard.

Special hazard identifiers go in the lower-most, or 6 o'clock, quadrant. The three recognized identifiers are:

to indicate water reactivity

OX to indicate oxidizing ability

to indicate radioactivity

In abbreviated form, the five degrees of risk for each of the three hazards are shown in Table 34-1. Consult NFPA 704 for more detailed definitions.

Recommended ratings for specific materials can be found in NFPA 49, *Hazardous Chemicals Data*, and NFPA 325M, *Fire Hazard Properties of Flammable Liquids, Gases, and Volatile Solids.* Be advised that the ratings given for a chemical are accurate for only the "commercially pure" material, as shipped. The ratings might not be accurate for diluted mixtures. Furthermore, a mixture of two or more chemicals may have to be evaluated separately if it is to receive the proper NFPA 704 rating.

Table 34-1. Identification of the fire hazards of materials.

Signal	Identification of Health Hazard Color Code: BLUE Type of Possible Injury
4	Materials that, on very short exposure, could cause death or major residual injury even though prompt medical treatment was given.
3	Materials that, on short exposure, could cause serious temporary or residual injury even though prompt medical treatment was given.
2	Materials that, on intense or continued exposure, could cause temporary incapacitation or possible residual injury unless prompt medical treatment was given.
1	Materials that, on exposure, would cause irritation but only minor residual injury even if no treatment was given.
0	Materials that, on exposure under fire conditions, would offer no hazard beyond that of ordinary combustible material.

(Continued)

Table 34-1. *(Continued)*

Signal	Identification of Flammability Color Code: RED Susceptibility of Materials to Burning
4	Materials that will rapidly or completely vaporize at atmospheric pressure and normal ambient temperature, or that are readily dispersed in air and will burn readily.
3	Liquids and solids that can be ignited under almost all ambient temperature conditions.
2	Materials that must be moderately heated or exposed to relatively high ambient temperatures before ignition can occur.
1	Materials that must be pre-heated before ignition can occur.
0	Materials that will not burn.

Signal	Identification of Reactivity (Stability) Color Code: YELLOW Susceptibility to Release of Energy
4	Materials that, in themselves, are readily capable of detonation or of explosive decomposition or reaction at normal temperatures and pressures.
3	Materials that, in themselves, are capable of detonation or explosive reaction, but require a strong initiating source or which must be heated under confinement before initiation or which react explosively with water.
2	Materials that, in themselves, are normally unstable and readily undergo violent chemical change, but do not detonate. Also materials that might react violently with water or that might form potentially explosive mixtures with water.
1	Materials that, in themselves, are normally stable, but that can become unstable at elevated temperatures and pressures or that might react with water with some release of energy but not violently.
0	Materials that, in themselves, are normally stable, even under fire exposure conditions, and are not reactive with water.

Source: Appendix A, NFPA 704, *Standard System for the Identification of the Fire Hazards of Materials,* NFPA, Quincy, MA, 1990.

Storage of Records

Good records are the lifeblood of many organizations, and the protection of valuable records from flame, heat, smoke, and water is important to an organization's survival. The exact protection measures used should be based on a survey to ensure that the proper records are selected for special protection. Not all records deserve the same degree of protection.

Records generally can be classified in one of two ways: records that are irreplaceable, such as those that give direct evidence of legal status and ownership, which are needed to sustain a business, and those records that can be reproduced from original sources only at considerable expense.

Other records might be useful, but they should be kept separate from vital and important records because they can constitute a fire exposure themselves. Bulk storage of less important paper records in file cabinets, on shelves, in palletized cardboard boxes, and so on, present enough combustible material to cause extensive fire spread and severely damage the building in which it is located. Photographic films and magnetic tapes with an acetate or polyester base have the same order of combustibility as paper, but tapes on plastic reels and in plastic cases can produce unusually high amounts of heat, smoke, and toxic gases.

Some storage and archival facilities now use high-density, mobile shelving systems that contain moveable shelves and racks to optimize the use of available space. Currently, there are no standardized protection criteria for such facilities. Each one must be handled on a case-by-case basis.

Automatic sprinklers are the primary form of fire protection for limiting the loss in bulk quantities of records. Special extinguishing systems using high expansion foam, carbon dioxide, and halon agents can be used in some unique situations, but selection of such systems should be weighed carefully.

Vaults

The term "vault" refers to a completely fire-resistive enclosure up to 5,000 cubic feet in volume that is used exclusively to store vital records. Vaults usually contain a substantial fuel load. In many instances, in fact, the contents of a vault are more of a hazard than any external fire exposure. A fire in an unprotected vault can be disastrous unless it is discovered immediately and extinguished.

In the past, the only penetrations permitted in vaults were the door openings. This prohibited sprinklers, fire and smoke detection units wired to a master panel, and even fixed lighting systems. Now vault standards permit penetrations for sprinkler piping and conduits so vault contents can be better protected. Work stations and mechanical equipment, such as air-handling and cooling equipment, are not permitted in vaults. Nor are ventilation penetrations. The ambient conditions within the vault must be controlled by means of indirect cooling and heating of the environment outside of the vault. In any event, water-type fire extinguishers or small hose, or both, should be available in an accessible location near the door of a vault.

File Rooms

File rooms are built as nearly like vaults as possible, but they are used for situations in which people work regularly with the records in the room. Thus, they usually have electric lights and steam or hot water heat. Any wall openings needed for air conditioning or ventilation must be equipped with fire dampers. Standard file rooms have a maximum ceiling height of 12 feet and a maximum volume of 50,000 cubic feet. File room doors can have vault door ratings or lesser ratings of 1/2 or 1 hour. Automatic sprinklers are desirable.

Archives and Records Centers

Bulk storage of paper records in separate buildings, in a major portion of a building, or in a room exceeding 50,000 cubic feet in volume requires special attention because of the large fire load it represents. The four basic factors that must be considered are exposure from nearby operations or buildings, the potential for ignition, the potential for fire spread, and the ability of the available fire control system to extinguish or control a fire with minimum damage to records.

Fire-resistive construction is essential to protect against exposure fires. Cleanliness, orderliness, and an absolute ban on smoking are the fundamentals of controlling the chances of ignition. The type of storage, whether steel cabinets or open shelf system, governs the potential for fire spread. Open shelves present a wall of paper at the face of the shelves, up which fire can spread rapidly to involve other rows of shelves.

Automatic sprinklers, backed up by an early-warning detection system, provide good protection in view of the rapidity with which fire can spread in the large open areas customarily found for archival storage. Catwalks in aisles inhibit overhead sprinkler protection and might necessitate special provisions.

Safes and Record Containers

Safes and containers are available with typical ratings of 4, 2, 1, and 1/2 hours. There are two types of containers and safes: Class 150 principally is for the storage of magnetic tapes, and Class 350 is for the storage of paper records. Insulated filing devices are available with a Class 350, 1/2-hour rating.

Bibliography

Cote, A. E., ed., *Fire Protection Handbook,* 17th edition, National Fire Protection Association, Quincy, MA, 1986. Chapters 5 and 6 of Section 8 discuss in detail the various systems that are available to identify the hazards of materials to minimize danger to emergency personnel. Chapters 30 and 34 of Section 2 give guidance on storage practices, facilities, and fire protection for goods and records in storage.

Linville, J. L., ed., *Industrial Fire Hazards Handbook,* 3rd edition, National Fire Protection Association, Quincy, MA, 1990. Chapter 48 discusses storage practices observed in industrial locations, including special storage facilities such as piers and wharfs, underground storage, air-supported structures, and so on.

NFPA Codes, Standards, and Recommended Practices

NFPA 30, *Flammable and Combustible Liquids Code.* Provides the framework for evaluating public fire prevention programs and addresses programs in zoning and enforcement, building regulations, fire prevention regulations, inspection and enforcement, fire investigation, and public fire safety education.

NFPA 43B, *Code for the Storage of Organic Peroxide Formulations.* Covers the basic requirements, segregated storage, cutoff storage, and detached storage of commercially available organic peroxide formulations in approved packages.

NFPA 43D, *Code for Storage of Pesticides in Portable Containers.* Covers both inside and outside storage of all forms of pesticides in portable containers other than fixed installations on transportation equipment.

NFPA 46, *Recommended Safe Practice for Storage of Forest Products.* Outlines recommendations to minimize hazards and control fire in storage areas that contain lumber, timber, wood chips, logs, and similar products.

NFPA 49, *Hazardous Chemicals Data.* Contains data on the fire hazards of several hundred chemical substances, including suggested hazard identification numbers for use with the NFPA 704 hazards identification system.

NFPA 81, *Standard for Fur Storage, Fumigation and Cleaning.* Covers protective practices for fur storage vaults and cleaning plants.

NFPA 231, *Standard for General Storage.* Contains guidance for the storage of combustible commodities in buildings with automatic sprinkler systems. Emphasis is on providing adequate sprinkler discharge for goods of different degrees of combustibility.

NFPA 231C, *Standard for Rack Storage of Materials.* Applies to the broad range of combustible commodities stored in racks over 12 feet high.

NFPA 231D, *Standard for Storage of Rubber Tires.* Covers indoor storage arrangements and fire protection requirements for large quantities of rubber tires.

NFPA 231E, *Recommended Practice for the Storage of Baled Cotton.* Covers storage of baled cotton in buildings and yards.

NFPA 231F, *Standard for the Storage of Roll Paper.* Covers storage of roll paper in buildings and structures.

NFPA 232, *Standard for the Protection of Records.* Contains requirements for vaults, file rooms, safes, containers, and other devices for the management of records.

NFPA 232AM, *Manual for Fire Protection for Archives and Records Centers.* Guidelines on fire protection for file rooms exceeding 50,000 cubic feet in volume and for all archives and records centers.

NFPA 325M, *Fire Hazard Properties of Flammable Liquids, Gases, and Volatile Solids.* A tabulation of the fire hazard properties of more than 1,600 substances, including suggested hazard identification numbers for use with the NFPA 704 hazards identification system.

NFPA 395, *Standard for the Storage of Flammable and Combustible Liquids at Farms and Isolated Sites.* Covers storage of hazardous materials in rural areas, where isolation from other structures makes it unnecessary to adhere to the more rigid requirements of NFPA 30.

NFPA 704, *Standard System for the Identification of the Fire Hazards of Materials.* Describes in detail the NFPA "704 Diamond" system for identifying health, fire, reactivity, and other related hazards that might be encountered during a fire or related emergency conditions.

CHAPTER 35

Storage and Handling of Flammable and Combustible Liquids

*A*s an inspector, you must be familiar with the physical and fire hazard properties that determine the risk associated with a variety of commonly used flammable and combustible liquids if you are to see to it that they are stored and handled safely. The distinction between a flammable and a combustible liquid is somewhat arbitrary, and the terms basically have the meanings of common usage. Strictly speaking, liquids either burn, in which case they are combustible, or they do not burn, in which case they are noncombustible. The word "flammable" connotes a greater fire risk than normal and serves to define a particular class of volatile combustible liquids, as will be discussed later in this chapter. For our purposes, the word "liquid" means a liquid that burns, unless otherwise identified.

At this point, you must recognize three things. First, it is the vapor given off by the liquid that burns, not the liquid itself, that is hazardous. You must be able to visualize where vapors will travel once they are released. Second, the greater the tendency of a liquid to give off vapors— that is, the more volatile the liquid is—the greater the risk of fire. While it is obvious that you must pay particular attention to these liquids, you also must be alert for operations in which less volatile liquids are heated, thus increasing their propensity to generate vapors. And finally, you must understand the physical and fire hazard properties of liquids to be able to judge the risk of an individual operation.

For more detailed information on some of the topics covered here, see the Appendix at the end of this book.

Physical Properties

Vapor Pressure. Vapor pressure is a measure of the pressure that the liquid exerts against the atmosphere above it. Just as the atmosphere exerts pressure on the surface of the liquid, the liquid pushes back. Vapor pressure normally is less than atmospheric pressure and is a measure of the liquid's tendency to **evaporate,** or move from the liquid to the gaseous state. This tendency also is referred to as **volatility,** which explains the use of the term "volatile" to describe liquids that evaporate very easily. The higher the vapor pressure, the greater the rate of evaporation and the lower the **boiling point.** Simply put, this means more vapors and increased fire risk. You must ensure that reasonable measures, such as local exhaust ventilation, have been taken to control vapors and that sources of ignition are either removed from the area or controlled.

Boiling Point. The boiling point is the temperature at which the vapor pressure of a liquid equals atmospheric pressure. At this temperature, atmospheric pressure can no longer hold the liquid in the liquid state, and the liquid boils. A low boiling point is an indication of high vapor pressure and a high rate of evaporation.

Vapor Density. Vapor density, sometimes referred to as **vapor-air density,** is the ratio of the weight of a volume of pure vapor to the weight of an equal volume of dry air, both at the same temperature and pressure. Vapor density determines whether the vapors will rise when released or sink to the ground. A vapor density less than 1 means that the vapor will rise and dissipate very quickly. This reduces the risk of ignition somewhat, but you should check for potential ignition sources that are in the likely path of the vapors. Such sources include ceiling-mounted or roof-level electrical equipment, light fixtures, and unit heaters. A vapor density of 1 means the vapor is just as dense as air, and the same precaution applies.

A vapor density greater than 1 indicates that the pure vapor is denser than air and will sink from its point of release, tending to flow downward and to settle in low areas. Inside buildings, you should pay close attention to below-grade areas, such as floor drains, sumps, trenches, and similar inadequately ventilated areas. This includes basements and crawl spaces. Outside, you should note the grading of the surrounding terrain and try to estimate the likely flow of vapors.

In the pure state, vapors from most flammable and combustible liquids are heavier than air. However, pure vapor will only be given off at or above the boiling point of the liquid. For all other conditions, the vapor is mixed with some air, and the density is thereby proportionately changed, approaching that of air itself. Regardless, you should understand that a mixture of vapor and air can be expected to travel at grade level, often for some distance, until it naturally disperses. Such mixtures can and have been known to ignite at some distance from their source, with flames spreading back to the source.

Specific Gravity. Specific gravity is the ratio of the density of one material to another, usually water. The density is expressed as weight per unit volume—for example, pounds per gallon or grams per liter. Most liquids are not as dense as water and, if not miscible with water, will float on top. Gasoline is a good example of this. Carbon disulfide, on the other hand, is an example of a liquid that is much denser than water and on whose surface water will therefore float.

Water Solubility. Water solubility is a measure of the tendency of a liquid to dissolve in, or mix with, water. It usually is expressed in terms of grams of liquid per 100 milliliters of water. Some liquids, such as acetone, alcohol, and amines, will mix completely with water, in all proportions. Other liquids, such as hydrocarbon fuels, will not mix with water at all.

The alert inspector will note the presence of water-soluble liquids and use this information to plan appropriate fire fighting tactics. Water-soluble liquids will destroy an ordinary foam blanket, thus requiring the use of special alcohol-resistant fire fighting foams. If a burning water-soluble liquid can be contained, it is even possible to dilute it to a noncombustible mixture using available hose streams.

Viscosity. The viscosity of a liquid is a measure of its resistance to flow, or its "thickness." Obviously, a viscous liquid will flow slowly and will be easier to contain. However, the viscosity of a liquid depends on its temperature, and most liquids will "thin out" and flow more easily when heated.

Temperature and Pressure Effects. Liquids are only slightly compressible, and they cannot expand indefinitely. Liquids will vaporize more rapidly as the temperature increases or as the pressure decreases.

NFPA 325M, *Fire Hazard Properties of Flammable Liquids, Gases, and Volatile Solids,* contains information on most of the above properties for many flammable and combustible liquids.

Fire Hazard Properties

Flash Point. The flash point of a liquid is the minimum temperature at which it gives off vapor in sufficient concentration to form an ignitible mixture with air near the surface of the liquid. It is a direct measure of a liquid's volatility, or its tendency to vaporize. The lower the flash point, the greater the volatility and the greater the risk of fire. Flash point is determined using one of several different test procedures and apparatus that are specified in Chapter 1 of NFPA 30, *Flammable and Combustible Liquids Code,* under the definition for "flash point."

Liquids with flash points at or below ambient temperatures are easy to ignite and burn quickly. Once ignited, the spread of flame over the surface of the liquid will be rapid because the fire need not expend energy heating the liquid to generate more vapor. Again, gasoline is a familiar example of such liquids. Liquids with flash points above ambient temperature present less risk because they must be heated to generate enough vapor to become ignitible; they are more difficult to ignite and present less potential for the generation and spread of vapor. A common example of this type of liquid is home heating oil (Fuel Oil No. 2), which must be atomized to a fine mist before it is easily ignited.

In discussing flash point, reference is sometimes made to the "fire point" of a liquid. Fire point is the temperature at which ignition of vapors will result in continued burning. As the term "flash point" suggests, the vapors generated at that temperature will flash, but they will not necessarily continue to burn. While the difference between flash point and fire point has some significance in flash point tests, it is ignored in practice, and the flash point is used to classify the liquid and to characterize its hazard.

For more detailed information on flash point and the various procedures by which flash point can be determined, see the *Manual on Flash Point Standards and Their Use.* Flash point will be discussed again under *Classification of Liquids.* Suffice it to say that the maxim "low flash, high hazard" applies.

Autoignition Temperature. Sometimes referred to as "spontaneous ignition temperature," "self-ignition temperature," or "autogenous ignition temperature," the autoignition temperature is the minimum temperature at which a liquid will self-ignite without an external source of ignition, such as a spark or pilot flame, under specified conditions and usually in air. In practice, autoignition results when an ignitible vapor-air mixture comes in contact with a hot surface or is introduced into a hot environment.

It is important to take autoignition temperature into account when selecting electrical equipment for areas in which ignitible vapor-air mixtures might be present. This is especially true of electrical equipment that heats with use, such as motors, transformers, and light fixtures. However, you should be aware of any other equipment that might provide a hot surface, such as drying ovens, hot air ducts, and hot process piping.

Flammable Limits. The lower flammable limit is that concentration of combustible vapor in air **below** which propagation of a flame will not occur. The upper flammable limit is that concentration of combustible vapor in air **above** which propagation of flame will not occur. Between these limits, ignition is possible, and the concentrations between these limits is thus known as the "flammable range." Mixtures within the flammable range are said to be ignitible. A mixture whose concentration is below the lower flammable limit is said to be too lean to be ignited. Conversely, a mixture that is above the upper flammable limit is said to be too rich to be ignited.

The flammable limits are important in calculating the volume of clean air for ventilating spray booths, drying ovens, and other such pieces of equipment to prevent internal explosions. Chapter 5 of NFPA 86, *Standard for Ovens and Furnaces,* includes information for these calculations. Flammable limits also are important in determining the explosion hazards of confined spaces where vapors are present. NFPA 69, *Standard on Explosion Prevention Systems,* should be consulted for additional information.

NFPA 325M contains information on most of the above properties for many flammable and combustible liquids.

Classifying Flammable and Combustible Liquids

The basic system for classifying liquids can be found in NFPA 321, *Standard on Basic Classification of Flammable and Combustible Liquids,* and in NFPA 30, Flammable and Combustible Liquids Code. For classification purposes, distinctions must be made between a gas, a liquid, and a solid. A gas is defined as a substance that has a vapor pressure of 40 psia (pounds per square inch, absolute) or more at 100°F. Any substance whose vapor pressure is below this is considered a liquid. Liquids also have a specified fluidity, and substances with less fluidity are treated as solids. The specified fluidity is that of 300 penetration asphalt, and the test procedure is described in ASTM D5, *Test for Penetration for Bituminous Materials.*

The broad categories of flammable and combustible liquids are defined as follows: flammable liquids have flash points below 100°F, and combustible liquids have flash points of 100°F or more. In order to apply the fire protection requirements of NFPA 30 and other NFPA codes and standards, these two groups are further subdivided, as shown in Table 35-1.

You should realize that NFPA's definitions of flammable liquid and combustible liquid are no longer the same as those of the U. S. Department of Transportation (DOT). In a recent major decision, DOT adopted a new classification system that defines a flammable liquid as any liquid with a flash point that does not exceed 141°F. Under certain circumstances, most containers holding Class II liquids must be placarded to indicate they are storing flammable liquid (see Title 49 of the *Code of Federal Regulations, Part 173*).

What impact do the new DOT definitions have on you, as an inspector, and on the proper application of fire protection standards? Actually, very little. Aside from its title and its definitions, NFPA 30 governs the storage and handling of liquids by their class designation. From a practical standpoint, the 1°F difference between the two systems at the boundary between Class II and Class IIIA is of little consequence.

You also should be aware that DOT does not regulate Class IIIB liquids that do not meet any other definition for a hazardous material. Likewise, the U. S. Occupational Safety and Health Administration (see Title 29 of the *Code of Federal Regulations,* Part 1910) does not regulate Class IIIB liquids whose only hazard is combustibility. However, NFPA 30 *does* regulate Class IIIB liquids.

Table 35-1. Classification of flammable and combustible liquids.

Classification	Flash point (°F)	Boiling point (°F)
IA	Below 73°	Below 100°
IB	Below 73°	100° and above
IC	73° to 100°	100° and above
II	100° to 140°	100° and above
IIIA	140° to 200°	100° and above
IIIB	200° and above	100° and above

Identification

Identifying the class of a liquid can be difficult. The sense of smell is not reliable, and many liquids are sold under names that give no indication of their potential fire hazard. The label on the container or the placard on the transportation vehicle will be helpful, as will the UN or NA number assigned under DOT's hazardous materials transportation rules. In many cases, however, you will have to rely on the Material Safety Data Sheet (MSDS) and any other information that must be available by federal and state right-to-know laws about all the hazardous materials on the premises. These sources include information about fire hazards, including flash point data, which you can use to determine the class of the liquid.

When in doubt, a flash point test will provide a positive determination. You can make a cursory estimate of the hazard of a liquid by placing a sample of the liquid in a small cup and trying to ignite the vapors. (Needless to say, this should be done in a safe location, such as in a laboratory hood or outdoors.) A flash of flame indicates that the liquid has a low flash point. However, you should not accept the absence of a flame as proof that the liquid will not burn. There are liquids—some halogenated hydrocarbons, for example—that do not have flash points, yet will burn when subjected to a sufficiently intense ignition source. Such liquids might not cause a fire, but they can be expected to add fuel to it.

For consumer commodities, the container label that is required by the Federal Hazardous Substances Act (see Title 16, *Code of Federal Regulations,* Part 1500.43a) will provide useful information. The words "Danger. Extremely Flammable" mean that the liquid's flash point is 20°F or less. "Warning Flammable" means the flash point is in the 20°F to 100°F range. "Caution. Combustible" means the flash point is in the 100°F to 150°F range. Absence of a label is no proof that the liquid will not burn, however.

Storage

The primary hazard involved in storing and handling flammable and combustible liquids is the accidental release of product, followed by the ignition of the spilled liquid. Accidental release usually results from container failure due to mishandling, corrosion, or puncture. Once a spill occurs, the likelihood of ignition increases significantly, and the resulting fire will present a greater challenge. If the spill takes place as a consequence of an existing fire, the severity of the incident will be magnified many times over.

Underground Tanks

Underground tanks, all of whose connections are made through the top of the tank shell, offer the most fire safe means of storing liquid. The tank is isolated from external fires, and physical damage and the chance of an internal ignition is extremely remote. (Cases of internal explosions of underground storage tanks are almost unheard of.) However, underground storage tank systems are subject to leaks that can go undetected for long periods of time. Released liquid can flow into the basements of adjacent buildings or into other subterranean structures, resulting in very serious fire hazard conditions that must be dealt with immediately. You should check NFPA 329, *Recommended Practice for Handling Underground Releases of Flammable and Combustible Liquids,* for information on this subject.

Special care must be taken when installing underground storage tanks to prevent damage to the tank and its piping that might cause future leaks. Excavation during installation must not undermine adjacent structures, and the tank must be situated so that it is not subject to any static loads from these structures. In areas subject to flooding or high groundwater levels, tanks must be secured to prevent them from being dislodged. Details of proper installation procedures are beyond the scope of this chapter. You are referred to Section 2-4 of NFPA 30; the Petroleum Equipment Institute's RP-100, *Recommended Practice for the Installation of Underground Liquid Storage Systems*; and manufacturers' recommendations for specific tank types and designs.

You are encouraged to review the rules promulgated by the U. S. Environmental Protection Agency (EPA) for installation of underground storage tank systems, which are found in Title 40 of the *Code of Federal Regulations,* Part 280. Under these rules, tanks and piping systems must be either suitably protected to resist corrosion or constructed of corrosion-resistant materials. There also are very specific rules for leak monitoring systems and for periodic testing of the entire storage system for tightness. As a result of these rules, a modern underground storage tank installation is likely to include double-walled tanks and double-walled piping, a monitoring system to detect leaks from the primary containment, groundwater monitoring wells around the installation, and an impervious liner in the excavation.

Outside Aboveground Tanks

Outside aboveground storage tanks are suitable for storing almost any quantity of liquid, from a few hundred gallons to several thousand barrels. Some of the various types of tanks used are shown in Figure 35-1. The smaller sizes, which will hold up to about 25,000 gallons, are typically factory-built, while the larger tanks are constructed on site. Chapter 2 of NFPA 30 applies in all cases. Essential features covered by NFPA 30 include proper design and construction; a well-engineered foundation; proper siting of the tank with respect to property lines, public roads, and nearby buildings; spill control, in the form of remote impounding or diking; normal venting and emergency relief venting from fire exposure; overfill prevention; and substantial pipe connections with an adequate number of properly placed valves to control flow in the event of fire or of breakage in the piping.

All of the above features should have been addressed at the design and construction stage, especially for the larger, site-built tanks. Consequently, you should pay close attention to the operating features and the maintenance of the facility. Where spills are controlled by diking, you should confirm that the dike can contain at least 100% of the contents of the largest tank within it, that the dikes are properly maintained, and that provisions have been made to drain accumulated rainwater from the dike. You should reconfirm this any time another tank is installed within the dike. If the diked area has been roofed over, as is becoming more common for small tank installations, you should ensure that vent discharge lines extend to above the roof. Finally, you should ensure that any fire protection systems on the site operate properly.

As an inspector, you probably will be more involved with smaller aboveground tanks. Over the past few years, the EPA's underground storage tank rules have been the impetus for abandoning small underground tanks in favor of aboveground tank systems that offer a number of desireable features, most directed at environmental protection. Some of these "new technology" aboveground tanks include one or more of the following: integral spill pans, double-wall construction, and thermal insulation. These tanks typically are factory-built and seldom exceed 25,000 gallons capacity.

Ordinary cone roof tank

Floating roof tank
Roof deck rests upon liquid
and moves upward and
downward with level changes

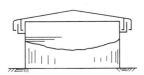

Lifter roof tank
Liquid-sealed roof moves
upward and downward with
vapor volume changes

Vapordome roof tank
Flexible diaphragm in
hemispherical roof moves in
accordance with vapor volume changes

Atmospheric storage tanks

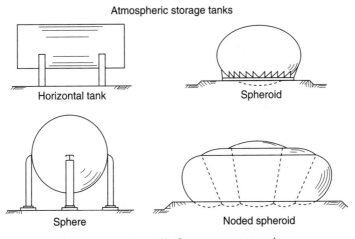

Horizontal tank

Spheroid

Sphere

Noded spheroid

Low pressure storage tanks or pressure vessels

Figure 35-1. Storage tanks for flammable and combustible liquids.

These tanks are installed in accordance with Chapter 2 of NFPA 30, as are the larger built-on-site tanks. You might also wish to refer to the Petroleum Equipment Institute's RP200, *Recommended Practices for the*

Installation of Aboveground Storage Systems for Motor Vehicle Refueling. This recommended practice includes detailed installation procedures specifically for these aboveground tanks.

You should be aware that NFPA 30A, *Automotive and Marine Service Station Code,* now permits the use of such tanks at retail service stations. However, special requirements, in addition to those found in Chapter 2 of NFPA 30, apply. These special requirements distinguish between aboveground tanks in dikes, aboveground tanks installed in vaults, and fire-resistant aboveground tanks. The complete set of requirements can be found in Section 2-4 of NFPA 30A.

You also should be aware that NFPA 30 now permits some of the new technology tanks to be installed without diking or remote impounding, the two accepted means of providing spill control, provided the tanks do not exceed 12,000 gallons capacity and meet certain other very specific requirements. Refer to the exception to 2-3.3.1 of NFPA 30.

Tanks Inside Buildings

Although not normally recommended, tanks often have to be installed inside buildings for process reasons or because the material stored must be kept under strict environmental control. Furthermore, many operators of small storage tank systems are choosing to build a roof over their tank storage areas or to enclose them entirely with a light-framed building. This is because many jurisdictions require that the rainwater that collects in the diked area be treated as a hazardous waste. Section 2-5 of NFPA 30 now includes a very detailed set of requirements for tanks housed in buildings. The requirements are too detailed to describe here, and, as is the case with outside aboveground tanks, most are dealt with at the design and construction stage. The requirements include siting and construction of the building, ventilation, drainage, venting tanks, connections to tanks, electrical equipment, and fire prevention control.

You should ensure that there is enough access and egress to provide unobstructed movement of personnel and fire protection equipment. You also should verify that the necessary ventilation is fully operational and adequate. NFPA 30 requires that there be enough ventilation to keep the concentration of vapors below 25% of the lower flammable limit. This applies to all liquids except Class IIIB. Refer to Section 2-5.3 of NFPA 30 for information on how this level of ventilation can be achieved. You also should confirm that the drainage systems are adequate and operable.

Tanks with weak roof-to-shell seams are not allowed inside buildings, and neither are floating roof tanks. Normal and emergency vents must terminate outside the building in all cases.

Storing fuel oil in inside tanks that hold not more than 660 gallons, with fill and vent connections outside, is an accepted practice under the requirements of Chapter 2 of NFPA 31, *Standard for the Installation of Oil-Burning Equipment.*

Portable Tanks

NFPA 30 defines a portable tank as a closed vessel that has a capacity greater than 60 gallons and is not intended for fixed installation. Portable tanks, if suitably constructed, are considered more desirable than smaller containers because they are equipped with pressure-relief devices that will relieve internal pressure if the portable tank is exposed to fire, thus preventing rupture. Being specifically designed for long-term reuse, they are also constructed more robustly than smaller fixed containers. Such tanks are widely used in the automotive, chemical, and paint industries. Not only are they a cost-effective way to transport, handle, and store liquids, but they also can be directly connected to processing equipment.

NFPA 30 requires portable tanks to be constructed of metal. You should be aware that the U. S. Department of Transportation allows the use of portable tanks constructed of heavy-gauge molded plastic enclosed in various types of overpacks for shipments of some flammable and combustible liquids. NFPA 30 considers such tanks suitable for transportation but does not permit them to be warehoused or stored in process areas.

Chapter 4, "Container and Portable Tank Storage," of NFPA 30 limits the maximum capacity of portable tanks to 660 gallons. This applies to all classes of liquid. Portable tanks that exceed 660 gallons are treated as fixed tanks subject to the requirements of Chapter 2, "Tank Storage," of NFPA 30.

Portable tanks occasionally are connected directly to process equipment. In such cases, the installation also must meet the applicable requirements of Chapter 5, "Operations," of NFPA 30.

Drums and Other Portable Containers

NFPA 30 recognizes the use of a number of different types of containers and specifies the maximum allowable sizes for the different liquid classes. Table 35-2 is taken from NFPA 30.

Table 35-2. Maximum allowable size of containers and portable tanks.

Liquids Container Type	Flammable Liquids			Combustible	
	Class IA	Class IB	Class IC	Class II	Class III
Glass	1 pt	1 qt	1 gal	1 gal	5 gal
Metal (other than DOT drums) or approved plastic	1 gal	5 gal	5 gal	5 gal	5 gal
Safety Cans	2 gal	5 gal	5 gal	5 gal	5 gal
Metal Drum (DOT Specification)	60 gal	60 gal	60 gal	60 gal	60 gal
Approved Metal Portable Tanks	660 gal	660 gal	660 gal	660 gal	660 gal
Polyethylene DOT Spec. 34, U.N. 1H1, or as authorized by DOT Exemption	1 gal	5 gal	5 gal	60 gal	60 gal
Fibre Drum NMFC or UFC Type 2A, Types 3A, 3B-H, or 3B-L, or Type 4A	—	—	—	60 gal	60 gal

Source: Table 4-2.3, NFPA 30, *Flammable and Combustible Liquids Code,* NFPA, Quincy, MA, 1993.

They are best stored outdoors away from buildings or in small detached storage buildings used only for such storage. Where drums are stored inside buildings, they should be stored in a special storage room that is protected by an automatic extinguishing system. Drainage from drum storage facilities should be provided and arranged in a way that facilitates fire control.

NFPA 30 now recognizes the use of moveable prefabricated hazardous materials storage buildings as an option for storing flammable and combustible liquids. If they meet the requirements for inside storage rooms, they can even be located within a building and shifted about on the factory floor as needs dictate. Use of these buildings outside is governed by a separate set of requirements in NFPA 30, Section 4-6.

Safety Containers

Safety containers have a maximum capacity of 5 gallons and come equipped with a spring closing lid and spout cover so that the can will safely relieve internal pressure when subjected to fire exposure. The spring also ensures that the cover will snap closed if the container is dropped while being used. Figure 35-2 shows the types of containers that can be used for storing and dispensing small quantities of flammable liquids inside buildings. The safety can is not intended for use in settings where the periodic release of flammable vapors could create a hazardous atmosphere.

Transfer and Dispensing

Flammable and combustible liquids can be transferred by gravity flow, by container-mounted pumps, or by a closed-pipe fixed pumping system. The latter is most often used for transferring large amounts of liquid and

Figure 35-2. Typical safety cans with pouring outlets with tight-fitting caps or valves normally closed by springs.

is the safest method of handling a large-quantity transferal.

Pumping Systems

Positive displacement pumps offer a tight shutoff and prevent the liquid from being siphoned when not in use. Centrifugal pumps do not provide a tight shutoff when taking suction under head, and siphoning of the liquid is possible. You should ensure that valves are provided to isolate pumps during maintenance or emergencies.

Gravity Systems

Gravity transfer most often is used to dispense liquids from containers. Dispensing valves should be of the self-closing type. You should be alert for signs that valves are blocked open, a very dangerous practice, and you should be aware that gravity flow is sometimes used where very volatile liquids are transferred from tanks. This is done to avoid vapor lock in the pumping systems. Make sure that isolation valves are provided in the dispensing lines from such tanks.

Compressed Gas Displacement Systems

Transfer of liquids by compressed gas displacement is allowed only under certain conditions. The vessels and containers between which transfer occurs and the transfer lines must be designed to withstand the anticipated operating pressure. Safety controls and pressure relief devices must be provided to prevent any part of the system from over-pressuring. Compressed air can be used to transfer Class II and Class III liquids, but only if handling temperatures are not at or above the flash point of the liquid. Inert gas must be used for Class I liquids and for Class II or III liquids heated to their flash points. Compressed air cannot be used because it increases the possibility of a vapor-air explosion inside the container being pressurized.

You should understand that compressed gas displacement keeps the system under constant pressure, so a pipe failure or careless valve operation can cause a considerable amount of product to spill. Adequacy of the safety and operating procedures is important and should be verified.

Dispensing Systems

Dispensing systems generally involve the transfer of liquid from fixed piping systems, drums, or 5-gallon cans into smaller end-use containers. Because the release of some vapor is practically unavoidable, dispensing must take place in designated areas. This includes dispensing from safety cans through closed piping systems, hand pumps, or similar devices, which transfer either by drawing liquid through an opening in the top of the tank or container, by means of gravity through a self-closing valve or faucet, through a hose equipped with self-closing valves, or by means of approved dispensing units, such as those used at service stations.

Designated areas should be protected adequately and ventilated or properly segregated from adjacent hazards.

Loss Control

The following basic loss control guidelines apply in principle to all operations in which flammable and combustible liquids are stored and handled.

Confinement of Liquids. The major objective of an effective loss control program is to confine liquids and vapors in their containers. A second objective is to minimize the effects of an accidental release. The following steps will help to achieve these goals:

1. Use equipment that is designed for flammable and combustible liquid storage. Such equipment should be vapor-tight, should have the minimum number of openings necessary, and should be de signed to relieve excess internal pressure to a safe location.
2. Equip open vessels and vessels with loose-fitting covers with overflow drains and emergency bottom dump drains that are piped to a safe location.
3. Handle small amounts of liquids in approved containers.
4. Provide adequate drainage systems to prevent the flow of liquids into adjacent work areas.

Ventilation. Ventilation is a loss prevention measure that can prevent the build-up of released vapors under normal operating conditions. However, ventilation cannot prevent ignitions where abnormal vapor releases occur.

The ventilation required for personnel health and safety greatly exceeds that required for fire safety. NFPA 30 requires that the ventilation necessary for fire safety be sufficient to ensure that the vapor concentration will not exceed 25% of the lower flammable limit. In addition to the traditional ventilation rate of 1 cfm per square foot of floor area, NFPA 30 also allows design of the ventilation system based on calculation of the anticipated fugitive emission of vapors and on actual monitoring of the space for build-up of vapors.

You should confirm that the ventilation system provides a sweeping action across the entire floor area and that the system exhausts to a safe location. The system should be interlocked so that the operation using flammable liquids will shut down if the ventilation is inadequate. Spot ventilation at the work site is also acceptable.

Control of Ignition Sources

All ignition sources should be controlled or eliminated in areas where flammable vapors could be present. Sources of ignition include open flames, heated surfaces, smoking, cutting and welding, frictional heat, static sparks, and radiant heat. Smoking, open flames, cutting and welding, and hot work should be controlled whether or not flammable vapors are present.

Specially classified electrical equipment may be needed in some areas (see Chapter 7). Generally, electrical equipment of the explosion-proof type is used, but nonclassified equipment can be housed in a purged enclosure. Refer to NFPA 496, *Standard for Purged and Pressurized Enclosures for Electrical Equipment,* for further information. NFPA 497A, *Recommended Practice for Classification of Class I Hazardous (Classified) Locations for Electrical Installations in Chemical Process Areas,* and NFPA 497M, *Manual for Classification of Gases, Vapors, and Dusts for Electrical Equipment in Hazardous (Classified) Locations,* are valuable resources for estimating the extent of the classified zone around vapor sources and for determining the proper type of electrical equipment to be provided.

Fire Protection

A wet pipe automatic sprinkler system is a preferred basic fire control system in areas used to store and handle flammable and combustible liquids. Containerized storage may require special sprinkler installations, including in-rack, ceiling-level sprinklers or large-drop sprinklers of special design. Storage tanks, vessels, and process equipment in chemical plants might require deluge water spray systems for cooling or fire control. Automatic or manually actuated foam extinguishing systems also are used in certain process and storage areas in which flammable and combustible liquids are handled, stored, and processed.

All tank foundations and supports should be of fire-resistive or protected steel construction. In small confined areas or inside special equipment or vessels, it might be desirable to provide special extinguishing systems to supplement the automatic sprinkler systems. Appropriate portable fire extinguishers also are necessary in the event of small liquid fires or fires in other combustibles.

Hydrants and small fire hose with adjustable stream nozzles should be provided in areas where flammable and combustible liquids are stored, handled, or used. Hose streams can be used to cool adjacent tanks and structures, to extinguish fires, and to clean up spills.

Specific Occupancies

In addition to NFPA 30, you may want to consult the following NFPA codes and standards for requirements for specific occupancies.

NFPA 30A, *Automotive and Marine Service Station Code.* This code covers both retail automotive service stations and private fleet fuel dispensing systems. It also covers fuel dispensing at marine facilities. Although primarily directed at the fuel dispensing system itself and fire safety within the service station building, it also addresses fire safety requirements for "quick lube" facilities and the use of aboveground storage tanks. The requirements for aboveground storage tanks differ markedly from those of NFPA 30.

NFPA 30B, *Code for the Manufacture and Storage of Aerosol Products.* The scope of this document is pretty much given in its title. It also allows one to classify the degree of hazard of the aerosol product. Its requirements for storing aerosols is quite extensive, and it even provides fire protection requirements for mixed flammable liquid/flammable aerosol storage.

NFPA 31, *Standard for the Installation of Oil-Burning Equipment.* This standard covers the installation of liquid-fuel-burning equipment, such as oil burners and oil-fired water heaters. Chapter 2 of this standard covers the installation of the fuel oil tanks and allows some latitude, compared to NFPA 30. It addresses the typical home heating oil tank and the use of special enclosures for fuel oil storage tanks.

NFPA 32, *Standard for Drycleaning Plants.* This standard covers drycleaning operations, both at drycleaning plants and at self-serve establishments open to the public.

NFPA 33, *Standard for Spray Application Using Flammable and Combustible Materials.* This standard covers spray application of paints, coatings, and so on by means of the compressed air, airless atomization, fluidized bed, and electrostatic methods. It provides requirements for the equipment, the spray area, spray booth construction, ventilation, liquid storage and handling, and special applications.

NFPA 34, *Standard for Dipping and Coating Processes Using Flammable or Combustible Liquids.* This covers the location of dipping and coating processes, the construction of the equipment, ventilation requirements, liquid storage and handling, and operations and maintenance.

NFPA 35, *Standard for the Manufacture of Organic Coatings.* This standard is specific to the coatings manufacturing industry and covers the manufacture of nitrocellulose-based coatings.

NFPA 36, *Standard for Solvent Extraction Plants.* This document is specific to the extraction of oil from oil-bearing seeds using hexane. It is very comprehensive and includes a description of the extraction process and the equipment used.

NFPA 37, *Standard for the Installation and Use of Stationary Combustion Engines and Gas Turbines.* This document covers the installation of engines and turbines and their fuel supplies for driving stationary equipment such as emergency generators and fire pumps. Its requirements for fuel storage differ from those of NFPA 30.

NFPA 45, *Standard on Fire Protection for Laboratories Using Chemicals.* This document covers the storage and handling of liquids in industrial and instructional laboratories.

NFPA 77, *Recommended Practice on Static Electricity.* This recommended practice provides guidance on proper bonding and grounding techniques to minimize ignition by static electric discharge.

NFPA 385, *Standard for Tank Vehicles for Flammable and Combustible Liquids.* This standard provides requirements for the construction of tank vehicles to be used in flammable and combustible liquids service. It also provides requirements for safe operation during loading and unloading.

NFPA 395, *Standard for the Storage of Flammable and Combustible Liquids at Farms and Isolated Sites.* This document provides requirements for storing liquids at isolated sites where full compliance with NFPA 30 is not considered necessary.

Bibliography

Benedetti, R. P., ed., *Flammable and Combustible Liquids Code Handbook,* 4th edition, National Fire Protection Association, Quincy, MA, 1990. An explanation of the provisions of NFPA 30, NFPA 30A, and NFPA 395, accompanied by the complete text of the codes.

Cote, A. E., ed., *Fire Protection Handbook,* 17th edition, National Fire Protection Association, Quincy, MA, 1991. Various chapters address properties of liquids and fire prevention practices in various applications.

Linville, J. L., ed., *Industrial Fire Hazards Handbook,* 3rd edition, National Fire Protection Association, Quincy, MA, 1990. The fire hazards involved in the use of flammable and combustible liquids in various processes are discussed in chapters dealing with the specific processes.

PEI/RP100-90, *Recommended Practices for Installation of Underground Liquid Storage Systems,* Petroleum Equipment Institute, Tulsa, OK, 1990. This recommended practice provides details on proper installation of underground storage tanks and piping.

PEI/RP200-92, *Recommended Practices for Installation of Aboveground Storage Systems for Motor Vehicle Refueling,* Petroleum Equipment Institute, Tulsa, OK, 1992. This recommended practice provides details on proper installation of aboveground storage tanks and piping for vehicle refueling operations.

Wray, H. A., ed., *Manual on Flash Point Standards and Their Use,* 1st edition, American Society for Testing and Materials, Philadelphia, PA, 1992. This manual discusses the use and proper selection of the different flash point test procedures.

Federal Regulations. These references are available from the U. S. Government Printing Office, Washington, D.C.

Title 16, *Code of Federal Regulations,* Part 1500.43(a). This citation provides rules for implementing the Federal Hazardous Substances Labeling Act.

Title 29, *Code of Federal Regulations*, Part 1910. This citation provides the rules for implementing the Occupational Safety and Health Act.

Title 40, *Code of Federal Regulations,* Part 280. This citation explains the U. S. Environmental Protection Agency's rules for underground storage tank systems.

Title 49 *Code of Federal Regulations,* Part 173. This citation provides the U. S. Department of Transportation's definitions of flammable and combustible liquids.

NFPA Codes, Standards, and Recommended Practices

NFPA 30, *Flammable and Combustible Liquids Code.* Covers safe storage and handling requirements, including bulk storage in tanks, piping systems and valves, warehousing of containers, incidental use, and operations.

NFPA 325M, *Fire Hazard Properties of Flammable Liquids, Gases, and Volatile Solids.* Summary of available data on the fire hazard properties of more than 1,600 substances.

NFPA 327, *Standard Procedures for Cleaning or Safeguarding Small Tanks and Containers*

Without Entry. Discusses procedures for safely removing flammable vapors, liquids, gases, or solids from small tanks or containers that cannot be entered.

NFPA 328, *Recommended Practice for the Control of Flammable and Combustible Liquids and Gases in Manholes, Sewers, and Similar Underground Structures.* Provides methods to control the hazards created by flammable liquids and gases in utility services beneath the street surface.

NFPA 329, *Recommended Practice for Handling Underground Releases of Flammable and Combustible Liquids.* Addresses procedures for safe and efficient recovery of hazardous liquids found unconfined at any underground location.

NFPA 386, *Standard for Portable Shipping Tanks for Flammable and Combustible Liquids.* Provides requirements for portable shipping tanks with a capacity between 60 and 660 gallons used to transport normally stable flammable and combustible liquids with a flash point below 200°F.

CHAPTER 36

Gas Hazards

*O*f the three states of matter—gas, liquid, and solid—gas is the only one with no shape or volume of its own, the only one that expands to fill the container it is in. A gas is always striving to get out of confinement, be it the vapor over a liquid or a material with a higher vapor pressure that has been compressed or liquefied to facilitate shipping. In those cases, any leak in the packaging will allow the material to escape until the pressure inside the container equals the pressure in the room or space outside it. Although the gas can be treated after it is released, it is far more effective to control the hazard by keeping the gas confined.

The most dramatic evidence of the hazard released flammable gases present is a fire or combustion explosion resulting from the ignition of a gas-air mixture in a confined space. However, an accumulation of any gas, except oxygen and air, can cause asphyxiation by displacing the oxygen in air from a room. Oxygen levels lower than 19.5% are hazardous; when the concentration goes below 4%, death can result in less than a minute. Because the human senses cannot detect most gases, people will inhale a gas normally, as though it was air.

Gas may be hazardous in other ways, too. Some gases are chemically reactive, either within themselves or on contact with other materials, and can generate hazardous heat and reaction products. Others are physiologically reactive and are toxic or poisonous.

Because a gas is so lightweight, it takes a lot of it to do a certain job. Except for gas distributed through pipelines from a supplier to a consumer, gases must be stored in containers. When a material's vapor pressure is high enough to allow it to be pressurized, or compressed, it can be placed in a concentrated form in pressurized containers as a high-pressure gas, a liquefied gas, or a refrigerated gas for transportation and storage. Such materials are called "compressed gases," defined by the U.S. Department of Transportation and Transport Canada as a material which exerts in its packaging an absolute pressure of 41 psia (2.8 bar) at

68°F. In addition to their individual properties, all compressed gases are hazardous materials because of their pressure. The volume of gas realized by converting it from a liquid state back into gas can be 200 to 850 times its volume as a liquid.

In the case of all compressed, liquefied, and refrigerated gases—including, but not limited to, cryogenic gases—the gas in a container at normal room temperature generally is under pressure ranging from about 100 psi to 2,600 psi. Very large storage vessels and transports of refrigerated liquids generally are designed for pressures below 25 psi; the liquids are converted to higher pressures outside the vessels. As noted before, however, a gas container is a major hazard simply because of the pressure inside it, which is independent of the chemical or physiological hazards of the gas inside.

Measures designed to keep gas confined thus dominate efforts to control gas hazards. These measures primarily are aimed at maintaining the integrity of containers by preventing leakage and by designing and testing them to prevent failure.

Gas Container Safeguards

Gas containers are either portable cylinders constructed to U.S. Department of Transportation (DOT) or Transport Canada (TC) regulations; containers that are part of cargo vehicles or railroad tank cars, also constructed to DOT or TC regulations; or pressure vessels constructed to the ASME boiler and pressure vessel codes. Large, low-pressure liquefied gas containers used for liquefied natural gas, propane, and ammonia are sometimes, with the permission of the authority having jurisdiction, constructed to other standards. However, there are increasingly fewer of these, so we will not address them.

DOT/TC and ASME code containers are built to working pressures that reflect the pressure of the gas contained. In the case of compressed gases, the working pressure is as high as it can be given the economics of container cost and container weight considerations—usually 2,000 to 3,000 psi. In the case of liquefied gases, the working pressure is determined by the vapor pressure of the liquid at liquid temperatures representative of the ambient temperature extremes in the United States and Canada—usually –65° to 130°F.

In both compressed gas and liquefied gas containers, the actual pressure varies directly with the gas or liquid temperature, increasing and decreasing with increases or decreases in temperature. If temperatures go above 130°F, the pressure inside the container may exceed the container's working pressure. In a liquefied gas container that is overfilled with liquid, heating the liquid will cause it to expand until the container becomes "liquid-full"—that is, until there is no vapor space left. Any small temperature increase at that point, to even less than 130°F, can cause the cylinder to rupture. To prevent this, federal laws limit the amount of liquid that may be charged into a cylinder of a given size. Applicable filling densities are specified in 49, *Code of Federal Regulations,* 173.304 or TC 73.304.

While containers can tolerate excess pressure to a degree, all liquefied gas containers are equipped with over-pressure limiting, or pressure relief, devices to limit the pressure. When these devices operate, they release gas, thus reducing the hazard. Cylinders containing highly toxic gases do not have pressure relief devices because the hazard of an accidental gas release is considered more dangerous than the possibility that the cylinder will fail due to pressure.

A fire exposure on a section of a container could not only cause the pressure in the container to rise, but could also weaken the container metal, which usually is steel or aluminum. Should this happen, the over-pressure relief devices might not be able to relieve the pressure enough to prevent an explosive container failure. This can be particularly true of liquefied gas containers because pressure is likely to be left in the container when the metal loses its strength, even though some pressure will be lost when the pressure relief valve reseats. This type of failure could cause a boiling liquid-expanding vapor explosion (BLEVE). BLEVEs are discussed in more detail in the *Fire Protection Handbook.*

As an inspector, then, you should look for any condition that is conducive to container failure. For example, combustibles located in the vicinity of a container can produce fire exposure so they must be kept clear of containers containing any gas.

Because the release of flammable gases can lead to fire exposure, flammable gas containers should not be stored close to containers of other types of gas. As a general rule, a 20-foot distance is needed to prevent the horizontal torch from a pressure relief device from seriously exposing another gas container. If this is not feasible, a noncombustible barrier as high as the relief devices—usually about 5 feet—with a fire-resistance rating of at least 1/2 hour should be used to separate the containers. Make sure that areas in which gases are being used are adequately ventilated and that liquefied gas containers are stored outdoors or in a well-ventilated area. Inside storage should not exceed the quantities listed in NFPA 55, *Standard for the Storage, Use, and Handling of Compressed and Liquefied Gases in Portable Cylinders,* or other NFPA standards.

Containers should be in good condition, free of dents, gouges, bulges, and corrosion. Portable DOT/TC containers have to be requalified for service at intervals prescribed in the regulations. This is done to verify their structural integrity. For low pressure containers, this is usually 12 years after manufacture; for high pressure containers, this is 5 or 10 years after manufacture, depending on the gas lading. They are then retested at intervals of 5 to 12 years, and each container is marked with the date of manufacture and the retest date. Containers that are not properly qualified cannot be refilled, although a cylinder that was filled before the retest date can remain safely in service well past the retest date.

Portable DOT/TC containers usually are not owned by their users but are owned by the gas suppliers. Inspection at the user site should show that all cylinders are properly labeled to identify the cylinder contents and to warn of the principal hazards. The most important safety statement on any gas container label is the name of the product in the container. If there is any doubt, the cylinder should be returned to the supplier.

Check the over-pressure relief device openings for signs of corrosion or of blockage by paint or other debris. Insects often build nests in relief device openings. Portable DOT/TC containers generally have either cylinder caps or permanently attached collars designed to protect the container valve from being broken off or damaged. Users should keep these cylinder caps in place at all times except when the container is hooked up in service.

Compared to their length, the diameter of high pressure compressed gas cylinders is small. Thus, they are rather easy to tip over. OSHA, NFPA, and other codes mandate that they be secured when being transported and stored. At cylinder filling operations, nesting is another acceptable method of storing. Liquefied gas containers and liquid cylinders are larger in diameter and therefore are more stable. Generally,

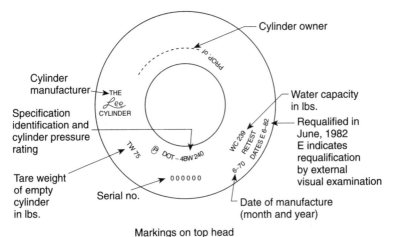

Markings on top head

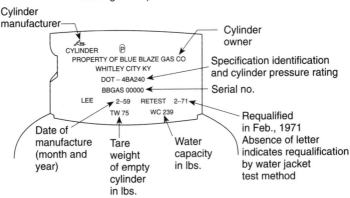

Markings on attached collar

Figure 36-1. Typical Department of Transportation (DOT) cylinder markings.

they need not be secured when being stored or used, but they must still be secured when being transported.

Gas piping is fabricated and installed according to NFPA standards and to the ASME *Code for Pressure Piping* (B 31) for specific gases and applications. With the exception of natural gas and, to a lesser extent, LP-Gas, most gas piping is installed aboveground. You should be alert to any signs of corrosion or poor support and note locations where piping may be subject to physical damage, especially areas in which there is vehicle traffic.

Released Gas Safeguards

By far the most common use for flammable gases is as fuel in gas-burning appliances and industrial heating equipment, with air, and in cutting and welding processes, with oxygen. Flammable gases are also used for medical purposes, principally with oxygen and nitrous oxide.

All of these uses, of course, involve the release of gas under controlled conditions, and you should be aware of the features of the devices that are used to maintain this control. On gas appliances, these include flame-failure gas shutoff devices. In industrial heating equipment, they include check valves. And in oxygen-fuel gas systems, these include check valves, flame arrestors, and pressure relief devices designed to prevent fuel gas and oxygen from mixing in piping and containers, to stop flame propagation, and to relieve excess pressure.

A new type of portable container is being used in both industrial and medical gas service. These containers, generally called "liquid cylinders" in the industry, are portable vacuum-insulated containers that hold either a cryogenic fluid, such as oxygen, nitrogen, or argon, or a refrigerated liquid, such as carbon dioxide or nitrous oxide. Although their safety record equals or exceeds that of cylinders or other containers, you should be aware of two major differences. First, they can contain much larger quantities of gas. Where a portable cylinder generally contains no more than 300 cubic feet of product, a liquid cylinder can hold over 6,000 cubic feet of product. Second, they often vent small amounts of product into the atmosphere by design. When product is not being withdrawn, the relief valve must balance the pressure build-up caused by gas vaporized when heat leaks into the container. Therefore, it is even more important than it is with other cylinders that the area in which they are used is adequately ventilated and that they are stored outdoors or in well-ventilated areas.

Nearly all domestic and commercial gas appliances are covered by ANSI or UL standards and are tested and listed by the American Gas Association Laboratories, Underwriters Laboratories, and other testing laboratories. If you find an appliance that is not listed, review the standard applicable to the appliance involved to determine its safety (see Bibliography).

Larger and more specialized industrial equipment is more diverse and might be custom-made. There are NFPA and ANSI standards for such equipment, which includes industrial ovens, furnaces, large boilers, unit heaters, direct make-up air heaters, and infrared heaters. Factory Mutual (FM) and Industrial Risk Insurers (IRI) have standards for other equipment, and FM approves ("lists," in NFPA terminology) many industrial gas system components.

Release of gas from containers and piping occurs, of course, and this escape must be stopped. This is true even if the gas is burning. In fact, a gas fire should be extinguished by stopping the leak or cutting off the gas flow because extinguishment with extinguishers will allow the remaining unburned gas to escape.

All systems involving compressed gas piped from manifolded cylinders or cryogenic storage tanks must have system pressure relief valves or devices downstream of the line pressure regulator to protect the system from regulator failure. This pressure relief device can be incorporated into the pressure regulator. The device should be vented outside the building to a safe location.

All containers are fitted with a valve that can be closed manually. Some containers are equipped with valves that will shutoff automatically when they sense excessive heat, as from a fire, or an excessive flow rate from the flow check valves. You should check the operating condition of such valves when they are used.

Over-pressure safety relief devices should only operate during true emergencies. However, such gas release commonly is caused by excessive ambient temperatures that are not due to fire exposure. As an inspector, you should see to it that compressed gas containers are not exposed to temperatures higher than 125°F and that cylinders and systems are not placed in areas in which temperatures may rise above 125°F. These areas include locations near heat-producing equipment and in poorly ventilated structures.

Storage areas should be ventilated to limit the concentration of released gas. This includes nonflammable gases, such as nitrogen and carbon dioxide, as well as flammable gases because the nonflammable gases may pose asphyxiation hazards.

LP-Gas Bulk Plants

Among the features that affect fire safety are such obvious items as fire extinguishers and "no smoking" signs, as well as the following special features. See Figure 36-2.

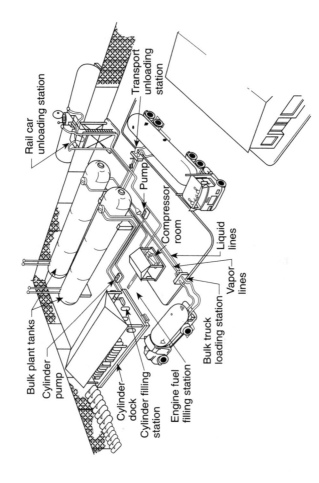

Rail car unloading station

Transport unloading station

Pump

Compressor room

Bulk plant tanks

Cylinder pump

Cylinder dock

Cylinder filling station

Engine fuel filling station

Bulk truck loading station

Liquid lines

Vapor lines

Figure 36-2. Typical LP-Gas bulk plant.

Tank Car Unloading: The railroad spur track should be at least 50 feet from the main line, and the plant should be surrounded by fencing. Wheel blocks should be provided under the car. The tank car and the liquid line should be equipped with valves to stop the flow of product in case of hose failure.

Truck Unloading: The unloading point for trucks carrying gas should have a concrete guard to prevent damage to the piping and hose racks. The truck and the unloading line should be equipped with valves to stop the flow of product in case of hose failure. Where necessary, a shed should be provided to protect the operator from the weather while he or she is monitoring the transfer operation.

Storage Tanks at the Plant: Tanks, marked to show that they are the proper type, should be mounted on substantial foundations or cradles and placed in such a way as to minimize exposure of buildings and equipment. Gauging devices and relief valves should be provided, and the tank outlet should be equipped with a valve to stop the flow in case a line breaks.

Pump Installation: Separate pumps and piping are required for butane and propane to prevent the two from mixing. The pumps, valves, and fittings must be designed for LP-Gas service, and the piping should be well supported. There should be a bypass in the pump discharge line. The installation also should have a pressure gauge and a pressure relief valve.

Truck Filling: The loading area should be paved and level. Wheel blocks should be provided for the truck, and the driver should have a remote control switch that allows him or her to instantly shut down loading. There should be a valve in the discharge line and a hose vent and relief valve on the discharge hose line. There also should be a vapor return hose line.

Cylinder Filling: The loading platforms, which should be at truck height to reduce the chance that cylinders will be dropped, should be built on solid fill and well ventilated at the floor level. Accurate weighing scales are required to prevent the cylinders from being overfilled. The fill line should be equipped with a bypass and a pressure gauge, and the pump should have a remote control switch that provides for immediate shutdown.

Occasionally, you will find special fire protection systems, such as fixed water spray or monitors. Such systems should be tested at intervals

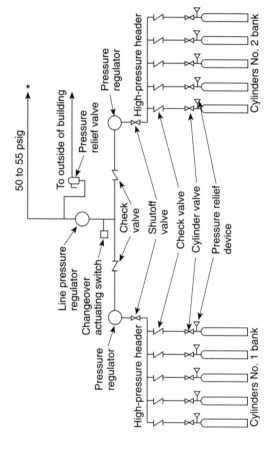

Figure 36-3. Typical cylinder supply system for nonflammable medical gas.

recommended by their installers, but at least annually. You should witness these tests.

Nonflammable Medical Gas Systems

Oxygen and nitrous oxide are used extensively in hospitals, nursing homes, dental offices, medical professional buildings, and other medical facilities for anesthesia, analgesia, and therapy. They are stored and used in both portable apparatus and permanent fixed piping systems, which pervade the facility. Facility owners and operators are very concerned about the reliability of the supply and distribution of these gases because they play such an important role in life safety.

Because oxygen and nitrous oxide are nonflammable, their hazard as oxidizing agents is not always recognized. In large leaks, both gases will lower the ignition temperature and accelerate the combustion of flammable and combustible liquids, gases, and solids. In addition, nitrous oxide, which is used as an anesthesia, can decompose explosively in a container if it is subjected to fire temperatures.

The key fire safety precept for both gases is to keep fire away from them, since their cylinders can be more dangerous than any other type of compressed gas cylinder during a fire. Nitrous oxide can decompose explosively, and oxygen cylinders can fail violently when the heated oxygen actually burns the steel or aluminum of which the cylinder is made at the first leak during a fire. Storage areas must be constructed of noncombustible or limited combustible materials, and there can be no combustible materials in the storage location.

Piping for such systems must be specifically cleaned to remove combustible matter, and joint brazing filler metal must have a melting point of at least 1,000°F to minimize the release of oxygen or nitrous oxide into a fire exposing the piping.

The geometry of these locations is spelled out in various standards, and ignition sources must be kept out of them. You should verify the administrative control procedures used in the facility.

Bibliography

Code for Pressure Piping, ASME B 31, American Society of Mechanical Engineers, 345 E. 47th St., New York, NY.

Cote, A. E., ed., *Fire Protection Handbook,* 17th edition, National Fire Protection Association, Quincy, MA, 1991. Several sections contain data and fire protection information on fuel gases and their use in various industrial processes.

Linville, J. L., ed., *Industrial Fire Hazards Handbook*, 3rd edition, National Fire Protection Association, Quincy, MA, 1990. Several chapters deal with industrial applications of fuel gases.

Lemoff, T. C., ed., *Liquefied Petroleum Gases Handbook,* 3rd edition, National Fire Protection Association, Quincy, MA, 1992. Commentary on NFPA 58.

The following documents deal with a wide variety of gas appliances and accessories. They are published by the American National Standards Institute, 1430 Broadway, New York, NY 10018.

ANSI Z 21.1, *Household Cooking Gas Appliances.*

ANSI Z 21.2, *Gas Hose Connectors for Portable Indoor Gas-Fired Equipment.*

ANSI Z 21.5.1A, *Gas Clothes Dryers, Volume I, Type 1 Clothes Dryers.*

ANSI Z 21.5.2, *Gas Clothes Dryers, Volume II, Type 2 Clothes Dryers.*

ANSI Z 21.10.1, *Gas Water Heaters, Volume I, Storage Water Heaters with Input Ratings of 75,000 Btu per Hour or Less.*

ANSI Z 21.10.3, *Gas Water Heaters, Volume III: Storage with Input Ratings Above 75,000 Btu per Hour, Circulating and Instantaneous Water Heaters.*

ANSI Z 21.11.1, *Gas-Fired Room Heaters, Volume I, Vented Room Heaters.*

ANSI Z 21.11.2, *Gas-Fired Room Heaters, Volume II, Unvented Room Heaters.*

ANSI Z 21.12, *Draft Hoods.*

ANSI Z 21.13, *Gas-Fired Low-Pressure Steam and Hot Water Boilers.*

ANSI Z 21.15, *Manually Operated Gas Valves.*

ANSI Z 21.17, *Domestic Gas Conversion Burners.*

ANSI Z 21.18, *Gas Appliance Pressure Regulators.*

ANSI Z 21.19, *Refrigerators Using Gas Fuel.*

ANSI Z 21.20, *Automatic Gas Ignition Systems and Components.*

ANSI Z 21.21, *Automatic Valves for Gas Appliances.*

ANSI Z 21.22, *Relief Valves and Automatic Gas Shutoff Devices for Hot Water Supply Systems.*

ANSI Z 21.23, *Gas Appliance Thermostats.*

ANSI Z 21.24, *Metal Connectors for Gas Appliances.*

ANSI Z 21.35, *Gas Filters on Appliances.*

ANSI Z 21.40.1, *Gas-Fired Absorption Summer Air Conditioning Appliances.*

ANSI Z 21.41, *Quick-Disconnect Devices for Use with Gas Fuel.*

ANSI Z 21.42, *Gas-Fired Illuminating Appliances.*

NSI Z 21.44, *Gas-Fired Gravity and Fan Type Direct Vent Wall Furnaces.*

ANSI Z 21.45, *Flexible Connectors of Other Than All-Metal Construction for Gas Appliances.*

ANSI Z 21.47, *Gas-Fired Central Furnaces (Except Direct Vent and Separated Combustion System Central Furnaces).*

ANSI Z 21.48, *Gas-Fired Gravity and Fan-Type Floor Furnaces.*

ANSI Z 21.49, *Gas-Fired Gravity and Fan-Type Vented Wall Furnaces.*

ANSI Z 21.50, *Vented Decorative Gas Appliances.*

ANSI Z 21.54, *Gas Hose Connectors for Portable Outdoor Gas-Fired Appliances.*

ANSI Z 21.56, *Gas-Fired Swimming Pool Heaters.*

ANSI Z 21.58, *Outdoor Cooking Gas Appliances.*

ANSI Z 21.60, *Decorative Gas Appliances for Installation in Vented Fireplaces.*

ANSI Z 21.61, *Gas-Fired Toilets.*

ANSI Z 21.64, *Direct Vent Central Furnaces.*

ANSI Z 21.66, *Electrically Operated Automatic Vent Damper Devices for Use with Gas-Fired Appliances.*

ANSI Z 21.67, *Mechanically Actuated Automatic Vent Damper Devices for Use with Gas-Fired Appliances.*

ANSI Z 21.68, *Thermally Actuated Automatic Vent Damper Devices for Use with Gas-Fired Appliances.*

ANSI Z 21.69, *Connectors for Movable Gas Appliances.*

ANSI Z 83.3, *Gas Utilization Equipment in Large Boilers.*

ANSI Z 83.4, *Direct Gas-Fired Make-Up Air Heaters.*

ANSI Z 83.6, *Gas-Fired Infrared Heaters.*

ANSI Z 83.7, *Gas-Fired Construction Heaters.*

ANSI Z 83.8, *Gas Unit Heaters.*

ANSI Z 83.9, *Gas-Fired Duct Furnaces.*

ANSI Z 83.11, *Gas Food Service Equipment Ranges and Unit Broilers.*

ANSI Z 83.12, *Gas Food Service Equipment Baking and Roasting Ovens.*

ANSI Z 83.13, *Gas Food Service Equipment Deep Fat Fryers.*

ANSI Z 83.14, *Gas Food Service Equipment Counter Appliances.*

ANSI Z 83.15, *Gas Food Service Equipment Kettles, Steam Cookers, and Steam Generators.*

ANSI Z 83.16, *Unvented Commercial and Industrial Heaters.*

NFPA Codes, Standards, and Recommended Practices

NFPA 50, *Standard for Bulk Oxygen Systems at Consumer Sites.* Recommends locations, distances between bulk systems and exposures, containers, and associated equipment.

NFPA 50A, *Standard for Gaseous Hydrogen Systems at Consumer Sites.* Contains requirements for containers, safety relief devices, piping, and other components.

NFPA 50B, *Standard for Liquefied Hydrogen Systems at Consumer Sites.* Contains requirements for containers, supports, marking, safety releases, piping, and other components.

NFPA 51, *Standard for the Design and Installation of Oxygen-Fuel Gas Systems for Welding, Cutting, and Allied Processes.* Addresses acetylene, hydrogen, natural gas, LP-Gas, MAP, and other stable gases.

NFPA 51A, *Standard for Acetylene Cylinder Charging Plants.* Contains safety requirements for design, construction, installation, operations, and fire protection.

NFPA 51B, *Standard for Fire Prevention in Use of Cutting and Welding Processes.* Covers practices and precautions for cutting and welding processes involving the use of electric arcs and oxy-fuel gas flames.

NFPA 52, *Standard for Compressed Natural Gas (CNG) Vehicular Fuel Systems.* Applies to general CNG and equipment qualification, engine fuel systems, storage, and dispensing systems.

NFPA 54, *National Fuel Gas Code.* Criteria for installation, operation, and maintenance of gas piping, appliances, and equipment.

NFPA 55, *Standard for the Storage, Use, and Handling of Compressed and Liquefied Gases in Portable Cylinders.*

NFPA 58, *Standard for the Storage and Handling of Liquefied Petroleum Gases.* Covers LP-Gas systems, liquid transfer, truck transportation, engine fuel systems, and buildings or structures housing LP-Gas distribution facilities.

NFPA 59, *Standard for the Storage and Handling of Liquefied Petroleum Gases at Utility Gas Plants.* Covers safe design, construction, and operation of LP-Gas equipment at plants supplying LP-Gas/air mixtures for utility application.

NFPA 59A, *Standard for the Production, Storage, and Handling of Liquefied Natural Gas (LNG).* Covers site selection, design, construction, and fire protection for LNG facilities.

NFPA 99, *Standard for Health Care Facilities.* Covers the use of oxygen.

CHAPTER 37

Combustible Dusts

*M*ost finely divided combustible materials, including metals, are subject to rapid combustion when dispersed in air, usually resulting in destructive explosions. The ease with which these dust/air mixtures ignite and their ability to propagate flame and generate damaging explosion pressures depend on a number of factors, such as particle size and shape, concentration, and moisture content. Although these factors cannot be addressed here in any detail, you can find information on specific combustible dusts in the *Fire Protection Handbook* (see Bibliography).

For the purposes of this manual, a dust particle is defined as a piece of material 150 microns or less in diameter. Basically, this means any material, not necessarily of regular shape, that is fine enough to pass through a 100-mesh sieve. Particles larger than 100 mesh can be considered "grit" and might not even pose any unusual hazards. For example, sawdust is primarily a collection of variously sized chips of wood. Although some very finely divided particles are present, they do not contribute much to the explosion potential of the mass, and sawdust presents little more than a fire hazard. In contrast, the fine floury dust generated by a sanding operation can be readily ignited and can explode quite destructively. Some severe dust explosions have occurred in sanding operations in plywood and particle board plants.

The concept of a dust explosion is sometimes not well understood because an explosion can result from a number of different physical, mechanical, and chemical processes. In terms of burning characteristics, the word "explosion" means either deflagration or detonation. A "deflagration" is a combustion reaction that travels slower than the speed of sound, while a "detonation" is a combustion reaction that travels at or above the speed of sound. A dust explosion that is, in fact, a detonation is very unusual.

In a typical dust explosion, the flame front will travel 3.3 to 33 feet per second. Although this is much faster than the flame speed in a typical fire, it is much slower than the pressure wave generated by the production and thermal expansion of the flammable gases. The pressure wave is responsible for most of the damage in a dust explosion and has two important characteristics: maximum pressure and maximum rate of pressure rise.

Dust Explosions

Dust explosions can be very destructive, the most vivid examples being those that occur in large grain elevators. In most cases, there actually is a series of explosions, and the first is frequently quite small. Although small in size and usually the result of a minor process malfunction, this first explosion is intense enough to dislodge any static dust on the walls, ledges, machinery, and other surfaces in the immediate vicinity. Because the pressure wave is moving much faster than the flame front, it knocks the dust loose and mixes it with air, creating a much larger dust cloud just in time to be ignited by the following flame front. This secondary explosion is much larger than the first and usually is very destructive. It can damage process equipment, easily destroy masonry walls, and trigger even larger subsequent explosions.

Rate of Pressure Rise

The rate of pressure rise is roughly the ratio of the peak pressure to the time interval during which the pressure is increased. It is the most important factor in determining the severity of a dust explosion. The size of explosion vents are largely determined by this rate of rise. For very rapid rates of rise, explosion vents might not be practical, and other protection devices might be necessary.

Maximum Explosion Pressure

The peak pressures most dust explosions reach under test conditions exceed 50 psi, although these peaks vary according to the particle size distribution, concentration, and other variables. When you consider that typical construction will withstand 1 psi or less, it becomes evident that even the most inefficient dust explosion will do considerable damage. In fact, most dust explosions are far from optimal. Rarely is there uniform dispersion or particle-size distribution; the damage that typically results is done at well below the explosion pressures that could have developed.

Duration

Another factor in explosion severity is the duration of the explosion pressure. Consider the wall of the dust collector in which an explosion occurs. The wall "sees" a steady increase of pressure to some peak value over a finite time span, assuming it does not rupture. Then the pressure begins to subside. If the pressure is plotted against time, the area under the curve is the total impulse imparted to the wall by the explosion. It is the total impulse, rather than the peak pressure, that ultimately determines the damage. This partly explains why dust explosions tend to be more damaging than gas explosions, even though they build pressure more slowly and do not usually peak as high.

Confinement

The gaseous combustion products of a dust explosion expand at a rate as high as sonic velocity and, in so doing, exert significant pressures on the surrounding enclosure. Unless the enclosure is strong enough to withstand the peak pressure developed, it will fail. For this reason, process equipment and the buildings in which it is located must be protected by explosion vents or some type of explosion-prevention system (see NFPA 68, *Guide for Venting of Deflagrations,* and NFPA 69, *Standard on Explosion Prevention Systems*).

Inerting

Laboratory tests have shown that the reduction of the oxygen concentration or the introduction of an inert powder can reduce the maximum explosion potential.

For most agricultural, plastic, and carbonaceous dusts, reducing the oxygen content below 10% by volume can prevent a dust explosion from occurring. Frequently, this is achieved by increasing the volume percentage of nitrogen or carbon dioxide in the enclosures or equipment handling the combustible dust.

For combustible metal dusts, such as aluminum or magnesium, however, this is not a satisfactory solution because these combustible metal dusts can react with these gases. In those cases, it would be necessary to use one of the inert noble gases, such as argon (see NFPA 69, *Standard on Explosion Prevention Systems*).

Introducing an inert powder to mitigate the effects of a dust explosion might not be practical because it takes relatively large amounts of the inert dust to be effective. This technique, referred to as "rock dusting," is limited mostly to coal mines, which generally require 65% of the total dust for a coal mine entry to be rock dust.

Evaluating the Hazard

When you are confronted with a dust explosion hazard, find out as much as you can about the material itself and the process conditions, including the size distribution of the dust particles. Next, compare the relative hazard of the dust.

The *Fire Protection Handbook* contains the explosion characteristics for common dusts. This information also may be available in some of the reports published by the U.S. Bureau of Mines, which are listed in the handbook and in the bibliography of this book. A note of caution, however: the U.S. Bureau of Mines data were generated using the Hartmann Apparatus. More recent data are generated in spherical vessels of 20 liters or 1 cubic meter and tend to be more consistent. Thus they are useful in designing explosion (deflagration) relief. The Hartmann data are limited as a relative indication of the hazard and should not be used to design dust explosion vents.

If you are confronted with a dust that has not been tested or are asked to evaluate one of the dusts described above, have a sample tested, preferably in the spherical test vessels noted above. You will want to know the maximum explosion pressure, the maximum rate of pressure rise, the minimum explosion concentration, and the concentration yielding the highest value of maximum pressure. You also might want to determine the minimum ignition energy and the layer ignition temperature.

Fire Hazards of Dusts

Combustible dusts are also a fire hazard because stationary deposits of dust provide an easy means for a fire to spread rapidly from its initial location. A flash fire of this nature could propagate so quickly that it might cause sprinklers to operate outside the sprinkler design area, limiting the system's ability to extinguish or control the fire.

Another characteristic of dust is its ability to act as thermal insulation. Thick deposits of dust on heat-producing equipment such as motors, shaft bearings, and similar components retard the flow of heat. The natural cooling effects of the equipment are therefore less efficient. Since the dust is organic, it will begin to degrade or carbonize, which tends to lower the ignition temperature of the dust. Eventually the dust will ignite or the equipment will fail because of high temperature, and a fire could result.

Particle Size

The smaller the particle size of the dust, the easier it is to ignite. This is because the ratio of surface area to volume increases tremendously as particle size decreases. Because of their smaller mass, smaller particles are less able to absorb energy from an external source. Once the dust has been ignited, it radiates energy to nearby particles more quickly and efficiently. It is also true that a decrease in particle size will increase the rate of pressure rise during an explosion and decrease the minimum explosive concentration and the energy necessary for ignition.

As a practical matter, however, a range of particle sizes will be present, and the behavior of a given dust sample will depend on particle-size distribution.

Concentration

There is a minimum concentration of dust in air below which propagating ignition will not occur. This is called the lower explosive limit (LEL), and, as stated above, it decreases with decreasing particle size. Plotting explosion pressures and rates of pressure rise against dust cloud concentration shows that both parameters are at a minimum value at the minimum explosive concentration, then rise to a peak value at a concentration near the so-called optimum concentration. However, it should be noted that the optimum concentration generally is considered to be the point at which the rate of rise is at a maximum. The maximum pressure does not always occur at the same point, varying very slightly. Once the optimum point is exceeded, both rate of pressure rise and explosion pressure decrease. Maximum explosive concentrations, described as the upper explosive limit, are very rarely determined and have no practical value.

The energy of the ignition source, the turbulence of the dust cloud, and the uniformity of dispersion all have some effect on the minimum explosive concentration, at least in laboratory tests. In the field, these influences are of secondary importance.

Moisture

The humidity of the air surrounding the dust particles has no effect on the course of a dust explosion. However, the moisture content of the dust particles can affect the potential for a dust explosion. A high moisture content tends to increase ignition temperature, ignition energy, and the minimum explosive concentration and tends to decrease the severity of the explosion. Again, these variations are of more interest in laboratory test work; they are of secondary importance in the field.

Other Factors

As would be expected, a decrease in the partial pressure of oxygen, either by vacuum or inert gas, will decrease the explosion hazard of a dust aerosol. In the production of metal powders, enough oxygen should be maintained in the system to permit controlled oxidation of the particle surface during the size reduction process. If this is not done, the metal particles will oxidize rapidly when exposed to air, and they may self-ignite.

The presence of a flammable gas in the dust/air aerosol greatly increases the hazard. Because they have a lower energy of ignition than the "pure" dust mixture, these so-called hybrid mixtures are easier to ignite, and they produce explosions that are much more violent than normally would be expected. The concentration of the flammable gas does not have to be at or above the lower flammable limit—considering the concentration of the flammable gas/air mixture alone, without the presence of the combustible dust—in order to achieve these effects. Such hybrid mixtures are encountered in fluid bed driers where a flammable solvent is being evaporated from a powder, for example, and must be provided with special safeguards, such as an inert gas atmosphere, which could reduce or even exclude the oxygen completely, or explosion protection systems.

Ignition Sources

Dust clouds and dust layers can be ignited by all the usual ignition sources, including open flames, electrical arcs, frictional and mechanical sparks, and hot surfaces. Ignition by electrical charge usually is ruled out. Dust clouds require 1 to 40 millijoules of energy for ignition to occur, compared to the 0.20 to 1 millijoules needed by flammable gases or vapors, making static discharge somewhat unlikely as an ignition source. The NFPA documents that deal with specific dust explosion hazards also address the control of ignition sources.

Prevention of Dust Explosions

Dust Control

Eliminating, or at least greatly reducing, the amount of airborne and static dust is the single most important means of preventing dust explosions. Dusts and materials that generate dust should be handled to the greatest extent possible in closed systems, either pneumatic or mechanical. In order to be effective, these systems must be dust-tight. Look for evidence of dust around the seams and joints of ducts or pipes and around access panels. If dust is evident, it may indicate a faulty gasket or mechanical damage to the conduit itself. Make sure hatches on bins and tanks are closed securely.

Keep in mind that these systems, whether they handle process material in bulk or collect fugitive dust, contain a dust/air mixture in the explosive range. Make sure there are adequate provisions for keeping tramp metal out. One method to consider using is a magnetic separator.

Good housekeeping is imperative. Any surface, either horizontal or vertical, on which dust can accumulate should be kept clean. There are two rules of thumb for judging the adequacy of housekeeping: If you cannot tell what color a surface is, it needs to be cleaned often. And if the dust deposits are thicker than a paper clip, cleaning is long overdue.

The frequency of cleaning will depend on conditions in the plant, such as the adequacy of dust collection systems and the tightness of the process equipment. Cleaning should be done by central vacuum systems. If portable systems are used, they should be suitable for Class II areas. Alternatively, soft brushes and dust pans made of conductive plastic or metal may be used.

Under no circumstances should dust be blown off with compressed air because doing this will just move the dust from one surface to another. Equipment that handles or produces dusts should be as tight as possible.

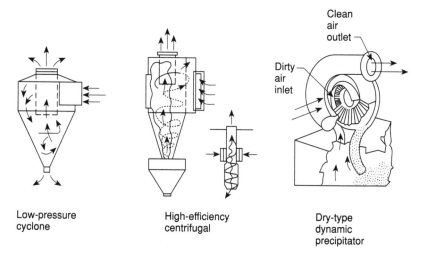

Clean
air
outlet

Dirty
air
inlet

Low-pressure
cyclone

High-efficiency
centrifugal

Dry-type
dynamic
precipitator

Figure 37-1. Examples of typical types of dust-collecting equipment.

Where equipment is loaded or unloaded by dumping, local dust collection pickups should be arranged. Dust control pickups should be initiated at drumming and bagging lines. Carefully review process schematics and the equipment itself to find those points at which dust aspirators might be needed. Such locations include hatch covers on bins, tanks, or vessels, and frequently opened access panels.

Process Equipment

If a dust explosion is going to occur, chances are that it will begin in a piece of equipment. It is impossible to prevent dust clouds from forming around equipment unless the material is handled as a slurry or a damp, cakey solid. Equipment maintenance is very important in these situations. Look for similar signs of abuse on drag or en-masse conveyers. Conveyer belts should not show any sign of excessive wear, and idler rollers should be free spinning to avoid frictional heating and possible failure of the conveyer belt.

Certain pieces of equipment are especially susceptible to dust explosions. These include mills, pulverizers, dust collectors, cyclone separators, and the various types of dryers.

There are several ways in which this equipment can be protected. It may be designed to contain the expected explosion pressure. It also may be fitted with explosion vents or equipped with an explosion-suppression system. Or the equipment enclosure may be blanketed with inert gas. Again, a careful review of the process will help when choosing the most suitable option.

You might need the help of qualified individuals to determine whether the equipment can withstand the expected overpressure. Explosion vents should never terminate inside the building. They should be located close to an outside wall and vented through a short, straight duct directly to the outside. Better yet, the vented equipment should be moved outside or to the roof of the building. Breather vents can terminate inside the building if they are fitted with filters. Check to make sure the filters are functioning properly.

Electrical Equipment

Electrical equipment in dust-prone areas that are well kept should be suitable for Class II, Division 2 locations, unless the dust happens to be electrically conductive. This would require that all electrical equipment be Division 1. Check to see that the conduit is properly sealed and that all electrical enclosures are tightly sealed. Process control equipment located within the process stream must be suitable for Class II, Division 2, or it must be intrinsically safe.

Ignition Sources

Assuming that a dust cloud will form eventually within a building, the next step is to prevent ignition. The most obvious items to control are smoking and welding operations. Make sure "no smoking" signs are posted in all operational areas and check to see that special areas are set aside for safe smoking. A hot work permit system should be in place for welding and cutting operations (see Chapter 45). Ancillary equipment should be checked for overheating, for slipping or chafing drive belts, and for other mechanical defects that might cause sparks. If there is a possibility that tramp metal or other foreign objects may enter the equipment, magnetic separators or screens may be needed.

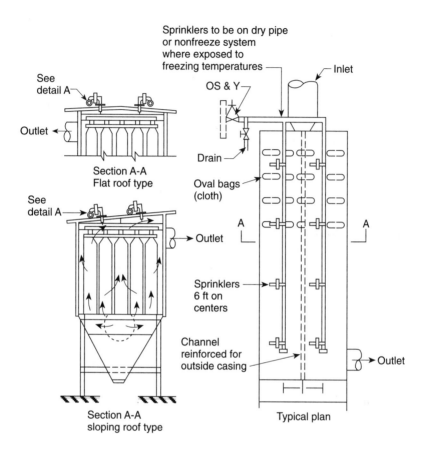

Sprinklers to be on dry pipe or nonfreeze system where exposed to freezing temperatures

Inlet

OS & Y

See detail A

Outlet

Section A-A
Flat roof type

See detail A

Outlet

Drain

Oval bags (cloth)

A ⌐   ⌐ A

Outlet

Sprinklers
6 ft on
centers

Channel
reinforced for
outside casing

Outlet

Section A-A
sloping roof type

Typical plan

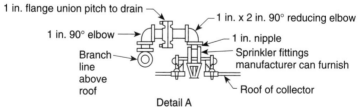

1 in. flange union pitch to drain

1 in. 90° elbow

1 in. x 2 in. 90° reducing elbow

1 in. nipple

Branch
line
above
roof

Sprinkler fittings
manufacturer can furnish

Roof of collector

Detail A

Figure 37-2. Sprinkler protection for a bag-type dust collector.

Fire Protection

Other chapters in this manual discuss what to look for when inspecting fire protection equipment—automatic sprinkler systems, hose connections, and portable fire extinguishers. In areas containing dust explosion hazards, you must also check to be sure that all hose connections are equipped with fine spray nozzles and that special fog nozzles will be used where high voltage electrical equipment is located. The plant fire brigade should understand that a coarse or solid water stream could throw dust into suspension, thus causing a primary or secondary explosion.

Where metal dusts are involved, quantities of sand, talc, foundry flux, or other specifically approved, inert extinguishing agents should be available to smother small fires. Make sure that only the approved types of water or portable extinguishers are used.

Bibliography

ASTM E1226-88, *Standard Test Method for Pressure & Rate of Pressure Rise for Combustible Dusts,* American Society for Testing & Materials, Philadelphia, PA, 1988.

Baker, W. E., and Tang, M. J., *Gas, Dust & Hybrid Explosions*, Elsevier Science Publishing Company, New York, NY, 1991.

Bartknecht, W., *Explosions — Course, Prevention, Protection*, Springer Verlag, New York, NY, 1981.

Bartknecht, W., *Dust Explosions— Course, Prevention, Protection,* Springer Verlag, New York, NY, 1989.

Cashdollar, K. L., and Hertzberg, Martin, *Industrial Dust Explosions,* American Society for Testing and Materials, Philadelphia, PA, 1987.

Coenen, W., and Meffert, K., *BIA-Handbuch -Erganzbare Sammlung der sicher-heitstechneschen Informations-und Arbeitsblatter fur betriebliche Praxis,* Berufsgenossenschaftliches Institut fur Arbeitssicherheit, Erich Schmidt Verlag GmbH & Co., Bielefeld, Germany, 1985.

Cote, A. E., *Fire Protection Handbook,* 17th edition, National Fire Protection Association, Quincy, MA, 1991. Section 3, Chapter 12, contains information on dust explosions.

Cross, Jean, and Farrer, Donald, *Dust Explosions,* Plenum Publishing Co., New York, NY, 1982.

Eckhoff, R. K., *Dust Explosions in the Process Industries,* Butterworth-Heinemann Ltd, Oxford, England, 1991.

Field, P., *Dust Explosions,* Elsevier Scientific Publishing Company, Amersterdam, The Netherlands, 1982.

Forschungsbericht Staubexplosionen: Brenn und Kenngrossen von Stauben, Hauptverband der gewerblichen Brerufsgenossenschaften e.V., Bonn, Germany, 1980.

Lunn, G. A., *Venting Gas & Dust Explosions— A Review,* Institution of Chemical Engineers, Rugby, England, 1984.

Lunn, G. A., *Guide to Dust Explosion Prevention & Protection: Part 3 — Venting of Weak Explosions and the Effect of Vent Ducts,* Institution of Chemical Engineers, Rugby, England, 1988.

Nagy, J., and Verakis, H. C., *Development and Control of Dust Explosions,* Marcel Dekker, Inc., New York, NY, 1983.

Palmer, K. N., *Dust Explosions and Fires,* Chapman & Hall Ltd, London, England, 1973.

Schofield, C., *Guide to Dust Explosion Prevention & Protection: Part 1—Venting,* Institution of Chemical Engineers, Rugby, England, 1984.

Schofield, C., and Abbott, J. A., *Guide to Dust Explosion Prevention & Protection: Part 2— Ignition Prevention, Containment, Inerting, Suppression and Isolation,* Institution of Chemical Engineers, Rugby, England, 1988.

NFPA Codes, Standards, and Recommended Practices

NFPA 61A, *Standard for Prevention of Fire and Dust Explosions in Facilities Manufacturing and Handling Starch*

NFPA 61B, *Standard for the Prevention of Fires and Explosions in Grain Elevators and Facilities Handling Bulk Raw Agricultural Commodities*

NFPA 61C, *Standard for the Prevention of Fire and Dust Explosions in Feed Mills*

NFPA 61D, *Standard for the Prevention of Fire and Dust Explosions in the Milling of Agricultural Commodities for Human Consumption*

NFPA 68, *Guide for Venting of Deflagrations*

NFPA 69, *Standard on Explosion Prevention Systems*

NFPA 497B, *Recommended Practice for Classification of Class I Hazardous (Classified) Locations for Electrical Installations in Chemical Process Areas*

CHAPTER 38

. . . .

Metals

M etals can burn. Some oxidize rapidly and reach flaming combustion; others oxidize so slowly that heat generated during oxidation dissipates before ignition occurs. Certain metals—notably magnesium, titanium, zirconium, hafnium, sodium, lithium, potassium, calcium, zinc, thorium, uranium, and plutonium—are combustible metals. In thin sections, as fine particles, or when molten, they can ignite easily; however, in massive solid form, they are difficult to ignite.

Aluminum, iron, and steel normally are not combustible, although they can ignite and burn when finely divided. Clean, fine steel wool, for example, can be ignited. Dust clouds of most metals in air are explosive. And most metals are combustible in high oxygen concentrations. Particle size, shape, quantity, and alloy and ambient conditions are important factors in assessing the combustibility of metals.

Temperatures produced by burning metals are much higher than temperatures of flammable liquid fires. Some hot metals continue to burn in nitrogen, carbon dioxide, or steam atmospheres, where fires of other materials would be extinguished.

All metals do not burn in the same way. Titanium produces little smoke; smoke from lithium is dense and profuse. Some water-moistened metal powders, such as zirconium, burn with near-explosive violence; yet the same powders, wet with oil, burn quietly. Sodium melts and flows; calcium does not. Some metals burn more readily after prolonged exposure to moist air, while exposure to dry air can make them more difficult to ignite.

If you know that the premises you are about to inspect has processes involving metals other than iron and steel, you should ascertain, before the inspection, the burning characteristics of the metals involved, the quantities involved, the types of processes involved, the arrangement made for the storage and handling of scrap, and the extinguishing agents used against combustible metal fires. Several good sources of information on combustible metals are the *Fire Protection Handbook,* the *Industrial Fire Hazards Handbook,* and NFPA codes on metals (see Bibliography).

Extinguishing Combustible-Metal Fires

Combustible-metal (Class D) fires are difficult to extinguish. Common extinguishing agents do not work well on them; in many cases they increase combustion. Many agents can be used to extinguish Class D fires, but a given agent does not necessarily work on all metals. Some agents work with several metals, others with only one. Commercially available agents are known as dry powders. They should not be confused with dry chemical agents that are suitable for flammable liquid and live electrical equipment fires. Some powders, such as G-1 powder, Na-X powder, Lith-X powder, Met-L-X powder, go by their trade names, and others such as talcum powder, sand, graphite, sodium chloride, copper powder, and soda ash are known by their common names. You must

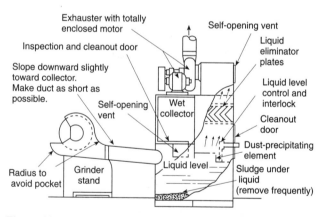

Figure 38-1. A schematic diagram of a liquid precipitation separator used with a fixed grinding unit handling combustible metal dust. Source: Figure 4-2.4(a), NFPA 480, **Standard for the Storage, Handling, and Processing of Magnesium Solids and Powders,** *NFPA, Quincy, MA, 1993.*

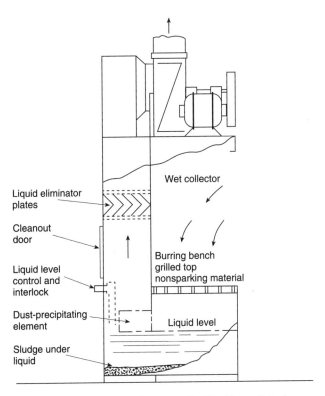

Liquid eliminator plates

Wet collector

Cleanout door

Liquid level control and interlock

Burring bench grilled top nonsparking material

Dust-precipitating element

Liquid level

Sludge under liquid

Figure 38-2. A schematic diagram of a liquid precipitation separator used with a portable grinding unit handling combustible metal dust. Source: Figure 4-2.4(b), NFPA 480, **Standard for the Storage, Handling, and Processing of Magnesium Solids and Powders,** *NFPA, Quincy, MA, 1993.*

understand the uses and limitations of any agent used. The references at the end of the chapter will acquaint you with them.

Controlling or putting out metal fires depends to a great degree on the method of application of the extinguishing agents and the training and experience of personnel who use them. In locations where combustible metals are present, ask to see the supply of dry powder agents on hand, their location, and the tools available to spread them on burning metal. Inquire about the training employees receive in extinguishing metal fires because these fires involve techniques not commonly encountered in conventional fire fighting. Emphasize that training is needed to get experience in techniques for specialized extinguishing agent application. Personnel responsible for controlling combustible metal fires should practice extinguishing fires of the metals used in their facility at an isolated outdoor location.

Magnesium

The ignition temperature of pure magnesium in large pieces is close to its melting point of 1,202°F, but magnesium ribbons and shavings can be ignited under certain conditions at about 950°F, and finely divided powder can be ignited at temperatures below 900°F. Magnesium principally is used in alloy form, and certain magnesium alloys can ignite at temperatures as low as 800°F. Thus, ignition temperatures can vary widely depending on the makeup of the alloys involved as well as the size and shape of the metal. Find out as much as you can about the alloys used and how the metal is processed. This will give you a good idea of the degree of hazard associated with the metals at a given facility.

Process Hazards

Magnesium and its alloys are readily machineable, and if the tools used are dull or deformed, frictional heat can ignite the chips and shavings created in machining operations. Machining magnesium usually is done dry, but any cutting fluids used must be of the mineral oil type. Water, water-soluble oils, and oils containing more than 0.2% fatty acids are hazardous and must not be used. Make sure these cooling liquids are not used by mistake and that the machines and surrounding work area are clean. Magnesium fires have been known to occur in machine beds. Waste magnesium is best kept in clean, covered, dry, steel, or other noncombustible drums, and the drums should be removed from the building at regular intervals. The machine operator must have an appropriate fire extinguishing agent immediately available.

Magnesium grinding is possibly more hazardous than machining. Magnesium dust clouds, made up of minute fine particles that could result from unprotected grinding operations, can be explosive if there is an ignition source. Make sure that grinding equipment used on magnesium has proper safeguards. An integral part of a good grinding installation is a liquid precipitation separator that converts the dust into a sludge. Fine particles from grinding generate hydrogen when submerged in water, but they cannot be ignited in this condition; however, fine particles resulting from grinding that are slightly wetted with water can generate enough heat to ignite spontaneously and burn violently because oxygen is extracted from the water with the release of hydrogen. Thus, it is important that grinding installations have interlocks that permit the grinder to operate only if the exhaust blower and water spray are working to keep the magnesium fines fully wetted.

Storage

Storage buildings housing magnesium preferably should be noncombustible, and the magnesium should be segregated from combustible materials. If magnesium is stored in combustible buildings, the buildings must be protected throughout by automatic sprinklers. Dry fine particles should be stored in noncombustible containers in a fire-resistive storage building, although a room with explosion venting also is acceptable. However, wherever stored, the fine particles must remain dry wherever they are stored to prevent the release of hydrogen. Scrap magnesium fine particles wet with coolants should be stored outdoors in covered, vented, noncombustible containers because they can spontaneously heat and generate hydrogen through reaction with the coolant.

Fire Extinguishment

In areas where magnesium is machined, ground, or similarly processed, a supply of extinguishing powder approved for use on a magnesium fire must be kept within easy reach of all operators. The powder can be kept in closed containers with easily removable covers and a hand scoop or in approved portable extinguishers designed for use with these powders. The powders available include G-1, which is composed of screened, graphitized foundry coke to which an organic phosphate has been added; Metal Guard, which is the same in composition as G-1 powder; and Met-L-X, which has a sodium chloride base to which has been added ingredients such as tricalcium phosphate to improve flow characteristics and metal stearates for water repellancy.

In general, water should not be used on magnesium chip fires because it can violently accelerate the fire. Automatic sprinklers, however, will extinguish the typical fire in a shop where quantities of chips are limited.

Castings, wrought products, and fabricated parts that are involved in a fire can be cooled and extinguished with coarse streams of water applied with a standard fire hose. Water fog must not be used because it can accelerate a magnesium fire rather than cool it. Finally, care must be used when applying water to magnesium fires where quantities of molten metal are present; the steam formation and metal-water reactions can be explosive.

For magnesium fires in heat-treating furnaces, dry powder, foundry fluxes, or approved gas can be used to extinguish the fire. If dry powder is used, the burning metal should be removed from the furnace, if possible. Fluxes and gas can be applied successfully to the burning metal in the furnace. Water is not to be used to fight magnesium fires in furnaces.

Because magnesium will burn in the presence of carbon dioxide and nitrogen, and will react violently with halogenated extinguishing agents, these extinguishing materials should not be used.

Titanium

Titanium, with an ignition temperature ranging from 630°F in dust-air clouds to 2,900°F in solid castings, has hazard characteristics similar to magnesium. Castings and other massive pieces are not combustible under normal conditions; however, large pieces can ignite spontaneously when they come in contact with liquid oxygen—truly an unusual condition. Small chips, fine turnings, and dust can ignite easily and burn with high heat release. It has been reported that fine turnings and very thin chips have been ignited by a match. Titanium dust also can be ignited in atmospheres of carbon dioxide and nitrogen.

Process Hazards

Heat generated during machining, grinding, sawing, and drilling of titanium can be enough to ignite the turnings and chips formed in the operations. Consequently, water-based coolants should be used in ample quantity to remove heat, and cutting tools should be kept sharp. Fine particles should be removed from the work area regularly and stored in covered metal containers.

Grinding of titanium requires a dust-collecting system discharging into a liquid precipitation separator. Large quantities of cooling fluid should be used to keep the sparking down.

Descaling baths of mineral acids and molten alkali salts can cause violent reactions with titanium at abnormally high temperatures. Titanium sheets also have ignited when they have been removed for descaling baths.

Titanium melting furnaces present a special problem. Several severe explosions have occurred in titanium melting furnaces when water inadvertently entered the melting crucible during the melting operation. The use of sodium-potassium alloy (NaK) as a crucible coolant has been developed for both laboratory and commercial use. While this reduces the danger of a furnace explosion, the handling of NaK presents its own hazards.

Storage

Large pieces of titanium do not present storage hazards. Dry scrap fine particles and titanium sponge, however, should be stored in covered metal barrels kept well away from combustible materials. Moist scrap should be stored outdoors in covered metal barrels because the scrap could generate hydrogen, and scrap wet with oils could heat spontaneously.

Fire Extinguishment

Where operations generate titanium fine particles, dust, and turnings, an adequate supply of approved extinguishing powder should be within easy reach of all machine operators. The powder can be kept in closed containers with easily removable covers and a hand scoop, or in approved portable extinguishers. The safest procedure to follow with a fire involving small quantities of titanium powder is to ring the fire with the extinguishing powder and allow the fire to burn itself out. Care must be taken to prevent the formation of a titanium dust cloud when applying extinguishing powder.

Tests conducted by Industrial Risk Insurers on titanium machinings in piles and in open drums showed water in coarse spray was a safe and effective means of extinguishing fires in relatively small quantities of chips.

Water-based (including foam), carbon dioxide, halon, and dry chemical extinguishers are not effective on titanium fires and should not be used.

Zirconium and Hafnium

The combustibility of zirconium increases as the average particle size decreases, but other variables, such as moisture content, also affect how easily zirconium will ignite. In massive form, zirconium can withstand extremely high temperatures without igniting, but clouds of dust of zirconium, in which the average particle size is 3 microns, have ignited at room temperature.

Massive pieces of zirconium do not ignite spontaneously under ordinary conditions, but they will ignite when an oxide-free surface is exposed to sufficiently high oxygen concentrations and pressure. Scrap chips, borings, and turnings can spontaneously heat and ignite if fine dust is present.

As with other combustible metals, the combustibility of hafnium is related to its size and shape. Large pieces are hard to ignite; turnings and chips ignite more easily. Hafnium is somewhat more reactive than titanium or zirconium of similar form. Unless inactivated, hafnium in sponge form can ignite spontaneously. When ignited, hafnium burns with very little flame, but it releases large quantities of heat.

Process Hazards

In general, processing recommendations for zirconium and hafnium are the same. Large flows of mineral oil or water-based coolant are required to prevent dangerous heating during machining. Turnings should be collected frequently and stored under water in cans. When zirconium dust is generated it should be captured in a liquid precipitation separator.

Zirconium powder should be handled under an inert liquid or in an inert atmosphere. If either zirconium or hafnium powder is handled in air, extreme care must be used because the small static charges generated can cause ignition.

Storage

Zirconium castings do not require special storage precautions because massive pieces of the metal can withstand very high temperatures without igniting. Zirconium powder, however, is highly combustible, and it should be stored and shipped in 1-gallon containers with at least 25% water by volume.

Storerooms for zirconium powder should be of fire-resistive construction and equipped with explosion vents. Cans in storage should be separated from each other to limit fire spread. Cans should be checked periodically for corrosion.

Fire Extinguishment

Fighting zirconium and hafnium fires requires the same approach as that recommended for titanium. Small quantities of the metals can be ringed with dry powder extinguishing agent and allowed to burn out. Fires in massive pieces of the metals can be fought with large quantities of water. Limited tests have indicated that water in spray form will have no adverse effect on burning zirconium turnings. Fires in enclosed spaces can be smothered with argon or helium.

Sodium, Lithium, Potassium, and NaK

The principal fire hazard with sodium is its rapid reaction with water. Hydrogen liberated in the reaction can be ignited by the heat of the reaction. Once sodium is ignited, it burns vigorously and forms dense clouds of caustic sodium-oxide fumes.

Lithium undergoes many of the same reactions as sodium; however, its reaction with water is not as vigorous, and not enough heat is generated to ignite the hydrogen given off in the reaction.

The fire hazards of potassium are very similar to those of sodium, but potassium is more reactive.

NaK is the term used for any of several sodium-potassium alloys. NaK alloys possess the same fire hazard properties as those of the component metals except that the reactions are more vigorous. All are liquids or melt near room temperature.

Process Hazards

A principal use of liquid sodium is as a heat-transfer medium. Where molten sodium is used in process equipment, steel pans should be located underneath to prevent contact and violent reactions of burning sodium with the moisture in concrete floors. There should be tray-type covers on the pans to catch the sodium and drain it into the pans through drilled holes. Any sodium flowing through the holes extinguishes itself in the pan. Information on sodium can be used as a guide in processing lithium, NaK, and potassium.

Storage

Because sodium reacts with water, it should be stored in drums and cases in a dry, fire-resistive room or building used exclusively for storing sodium. And because sprinklers cannot be used, combustible materials should not be stored in the same area as sodium. Check to see that no water or steam pipes are located in the storage area and that sufficient heat is maintained to prevent moisture condensation. Natural ventilation at a high spot in the room can vent any hydrogen that might be released by accidental contact of sodium with moisture. In general, storage recommendations for lithium, NaK, and potassium are the same as those for sodium.

Fire Extinguishment

Never use aqueous-based extinguishing agents on fires of sodium, potassium, or lithium because they would cause a violent reaction. The dry powders developed for metal fires and dry sand, dry sodium chloride, and dry soda ash are effective extinguishing agents. Sodium burning inside a piece of apparatus usually can be extinguished by closing all openings. Fire extinguishing recommendations for sodium fires also apply to lithium, NaK, and potassium fires. Copper powder is an extremely effective extinguishing agent for lithium fires.

Calcium and Zinc

The moisture in the air governs the flammability of calcium. If ignited in moist air, it burns without flowing. Finely divided calcium will ignite spontaneously in air.

Sheets, castings, or other massive forms of zinc do not present serious fire hazards because they are difficult to ignite. Once ignited, however, zinc shapes can burn vigorously, and, zinc generates an appreciable amount of smoke when it burns.

Normally Noncombustible Metals

Aluminum

Aluminum, in its usual forms, has a sufficiently high ignition temperature so that its burning is not a factor in most fires. Aluminum only presents a special fire problem in powder or other finely divided forms. Under certain conditions powdered or flaked aluminum can be explosive.

Aluminum in contact with magnesium is much more combustible, possibly because they form an alloy.

Aluminum dust fires should be extinguished with approved dry powders. Nearly all vaporizing liquid fire extinguishing agents react violently with burning aluminum, usually intensifying the fire and sometimes exploding. Water hose streams should not be used because the impact of the water stream can lift enough dust into the air to produce a strong dust explosion. In addition, water reacting with aluminum can give off hydrogen.

Iron and Steel

Iron and steel usually are not considered to be combustible; however, steel in the form of fine steel wool or dust can be ignited in the presence of excess heat, such as from a torch. Steel wool is more likely to ignite when it is saturated with a flammable solvent.

There have been reports of fires in piles of steel turnings and other fine scrap that presumably contained some oil or other material that promoted self-heating. Spontaneous ignition of water-wetted borings and turnings in closed areas, such as ships' hulls, have been reported.

Radioactive Metals

Radioactive metals include those that occur naturally, such as uranium and thorium, and those that are produced artificially, such as plutonium and cobalt-60. It is important to remember, however, that radioactivity cannot be altered by fire, and radiation will continue wherever the radioactive metal spreads during a fire. Due to radioactive contamination, smoke from fires involving radioactive materials frequently causes more property damage than the fire.

Uranium

Uranium generally is handled in such massive forms that it does not present a significant fire risk unless exposed to a severe and prolonged external fire. In finely divided form it ignites easily, and scrap from machining operations can ignite spontaneously. Dust from grinding has ignited, even under water, and fires have occurred spontaneously in drums of coarse scrap after prolonged exposure to moist air. Machine chips, if not adequately quenched with coolant, will self-ignite and burn in air from the heat of machining.

Thorium

Powdered thorium usually is compacted into small, solid pellets. In that form it can be stored safely or converted into alloys with other metals. Improperly compacted thorium pellets have slowly generated enough heat through absorption of oxygen and nitrogen from the air to raise the temperature of a steel container to red heat. Because of its low ignition temperature, powdered thorium should not be handled in air because the friction of the particles falling through air or against the edge of a glass container can ignite the powder electrostatically. Thorium powder usually is handled in a helium or argon atmosphere.

Plutonium

Plutonium can be ignited more easily than uranium. Normally it is handled by remote control under an inert gas or dry air atmosphere. In finely divided form, such as dusts and chips, plutonium is subject to spontaneous ignition in moist air.

Plutonium metal is never exposed intentionally to water, in part because of fire considerations. Plutonium, which ignites spontaneously, normally is allowed to burn under conditions limiting both fire and radiological contamination spread.

Bibliography

Cote, A. E., ed., *Fire Protection Handbook*, 17th edition, National Fire Protection Association, Quincy, MA, 1991. Section 3, Chapter 13, "Metals," is a comprehensive resource on the fire hazards of metals; the safeguards to observe in their processing, storage, and handling; and the fire extinguishing methods that can be used. Section 5, Chapter 21, describes the many different extinguishing agents that can be used on combustible metal, or Class D, fires.

Linville, J. L., ed., *Industrial Fire Hazards Handbook,* 3rd edition, National Fire Protection Association, Quincy, MA, 1990. Chapter 30 explains in detail the hazards involved in machining various metals and the safeguards that can be applied against fire hazards.

Purington, R. G., and Patterson, H. W., *Handling Radiation Emergencies,* National Fire Protection Association, Quincy, MA, 1977. A guide to handling fire emergencies involving radioactive materials in all forms.

NFPA Codes, Standards, and Recommended Practices

NFPA 65, *Standard for the Processing and Finishing of Aluminum.* Covers safety requirements for operations where fine aluminum dust or powder is liberated.

NFPA 480, *Standard for the Storage, Handling, and Processing of Magnesium Solids and Powders.* Gives guidance on measures that can be taken to control the fire and explosion hazards in the storage, handling, and processing of magnesium and magnesium alloys.

NFPA 481, *Standard for the Production, Processing, Handling, and Storage of Titanium.* Covers the properties and characteristics of titanium including sponge production, melting powder, scrap production, and mill operations.

NFPA 482, *Standard for the Production, Processing, Handling, and Storage of Zirconium.* Contains information on the fire and explosion hazards of zirconium and the fire prevention and protection practices, such as dust collection and the disposal of zirconium scrap, that can be taken to control the hazards.

NFPA 651, *Standard for the Manufacture of Aluminum Powder.* Covers the manufacture of aluminum and magnesium flakes, powders, pastes, or atomized granules and explosive aluminum or magnesium alloys.

CHAPTER 39

Chemicals

*W*hen chemicals are involved, safe and effective fire control measures require a knowledge of their hazardous properties. For the purpose of this discussion, chemicals are classified according to their combustibility, instability, reactivity with air or water, corrosivity, toxicity, oxidizing capability, and radioactivity.

Solid Combustible Chemicals

Several chemicals are solids at room temperature and are hazardous due to their combustibility.

Aluminum and Magnesium

These metals, when in finely divided form—that is, when powdered—have the potential to be severe fire and dust explosion hazards. They are easily ignited, and the fire can only be controlled with special extinguishing agents.

Carbon Black

Carbon black is most hazardous immediately after it is manufactured. After thorough cooling and aging, it will not ignite spontaneously, although it can generate heat in the presence of oxidizable oils.

Nitroaniline

This combustible solid melts at 298°F and has a flash point of 309°F. Explosive decomposition can occur during a fire.

Nitrochlorbenzenes

These isomers melt between 90°F and 183°F and have a flash point of 261°F. Its combustion byproducts are toxic.

Sulfides

Most sulfides are easily ignited as they liberate hydrogen sulfide with water. Phosphorus pentasulfide can ignite spontaneously in the presence of moisture as it decomposes. Phosphorus sesquisulfide is highly flammable, with an ignition temperature of 212°F.

Sulfur

Molten sulfur has a flash point of 405°F and an ignition temperature of 450°F. If impure it can liberate toxic and flammable hydrogen sulfide. Finely divided sulfur dust is an explosion hazard. Sulfur also forms explosive mixtures with powerful oxidizers such as chlorates and perchlorates.

Naphthalene

This chemical is combustible in both the solid and liquid forms, and its vapor and dust form explosive mixtures with air.

Some solids are likely to cause a fire or explosion through friction, absorption of moisture, or exposure to air or moderate heat. Some such chemicals, though by no means all, are listed in Table 39-1.

Unstable Chemicals

Certain chemicals spontaneously polymerize or decompose with the liberation of heat when contaminated or even when pure. Such reactions can become violent.

Acetaldehyde

Acetaldehyde forms explosive peroxides when exposed to oxygen from the air. Aldehyde also can undergo an addition-type reaction with certain catalysts, and the reaction can be dangerous.

Table 39-1. Typical oxidizing materials.

Bromates	Nitrates
Chlorates	Perchlorates
Chlorites	Peroxides
Hypochlorites	Permanganates
Hydrosulfites	Persulfates

Ethylene Oxide

Ethylene oxide can polymerize or decompose violently when catalyzed by iron rust, aluminum, alkali metal hydroxides, and anhydrous chlorides of iron, tin, or aluminum. It also reacts vigorously with alcohols, organic and inorganic acids, and ammonia.

Hydrogen Cyanide

This chemical is both highly flammable and poisonous, and the liquid can polymerize explosively. The flash point is 0°F, and the explosive range is from 5.6 to 40%.

Nitromethane

Nitromethane decomposes violently at 599°F and 915 psig. There have been industrial accidents in which undiluted nitromethane was detonated by shock at room temperature.

Organic Peroxides

These materials are combustible and can decompose. Heat, shock, or even friction can cause many organic peroxides to decompose explosively. As a result, most organic peroxides are shipped, stored, and handled with inert diluents to reduce their decomposition potential.

Styrene

The polymerization reaction of styrene increases as temperature increases. Eventually, the reaction can become violent unless it is controlled

Water and Air-Reactive Chemicals

The heat liberated during the reactions of certain chemicals with air or water can be great enough to ignite nearby combustibles.

Alkalies

Caustics or alkalies, although noncombustible, can react with water and generate enough heat to ignite combustibles.

Alkylaluminums

These compounds are pyrophoric—that is, they ignite spontaneously on exposure to air—and react violently with water. As a result, they generally are found in solutions with hydrocarbon solvents.

Anhydrides

Acid anhydrides are compounds of acids from which the water has been removed. They react with water, sometimes violently, to regenerate acids.

Carbide

Carbides of some metals react explosively on contact with water. Calcium carbide reacts with water to produce acetylene, and, without careful control, the heat of reaction will ignite the acetylene.

Charcoal

Under some conditions, charcoal reacts with air at a rate that will cause the charcoal to ignite.

Hydrides

Metal hydrides react with water to form hydrogen gas, which may be ignited by the heat of reaction.

Oxides

Oxides of some metals and nonmetals react with water to form alkalies and acids, respectively. Calcium oxide, or quicklime, reacts vigorously with water and liberates enough heat to cause some combustible to ignite.

Phosphorus

There are two forms of phosphorus. White phosphorus is pyrophoric and extremely toxic. Red phosphorus, although less hazardous, is combustible and can be converted to the white form under fire conditions

Sodium Hydrosulfite

On contact with moisture from the air, sodium hydrosulfite heats spontaneously and can ignite nearby combustibles.

Corrosive Materials

Corrosive materials have a destructive effect on living tissues. While some are oxidizers, they are classified separately to emphasize their injurious effect on contact or inhalation.

Inorganic Acid

Concentrated aqueous solutions of the inorganic acids—sulphuric, nitric, and hydrochloric—are not combustible. The chief hazard is the danger of leakage and possible mixture with other chemicals or combustible materials nearby, which could create a serious fire or explosion hazard.

Halogens

The chemicals of the halogen family—fluorine, chlorine, bromine, and iodine—differ from each other, with their fire hazard potential decreasing in the order listed. Halogens are noncombustible and act as oxiders. They are also toxic chemicals.

Toxic Chemicals

Most chemicals are not considered toxic unless taken orally or inhaled in relatively large quantities. However, a few can cause serious illness or death when they come in contact with the body or when they are swallowed or inhaled in small quantities. Gases and vapors that are dangerous to life when mixed in small amounts in air are considered to be extremely dangerous poisons. These chemicals are listed in Table 39-3.

Table 39-2. Typical corrosives.

Antimony pentachloride	Hydrofluoric acid
Benzoyl chloride	Nitric acid
Bromine	Oleum
Chlorine	Perchloric acid (under 72%)
Chlorine trifluoride	Sodium hydroxide (caustic soda)
Chromic acid	Sulfur chloride
Fluorine	Sulfur trioxide
Hydrochloric acid	Sulfuric acid
Chlorosulfonic acid	

Table 39-3. Typical toxic chemicals and conditions for the greatest hazard.

Dangerous when small amounts are mixed in air:

Acrolein	Germane
Aluminum phosphide	Hydrogen cyanide
Boron trifluoride	Hydrogen sulfide
Choloropicrin	Methyl bromide
Cyanogen	Nickel carbonyl
Diborane	Phosgene
Fluorine	Phosphine

Dangerous toxins that are hazardous when taken orally or on contact:

Acrylonitrile	Endrin
Allyl alcohol	Ethyleneimine
Antimony pentafluoride	Methyl hydrazine
Arsenic compounds	Nicotine
Arsine	Nitrobenzene
Bromine pentafluoride	Nitrochlorobenzene
Chlorine	Parathion
Cyanides	Phenol (carbolic acid)
Diketene	Stibine
Dimethylhydrazine	Tetraethyl lead
Dimethyl sulfate	Thionyl chloride

Oxidizing Chemicals

Most oxidizing chemicals are not combustible, but they can increase the ease of ignition of combustible materials and will increase the intensity of burning. Some oxidizing agents are susceptible to spontaneous decomposition. However, most are stable unless they are contaminated. If they are contaminated by organics, many of them can spontaneously ignite and may undergo explosive reactions.

Nitrates

Inorganic nitrates are widely used in fertilizers, salt baths, and other industrial applications. When exposed to fire, they can melt and release

Table 39-4. Typical combustible solids and conditions for the greatest hazard.

Danger from heating due to absorption of moisture:

Alkylaluminums	Phosphorous pentasulfide
Aluminum chloride	Potassium
Aluminum dust	Potassium peroxide
Calcium	Sodium
Calcium carbide	Sodium hydride
Calcium oxide	Sodium hydrosulfite
Lithium	Sodium peroxide
Lithium hydride	Tricholorisocyanuric acid
Magnesium (finely divided)	Zinc dust

Dangerous in air:

Diborane	Phosphorous (white)
Diethyl ether	Sodium hydride
Lithium	Zirconium dust

Danger from subjection to heat:

Antimony pentasulfide	Dinitrobenzene
Calcium	Phosphorus pentasulfide
Cellulose nitrate	Phosphorus sesquisulfide
Dinitroaniline	
All oxidizers when mixed with	
combustible or organic material.	

oxygen, causing the fire to intensify. Molten nitrates will react violently with organic materials. Solid streams of water used to fight nitrate fires may produce steam explosions. In addition, most nitrates are water-soluble, and a solution of nitrates absorbed by a combustible material makes that material extremely easy to ignite once it has dried.

Nitric Acid

Although nitric acid generally is considered a corrosive, it will markedly increase the ease with which an organic material that comes in contact with it or its vapors ignites. The use of even dilute nitric acid solutions to clean organic residue from equipment can lead to an explosion.

Nitrites

Nitrites are more active than nitrates as oxidizing agents. Mixtures with combustible substances should not be subjected to the heat of a flame. Certain nitrites, notably ammonium nitrite, are explosive by themselves and must be avoided.

Inorganic Peroxides

Sodium, potassium, and strontium peroxides react vigorously with water and release oxygen and large amounts of heat. If organic or other oxidizable material is present when such a reaction takes place, a fire or explosion is likely to occur.

Mixtures of barium peroxide and combustible or readily oxidizable materials are explosive. They are easily ignited by friction or a small amount of water.

Hydrogen peroxide is a strong oxidizing agent that can cause combustible materials with which it remains in contact to ignite, especially at concentrations above 35%. Contamination of a storage tank containing hydrogen peroxide can result in an explosion. At a concentration above about 92%, hydrogen peroxide can be exploded by shock.

Chlorates

When heated, chlorates liberate oxygen more readily than do nitrates. When mixed with combustible materials, they can ignite or explode spontaneously. Drums containing chlorates can explode when heated.

Chlorites

Sodium chlorite is a powerful oxidizing agent that forms explosive mixtures with combustible materials. When it comes in contact with strong acids, it releases explosive chlorine dioxide gas. Chlorites decompose explosively at lower temperatures than chlorates.

Dichromates

Among the dichromates, most of which are noncombustible, ammonium dichromate is the most hazardous. It may explode on contact with organic materials, and it decomposes at 338°F, releasing nitrogen gas. Closed containers rupture at the decomposition temperature. Other dichromates release oxygen when heated and react readily with oxidizable materials.

Hypochlorites

Calcium hypochlorite can cause combustible organic materials to ignite on contact. When heated, it gives off oxygen. It is sold as a bleaching powder and, when concentrated, as a swimming pool disinfectant.

Perchlorates

Perchlorates contain one more oxygen atom than chlorates do. They have similar properties, but perchlorates are more stable than chlorates. Ammonium perchlorate has great explosive sensitivity when contaminated with an oxidizable impurity. The pure material in finely divided form is classified as an explosive.

Permanganates

Mixtures of inorganic permanganates and combustible material can be ignited by friction, or they may ignite spontaneously in the presence of an inorganic acid.

Persulfates

These are strong oxidizing agents that can explode during a fire. An explosion can also follow an accidental mixture of a persulfate with a combustible material.

Bibliography

Cote, A. E., ed., *Fire Protection Handbook,* 17th edition, National Fire Protection Association, Quincy, MA, 1991.

Linville, J. L., ed., *Industrial Fire Hazards Handbook,* 3rd edition, National Fire Protection Association, Quincy, MA, 1990.

NFPA Codes, Standards, and Recommended Practices

NFPA 43A, *Code for the Storage of Liquid and Solid Oxidizers.* Recommends practices for reducing fire and explosion hazards of liquid and solid oxidizing materials in storage.

NFPA 43B, *Code for the Storage of Organic Peroxide Formulations.* Covers the basic requirements for commercially available organic peroxide formulations in approved packages, including segregated storage, cutoff storage, and detached storage.

NFPA 45, *Standard on Fire Protection for Laboratories Using Chemicals.* Provides basic requirements for protection of life and property in laboratory work areas where hazardous chemicals are handled.

NFPA 49, *Hazardous Chemicals Data.* Provides data involving chemicals that are health hazards, have a reactivity rating, or pose unusual storage or fire fighting problems.

NFPA 490, *Code for the Storage of Ammonium Nitrate.* Outlines safe storage procedures for fertilizer-grade ammonium nitrate in the form of crystals, flakes, grains, or prills.

NFPA 491M, *Manual of Hazardous Chemical Reactions.* Contains information about more than 3,500 potentially dangerous chemical reactions.

NFPA 495, *Explosive Materials Code.* Provides regulations for safety in the manufacture, storage, transportation, and use of explosives and blasting agents commonly used in mining, quarrying, road building, harbor improvement, and similar operations.

NFPA 655, *Standard for Prevention of Sulfur Fires and Explosions.* Discusses methods of eliminating or reducing hazards encountered in the crushing and pulverizing bulk and liquid sulfur.

NFPA 704, *Standard System for the Identification of the Fire Hazards of Materials.* Describes the key method of marking containers to indicate the relative reactivity, flammability, and health hazards of materials in storage.

NFPA 801, *Recommended Fire Protection Practice for Facilities Handling Radioactive Materials.* Covers practices aimed at reducing the risk of fire or explosion and minimizing the associated damage by radioactive contamination.

NFPA 802, *Recommended Fire Protection Practice for Nuclear Research and Production Reactors.* Provides recommendations for the safe design, construction, operation, and protection of nuclear research facilities.

NFPA 803, *Standard for Fire Protection for Light Water Nuclear Power Plants.* Provides fire safety guidelines for light water nuclear electric generating facilities, including operating personnel, equipment, and operations.

CHAPTER 40

Plastics and Rubber

*P*lastics and rubber are all part of the family of materials called polymers, which are now found throughout society in innumerable variations. Almost all are combustible to some extent, and some burn with extreme rapidity, producing large amounts of dense smoke. In most instances, it is impossible to determine the burning characteristics of a material simply by looking at it. Because the product appears in so many variations and its uses are so diverse, this chapter cannot present more than general guidelines that will tell you what to look for and how to take the proper fire safety precautions. You may have to refer to the handbooks, codes, and standards that are listed in the bibliography to obtain specific information on protection for a particular application.

General Uses

Small amounts of plastics and rubber are seldom of concern—one styrofoam cup is hardly significant. However, stacks of polystyrene foam stored in a warehouse could overpower a sprinkler system that has not been designed for the hazard. In general terms, plastics being stored and used need the same protection that similar amounts and arrangements of wood, cardboard, paper, fiberboard, natural fabrics, and other common cellulosic materials do. Their burning rates often are similar, but some materials and situations warrant extraordinary protective measures.

Foam plastic and foam rubber tend to burn faster and more intensely, generating more smoke and toxic gases, than other forms of the same polymer. Inhibitors, or flame retardants, can slow ignition or flaming, but these additives or other treatments are generally ineffectual in a fully developed fire. Ordinary sprinkler protection might be inadequate to protect lives or the building.

When used as wall and ceiling insulation in buildings, foam plastics—typically rigid polyurethane, polyisocyanurate, and polystyrene—must be completely covered on the inside of the building by a fire-resistant barrier, such as gypsum wallboard 1/2 inch or thicker. This is true even if the material has a low flame-spread rating under standard test procedures. Consult NFPA *101, Life Safety Code,* and the local building code for details.

Foam rubber and foam plastics in mattresses and furniture cushions can be of concern where people sleep, particularly in institutional occupancies. The cigarette ignition resistance of mattresses and mattress pads is controlled by Part 1632, *Code of Federal Regulations,* Title 16. Title 16 also contains standards for the flammability of clothing textiles, vinyl plastic film, children's sleepwear, and carpets and rugs.

NFPA 260, *Standard Methods of Tests and Classification System for Cigarette Ignition Resistance of Components of Upholstered Furniture,* provides a Class I designation for components that meet the test criteria. The Upholstered Furniture Action Council has adopted this standard as part of a voluntary industry program to reduce the liklihood of cigarette ignition in upholstered furniture. The program requires that a Class I barrier be provided between nonconforming, or Class II, fabrics and conventional polyurethane cushions.

Cellulose nitrate, also known as nitrocellulose or pyroxylin, is recognized as one of the most hazardous plastics: It begins to decompose dangerously at relatively low temperatures. Special rules have been written for its storage and handling (see NFPA 40, *Standard for the Storage and Handling of Cellulose Nitrate Motion Picture Film,* and 40E, *Code for the Storage of Pyroxylin Plastic*).

When you have questions about the hazard of the material or product, you can rely on the standard fire test methods that are valid for the application. A number of tests are commonly used, either singly or in combination. However, one of them—the Steiner Tunnel Test, ASTM E84, which typically is used to evaluate the surface burning characteristics of interior finish materials—may not give a true indication of the actual hazard presented by many plastics. See the *Fire Protection Handbook* for more detailed information. The results of small-scale, "bunsen burner" tests are often suspect when dealing with large amounts of plastic because the small flame does not simulate the much greater intensity of the fire exposure under real-life conditions.

Some general guidelines can be given for situations often encountered. Plastic glazing materials, such as Plexiglas®, Lucite®, and polycarbonates, should not be used in applications where their combustibility is objectionable or where a fire rating is required. This precludes the use of plastic glazing in fire walls, fire doors, fire-rated corridor partitions, and smoke barriers.

Thin plastic laminates, such as Formica® and vinyl wall covering, can be considered to take on the burning characteristics of the substrate to which they are applied. For example, they would be low on gypsum wall board or metal, moderate on wood particle board, and high on foam plastic. If in doubt, you should ask for documentation of the flame-spread rating that has been developed under such test methods as the ASTM E 84 tunnel test. The tunnel test, by itself, is not adequate to evaluate the burning characteristics of foam plastics.

In air plenums and some other applications, the flammability of the plastic insulation on wiring that is not in a conduit is now often limited by code. Typically, however, polyvinyl chloride, polyethylene, and other commonly used plastics pose an insignificant hazard in this application. This is not the case where many cables are grouped or bunched together, as they are in cable trays and cable chases extending vertically through a building. Self-propagating fires can occur under such conditions, with serious consequences in such occupancies as power plants, large computer installations, and telephone exchanges. Special protection, such as fire stops at floor and fire wall openings, special coatings on the wiring, special flame-resistant insulation, and so on, might be necessary in these situtations.

Because plastics and rubber are Class A materials, water-type fire extinguishers and hose lines are appropriate for fire fighting. Halon and multipurpose extinguishers are suitable when used in accordance with their labeling.

Warehousing

In warehouses, the often intense fires that can develop rapidly in concentrations of plastics and rubber require the installation of specially engineered, high-density automatic sprinkler systems and, at times, other measures, such as smoke and heat vents. You should verify that the fire protection plan takes into account storage of large quantities of items such as rubber tires, plastic packing materials, and plastic insulating materials.

NFPA 231, *Standard for General Storage,* and NFPA 231C, *Standard for Rack Storage of Materials,* are especially useful for evaluating the potential hazards of different types of combustible materials stored in warehouses. Plastics and rubber are divided into three groups according to their potential for creating difficult-to-extinguish fires in stored products, as indicated in Table 40-1. Four commodity classifications are established, as follows:

- Class I encompasses essentially noncombustible products in paper or cardboard cartons or wrappings, with or without wooden pallets.
- Class II is composed of Class I products in wooden or multilayer cardboard containers, with or without pallets.
- Class III contains wood, paper, or natural cloth products or Group C plastics, with or without pallets. A limited amount of Group A or B plastics may also be included.
- Class IV is composed of any of the above, with an appreciable amount of Group A or B plastics in ordinary corrugated cartons or with Group A or B plastic packing, with or without pallets.

Table 40-1 Classification of Plastics and Rubber

Group A
Acrylonitrile-butadiene-styrene copolymer (ABS)
Acrylic (polymethyl methacrylate)
Acetal (polyformaldehyde)
Butyl rubber
Ethylene-propylene rubber (EPDM)
Fiberglass reinforced polyester (FRP)
Natural rubber (if expanded)
Nitrile rubber (acrylonitrile-butadiene rubber)
Polybutadiene
Polycarbonate
Polyester elastomer
Polyethylene
Polypropylene
Polystyrene

(Continued)

Table 40-1. *(Continued)*

Polyurethane
Polyvinyl chloride (PVC—highly plasticized; for example, coated fabric, unsupported film)
Styrene acrylonitrile (SAN)
Styrene-butadiene rubber (SRB)
Thermoplastic polyester (PET)

Group B
Cellulosics (cellulose acetate, cellulose acetate butyrate, ethyl cellulose)
Chloroprene rubber Fluoroplastics (ECTFE—ethylene-chlorotrifluoroethylene copolymer;
    ETFE—ethylene-tetrafluoroethylene copolymer; FEP—fluorinated ethylene-propylene
    copolymer)
Natural rubber (not expanded)
Nylon (nylon 6, nylon 6/6)
Silicone rubber

Group C
Fluoroplastics (PCTFE—polychlorotrifluoroethylene; PTFE—polytetrafluoroethylene)
Melamine (melamine formaldehyde)
Phenolic Polyvinyl chloride (PVC—rigid or lightly plasticized; for example, pipe, pipe
    fittings)
Polyvinylidene chloride (PVDC)
Polyvinyl fluoride (PVF)
Polyvinylidene fluoride (PVDF)
Urea (urea formaldehyde)

Note: These categories are based on unmodified plastic materials. The use of fire- or flame-retarding modifiers or the physical form of the material may change the classification.

More detailed specifics on the proper classification for different commodities can be found in NFPA 231 and NFPA 231C. Additional guidance for the hazard presented by individual elastomeric materials is available in Chapter 34 of this book, in the *Chemical Safety Data Sheets* issued by the manufacturers of plastics, and in Factory Mutual data sheets.

Manufacturing and Fabrication

In factories that produce plastics or plastic products, the operations are divided into three general categories, synthesizing, conversion, and fabrication. Each of these has special fire problems you must take into consideration.

Synthesizing, or manufacturing, is the mixing of the basic plastic materials, or feedstock. Sometimes coloring agents or other substances are added. Conversion is the process of molding, extruding, or casting the plastic so that it will flow into a shape it will retain after cooling. Considerable heat is required for both of these processes.

Fabricating includes bending, machining, cementing, decorating, and polishing plastic, sometimes using other materials that might be flammable or reactive. For example, the thermoplastic ABS is a combination of acrylonitrile, butadiene, and styrene. Two of these materials are low flash-point flammable liquids, and the third is a gas with an ignition temperature of 804°F. A molding process might be used to combine a flammable resin with nonflammable glass fibers or with heat-resistant silicones.

Among the hazards to be considered for each of these operations are combustible dusts, flammable solvents, electrical faults, hydraulic fluids, and the storage and handling of large quantities of combustible raw materials and finished products. To help you evaluate a given situation, you can refer to the standards and to other documents published by NFPA, Underwriters Laboratories, Inc., Factory Mutual Research Corporation, and many other reliable sources of technical information.

Suspensions of plastics and rubber dusts in air form explosive mixtures, as is the case for organic materials in general. Special explosion prevention measures must be taken to prevent ignition or to minimize the dust concentrations in manufacturing and fabricating operations (see Chapter 37 in this book).

In the plastics manufacturing process, thermoplastic compounds usually are melted by heat, then forced into a mold or die for shaping. In their original state, these compounds can be in the form of pellets, granules, flakes, or powder, and each of these forms can produce dust.

Thermosetting resins may be in the form of a liquid or a partially polymerized molding compound. Considerable heat is needed to mold either form.

Other manufacturing processes include blow molding, which produces hollow products, such as bottles, gas tanks, and carboys, and calendering, the process of converting thermoplastics into film or sheeting or applying a plastic coating to textiles or other materials. Casting uses thermoplastics or thermosets to make products by pouring the hot liquid into a mold, then letting it cool until it is solid. In coating, thermoplastic or thermo-

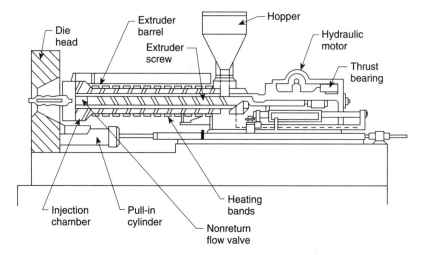

Figure 40-1. Diagram of a reciprocating screw injection molding machine in which plastic pellets are compacted, melted, and injected into a die, where the molten plastic is allowed to cool and harden. (Society of the Plastics Industry)

setting materials are applied to metal, wood, paper, glass, fabric, or ceramics. In compounding, additives are mixed with resins by kneading mixers or screw extruders. Compression molding uses heat and pressure to squeeze or press material into a certain shape, while extrusion uses a screw thread or some other form of propulsion to shape a thermoplastic material into a continuous sheet, film, rod, cable, cord, or other product. Foam plastics molding uses foam plastics in casting, calendering, coating, or rotational molding. High-pressure laminating uses heat and pressure to join materials. Injection molding involves the impinging of two or more high-pressure reactive streams in a mixing chamber, then injecting the mixture into a mold. Reinforced plastics processing combines resins with reinforcing materials. Rotational molding involves the movement of powdered plastic or molding granules in a moving, heated container. Transfer molding is the curing of thermosetting plastics in a mold under heat and pressure.

Molding and extrusion operations require temperatures of 300°F to 650°F, depending on the plastic being processed. Because the upper temperatures are beyond the practical use of heat-transfer fluids, electrical-resistance heating is most commonly used. Sometimes, however, controllers do not operate correctly, and the temperatures become excessive. If plastic feedstock is allowed to remain in equipment, it might decompose under excessive or prolonged temperatures and release combustible gases. To reduce this hazard, the molding and extruding areas should be cleaned frequently.

In all of these operations, the potential fire danger is influenced by the temperatures reached in these processes, the fire characteristics of the solids and liquids used, the type of portable and automatic fire extinguishing equipment, and the condition of manual and automatic fire alarms. Sources of heat include the equipment's operating temperatures, the electrical equipment and wiring, static sparks, friction, matches, and smoking materials.

Static sparks are common in plastic manufacturing because plastics are good electrical insulators. The movement of film across rolls or guides can generate sparks, as can transmission belts. The hazard is reduced if the equipment is correctly grounded and tinsel conductors are used on moving films or filaments.

Another potential ignition source are the temperatures reached in hydraulic systems for clamping molds or providing pressure to the rams

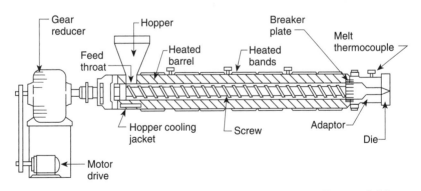

Figure 40-2. A basic single-screw extruder in which plastic pellets are fed from a hopper, driven forward, and melted. The molten plastic is fed through the adapter into the die. (Society of the Plastics Industry)

or screws that force plastic by compression, transfer, or injection molding. These temperatures might exceed the ignition temperature of some petroleum fluids.

Fire Protection

The burning of plastics is influenced considerably by their physical form. Molding pellets in bulk storage will burn differently than certain finished products, such as containers, polyvinyl envelopes, or insulated cables. Dust and some granules can flare rapidly on the surface of equipment, but a solid compound in a mold might be easy to extinguish.

In most situations, water is the most appropriate extinguishing agent for fires involving plastics, and it should be available in large quantities. A plastics manufacturing plant should be equipped with automatic sprinklers, standpipe and hose systems, water-type portable extinguishers, and perhaps special automatic extinguishing systems for flammable liquids and electrical fires. Because of the many variables involved in plastics and their fire behavior, the arrangement of fixed extinguishing and explosion-suppression systems and of portable extinguishing equipment should be designed specifically for each plant.

If large quantities of stored plastics are exposed to fire, fire fighters should direct hose streams onto them to cool them and prevent them from melting into the more flammable liquid state. At the same time, they must be careful not to agitate any dust that may be in the area, be it plastic dust, wood dust, or some other type of dust.

When a fire involves plastics, the potential for dense, noxious smoke must be considered, and the fire area should be evacuated. The fire officer in charge of responding fire fighters must be told immediately of the respiratory hazards and the need for protective breathing apparatus.

Bibliography

Cote, A. E., ed., *Fire Protection Handbook,* 17th edition, National Fire Protection Association, Quincy, MA, 1991.

Fire Protection Guide on Hazardous Materials, 9th edition, National Fire Protection Association, Quincy, MA, 1986. This publication contains NFPA 49, NFPA 325M, NFPA 491M, and NFPA 704 and related commentary that can be used to identify the hazardous properties of most of the chemicals in commerical use today.

Linville, J. L., ed., *Industrial Fire Hazards Handbook,* 3rd edition, National Fire Protection Association, Quincy, MA, 1990. A comprehensive description of industrial fire risks, life safety from fire, and general and specific fire hazards in a large variety of industrial manufacturing, processing, and assembly plants.

Standard Test Method for Surface Burning Characteristics of Building Materials, ASTM E 84, American Society for Testing and Materials, New York, NY.

NFPA Codes, Standards, and Recommended Practices

NFPA 40, *Standard for the Storage and Handling of Cellulose Nitrate Motion Picture Film.* Provides data on film cabinets, vaults, archival vaults, projection rooms, and film exchanges.

NFPA 40E, *Code for the Storage of Pyroxylin Plastic.* Covers safe storage in manufacturing buildings, warehouses, jobbing shops, and retail outlets.

NFPA 49, *Hazardous Chemicals Data.* Provides data involving chemicals that are a health hazard, have a reactivity rating, or present an unusual storage or fire fighting problem.

NFPA 69, *Standard on Explosion Prevention Systems.* A description of the equipment and systems needed to keep oxidant and combustible concentrations below hazardous levels. Discusses the functions, inspection, and maintenance of explosion-suppression systems and the requirements for inert gas systems.

NFPA 70, *National Electrical Code.* Contains requirements for all standard types of electrical installations.

NFPA *101, Life Safety Code.* Addresses construction, protection, and occupancy features necessary to minimize danger to life from fire, smoke, fumes, and panic. Identifies criteria for designing egress facilities to permit prompt escape from buildings or into safe areas within a building.

NFPA 325M, *Fire Hazard Properties of Flammable Liquids, Gases, and Volatile Solids.* Summary of available data on the fire hazard properties of more than 1,600 substances.

NFPA 491M, *Manual of Hazardous Chemical Reactions.* Describes more than 3,500 potentially dangerous chemical reactions.

NFPA 654, *Standard for the Prevention of Fire and Dust Explosions in the Chemical, Dye, Pharmaceutical, and Plastics Industries.* Describes the classification and hazardous ratings of plastics; practical measures of building construction, area segregation, and venting; methods of preventing explosions and minimizing damage to equipment; and fire protection needed for buildings and apparatus.

NFPA 704, *Standard System for the Identification of the Fire Hazards of Materials.* Describes key method of marking containers to indicate the relative reactivity, flammability, and health hazards of materials in storage.

CHAPTER 41

Explosives and Blasting Agents

*T*o maintain an effective level of fire protection in a plant that manufactures, or transports explosive materials, you must examine the entire plant, know the characteristics of the materials in it, and correct hazardous situations. Your task is to find, identify, and correct or remove all factors that are dangerous. If you are inspecting plants or motor terminals where explosives are present, you should be concerned with general fire safety practices, and combinations of chemicals and liquids that have a wide range of sensitivity, potential flame, and explosive power. You should also know about the extent and efficiency of existing fire protection and the plans for controlling fires or explosions. You should stress to plant personnel the importance of good safety, housekeeping, and fire protection practices; otherwise sparks, flames, impact, or the decomposition of explosive materials could cause catastrophic destruction. You should be familiar with codes and standards on explosive materials. (See Bibliography).

Definitions

To understand potential problems, you should be familiar with the terms and definitions that apply to explosive materials. The following are brief definitions of some important terminology.

Blasting Agent: A material or mixture intended for blasting that is mixed or made to have sufficient insensitivity to shock, fire, sparks, electrostatic effects, impact, and exposure to heat.

Explosive: A chemical compound, mixture, or device whose primary or common function is to create an explosion, or which, by chemical reaction within itself, is able to function in a similar manner.

Composite Propellants: A mixture of an oxidizer with an elastomeric fuel compound that is used in gas generators and rocket motors.

Detonating Cord: A flexible cord that contains a center core of high explosive, which is used to initiate other explosives.

Detonator: Any device for initiating detonation.

High Explosive Materials: Materials that produce a high rate of reaction, high-pressure development, and a detonation wave in the explosion.

Low Explosive Materials: Materials that produce deflagration or a low rate of reaction and pressure.

Oxidizing Materials: Any solid or liquid that readily yields oxygen or other oxidizing gas that readily reacts to oxidize combustible materials.

Propellant: An explosive that normally functions by deflagration and normally is used for propulsion.

Primer: A unit, package, or cartridge of explosive material with a detonator or detonating cord attached to a detonator, which is used to initiate blasting agents or other explosives.

Sensitivity: The tendency of explosive material to detonate on receiving impact, shock, flame, heat, or other influence that can cause explosive decomposition.

Special Industrial Explosive Materials: Shaped materials, sheet forms and other extrusions, pellets, and packages of high explosives used in metal fabrication and for reducing scrap metal.

Water Gel: Any explosive or blasting agent that contains a substantial portion of water.

In addition to these you should understand the classification of explosives as defined in the Hazardous Materials Regulations of the U.S. Department of Transportation. These are:

Division 1.1: Explosives for which the major hazard is mass explosion. It includes, but is not limited to, detonating materials, since some substances, such as black powder, deflagrate violently. This division corresponds closely to the old Class A. Examples include: dynamite, desensitized nitroglycerin, lead azide, mercury fulminate, black powder, some detonators, and boosters.

Division 1.2: Explosives for which the major hazard is dangerous projections, such as fragments. This division has no clear-cut equivalent in the traditional U.S. classification scheme. Examples include certain types of ammunition and explosive components and devices.

Division 1.3: Explosives for which the major hazard is radiant heat or violent burning, but for which there is no blast or projection hazard. This division corresponds closely with the old Class B. Examples include propellants such as smokeless powder.

Division 1.4: Low hazard explosives with no mass explosion hazard and no projection of fragments with appreciable size or range. This division corresponds closely with the old Class C. It includes articles containing division 1.1, or 1.3 or both, materials in limited quantities, such as small arms ammunition.

Division 1.5: A detonable explosive material with acceptably low sensitivity to shock, heating under confinement, fire, and incendiary sparks. This division corresponds closely with the old blasting agent classification.

Division 1.6: Explosive articles containing extremely insensitive explosive substances. This division has no clear-cut equivalent in the traditional U.S. classification system. It includes certain specialized ordnance items.

Forbidden explosives: Explosives for which transportation is forbidden because of instability, high sensitivity to various stimuli, incompatibility of components, or other reasons. It also includes any explosive, regardless of properties, that has not been approved by DOT for transportation.

Mixing Plants and Vehicles

Certain principles of fire safety are common to every area of manufacture, transportation, and storage of explosive materials. Each area and its equipment should be clean and free of deposits of the materials. Matches and other smoking materials cannot be permitted in the area. Buildings must be made of noncombustible materials or of sheet metal on wood studs. Floors must be made of concrete or some other nonabsorbent material. Portable fire extinguishers and other appropriate equipment should be fully charged and readily available. Primers and detonators should be kept separate from the explosive materials.

In addition to these principles, you, as an inspector, will have to consider the less obvious weaknesses or violations of fire safety, such as the relative cleanliness and order of the building interior and the work stations. Check to see if aisle space and other passageways are clear of obstructions. Note whether there are accumulations of cloth, paper, or other combustibles and whether there are residues of flammable liquid or grease on equipment or the floor. Watch for accumulations of dust on walls and equipment. Check the heating equipment to verify that it does not produce flame or sparks inside the building.

Verify that portable fire extinguishers have been inspected and charged within the last year and are at their designated locations. Inspect the systems of automatic extinguishing or explosion-suppression equipment to make certain that they are in good condition and ready to operate. Observe how unopened and emptied containers are stored and used, and look into the emptied containers to see if they have residues of hazardous products.

Examine all electrical outlets and operating machinery for possible misuse or overloading, and check the main board for condition of fuses and circuit breakers.

Observe how containers are arranged and handled in the storage and shipping areas and check how vehicles and lifting equipment are operated. Watch particularly for containers or spills of oil or other flammable liquids.

You should also check conditions in areas used for manufacturing, transporting, and storing the materials.

Motor Vehicle Terminals

Explosives motor vehicle terminals include explosives interchange lots, explosives less-than-truckloads lots, maintenance shops, driver rest facilities, or a combination of these facilities. At each of these places, large quantities of sensitive explosive materials are brought near each other and can be vandalized or accidentally set on fire. Thus, each of these places requires certain fire prevention measures.

Interchange lots should be separated by at least 100 feet from other facilities. Weeds, underbrush, vegetation, and other materials should be cleared for at least 25 feet from the lot, and adequate warning signs should be posted. Fences, gates, and security patrols should be used as backups to these measures.

Portable fire extinguishers should be placed in appropriate locations, and hoses can be connected to hydrants and standpipes. Lots should be protected by natural or artificial barricades.

At least 5 feet should separate vehicles parked side by side or back to back; these should be 25 feet between vehicles loaded with explosives.

Smoking, matches, open flames, spark-producing devices, and firearms should not be permitted within 50 feet of the lot.

Blasting Agents

Blasting agents are manufactured so that the final product is relatively insensitive; however, the materials from which they are made have their own hazards. Blasting agents consist of an oxidizer mixed with a fuel. Oxidizers are sensitive to heat, friction, impact, and impurities, so they must be processed and stored accordingly. Under fire conditions, they yield oxygen and vigorously support combustion. Ammonium nitrate, for example, is a compound produced by reacting nitric acid with ammonia, and the end product will be fertilizer grade, dynamite grade, nitrous oxide grade, or some other mixture. It is capable of detonating with about half the blast effect of explosives if it is heated under confinement that permits pressure buildup, or is subject to strong shock such as from an explosion.

Fuel oil storage must be outside the mixing plant and located so that oil will drain away from the plant if the tank ruptures, and the mixing building must be well ventilated. Check that emergency venting systems operate correctly.

Internal combustion engines used for generating electric power must be located outside the mixing building, or they must be shielded by a firewall. Spark emission can be hazardous to materials in the plant.

Mixing and packaging materials must be compatible with the composition of the blasting agent.

The flash point of No. 2 fuel oil, 125°F, is the minimum permissible for hydrocarbon liquid fuel for the agent mix.

Metal powders, such as aluminum, are sensitive to moisture, and should be secured in covered containers. And solid fuels, including metal powders, of small size create accumulated dust. The dust can be removed by vacuuming with appropriate nonsparking equipment or by washing.

There should be no drains or piping in the floor where molten materials can flow and be confined during a fire.

Empty ammonium nitrate bags must be disposed of daily in a safe manner.

The entire building should be cleaned thoroughly on a regular basis.

Smoking, matches, open flames, spark-producing devices, and firearms should not be permitted within 50 feet of the building. And the area around the plant should be cleared of brush, dried grass, leaves, and litter within at least 25 feet of the building.

Explosives should not be stored within 50 feet of the building. And those that are not in the process of being manufactured, transported, or used should be stored in appropriate magazines or in storage buildings that meet the requirements of NFPA 495, *Explosive Materials Code.*

Ammonium Nitrate

Facilities used for mixing, handling, and storing ammonium nitrate should have the same fire precautions as those used for other oxidizers. Because this compound is sensitive to contamination and heat, you, as an inspector, should watch for these two influences.

Buildings in which this compound is stored must not be taller than one story and should not have basements, unless the basement is open on one side. There should be adequate ventilation or automatic emergency venting.

All flooring in storage and handling areas must be noncombustible or protected from impregnation by ammonium nitrate. There must be no open drains, traps, tunnels, pits, or pockets where the compound can accumulate in a fire.

Containers of ammonium nitrate should not be stored if the temperature of this agent exceeds 130°F. Bags of it should be stored at least 30 inches away from building walls and partitions. Storage piles should be no higher or wider than 20 feet, and should not exceed 50 feet in length, unless the building is of noncombustible construction or protected by automatic sprinklers. Storage piles must be at least 3 feet below the roof or beams overhead. Aisles must be at least 3 feet wide with at least one service or main aisle that is at least 4 feet wide.

Bins for storing ammonium nitrate in bulk should be kept free of any contaminating materials. Aluminum or wooden bins should be used because ammonium nitrate is corrosive and reactive in combination with iron, copper, lead, and zinc. The storage should be clearly identified by signs reading "AMMONIUM NITRATE" in letters that are at least 2 inches high.

This material must not be stored in piles of excessive height. The pressure setting of the mass is affected by humidity and pellet quality as well as temperature. Temperature cycles through 90°F and high atmospheric humidity can be hazardous to this product.

Ammonium nitrate can be affected by a wide range of contaminants, including flammable liquids, organic chemicals, acids, and other substances. It is important that these contaminants be kept out of the storage building or kept at some distance, and they should be shielded from this agent.

Electrical installations must meet the requirements of NFPA 70, *National Electrical Code,* for ordinary locations, and be designed to minimize corrosive damage. Spilled materials and discarded containers must be removed and disposed of promptly. Open flames and smoking should be prohibited from these storage buildings.

Fire Protection

Areas where ammonium nitrate is stored, handled, and processed should be protected by automatic sprinkler systems. These should be supplemented by portable fire extinguishers, standpipe systems, and fire hydrants.

If fire starts in such a processing plant, the ammonium nitrate must be doused with large quantities of water until the burning is extinguished. If the fire grows beyond control, all personnel should leave the area. If the building is not automatically ventilated, it should be manually ventilated if possible. The fire should be approached from upwind because the vapors of burning ammonium nitrate are very toxic. Fire fighters should wear self-contained breathing apparatus, and persons without this protective equipment should be ordered to leave the area.

After the fire is extinguished, loose and contaminated ammonium nitrate should be dumped in water or buried, if that is acceptable to environmental authorities. The remainder can be dissolved, flushed, or scrubbed from all areas. Wet, empty bags and containers should be flushed, permitted to dry, and then burned.

Bibliography

Cote, A. E., ed., *Fire Protection Handbook,* 17th edition, National Fire Protection Association, Quincy, MA, 1991. Section 3, Chapter 9 contains data on storage distances and fire protection for explosives and blasting agents.

NFPA Codes, Standards, and Recommended Practices

NFPA 70, *National Electrical Code.* Contains the requirements for all standard types of electrical installations, including those that are essential for explosives mixing plants.

NFPA 490, *Code for the Storage of Ammonium Nitrate.* Outlines safe storage procedures for fertilizer-grade ammonium nitrate in crystals, flakes, grains, or prills.

NFPA 495, *Explosive Materials Code.* Covers security and safety, blasting agents, water gel and emulsions, transportation, aboveground storage, and other essential information.

NFPA 498, *Standard for Explosives Motor Vehicle Terminals.* Covers fire safety requirements for explosives interchange lots and less-than-truckload lots, with particular emphasis on vehicle parking, control of ignition sources, security against trespassers, and employee training.

CHAPTER 42

Fireworks and Pyrotechnics

*T*his chapter only addresses special safety considerations for the manufacture and storage of pyrotechnic materials. Normal manufacturing and chemical safety issues are covered elsewhere in this manual.

As a group, facilities that manufacture or distribute fireworks or other civilian pyrotechnic products present a special and difficult challenge to inspectors. This is because of the vast range of potential hazards associated with these products. During a fire, some pyrotechnic materials will burn with little violence, even in very large quantities, while others will explode with a force rivaling high explosives, even in relatively small quantities. Some pyrotechnic materials are difficult to ignite, making accidental ignition extremely unlikely, while others are so easily ignited that exceptional precautions must be exercised constantly during their preparation and use.

Obviously, the safety precautions needed may vary greatly from one type of facility to another and even between different areas of the same facility. For these reasons, and because it is unusual for an inspector to be familiar with the characteristics of the vast number of different pyrotechnic materials, it is important that you enlist the active cooperation and participation of the facility's safety manager.

The range of civilian pyrotechnic products is vast, and the differences in their manner of functioning is extreme. Unfortunately, NFPA 1124, *Code for the Manufacture, Transportation, and Storage of Fireworks,* and NFPA 1125, *Code for the Manufacture of Model Rocket Motors,* address only fireworks and model rocket motor manufacturing. Thus, these are the only facilities this chapter will address specifically. However, what represents safe practice for the manufacture and storage of fireworks and model rocket motors generally is applicable to the manufacture and storage of other civilian pyrotechnic products, as well.

Definitions

Civilian pyrotechnic products: These are commercial nonmilitary products deriving at least part of their energy from the burning or explosion of a pyrotechnic composition. Some examples are fireworks, model rocket motors, highway flares, signaling smoke devices, pest and predator control devices, pyrotechnic theatrical special effects, and automobile airbags.

Consumer fireworks (formerly common fireworks): Consumer fireworks are those devices intended for use by the general public where state and local laws permit. They contain limited quantities of pyrotechnic composition and include cone and cylindrical fountains, roman candles, small sky rockets, mines and shells, certain firecrackers and sparklers, and other devices (see Figure 42-1). Consumer fireworks are classified as Explosives 1.4 G (formerly Class C explosives) by the Department of Transportation (DOT). Unless specifically exempted, the devices must comply with construction, performance, labeling, and chemical composition regulations promulgated by the DOT and Consumer Product Safety Commission (CPSC).

Display fireworks (formerly special fireworks): These fireworks are larger and more powerful than consumer fireworks and are intended for use only by trained operators in outdoor displays for which the appropriate licenses or permits have been obtained. The DOT classifies display fireworks as Explosives 1.3 G (formerly Class B explosives).

Model rocket motor: This is a solid propellant motor that conforms to the standards for rocket motors as set forth in NFPA 1122, *Code for Model Rocketry* (formerly *Code for Unmanned Rockets*). Model rocket motors are classified as a Toy Propellant Device 1.4 G (formerly Class C explosives) by the DOT. By DOT exemption, however, most manufacturers may ship model rocket motors as a flammable solid.

Novelties and trick noise-makers: These items are not considered fireworks for regulatory purposes. When test data are submitted to the DOT, the DOT may classify these devices as Explosive 1.4 S, or they may not regulate them as hazardous materials at all.

Process building: A process building is any mixing building, any building in which pyrotechnic composition is pressed or otherwise prepared for finish or assembly, or any finishing or assembly building.

Pyrotechnic composition: A pyrotechnic composition is a chemical mixture containing fuel(s) and oxidizer(s) in the proper proportion that is

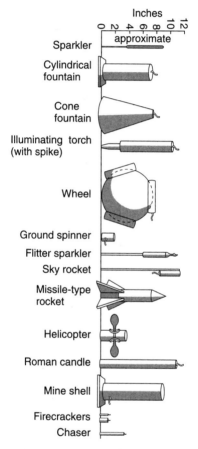

Figure 42-1. Types of consumer fireworks.

NFPA INSPECTION MANUAL

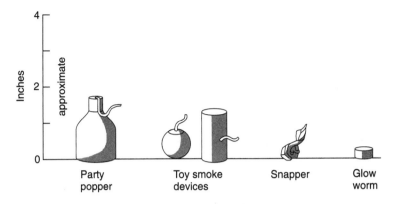

Figure 42-2. Types of novelties and trick noise-makers.

designed to produce, when ignited, a visible or audible effect by a combustion or deflagration process. The effects include the production of light, color, smoke, motion, or noise.

Salute powder: Salute powder is a pyrotechnic composition that makes a loud report when ignited and constitutes the sole pyrotechnic mixture in a salute. Flash powder is an example of salute powder.

General Pyrotechnic Safety Considerations

Obviously, you inspect a facility to evaluate its safety, and safety is said to be achieved when risk is reduced to acceptable levels. In essence, there are two components to risk: probability and consequence. Thus, risk can be managed either by minimizing the probability of an accident or by minimizing the consequences of that accident. In the manufacture, storage, and use of pyrotechnic materials, it is appropriate to look to minimizing both probability and consequence.

Generally, pyrotechnic accidents are the result of unintentional ignitions, and the consequence of an accident is directly related to the amount of material accidentally ignited and to the number of persons exposed to the accident. By introducing measures that reduce the chance of accidental ignitions and keeping the amount of pyrotechnic materials and the number of people in work areas to a minimum, a facility will remain relatively safe.

Concern for safety should be greatest during manufacturing operations such as mixing, pressing, and loading pyrotechnic compositions. This is when the probability of accidental ignition and the quantity of pyrotechnic materials present is the greatest, and when propagation in the event of an ignition is likely to be most rapid. Accordingly, these operations deserve the most attention during inspection.

Once a pyrotechnic composition has been loaded into a container and is no longer exposed, the probability of an accidental ignition is greatly reduced, as is the rate of fire spread if there is an ignition. This is particularly true for products, such as consumer fireworks and model rocket motors, that contain limited amounts of pyrotechnic composition. Tests on large quantities of consumer fireworks have shown that, while they may burn vigorously once ignited, they do not pose a mass explosion hazard. Thus, finishing operations such as labeling and packaging, during which little if any pyrotechnic composition is exposed, are lower hazard activities, as is the storage of completed consumer fireworks and model rocket motors.

For larger pyrotechnic items, such as display fireworks, the probability of accidental ignition during finishing and storage is similarly reduced. However, larger pyrotechnic items have a greater individual explosion potential than consumer fireworks. Once started, a fire in such items will spread very rapidly, and an explosion is likely during a mass fire.

Pyrotechnic Inspection Guidelines

The U.S. Bureau of Alcohol, Tobacco, and Firearms (BATF) regulates the commercial production of pyrotechnic composition, its use in manufacturing, and the storage and use of larger items, such as display fireworks. To help their inspectors prepare to examine fireworks facilities, the BATF has produced a videotape (see Bibliography). Any fire service inspector not familiar with pyrotechnic manufacturing would benefit from viewing this video before conducting an inspection.

While inspecting a facility, you must follow the safety requirements established by that facility. For example, you many have to wear cotton clothing to minimize the generation of static electricity, limit your use of cameras and other battery-operated equipment, and remove cigarette lighters and matches before entering the facility.

Cleanliness and good housekeeping are critical in reducing the likelihood of an accidental ignition and the spread of a pyrotechnic accident. Significant quantities of pyrotechnic dust present a real danger. Spills of pyrotechnic composition must be cleaned up immediately. Contaminated work clothing should not be worn outside the facility and should be laundered frequently.

As an inspector, you must address all potential ignition sources. In process buildings, electrical equipment must be suitable for Class II, Division I, Group E locations, and the electrical wiring must be sound. There must be no open-flame heating and no high-temperature heating surfaces. Trash should not be allowed to accumulate anywhere in the facility, and brush and dry grass should be controlled.

In large measure, it is the distance between work areas that determines whether and how fast a fire or explosion will spread from one work area to another. Consult NFPA 1124 for the recommended separation distance at fireworks manufacturing and storage facilities. NFPA 1124 generally is applicable to facilities manufacturing other civilian pyrotechnic products, as well.

The severity of a pyrotechnic accident is directly related to the amount and explosive potential of the pyrotechnic composition involved. For this reason, the BATF has limited the amount of pyrotechnic composition and salute powder allowed in any process building to 500 pounds and 10 pounds, respectively. However, the amount of pyrotechnic material present always should be the minimum practical amount; large quantities of raw materials and finished product should not be allowed to accumulate in any process building.

At the end of the work day, all pyrotechnic materials must be stored properly. Display fireworks and pyrotechnic compositions must go into magazines that comply with BATF regulations, while consumer fireworks and model rocket motors may be stored in a variety of structures. See NFPA 1124 and NFPA 1125 for guidance. Raw chemical materials also must be stored and handled safely.

There should be no more people present in any process building or magazine than are needed to conduct the operation. A facility with a number of small process buildings, each with one or two persons working in them, is greatly preferred over a facility with large process buildings with many workers in each building.

A fire involving bulk pyrotechnic composition or display fireworks is likely to spread so rapidly that sprinklers may not be effective. For this reason, the building should be constructed in such a way that personnel can leave their work areas easily and reach relative safety. Fireworks process buildings must be one story high with no basement, and buildings or rooms larger than 100 square feet must have at least two exits, which should be located such that no point within the building or room is more than 25 feet away.

Finally, you should review the facility's emergency procedures and evacuation plan in case of fire or other pyrotechnic accident.

Bibliography

Bureau of Alcohol, Tobacco, and Firearms, Explosives Law and Regulations, ATF Publication P5400.7, Washington, D.C. Contains BATF's magazine requirements for the storage of special fireworks, as well as license and permit regulations.

Bureau of Alcohol, Tobacco, and Firearms, Fireworks Manufacturing Safety, Washington, DC. A video presentation of information on pyrotechnic safety, including the materials used in the manufacture of fireworks, typical manufacturing methods, and a tour of a fireworks manufacturing facility.

Conkling, J. A., "American Fireworks Manufacturing: An Industry in Transition," *Fire Journal,* September 1986, pp. 41–47, 66-70. Contains a survey of the current regulatory agencies that oversee the fireworks industry. Presents results of several tests of fireworks output.

Consumer Product Safety Commission Regulations, Title 16, Code of Federal Regulations, Parts 1500 and 1507. These regulations govern common fireworks intended for use by individuals where state and local laws permit the use of fireworks.

Department of Transportation Regulations, Title 49, Code of Federal Regulations, Parts 100-177. These regulations include the definitions of common and special fireworks and the requirements for approval for transportation purposes.

NFPA Codes, Standards, and Recommended Practices

NFPA 43A, *Code for the Storage of Liquid and Solid Oxidizers.* Covers storage requirements of oxidizers used in pyrotechnic compositions.

NFPA 70, *National Electrical Code.* Contains the requirements for all standard types of electrical installations, including those that are essential for fireworks manufacturing plants.

NFPA 495, *Explosive Materials Code.* Covers security and safety, blasting agents, water gel and emulsions, transportation, aboveground storage, and other essential information.

NFPA 497M, *Manual for Classification of Gases, Vapors, and Dusts for Electrical Equipment in Hazardous (Classified) Locations.* Covers the selection of special electrical equipment for hazardous (classified) areas.

NFPA 1124, *Code for the Manufacture, Transportation, and Storage of Fireworks.* Covers the safe manufacture, transport, and storage for common and special fireworks.

NFPA 1125, *Code for the Manufacture of Model Rocket Motors.* Covers the manufacture of model rocket motors.

CHAPTER 43

Heat-Utilization Equipment

*H*eat is a predominant factor in many industrial processes. It is used to provide energy for operating machinery and to change the physical form or character of raw materials to adapt them to some human need. Heat is used in boiler furnaces to transform water into steam, which drives the turbine generators in power plants, which provide electric power. The electric power, in turn, is used for lighting, for operating machinery, or for initiating chemical reactions, such as those required to smelt aluminum. Heat is used in ovens, kilns, and dryers to cure, change, or preserve materials and products.

By its very nature, heat-utilization equipment presents serious fire hazards. As an inspector, you must be familiar with the types and functions of heat-utilization equipment so that you can recognize the associated hazards and see that the necessary maintenance and protective measures are taken to ensure life safety and fire safety. This chapter describes in some detail the various types of heat-utilization equipment and how the controlled fires and explosions used in these types of equipment can be maintained at safe levels.

Boiler-Furnaces

Boiler-furnaces, or boilers, are used to turn water into steam, which can be used to drive electric generators, one of steam's most important uses in industry. Steam can also be used directly to power steam-driven machinery, to provide process steam, or to heat a building.

There are two basic types of boilers: water-tube and fire-tube. In water-tube boilers, water is circulated through tubes heated by hot combustion gases. In fire-tube boilers, the combustion gases pass through tubes immersed in circulating water.

Basically, the combustion of fuels in boilers involves carbon, hydrogen, and sulfur burned with oxygen from air. The heat released is about 14,000 Btu per pound of carbon and 61,000 Btu per pound of hydrogen. The sulfur plays little part in the production of heat, but it can be a major source of corrosion and pollution.

Oil, natural gas, and pulverized coal are the most common boiler fuels. Some industries also use waste products, including gases, flammable liquids, wood waste, and sawdust. Municipal refuse is used in some types of boilers, which may require special precautions.

No matter what fuel is used, the combustion process results from the continual introduction of fuel and air in a combustible mixture. The flow rates of fuel and air, the fuel-air ratio, and the ignition source must be controlled. If any of these factors is out of balance or is interrupted, a boiler explosion can occur.

Figure 43-1. Installation for combination oil and gas firing in a large electric utility boiler.

Boiler operation requires different outputs to meet varying load conditions. The operating range, or load, of a boiler is the ratio of the full load to the minimum load at which it will operate reliably and produce complete combustion without changing the number of burners in operation.

To burn efficiently, oil must be atomized, either by steam or mechanical atomizers. Steam atomizers produce a steam-fuel emulsion that atomizes the oil by the rapid expansion of the steam when it is released into the furnace. Steam atomizers perform more efficiently over a wider load range than other types, normally atomizing properly down to 25% of rated capacity.

Premix gas burners mix fuel and air before they are introduced into the burner-nozzle, while external-mix gas burners mix the fuel and air outside the nozzle. Multiple-speed external-mix burners provide high ignition stability and are replacing many other types.

A multifuel-fired furnace with multiple-speed burners and proper control equipment can be changed from one fuel to another without a change in load or fuel pressure. Simultaneously firing natural gas and oil is acceptable in this type of burner.

Pulverized coal-fired systems may be arranged in several ways because of the many functions necessary. Coal must be transported to the pulverizer in measured and controlled quantities, and the air-coal stream from the pulverizer must be kept within a specific temperature range to increase efficiency and reduce the hazard of coking and fire. The coal-air mix is combined with a controlled amount of secondary air at the burner. The fuel must be consumed completely in a continuous process with no more than a trace of combustibles in the stack gas and ash hoppers. The amount of oxygen in the initial combustion zone is limited to control stack emissions. Dual register burners proportion the air between the fuel-rich ignition zone and the secondary combustion zone to ensure full combustion.

The principal hazards of boiler furnaces are explosion and fire. Explosions result when combustible fuel-air mixtures that have accumulated in confined spaces ignite. Generally, these accumulations are the result of equipment malfunction or operator error, such as the failure to purge the furnace between unsuccessful attempts to light off the burner. Loss of flame from an interruption in fuel or air delivery or in ignition energy might also permit such an accumulation.

Ovens and Furnaces

Ovens are defined as chambers used for baking, heating, or drying or as chambers equipped to heat objects within. Furnaces are enclosures in which energy in a nonthermal form is converted to heat by the combustion of a suitable fuel. Ovens usually are classified as heating devices that operate at temperatures below 1,400°F, although this does not always apply. Some ovens, such as coke ovens, operate at temperatures above 2,000°F, while others, such as bakery ovens, operate at temperatures below 1,400°F.

The NFPA system classifies ovens and furnaces as belonging to Class A, B, C, or D. Class A ovens and furnaces include equipment operating at or near atmospheric pressure in which the flammable volatiles or the combustible residue of the objects processed present a potential fire or explosion hazard. Flammable volatiles or residues are produced by paints and powders or by finishing processes such as dipping, spraying, coating, impregnation, polymerization, or molecular rearrangement. NFPA 86, *Standard for Ovens and Furnaces*, addresses Class A ovens and furnaces.

NFPA 86 also addresses Class B ovens and furnaces, which operate at approximately atmospheric pressure and produce no hazardous flammable or combustible volatiles or residues.

Class C furnaces present an explosion hazard because they use a flammable or other special atmosphere. This type of furnace can use any heating system and includes the atmosphere generator when one is used.

Atmosphere generators provide the special gases required for some heat-utilization processes. Generally, these atmospheres are toxic, flammable, explosive, or a combination of all three. Exothermic generators produce the gas by partially or completely burning fuel gas at a controlled ratio, usually 60 to 100% aeration, while endothermic generators use a ratio of less than 50%. Ammonia dissociators produce dissociated ammonia—25% hydrogen and 75% ammonia—from ammonia through a temperature reaction with a catalyst. Special atmosphere generators must have adequate supervisory controls. NFPA 86C, *Standard for Industrial Furnaces Using a Special Processing Atmosphere,* provides information on protective equipment for atmosphere generators and on Class C furnaces.

Class D furnaces are vacuum furnaces operating at temperatures up to

5,000°F and at pressures below atmospheric. Such furnaces can use any type of heating system and also might use special atmospheres. They are discussed in NFPA 86D, *Standard for Industrial Furnaces Using Vacuum as an Atmosphere.* More complete information on the characteristics and uses of each of these ovens and furnaces can also be found in the *Fire Protection Handbook.*

Batch- and Continuous-Type Ovens and Furnaces

Ovens and furnaces also are designated as "batch" or "continuous" types. In batch type equipment, the temperature remains constant. The material is introduced and stays in place until the process is complete, when it is removed, usually through the opening by which it entered. Material moves through continuous-type ovens and furnances on some kind of conveyor. The temperature might remain constant throughout or it might be divided into varying zones.

The most common methods of transferring heat to the materials being processed are through direct contact with the products of combustion, convection and radiation from the hot gases, and reradiation from the hot walls of the furnace.

There are two types of oven and furnace heaters: direct-fired and indirect-fired. Direct-fired ovens heat by contact with the products of combustion, while indirect-fired ovens heat by radiation from heated tubes of air. Indirect-fired ovens are safer because dangerous fuel-air mixtures do not readily fill the enclosure. Nonetheless, vapors from a flammable-liquid drying process could cause explosions.

There are several different firing arrangements for these heaters, both internal and external, direct and indirect. Many different sources of heat may be used for ovens or furnaces, including gas and oil burners, electric heaters, infrared lamps, electric induction heaters, and steam radiation.

Ovens and furnaces should be installed where they present the least possible hazard to life and property. They may have to be surrounded by walls or partitions. In any case, the area should be adequately ventilated and be equipped with proper explosion venting. Operating and control equipment should be tested regularly, and all portions of the oven or furnace and its attachments should be cleaned on a regular schedule.

After-Burners and Catalytic Combustion Systems

After-burners and catalytic combustion systems are used to conserve fuel and to reduce fumes, odors, vapors, and gases to acceptable exhaust products, such as carbon dioxide (CO_2) and water vapor. Some exhaust from ovens and furnaces may require special treatment to remove particulates, halogens, hydroxides, and sulfur and nitrogen oxides.

After-Burners

After-burners, or direct-flame incinerators, burn organic solvent vapors, organic dusts, and combustible gases. The fumes must be heated to autoignition temperatures, and there must be enough oxygen to complete

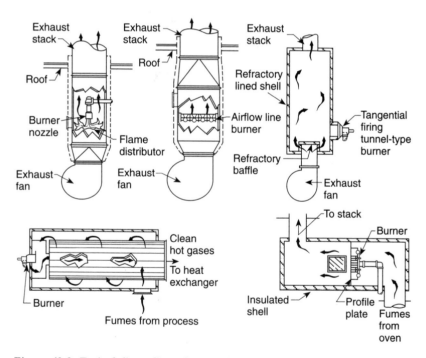

Figure 43-2. Typical direct-flame fume incinerators. (Maxon Premix Burner Co., Inc.)

the chemical reaction. More than 16% oxygen is required to keep the fumes at or less than 25% of the lower explosive limit (LEL). If there are adequate combustible gas analyzers and interlocks, the fumes may rise as high as 50% of the LEL.

Operating temperatures in the combustion chamber usually are between 1,200°F and 1,500°F. Conversion to CO_2 at 92% efficiency at 1,300°F and at 96% at 1,450°F have been reported in tests.

After-burner combustion chambers may be lined either with heavy refractory materials or light refractory materials. If heavy materials are used, the chambers must have external burners. Line burners may be used on chambers lined with light refractory materials.

If the fumes to be incinerated are inert gases with low combustible content, they can be mixed with air and burned. If they are combustible and concentrated from 25 to 100% of the LEL, they should be diluted with air before they are transferred to the incinerator. Combustible fumes above the LEL normally are furned in flare stacks or used as fuel in heating equipment, a process that requires special equipment and control.

Catalytic Combustion Systems

A catalytic combustion system uses a catalyst to speed up the combination of fuel-air or fuel-gas mixtures. Catalytic heaters can be used to burn a fuel gas, releasing much of the energy as radiation to the processing zone, or they may be used in the oven exhaust to release heat from evaporated by-products to a heat exchanger.

There are three types of catalytic combustion elements: all-metal mats, which are used as fuel-fired radiant heaters or to oxidize combustibles in fume-air mixtures; ceramic or porcelain elements, which use rare-earth elements, platinum, or metallic salts as catalysts; and beds containing pellets or granules that are kept between screens, but are free to migrate within the bed.

Heat Recovery

Heat exchangers often are used to make process and fume incineration more economical. For this same reason, heat may also be directly recirculated. When applied to heat generation and fume incineration, such heat recovery can supply a significant portion of the heat requirements.

Recovered heat can be used as a primary or supplementary source of process heat, to heat some process zones in a multizone process, to heat other nearby processes, to pretreat fumes to incinerators, to heat make-up air, and as a waste heat boiler servicing multiple requirements.

When combustible deposits and flammable liquids are heated to high temperatures within a heat exchanger, they present fire and explosion hazards. Dirty stream deposits can make the heat exchanger inoperable.

Lumber Kilns

Lumber kilns are valuable because they can dry freshly cut wood more quickly and efficiently than outdoor or natural seasoning. Natural drying often results in waste and loss because it causes excessive warping and cracking. Though often called "dry kilns," wood dryers usually use some moisture to maintain the wood at a uniform moisture content during the drying process. This reduces warping, checking, and cracking.

Lumber kilns may be classified by the method of heating they use, by their method of air circulation, or by their method of operation.

In batch, or compartment, kilns the lumber remains stationary during the entire process. In continuous kilns, lumber enters at one end and, over a period of time, moves to the discharge end.

Kilns may be heated either directly or indirectly. In directly heated kilns, hot gases produced by burning oil, gas, sawdust, or some other fuel are passed through the stacked lumber. Direct heating can also be accomplished by using an open oil or gas flame to heat large metal surfaces, which act as heat exchangers. Steam, circulated through pipes located at the bottom or top of the kiln, is a common source of heat for indirectly heated kilns. Hot gases circulated through ducts and electrical resistance heaters also are used.

In natural circulation kilns, heated air rises through the stacked lumber. As it cools, it travels down to the heater and is reheated. During the first part of the drying cycle, the air moves upward at the sides of the kiln and down through passages within the stack. When the moisture has been reduced to about 10 to 20% the heated air is directed upward through the center. Vents in the wall or roof exhaust the air and moisture.

In forced-circulation kilns, blowers, internal or external, move air over and through the stack. Heating elements and blowers are located either at the bottom or top of the kiln.

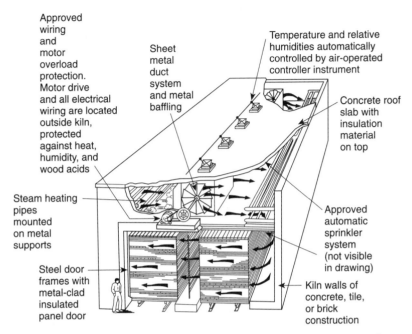

Approved wiring and motor overload protection. Motor drive and all electrical wiring are located outside kiln, protected against heat, humidity, and wood acids

Sheet metal duct system and metal baffling

Temperature and relative humidities automatically controlled by air-operated controller instrument

Concrete roof slab with insulation material on top

Steam heating pipes mounted on metal supports

Steel door frames with metal-clad insulated panel door

Approved automatic sprinkler system (not visible in drawing)

Kiln walls of concrete, tile, or brick construction

Figure 43-3. A forced-circulation, double-track compartment kiln. Note that automatic sprinklers are installed above and below the platform between the kiln and the overhead fan room.

Although the air-flow systems in batch and progressive kilns are similar, there is one minor difference. In progressive kilns, the air moves from the dry end to the green end. Because the air has lost heat and picked up moisture, the rate of drying is slower at the green end.

Fire Hazards

Lumber kilns present serious fire hazards, especially when they use direct-fired or high-pressure steam systems and when the structure itself is combustible. Direct-fired kilns are analogous to Class A ovens and require the combustion controls specified for drying ovens in which the heating fuel is introduced into the oven itself.

Kilns should be of fire-resistive or heavy-timber construction. They are subject to extreme variations in temperature and humidity and to unusual degrees of expansion and contraction, which reduce their structural stability.

Dehydrators and Dryers

In some respects, dehydrators and dryers for agricultural products are similar to lumber kilns. The basic purpose of each is to remove moisture from an organic material. Kilns introduce some moisture into the process for control purposes only; dehydrators and dryers do not.

Dehydrators and dryers are classified as batch, bulk, and continuous, depending on the arrangement and operation of the drying chamber. Batch dryers can be either fixed or portable. They can be of the gravity type, and include pan dryers for sugar, puree, sludges, and other products. In batch dryers, heated air is introduced into a perforated plenum. The product to be dried is fed from overhead and loses moisture as it passes downward. Exhaust air escapes through openings in the dryer's outer wall.

Bulk dryers are used to dry seeds, grains, nuts, tobacco, hay, and forage in the bin, crib, or compartment in which the product is to be stored. Such dryers commonly introduce dry, heated air below a perforated floor. The air rises through the product, carrying moisture to exhaust vents.

In continuous gravity dryers, wet material enters at the top of a silolike structure. Warm air is blown into the upper half to dry the falling material, which continues through a zone of cool air to the bottom, where it is conveyed to storage or a process step.

Continuous dryers include drum dryers for milk, puree, and sludge; spray dryers for milk, eggs, and soap; flash dryers for chopped forage crops; gravity dryers for small grains, beans, and seeds; tunnel dryers for fruits, vegetables, grains, seeds, nuts, fibers, and forage crops; and rotary dryers for milk, puree, and sludge. Tunnel dryers also can be batch dryers and can be further classified according to their airflow and to their need for intermediate heating.

Dryers for agricultural products are either direct-fired or indirect-fired, heated electrically or by using a heat-transfer medium, such as steam. Heaters may be oil-fired, gas-fired, or solid-fuel-fired. When gas-fired

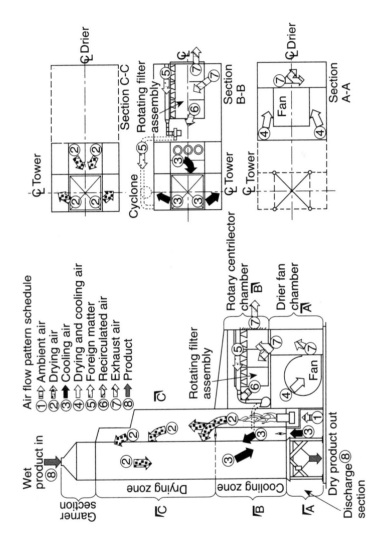

Figure 43-4. A continuous gravity dryer.

infrared heaters or lamps are used, the focal length should be such that the surface of the product does not reach autoignition temperatures. Electrical infrared lamps should be located where they cannot collect combustible dust.

Excluding those required for burners and heating equipment, dryer controls should include a method for automatically shutting down the dryer in the event of fire or excessive temperature. When the product is fed automatically from the dryer to a storage building, the controls should also include a thermostat in the exhaust system. In the event of excessive temperature, the thermostat should shut off heat to the dryer, stop the airflow (except when the product is in suspension), stop the product flow, and sound an alarm. In a combustible dryer, a thermostat should shut off heat when the temperature reaches 165°F but permit a flow of unheated air and sound an alarm. Among the other dryer controls necessary are a device to shut off heat if airflow through the dryer stops and a high-limit thermostat between the heat-producing unit and the dryer.

An agricultural product dried by heat must be adequately cooled before it is stored or packaged to prevent subsequent ignition. The amount of cooling necessary depends on the material, its spontaneous heating, and the way it is to be packaged or stored. NFPA 61B, *Standard for the Prevention of Fires and Explosions in Grain Elevators and Facilities Handling Bulk Raw Agricultural Commodities,* contains specific requirements for grain dryers.

Oil Quenching

Oil quenching is a method of imparting desirable characteristics to metals and metal products by metallurgical changes. The process presents several serious fire hazards, chief among them the combustible character of the quenching oils and the elevated temperatures often required. Other contributors to the hazards are special atmospheres, the size and shape of the work being processed, oil volume, the location of furnaces and quench tanks, and exposure to other process or storage facilities.

The most critical step in the oil quenching process is the entrance of the product into the quench, which must be rapid and complete. Partial immersion is the cause of most quench oil fires. There must be minimal splashing, and the quench oil should not overflow.

Chutes, elevators, cranes, hoists, conveyors, or a combination of these move the work into, through, and out of the quench. They must be designed and maintained properly, so that parts and products move without jamming. Elevating mechanisms must be supported adequately to prevent the load from tilting, and guides are necessary in the tank to ensure uniform movement and prevent wedging, which could result in partial immersion. Baskets and elevators cause more partial immersions than any other method.

The work must be drained at the end of the quench cycle, or an excessive amount of oil will be wasted. Usually, the work is still warm when it is drained, and the oil could vaporize, making it susceptible to ignition. Vapors will condense on surfaces and add to the seriousness of any fire at this point.

Quench oil must be kept within certain specified temperatures. Generally, this requires a cooling system to prevent overheating. A cooling system failure that permits water to enter the quenching oil is particularly hazardous because hot work entering the bath can convert the water to steam and cause a boilover. Quench oil should be tested regularly. If the water content reaches 0.50% by volume, the oil is no longer safe to use.

The quantity of oil in the quench tank must be controlled carefully. If the oil level is too low and a large load is immersed, the oil can overheat and ignite. Too much oil will result in an overflow. The distance between openings in the tank wall and the level of the liquid when a full load is submerged should be at least 6 inches. Adequate, fully trapped drains should carry overflow to a safe location or into special tanks.

Bottom drains should be provided so that a quench tank can be emptied under serious fire conditions. Gravity drains or special pumps sized in such a way that the tank can be emptied within 5 minutes may be used. Such drains must be used only by well-trained persons because improper use can result in greater hazard. If a flammable gas atmosphere is maintained above the oil, removing the oil can create a negative pressure that may result in a higher potential for fire or explosion. Established drain pipe sizes are listed in the *Fire Protection Handbook*.

When the system is automatically shut down, the work load should be completely immersed or completely removed from the quench. All safety controls and interlocks should be tested on a regular schedule.

Inspection Reminders

Keep the following questions in mind when inspecting heat-utilization equipment:

1. Is there evidence of fuel or hydraulic fluid leaks?
2. Is there enough insulation or clearance where ducts or stacks pass through combustible walls, floors, or roofs?
3. Are interlock safety systems intact?
4. Is there evidence of corrosion, especially where fuel with a high sulfur content is used?
5. Is the natural or mechanical ventilation adequate to remove flammable vapors?
6. Have provisions been made for explosion venting where needed?

Good maintenance procedures for heat-utilization equipment include regular and frequent checks of safety devices and circuits. Ask to see the inspection reports, and note any abnormalities that could signal a potential hazard.

Bibliography

Cote, A. E., ed., *Fire Protection Handbook,* 17th edition, National Fire Protection Association, Quincy, MA, 1991.

Linville, J. L., ed., *Industrial Fire Hazards Handbook*, 3rd edition, National Fire Protection Association, 1990.

NFPA Codes, Standards, and Recommended Practices

NFPA 30, *Flammable and Combustible Liquids Code.* Covers requirements for piping, valves, and fittings used for flammable liquids.

NFPA 31, *Standard for the Installation of Oil-Burning Equipment.* Covers requirements for stationary and portable oil-burning equipment, tanks, piping, and accessories.

NFPA 34, *Standard for Dipping and Coating Processes Using Flammable or Combustible Liquids.* Covers requirements for coating, finishing, and treating processes.

NFPA 54, *National Fuel Gas Code.* Covers criteria for the installation, operation, and maintenance of gas piping and appliances.

NFPA 58, *Standard for the Storage and Handling of Liquefied Petroleum Gases.* Provides general provisions for LP-Gas equipment and appliances.

NFPA 61B, *Standard for the Prevention of Fires and Explosions in Grain Elevators and Facilities Handling Bulk Raw Agricultural Commodities.* Covers prevention of dust explosions and ways to minimize the damage if an explosion should occur. Also covers fumigation of commodities and storage spaces.

NFPA 68, *Guide for Venting of Deflagrations.* Covers fundamentals of explosion venting.

NFPA 70, *National Electrical Code.* Includes electrical requirements in hazardous atmospheres.

NFPA 85C, *Standard for the Prevention of Furnace Explosions/Implosions in Multiple Burner Boiler-Furnaces.* Provides requirements for the design, installation, operation, and maintenance of boiler-furnaces using natural gas, oil, or coal, and their fuel-burning systems and related control equipment. For boilers with fuel input greater than 12,500,000 Btu/hr.

NFPA 85H, *Standard for Prevention of Combustion Hazards in Atmospheric Fluidized Bed Combustion System Boilers.* Provides combustion safeguard criteria for atmospheric fluidized bed boiler furnaces with fuel input greater than 12,500,000 Btu/hr.

NFPA 86, *Standard for Ovens and Furnaces.* Details requirements for location, construction, operation, heating system, ventilation, safety control equipment, and fire protection for Class A and B ovens and furnaces.

NFPA 86C, *Standard for Industrial Furnaces Using a Special Processing Atmosphere.* Covers Class C industrial furnaces that use a special processing atmosphere, including salt baths and integral quench furnaces. Sets requirements for location, construction, heating system, safety controls, operation, and fire protection.

NFPA 86D, *Standard for Industrial Furnaces Using Vacuum as an Atmosphere.* Applies to the design, construction, and protection of Class D industrial furnaces that operate at above ambient temperatures to over 5,000°F and at pressures normally below atmosphere to 10-8 Torr.

NFPA 120, *Standard for Coal Preparation Plants.* Specifies safety requirements for design, construction, and operation of coal preparation plants.

NFPA 850, *Recommended Practice for Fire Protection for Electric Generating Plants.* Gives recommendations for fire prevention and protection for gas-, oil-, or coal-fired steam electric generating plants during design, construction, and operation.

NFPA 8501, *Standard for Single Burner Boiler Operation.* Information on design, installation, operation, and maintenance for boilers with fuel input greater than 12,500,000 Btu/hr that use single burners firing natural gas, fuel oil, or both.

NFPA 8503, *Standard for Pulverized Fuel Systems.* Details requirements for the design, installation, operation, and maintenance of pulverized fuel systems and for personnel safety around such systems.

NFPA 8505, *Recommended Practice for Stoker Operation.* Gives information and guidance for stoker-equipped boiler-furnaces firing fuels such as coal, wood, rubber tires, municipal waste, and so on with a fuel input greater than 400,000 Btu/hr.

CHAPTER 44

Spray Painting and Powder Coating

Introduction

Processes involving spray application of materials that are flammable or combustible—whether they be in the form of liquids or powders—also involve the risk of fire. Since two sides of the fire triangle—air and fuel—are routinely present and already mixed, a source of ignition is the only thing needed to start a fire.

Although spray painting is the most familiar of these processes, similar equipment is used in industry for applying other materials including lubricants, sealants, waxes, colorants, flavors, pharmaceuticals, and structural layers of products. Among these materials the fire hazards and means for controlling them generally are similar in principle and differ only in detail.

Hazardous Characteristics of Spray Painting Processes

Solventborne Coatings

Flammable vapors are present at all stages of the spray painting process. They come from coating materials in storage, during preparation for the application process, from containers, and from the spray process itself.

Residues of the process are readily ignitable, and resulting fires develop quickly and have a high rate of heat release. Residues of some process materials, particularly air dry enamels and varnishes, can spontaneously heat and ignite.

Containers for process liquids can leak or spill, and exposure of the containers to process fires could result in BLEVEs if there is not adequate pressure relief.

Mixing some coating components with other components may cause a chemical reaction, which could lead to uncontrolled heating. Other components, such as organic peroxides, are inherently unstable, and they may decompose violently if they are contaminated or suddenly heated.

Cleanup solvents used to remove residues from spray apparatus and the spray booth may be flammable. Overspray residues and leftover materials from cleanup usually are classified as hazardous wastes.

Spray booth and exhaust ducts may be heated to incandescence in a residue fire and must be constructed to withstand severe fire conditions.

Waterborne Coatings

Waterborne coatings may release flammable vapors. These materials commonly exhibit a flash point, but generally they will not continue to burn after an initial flash.

Spray patterns and the liquid supplies used in the process generally are not ignitable in the condition in which they are used, but they may become ignitable if virtually all of the water content is evaporated.

Residues after these coatings have dried have burn characteristics comparable to those from solventborne coatings. Some residue accumulations may spontaneously heat and ignite.

Materials used for cleaning residues from equipment and spray booths may be flammable.

Powder Coating

No flammable vapors are produced at any stage of powder coating—not in storage, in process, nor from residues.

Airborne dust within the spray pattern will burn vigorously, but residues deposited on surfaces are not readily ignitable. If the spray is interrupted immediately after ignition, the fire will extinguish itself without further effort. If feed to the spray guns is sustained, the flame will continue to heat surrounding materials, causing the collector filters and powder residing in the collector hopper to ignite.

Cyclone or bag-house type dust collectors and airborne dust in any confined enclosure can explode if ignited.

Oversprayed coating materials normally are recycled to be reused in the process.

After exhaust air passes through process filters, it is normally discharged back into the workplace.

Spray booths commonly are constructed of plastic materials to prevent overspray from adhering.

Differences Between Manual and Automatic Spray

Each coating process may be done with manual or automatic spray guns or with a combination of the two in the same operation. Manual and automatic spray devices operate in much the same way. Automatic operations, however, may involve numerous spray guns used within the same booth and may be unattended during operation. Unless there is a special flame detection apparatus, the spray guns may continue to operate after a fire has ignited, severely aggravating the results. Hand spray operators will notice a fire immediately and release gun triggers to interrupt the supply of sprayed fuel to the fire, leaving residue fire considerations as the major remaining concern.

Electrostatics

In a production setting any coating process may be augmented with electrostatics. In this arrangement, the spray device has a means for introduction of high voltage (between 50,000 and 120,000 volts), which will enhance deposition of the sprayed paint onto the work piece. In this high voltage environment any electrically conductive object that is not grounded may discharge electrical sparks that could ignite a fire. Stringent grounding discipline is required.

Spray Booths and Rooms and Open Spray Areas

Spray Booths

Production spray painting of objects up to the size of automobiles routinely is done in a power-ventilated enclosure referred to as a spray booth. The objects may be brought to the booth manually or by a conveyor, and the booth may appear in any one of a wide variety of designs. Although the booth typically will enclose the object during painting, in some designs it will be adjacent to the object and will surround the object and the spray process with a controlled stream of air that will capture all vapors and overspray and carry them into a collector. No vapors or overspray should escape.

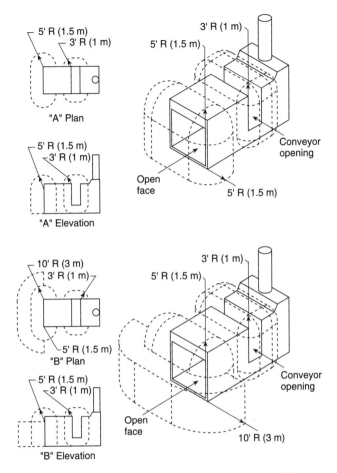

Figure 44-1. Class I or Class II, Division 2 locations adjacent to a closed top, open faced or open front spray booth. (Top) When ventilation system is interlocked with spray equipment. (Bottom) When ventilation system is not interlocked with spray equipment. Source: Figure 2, NFPA 33, **Standard for Spray Application Using Flammable and Combustible Materials,** *NFPA, Quincy, MA, 1989.*

Spray booths range in size from larger than a railroad box car to smaller than a bread box. They must be constructed of materials that will withstand a nominal process fire without collapsing. Booths and exhaust ducts most commonly are constructed of steel of at least 18 MSG (1.3 mm) thickness, but they may also be constructed of masonry or other materials. Aluminum or structural plastics are permitted for powder booths since residues are not readily ignitable and a fire is expected to last no longer than a second.

The principle components of a spray booth are the enclosure, the overspray collector, and the exhaust system. The interiors of all of these components are classified as Division 1 hazardous areas.

Open-Face Spray Booths

Spray enclosures most commonly are configured as boxes with one side open. The object to be painted is situated either within the box or at its open side during spraying and, if the booth operates properly, all-over spray will be captured by the airflow and contained within the enclosure. See Figure 44-1 for delineation of the Division 2 area outside the openings of the spray booth.

Enclosed Spray Booth

Enclosures also can be designed as a tunnel, with openings at either end for entry and exit of a conveyor carrying objects, such as automobile bodies, through the process zone. Airflow in this type of booth usually is introduced through filters in the ceiling and exhausted through floor gratings.

In larger models, the booth will accommodate painters and spray equipment, while in smaller models the painters and spray gun mounts will be outside spraying inward through openings of limited size. See Figure 44-2. See Figure 44-3 for delineation of the Division 2 hazardous area outside of openings.

To diminish the chance of fire spread, spray booths should be separated from other processes, from stored combustible materials, and from combustible structures by at least 3 feet. If a side of the spray booth does not need to be accessed for maintenance purposes, it may be located closer to a masonry or fire-resistant wall.

Processes that do not use a conveyor, such as automobile or furniture refinishing, may have booths that are totally enclosed during operation,

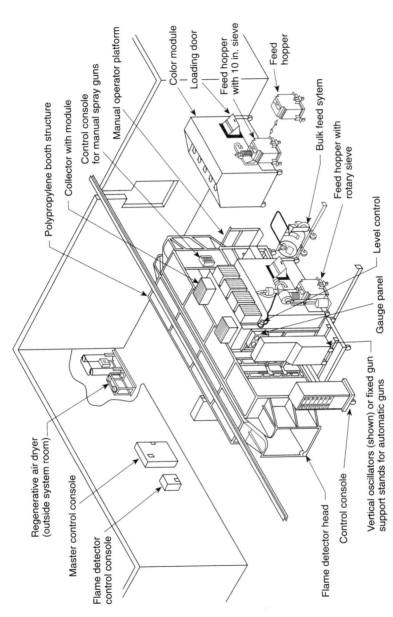

Regenerative air dryer
(outside system room)

Master control console

Flame detector
control console

Polypropylene booth structure

Collector with module

Control console
for manual spray guns

Manual operator platform

Color module

Loading door

Feed hopper
with 10 in. sieve

Feed
hopper

Bulk feed sytem

Feed hopper with
rotary sieve

Level control

Gauge panel

Flame detector head

Control console

Vertical oscillators (shown) or fixed gun
support stands for automatic guns

Figure 44-2. Integrated powder spray booth/recovery system. (Nordson)

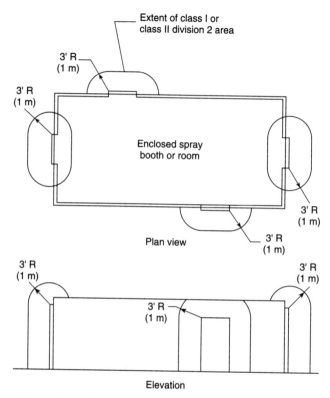

Figure 44-3. Class I or Class II, Division 2 locations adjacent to openings in an enclosed spray booth or room. Source: Figure 3, NFPA 33, Standard for Spray Application Using Flammable and Combustible Materials, NFPA, Quincy, MA, 1989.

with air intake through installed duct work or through a filter bank in a wall or a door.

The Division 2 area outside the booth normally would extend only 3 feet from a door or opening.

The Overspray Collector

This component of the spray booth is intended to capture and remove particulate matter from the exhaust air stream, allowing vapors to pass and be discharged. They may appear either as dry systems or involve use of a liquid for this purpose.

Maze-Type Dry Collectors

In its simplest form this type of collector looks like a maze of steel panels or chains or one of folded paper through which the airstream is drawn with the intention that particles will impact with the obstructions and be collected upon them. This collector is not very efficient; it allows considerable amounts of contaminants to pass through the maze to subsequently be deposited in the exhaust duct, on the fan, and on the building roof around the stack discharge point.

Dry-Filter Type

Dry filters made of shredded paper or of fiberglass mats are more efficient at trapping overspray. If cloth second-stage filters are used, virtually no contaminants are allowed to pass through to foul the stack.

In powder coating processes, the dry filters used are engineered to stop all of the particulate material and not allow any to bypass into the exhaust system.

In liquid coating systems the residues accumulated on dry collectors usually are readily ignitable and, especially on vertical filters, will burn violently. Fouled filters that have been removed from the spray booth but which are then stored in drums or boxes can spontaneously heat and ignite. Unless they are removed immediately from the factory, these filters must be immersed and stored in water until they are removed from the premises.

Residues in a powder collector will not spontaneously ignite and they are not readily ignitable. Their hazardous characteristics are comparable to those of wheat flour or powdered sugar.

Water Wash Collectors

The water wash collector separates contaminants by passing the exhaust air stream through a series of sprays or waterfalls that scrub out particles of overspray and keep them submerged in a water tank. See Figure 44-4.

Special chemicals must be added to the water and maintained at the proper concentration to render the paint particles nonadhesive and thus prevent them from forming large sticky curds that can plug spray nozzles

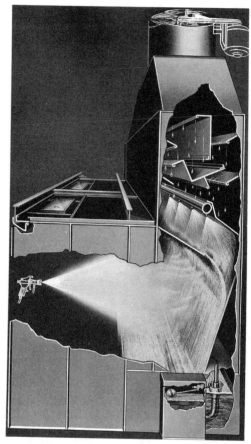

Figure 44-4. Water wash booth. (DeVilbiss)

or adhere to overflow weirs and produce gaps in the waterfalls or
scrubbers.

Such gaps, if permitted to form, will permit overspray to pass through
the collector and into the exhaust duct where it can accumulate as dry
residue.

As long as it is properly maintained, the water wash collector contributes substantially to fire safety by keeping residues submerged in water
and unavailable as fuel for fire.

The Exhaust System

For liquid coating processes, this component of the spray booth is comprised of a plenum downstream of the collector, a fan, and duct work leading to a discharge point outside the building. For powder coatings, the discharge is recirculated back to the work space within the building through a secondary set of filters.

The fan may be located near either end of the duct and should be of nonsparking structure (AMCA Class C). Its rotating shaft should have heavy-duty bearings, and the motor should not be exposed to the exhaust air stream unless listed for that service.

The exhaust system should have access doors or easily opened joints to facilitate inspection of the duct work interior and cleanout of residues. The duct must be constructed of suitable materials and be supported to prevent collapse under fire conditions. (The duct may be heated to cherry red during a thermally drafted residue fire, substantially weakening the originally expected strength, and the load of water from internal sprinklers must be considered if horizontal duct runs are present.)

Spray Rooms and Open Floor Spraying

Some objects to be painted, such as large, heavy machinery or structural steel fabricated components, are beyond the size that can be brought practically into a spray booth. They may be accommodated either in a spray room or under open floor conditions.

Spray Room

A spray room differs in operation from a spray booth in that no attempt is made to provide exhaust air velocity that will carry overspray into a collector; powered exhaust is provided only to carry away vapors. Spraying may take place anywhere in the room, and overspray is permitted to fall to the floor, from which it must be mechanically removed to prevent excess accumulation.

Spray rooms should be separated from other occupancies by structures with at least a 1-hour fire-resistance rating. The entire interior of the spray room is classified as a Division I fire hazard with Division 2 extending 3 feet outside of doors.

Exhaust systems associated with spray rooms are treated with the same fire control considerations as those associated with spray booths. Spray rooms should be separated from other occupancies of the building by construction with at least a 1-hour fire-resistance rating.

Open Floor Spraying

Another approach used for infrequent spraying of large objects involves spray painting on the open factory floor without an enclosure or a dedicated ventilation system. This is referred to as open floor spraying, and it requires the establishment of rather extensive surrounding areas classified as hazardous during operation. The Division 1 area usually is designated to be as extensive as the visible spray and the wet paint surfaces remaining on the object, and the Division 2 area extends 20 feet further horizontally and 10 feet vertically beyond the Division 1 area. See Figure 44-5.

Spray Apparatus

The devices that actually produce the paint spray are known as spray guns and exist in both hand-held and automatic forms. See Figures 44-6 and 44-7.

Paint is supplied to the spray device through a hose originating in a reservoir that may be a pressurized tank, or a "pressure pot," an unpressurized tank associated with a pump, or, for powder coating, a feed hopper with a pneumatic ejector type pump. Depending on the scale of the painting operation, this reservoir may be as small as 1 gallon or as large as 100 gallons. Several reservoirs supplying different colors or types of paint may be associated with a single spray booth or room.

To lessen the effects of exposure during spray booth fire conditions, the supply reservoirs should be separated from the spray booth by several feet. Since hoses may be expected to burn off in a fire, pressurized paint supplies should be interlocked with a fire alarm to prevent the paint from being delivered into the spray booth during a fire.

In automatic operations at their simplest, the atomizers are mounted on "fixed gun stands" and are triggered on and off by a controller as the objects to be painted pass by on a conveyor. In increasing order of complexity, the guns are mounted in an array on a machine called a "reciprocator" to stroke back and forth, or up and down, like strokes of a paint brush as the work passes. The guns may be on constantly or may be triggered to spray only the work pieces. Some reciprocators function as two-axis or even three-axis machines. In the most complex arrangements,

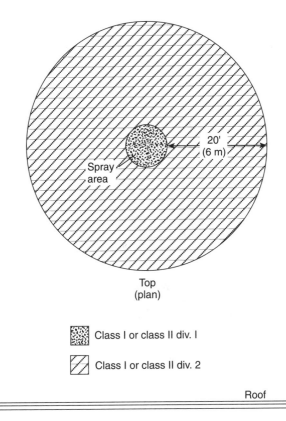

Top
(plan)

Class I or class II div. I

Class I or class II div. 2

Roof

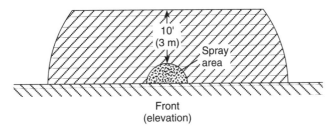

Front
(elevation)

Figure 44-5. Class I or Class II, Division 2 locations adjacent to an unenclosed spray operation. Source: Figure 1, NFPA 33, **Standard for Spray Application Using Flammable and Combustible Materials,** *NFPA, Quincy, MA, 1989.*

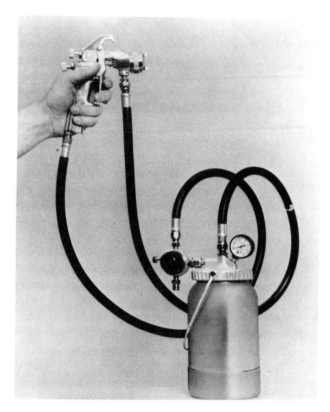

Figure 44-6. Hand air spray gun with fluid supplied from 2-qt pressure pot. (DeVilbiss)

the guns are manipulated by a machine called a "robot" that can move the gun to any position within the area swept by its arm and point in any direction just as if it were hand-held. Triggering is controlled by a computer that also runs the movements of the robot.

Control of Fire Risk

The risk of fire can be kept to an acceptable level through a combination of efforts directed toward control of ignition sources, limitation of

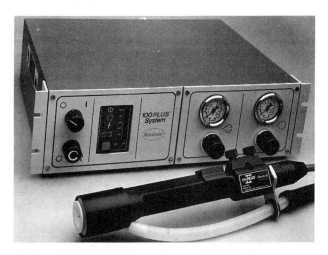

Figure 44-7. Automatic powder gun. (Nordson)

available fuel quantities, isolation of the process, explosion prevention, and provision of adequate means for extinguishment.

Simply stated, the person who adequately manages his or her process must do those things that will tend to prevent a fire from starting and those things that will limit the size of any fire that does occur to a scale that can be quickly extinguished with immediately available resources.

If these things are done, the process can be operated with minimal risk to life and property.

Summary Checklist for Control of Fire Risk

Ignition Avoidance

All recognized sources of ignition must be excluded from the area designated as hazardous, including: open flames such as process heaters, pilot lights, torch welding and cutting operations, cigarette smoking, and space heaters; hot surfaces that may result from prior operations, heat treatment, welding and flame dry off operations, shearing, drilling, and

Figure 44-8. Electrostatic disc. (Ransburg)

grinding operations, friction from binding conveyor components, over-heated bearings, or from hot surfaces of lamps; and sparks resulting from grinding or welding operations, flame cutting, or embers from poorly adjusted overhead fuel burning heaters.

Sparking from open electrical contacts must be avoided by ensuring that all electrical devices within the hazardous area are appropriately approved and listed.

Reactive finishing materials that may overheat if mixed inappropriately must be rigidly controlled in accordance with the process. For example, coating materials that heat after mixing as a result of a chemical reaction may remain at perfectly acceptable temperatures when spread as a thin film onto a product. But the same materials may heat sufficiently to burst into flames if mixed in a pail or bucket that has insufficient surface area to dissipate the heat.

Coating residues that can spontaneously heat, such as air drying enamels and varnishes, must not be allowed to accumulate excessively in collector filters or in wiping rags. Fouled filters that have been removed from spray booth collectors must be removed from the factory immediately or immersed in water and kept immersed until removal to prevent spontaneous ignition.

Unstable materials such as organic peroxides and nitrocellulose materials must be meticulously managed to prevent contamination or excess temperatures that may cause spontaneous decomposition and ignition.

Sparking as a result of discharge of static electricity accumulations must be prevented by thoroughly grounding all electrically conductive objects in the process area. All spray equipment, flammable liquids handling equipment, spray booth components, and associated apparatus, and the conveyors must have ground conductors connected to a common building ground.

Contact points on conveyor racks and rack-to-workpiece contacts must be kept clean and have a resistance of less than 1 megohm at all times.

The floor within the process area should be electrically conductive, and shoes worn by all personnel entering the hazardous area should be of static-dissipative type. If the floor is covered by insulative residues, there must be alternative means for grounding personnel, such as a lanyard with a wrist strap.

Whether or not electrostatic apparatus is installed, static electricity is a common source of ignition of flammable vapors in situations where overspray falls to the floor to form a sticky residue. In walking only three or four steps across the sticky residue, an individual can accumulate a high enough electrostatic voltage on his or her body to discharge an incendive spark when approaching a grounded object. In order to prevent this type of ignition, through prevention of static accumulation, it is critically important that a reliable means of grounding the human body be provided at all times.

Fuel Quantity Limitations

The total quality of fuel permitted in the process area must be restricted to the minimum needed for one shift or one day of operation.

Ready operating supplies should be kept in an area separate from the spray area to prevent their involvement in a spray booth fire.

Pressurized supplies of coating materials should have emergency shutoffs, both manual and automatic interlocked with the fire alarm to prevent additional fuel from being poured into a spray booth fire when hoses are burned off.

Hose materials should have nominal resistance to fire. For example, polyethylene tubing will melt off immediately when exposed to fire, while rubber hoses will be more resistant and Teflon$^{(TM)}$ hoses even more resistant.

Overspray residues within the spray booths, the collector, and the exhaust duct work must not be allowed to accumulate to a quantity that will produce a fire too big and too vigorous for the installed extinguishing system to suppress. Accumulation beyond approximately 1/8-inch thickness should draw careful consideration.

Use of a water wash overspray collector, which keeps collected residues submerged in water, is strongly favored over the dry filter alternative, which usually retains the residues in a configuration that will produce a severe fire when ignited.

Isolation of Process

The spray painting process should be separated from other manufacturing processes and occupancies, both to prevent ignition and to retard fire spread.

Spray booths in which flammable materials are used and in which readily ignitable residues accumulate should be of fire-resistant construction. Spray rooms should have at least a 1-hour fire-resistance rating separating them from other occupancies.

Spray booths should be of the appropriate type, size, and material for the process in which they are being used. Air velocity and volume must capture and contain over-spray to the spray booth.

Exhaust systems that may accumulate readily ignitable residues must be structured and supported to prevent them from collapsing in a fire. They must have adequate clearance from combustible construction, such as at roof penetrations, and they should discharge free of the building to prevent vapors from re-entering.

Explosion Prevention and Pressure Relief Venting

Since ignitable concentrations of vapors or combustible dust routinely exist in several parts of the process—in flammable liquid containers, within the spray process zone, within dust collectors—conditions that will produce an explosion must be prevented.

All flammable liquid reservoirs and closed containers of supply materials must have pressure release vents. To prevent a BLEVE from happening if exposed to a process fire, approved pressure/relief vent devices should be installed on all flammable liquid shipping containers over 5-gallon capacity.

Although ignitable concentrations are expected within the spray pattern, there must be sufficient exhaust airflow to prevent ignitable concentrations from being induced into the exhaust system. Flammable vapors should be diluted to less than 1/4 LFL (Lower Flammable Limit) and ignitable dusts should be diluted to less than 1/2 MEC (Minimum Explosive Concentrate) in ducts leading to powder collectors that are connected to a separate collector, such as a cyclone or bag house, through duct work. An interlock should prevent triggering of automatic spray guns unless the exhaust system is operating.

For powder coating systems, dust collectors that are integrated into the spray booths and are designed to eliminate the confinement necessary for formation of an explosion are preferable to more conventional dust collectors such as a cyclone or bag house, which is connected to duct work and is capable of exploding.

Cyclones, bag houses, and long duct work runs associated with powder coating facilities must have appropriate pressure release venting and duct work to discharge relieved pressure and products of combustion to the exterior of the building. The maximum acceptable length of pressure relief duct work is approximately 10 feet. All process and pressure relief duct work associated with this type of equipment must be constructed to withstand the maximum pressure expected in an explosion. Duct work must have welded longitudinal seams and bolted flange-type joints.

All automatic powder coating installations must have fast-acting flame detectors that will respond within a half second to shut down the process, sound an alarm, and close dampers in any associated duct work between the booth and collector. Prompt shutoff of a supply of airborne combustible dust will extinguish a process fire before enough time has elapsed for embers to form that may be carried through the duct work to ignite the collector. Dampers in the duct work further contribute to interruption of the air flow which would be necessary to transport the embers.

Extinguishment

All spray booths are required to have installed approved automatic fire extinguishing systems. The systems should protect not only the spray process area but the overspray collector and the exhaust system as well. While automatic sprinklers both inside the process enclosure and at ceiling level are recommended, other systems may be appropriate with consideration given to the process, to the materials used, and to the surrounding circumstances.

Interlocks should shut down the process in the event of fire, paint hose rupture, conveyor wreck, ventilation failure, or similar event. They should be integrated with the fire alarm and the emergency stop control to shut down the spray process, interrupt all fuel supplies, and all energy inputs including electrical, compressed air, and hydraulic. The conveyor and all gun movers should be brought to a stop.

Automatic flame detectors with a response time of a half second or less should be installed in all automatic electrostatic systems for fluid or powder spray. Flames in spray patterns of both liquid and powder guns have very high heat release rates, which, if continued, will quickly heat residues and boost the rate of flame spread. Fast-acting flame detectors connected to the interlock almost instantly shut down the spray gun fires in the event of ignition, thus preventing residues from being heated and enhancing chances of prompt extinguishment.

In liquid spray systems where residues are expected to be readily ignitable, thus producing a persistent fire with large volumes of smoke, the air makeup and exhaust ventilation system should be kept in operation during fire conditions.

In powder coating operations where residues are **not** readily ignitable and no persistent fire is expected, the exhaust system should be shut down to prevent fanning of any flames which might then heat residues to ignition temperature.

In spray operations using flammable liquids and readily ignited residues, smoke produced by a fire may completely fill the building or the room containing the spray operation in less than a minute, thereby threatening egress and making attack of the fire by fire fighters almost impossible. The installation of fire curtains and of smoke and heat vents over such operations is recommended to limit the opening of sprinklers to the area immediately above the fire and to aid in clearing smoke so that fire fighting operations may be conducted.

A supply of appropriate hand extinguishers should be readily available to operating personnel in all spray finishing operations.

Training

An on-going training program should be in place for supervision and production employees. Topics to be addressed should include the finishing process, the material used, manufacturers' operating instructions for the apparatus, identification of hazards and means for controlling them, and emergency procedures. Records should be on hand with reference materials for the course content and memoranda of attendance records for each date that training has been conducted. There also should be a realistic program for refresher training.

Manufacturers' instruction manuals for all process apparatus should be on hand.

Inspection of Apparatus and Procedures

Apparatus should be inspected and procedures reviewed on a routine basis and after incidents using a check list to assure that all critical items are inspected.

Values determined during inspections—such as air flows, pressures, electrical current—should be compared with acceptable baseline values during nominal operation to aid in detecting misadjustments or deterioration of apparatus.

Reports of inspection results should be reviewed by management and retained in files for future comparison.

Maintenance

Any equipment damage or wear should be repaired promptly to the original manufacturer's specification. All repairs to equipment listed for hazardous area operation should be made using only replacement parts specified or supplied by the original manufacturer and in strict accordance with the manufacturer's instructions in order to maintain the validity of the safety listing and to assure continued operation in accordance with original specifications.

A permit system must be in place to control all hot work in spray operation areas and for all hot work performed on the spray booth, overspray collector, and exhaust system, including welding, torch cutting, drilling, and sawing operations. All residue should be removed before hot work begins on booth enclosure, collector, or duct work.

Written instructions should be available describing in detail the procedure for removing readily ignitable residues from process equipment or floors. This procedure should specify clearly any chemical substances to be used, require the use of nonsparking scraping tools, require wetting of residues before scraping, and describe in detail the procedure for disposing of residues that have been removed.

A fire guard equipped with appropriate extinguishing equipment should be posted during all hot work and residue removal operations and for a reasonable time after those operations have been completed.

Storage and Handling of Materials and Residues

Written instructions should be on hand describing procedures for storing and handling as well as disposing of all hazardous process materials and residues.

Materials in excess of what is needed for the current day's production should be removed from the process area and kept in a storage area.

Residues should be placed in covered metal containers and removed immediately from the factory. Filters fouled with overspray residues should be immersed in water in metal containers and removed promptly from the factory.

Protective Clothing for Personnel

All persons entering the hazardous process area should be equipped with appropriate protective clothing. To protect from flash fire during process operations, maintenance, and clean-up, exposed personnel should be dressed in clothing providing maximum skin coverage and adequate resistance to flame. Textiles such as Nomex$^{(TM)}$ IIIA or equivalent are most suitable for these tasks.

Bibliography

Instruction manuals of equipment suppliers.

NFPA Codes, Standards, and Recommended Practices

NFPA 33, *Standard for Spray Application Using Flammable and Combustible Materials.*

NFPA 68, *Guide for Venting of Deflagrations.*

NFPA 69, *Standard on Explosion Prevention Systems.*

NFPA 77, *Recommended Practice on Static Electricity.*

NFPA 91, *Standard for Exhaust Systems for Air Conveying of Materials.*

CHAPTER 45

. . . .

Welding and Cutting

W elding and cutting operations have been known to cause as many as 20,000 fires in an average year and have led to direct property damage of almost $224 million per year.[1] This should not surprise the experienced fire inspector, who has seen the hazard potential and the dangers of these common operations.

Cutting and welding operations are hazardous for a number of reasons. First, they normally use flames burning at temperatures of 4,000°F to more than 5,000°F or electric arcs that are hotter than the surface of the sun. They may take place in areas in which containers of fuel gas and oxygen and other combustible materials are present or in areas filled with tools and equipment that may hinder movement during an emergency. Cutting and welding can produce bursts of molten metal sparks that cause burns and other injuries and create brilliant flares of light that can harm unprotected eyes. Together, these factors create a fire and explosion hazard.

As an inspector, you should understand how welding and cutting operations can be performed to minimize the hazards and improve work place safety. You should also be aware of the regulations and standards that apply to these processes.

The NFPA and the American Welding Society (AWS) publish a number of safety and health documents that are recognized by the industry as the major source of information and serve as the basis of many of the federal and state regulations. Two of the most important are ANSI/ASC Z49.1, *Safety in Welding and Cutting,* published by the

---

[1] Manz, A. F., "Who Needs Fire Watchers for Welding and Cutting?", *Fire Journal,* National Fire Protection Association, Quincy, MA, Vol. 83, No. 1 (Jan/Feb 1989), p. 58.

American Welding Society, and ANSI/NFPA 51B, *Standard for Fire Prevention in Use of Cutting and Welding Processes,* published by the NFPA. These two documents are the basis of OSHA 29 CFR 1910 Subpart Q, "Welding and Cutting, General Industry Standards." You should be familiar with these two documents, as well as the OSHA standards. The American National Standards Institute (ANSI), OSHA, the American Petroleum Institute, and others also publish pertinent documents.

The Processes

There are two major categories[2] of welding and cutting processes with which we are concerned. These are processes using oxyfuel gas and electric processes. The oxyfuel processes use gases such as acetylene, propane, propylene, and methane in combination with oxygen or air, while the electric arc processes use alternating currents (AC) and direct currents (DC) at voltages ranging as high as 400 volts, depending on the specific process. Electric arc processes include shielded metal arc welding (SMAW), gas metal arc welding (GMAW), flux-cored arc welding (FCAW), gas tungsten arc welding (GTAW), plasma arc welding (PAW), plasma arc cutting (PAC), carbon arc cutting-air (CAC), and a number of non-arc resistance welding variations. These processes can be manual or mechanized, and they can be done with portable or stationary equipment and machines.

The Electric Arc Processes

Electric arc processes are those that use an arc as the source of heat for melting and joining metals. The heat is controlled and concentrated, and some of the process variations use a filler metal. In most cases, the arc is struck between the metal to be welded and an electrode, which is maneuvered along the weld joint of the work pieces. The electrode may be consumable or nonconsumable, and the arc may or may not be shielded by a flux or shielding gas. The shielding protects the electrode and the molten work piece metal from the reactive effects of the room atmosphere.

---

[2]The terms and definitions used here are taken from AWS A3.0, *Terms and Definitions.*

Shielded metal arc welding: This is one of the oldest welding processes and one of the easiest to use. Commonly known as "stick welding," "covered electrode welding," "electric arc welding," and "rod welding," it is used to weld most of the common metals in any position with a minimum of investment in equipment. The decomposition of the electrode covering provides the shielding, and the melting electrode provides the filler material. Power can be either AC or DC, depending on the electrode coating.

Gas metal arc welding: This process appeared on the scene in the late 1940s, and there are many popular commercial versions. It uses a consumable wire electrode fed from a reel through a conduit to a welding gun, or torch. A nozzle on the end of this gun delivers a shielding gas to the arc. Direct current normally is used with this process; it can be steady state or of a pulsating nature. Among the commercial terms used to describe this process and its variations are MIG (metal inert gas), MAG (metal active gas, such as CO_2 and its mixtures), SHORT ARC, DIP TRANSFER, MICROWIRE, and SIGMA.

Flux-cored arc welding: This process uses much the same equipment as the gas metal arc welding process. In this case, however, the arc zone usually is shielded by the decomposition during welding of a granular flux, which is contained in the center of the tubular wire electrode. The electrode is made from a strip formed into a continuous tube, like a straw. Gas shielding may also be used with the process to supplement the flux shielding.

Gas tungsten arc welding: This process uses a nonconsumable electrode of tungsten. The tungsten may be pure, or it may contain alloying material, such as thoria, zirconia, or rare earth oxides of a few percent. The arc zone is shielded with an inert gas, such as argon or helium, and with a small amount of oxygen on occasion. This process commonly is called HELIARC, TIG (tungsten inert gas), and ARGONARC; in Europe, it is sometimes known as WIG—wolfram is German for tungsten—welding. It uses both AC and DC power.

Plasma arc welding: The plasma arc process is similar to the gas tungsten arc process, except that the plasma arc and its shielding gas are forced through a small orifice in a nozzle placed over the end of the torch. The constricting action of the orifice increases both the heat and the columnar stiffness of the arc. Additional shielding gases are used in this process, and they are introduced to the arc zone by a secondary shielding nozzle surrounding the end of the torch.

Submerged arc welding: This group of processes uses a granular flux material to bury the arc, which operates beneath the flux and is hidden from view. Decomposition of the flux helps the metallurgical reactions taking place in the molten metal puddle and provides an atmosphere for the arc. The process uses a wire electrode fed from a reel in much the same fashion as gas metal arc welding. It does not use auxiliary shielding gas.

Electroslag welding: This process is similar to submerged arc welding, but there is no arc after the process is established. An arc is used initially to melt a certain amount of flux, then extinguished, after which the hot molten flux conducts current from the end of the consumable electrode to the work piece. The current passing through the molten flux generates the welding heat by resistance heating phenomenon.

Plasma arc cutting: The equipment for this process is much the same as that used in plasma arc welding, but the velocity of the gas and the intensity of the arc passing through the orifice are much greater. Reactive gases are introduced to increase the heat released in the arc zone, a process that causes an intense jet to issue from the end of the torch. Because of the intense noise and radiation, the cutting is done underwater using specially designed equipment. Sheet metal is cut in the open air.

Air carbon arc cutting/carbon arc cutting air: This process uses a carbon electrode, held by jaws at the end of a torch holder, and a jet of compressed air, which runs alongside the electrode. The electric arc between the carbon electrode and the work piece melts the metal into a puddle, and the compressed air jet blows it out of the puddle. The shower of sparks can be thrown 30 feet or more.

The Oxyfuel Gas Processes

These processes use fuel gas and oxygen or air obtained from cylinders or a manifold. The gases are delivered to a torch through valves and regulators at the proper pressure and quantity, are mixed in the torch, and are burned at the end of the torch tip. The tips are designed to operate with the specific fuel gas chosen, some of which are lighter than air and some heavier. The temperature of the flame is controlled by the ratio of the fuel gas-oxygen mixture.

Oxyactylene welding and cutting: These processes use acetylene fuel gas to generate the flame. In combination with oxygen, acetylene burns at a higher temperature than any other fuel gas. By adjusting the ratio of oxygen to fuel, the OAW flame can be made reducing, oxidizing, or neutral. When a central jet of pure oxygen is introduced into the flame through a port in the end of the torch tip, the flame will cut steel. The work piece is first heated red/white hot at the place the cutting will start, then the oxygen jet is turned on with a lever on the torch handle. The oxygen literally ignites the hot metal and burns it away. The molten material is blown from the cut by the action of the flame and the oxygen jet. OAC can throw molten metal and slag to over 30 feet.

Brazing: Brazing is broadly defined as a welding process in which the base metals are heated but not melted. Joining is accomplished with a filler metal, which has a melting temperature above 840°F, and a flux, and the molten brazing material is distributed in the joint by capillary action. Brazing can be accomplished with almost any fuel gas in combination with oxygen or air.

Other Uses of Flames

Skilled workers use oxyfuel gas flames for a variety of operations. These include forming by means of heating to facilitate bending or straightening; conditioning by annealing, flame-hardening, and flame-softening; and surface preparation by removing scale, rust, and surface blemishes.

The Hazards of Welding and Cutting

The major hazards of welding and cutting are described on the labels prescribed by ANSI Z49.1 and OSHA standards, which appear on all welding materials and equipment. These hazards include potential over-exposure to fumes, gases, and radiation; electric shock; fires and explosions; noise; spatter and sparks; and general work place hazards.

As an inspector, you should be particularly alert for any circumstances that could lead to fires and explosions, although you should also watch for the other hazards welding and cutting present.

Clothing

Frayed clothing can be ignited easily and should not be worn in an active welding and cutting work area. Sparks and spatter can become trapped in rolled-up sleeves, cuffs, and pockets, which should be emptied of flammable or combustible material, closed, and buttoned. Materials that can melt and cause burns should not be worn as clothing near welding and cutting operations. Clothing should provide enough coverage to protect skin from radiation and spatter burns. Outer garments, such as overalls and jumpers, should be free of oil and grease.

Ventilation

You can be overexposed to fumes and gases if the ventilation in the work area is not adequate. These fumes and gases cannot be classified simply because they depend on the process, the intensity of the heat source, the materials used, and other factors. Besides those fumes that emanate from the metals and welding materials, you may be exposed to gases such as carbon dioxide, carbon monoxide, ozone, and nitrogen oxides. Adequate ventilation will protect you from overexposure.

Areas Containing Combustibles

Welding and cutting should only be done in areas specifically designed for the work. If the area is inappropriate, the operation should be moved to a safe area. Where this is not possible, the nearby fire hazards should be transferred to a safe place. If neither the work nor the fire hazards can be moved, the hazardous materials must be protected from the heat, slag, sparks, and spatter of the process. Welding and cutting work should not be undertaken unless all combustibles in the area have either been moved away or protected from ignition and the atmosphere is nonflammable.

The work area should be swept clean, and combustible floors should be wet down or covered with damp sand, sheet metal, or the equivalent. If water is used, personnel must be protected from electric shock. Be sure that all cracks and openings in the floor are covered or closed to prevent sparks and spatter from falling to the floor below or onto flammable dusts and particles trapped in the crevices. The same precautions should be taken near open windows and doorways.

Fire Protection

Fire prevention and related activities are the joint responsibility of the management, the supervisors, and the workers. Management must see that the workers and their supervisors are trained to safely operate the processes used, that the hazards are communicated, that the work areas are approved for the hot work, and that approved equipment is used.

Supervisors are responsible for seeing that the work area is safe for the work performed, that authorization is given to start work, and that the workers have the proper tools and protective equipment. The workers must have permission before they begin any hot work and should only continue to cut or weld where the conditions remain unchanged and safe.

Hot Work Authorization

On occasion, a hot work permit system is warranted. The system used will depend on circumstances, but it should at least include an inspection and authorization steps before the work is allowed to begin. Refer to NFPA 51B, *Standard for Fire Prevention in Use of Cutting and Welding Processes,* for a sample hot work permit.

Fire Watchers

Fire watchers should be used wherever there is a possibility that a large fire might develop. They should also be used when there are combustibles within 35 feet of the operation and when openings in the floor or wall within a 35-foot radius of the operation expose combustible materials in adjacent areas, including concealed spaces in floors and walls.

Watchers are also necessary when the hot work is likely to ignite combustible materials adjacent to metal walls near the operation. Ship work performed on tank shells, decks, walls, overheads, and bulkheads should be supervised if there is any possibility that sparks or heat transfer will introduce a fire hazard into the adjacent area.

Fire watchers must be trained to use extinguishing equipment and must be able to sound the alarm system. They should continue to watch for fires for at least 30 minutes after the hot work has been completed.

Sprinklers

If the heat of the welding and cutting operation is likely to cause the automatic sprinkler system to operate, you can temporarily cover the sprinklers in the immediate vicinity with noncombustible material or damp cloths. Be sure to remove the temporary protection when the operation is complete.

Containers that Have Held Hazardous Substances

The term "container" refers to jacketed vessels, pipes, tanks, covered parts, and other equivalent items, each of which should be considered to have contained flammable, toxic, explosive, or reactive material that the hot work will activate. Hot work should not be permitted on such containers unless they have been inspected and certified as safe for the job. You should not assume that the container will remain safe during the job: the heat of the work may release hazardous substances hidden in the crevices and corners of the container. For further information, refer to AWS F4.1, *Recommended Safe Practices for the Preparation for Welding and Cutting of Containers and Piping That Have Held Hazardous Substances.*

Inspection Reminders

Regulators

Regulators are not interchangable among the designated gas services at the site. They should be used only for the gas and pressure for which they are labeled. This will prevent them from failing and releasing potentially hazardous gases.

Oxygen gauges should be marked "Use No Oil." Oxygen-enriched fires burn with great violence, so it is imperative that damaged nuts and connections are replaced to avoid leaks and that all connections are checked with leak detection fluid before the system is used. Only qualified technicians should be allowed to repair regulators.

Torches

The only torches that should be used are those that have been approved by a nationally recognized testing laboratory, those that meet nationally recognized standards, and those that have been tested and found to be safe. They are to be ignited only by friction lighters, stationary pilot flames, or some other suitable means of ignition. Matches are unsuitable because the torch gases can blow out their flames, allowing too much gas to escape into the work place.

All torches must be shut off when they are not going to be used for a substantial period of time, such as during lunch or overnight. Remove the torches from confined spaces when the work stops for the night, or make sure that the gas supply system has been turned off. This will prevent gas, which can cause fires and explosions, from leaking from the torch and accumulating in the work area.

Hose

In the United States, fuel gas hoses generally are red and oxygen hoses generally are green. Black is used for inert gas and air hoses. Do not mix these colors. Sometimes hoses are taped together for convenience and to prevent them from tangling. When this is the case, not more than 4 inches in each foot of hose should be covered by the tape. This will allow gases to escape when cracks and defects appear in the hose. Check the hoses for any damage that could cause leaks, and replace or repair burned and damaged sections. Make sure that all connections are tight and leak-free. Welding and cutting gas connections should not be compatible with the breathing air connections.

Flash Arrestors and Protective Devices

Unless required by a standard, most such devices are optional. When an approved device, such as a reverse flow check valve or flash back arrestor, is used, it should be used and maintained in accordance with the manufacturer's instructions. These devices are not a substitute for proper system maintenance.

Cylinders

Cylinders that show signs of severe damage, corrosion, or fire exposure must not be used. The cylinder temperature should not be allowed to exceed 130°F. Make sure that all labels and markings on the cylinder are legible; never use a cylinder whose contents are not known.

Cylinders should never be stored where they may be exposed to physical damage or to tampering. Nor should they be placed where they can impede passage. They should be kept where they will not be knocked over and should be chained or restrained to keep them from falling. Storage locations should be constructed in accordance with the requirements of NFPA and ANSI standards or the local construction codes.

Bibliography

Accident Prevention Manual for Industrial Operations: Engineering and Technology, 8th edition, National Safety Council, 1980. Provides detailed operating procedures for oxyfuel gas welding equipment.

Cote, A. E., ed., *Fire Protection Handbook,* 17th edition, National Fire Protection Association, Quincy, MA, 1991.

Linville, J. L., ed., *Industrial Fire Hazards Handbook*, 3rd edition, National Fire Protection Association, Quincy, MA, 1990.

Safety in Welding and Cutting, ANSI Z 49.1, American Welding Society, Miami, FL. Chapter 5 provides recommendations on ventilation and covers single cylinder systems and arc welding.

NFPA Codes, Standards, and Recommended Practices

NFPA 51, *Standard for the Design and Installation of Oxygen-Fuel Gas Systems for Welding, Cutting, and Allied Processes.* Applies to acetylene and oxygen cylinder storage and use, and covers MAP, other stable gases, and acetylene generation.

NFPA 51B, *Standard for Fire Prevention in Use of Cutting and Welding Processes.* Covers practices and precautions for cutting and welding processes involving the use of electric arcs and oxyfuel gas flames.

NFPA 306, *Standard for the Control of Gas Hazards on Vessels.* Deals with vessels that are to be repaired. Particularly useful for those who inspect ships in port that are carrying or have carried combustible or flammable liquids, flammable compressed gases, bulk chemicals, or other hazardous cargo.

NFPA 327, *Standard Procedures for Cleaning or Safeguarding Small Tanks and Containers Without Entry.* Explains the hazards of these operations and the procedures for flushing or inerting the containers to reduce flammable vapors before using a torch.

CHAPTER 46

Hazards of
Special Occupancies

*A*ll industrial and manufacturing plants have one sort of fire hazard or
another, many of which are common to all and some that are unique to
specific processes. Thus, fire control, suppression, and extinguishment
can be much more difficult and the consequences more disastrous. This
chapter describes how some of these hazards arise across a range of
industrial and commercial processes and facilities, and it points out the
hazards specific to special occupancies without many details about the
processes themselves.

The existence of a potential hazard, such as the presence of flammable
liquids in a facility, should not be construed as a hazardous condition.
Codes and standards define what is acceptable. Many facilities and
processes are unique, and the level of hazard often is reduced by the
physical details, operating procedures, or special local conditions of the
plant. These factors should be borne in mind in any inspection or
evaluation of the hazard level of a facility.

Electric Generating Stations

Large-scale electric generating plants use fuel oil, coal, gas, water, or
nuclear fuel to produce electricity. Hydroelectric generating plants, or
plants using water to produce electricity, have no primary fuel fire
hazards (see Bibliography), and gas turbines are used to produce a
smaller output than generating plants.

The fire hazards in coal- and oil-fired generating plants are associated
with the storage and transmission of the fuel, boiler explosions, failure of
lubrication and hydraulic oil lines, leakage of the hydrogen used to cool
turbine generators, failure of oil-insulated transformers, and deterioration

of cable insulation in spreading rooms. (See NFPA 850, *Recommended Practice for Fire Protection for Electric Generating Plants,* for more information.)

Coal can heat spontaneously in storage yards, bunkers, and conveying equipment, and such fires are difficult to control. All possible sources of ignition should be eliminated by prohibiting smoking and open flames in coal storage areas. Coal dust accumulations should be avoided by operating a continuous collection system and with careful housekeeping practices.

The potential for spontaneous ignition of stored coal depends on many factors including the type of coal, its moisture content as well as storage, pile packing density, and size. When high volatility coals are used procedures often are in place for minimizing conditions that would cause spontaneous heating.

Pulverized coal is entrained in air and carried to the boiler. Pulverizers should have separators to remove tramp metal that might cause ignition. Failure of the feed pipe, from erosion or another cause, can release an explosive cloud of dust.

Explosion hazards exist to varying degrees in pulverized coal-handling equipment. The type of coal and its characteristics, the construction of the coal-handling equipment, and the relative importance of the equipment should be evaluated in order to determine the need for automatic-detection and fixed-suppression devices.

Oil-fired boilers often use heavy fuels, which must be heated for pumpability and atomization. All oil tank heaters should have thermal-limiting devices to prevent the oil from overheating, and flow-through heaters should have a switch to stop the heating if circulation is interrupted.

All fuel-handling equipment should be located outside of tank dikes. Pumps should have filters to prevent damage, and there should be a curb and drain system for pump seal leakage. Oil is carried to the boiler at about 135°F and at pressures of up to 1,000 psi. Rupture of an oil line can cause an extensive spill or an atomized spray. Fuel oil piping should be of all-welded construction with a minimum of connections. Hot surfaces are an ignition hazard. Automatic sprinkler or water spray systems often are provided at the boiler front where fuel oil is present close to hot surfaces.

Boiler explosions result from uneven or low fuel flow causing a loss of flame in a portion of the boiler. Continued introduction of fuel builds an explosive "cloud," which often finds a source of ignition from other flames or hot boiler surfaces. Therefore, all boilers should be equipped with process interlocks that prevent the introduction of fuel without an ignition source and shut the fuel supply off upon loss of flame. Such interlocks are considered standard equipment on all boilers.

Turbine generators require substantial systems for lubricating and hydraulic oils, and these present significant hazards. Oil lines should be installed away from valve bonnets, steam pipes, steam chests, and other turbine parts operating at or above 700°F. High-pressure oil lines should be run inside another pipe to contain oil from leaks.

Lube oil and hydraulic oil systems should be properly protected. Water spray or local application gaseous extinguishing systems are often provided in the vicinity of turbine bearings where lubricating oil connects to the turbine in the vicinity of potential hot surfaces. Turbine generators can be cooled with hydrogen, which, if not carefully controlled, is a severe hazard.

Many electric generators are cooled and insulated with hydrogen gas. The hydrogen is sealed in the generator through seals utilizing oil. The "seal oil unit" has potential hazards similar to those of lubricating and hydraulic oil.

Most central electric generating plants are built and protected to an established level of fire risk acceptable to the utility and its insurance carriers. The level of protection varies between facilities often because the owners' tolerance for risk varies. Fires in electric generating plants are relatively rare. The need for continued uninterrupted operation, the high capital cost of machinery and facilities, and long replacement times help ensure that such facilities are adequately protected.

Nuclear Energy Plants

The fire hazards of nuclear power plants are low compared to those of fossil-fuel power plants. Nuclear power plants are subject to stringent federal regulations for all aspects of design, construction, and operation. The requirements for control and mitigation of fire hazards are set by the Nuclear Regulatory Commission. Hence, nuclear power facilities generally are much better protected than fossil-fuel plants.

The primary objective for the safety of nuclear power facilities is preventing the release of radiation and exposure to personnel. Fires are potential causes of unwanted release and subsequent exposure to radiation; hence, all fire safety provisions of nuclear power plants are carefully controlled and regulated.

While the reactor itself poses no fire hazard, particularly in comparison to fossil fuel power facilities, there are a range of potential fire hazards in nuclear power plants.

There can be oil fires involving reactor coolant pump motors and emergency turbine-driven feedwater pumps; fuel fires at diesel-driven pumps and emergency generators; and fires involving charcoal in filter plenums. Fires can occur in cable insulation, combustible waste and organic resins, and in protective coatings.

There can be fires of flammable off-gases, turbine lubricating oil, and hydrogen seal oil. Hydrogen off-gas is flammable and radioactive. It is held in decay tanks before recombination with oxygen or venting to the atmosphere. Off-gas systems must be monitored constantly for oxygen. Hydrogen cooling gases and hydraulic fluids from turbine controls can leak.

Most of these hazards are similar to those found in conventionally fueled generating plants, and the safeguards are similar. Records indicate that the construction stage is the most vulnerable period for fire damage in nuclear plants (see NFPA 803, *Standard for Fire Protection for Light Water Nuclear Power Plants*).

Computer Centers

Computer rooms and facilities pose a relatively low fire risk. The major fire protection problem associated with these facilities is their high replacement cost and cost caused by operation interruption. Computer facilities are often separated from the remainder of the building by a fire-resistive barrier to prevent fires that originate outside the space from damaging the computer room.

Computer room fires caused by computer equipment faults are relatively rare. Electrical distribution equipment and associated power cabling is a special concern. Concentrations of power and data transmission cable in the subfloor area are typical (see NFPA 75, *Standard for the Protection of Electronic Computer/Data Processing Equipment*).

The storage of ordinary combustible materials such as printer paper, magnetic tape storage, forms, and boxes should be minimized in the computer room or stored in metal cabinets.

Computer facilities often are protected by total flooding gaseous extinguishing systems. The integrity of the enclosure as well as proper functioning of all detection, alarm, and discharge devices. HVAC interlocks and similar devices must be routinely tested. If there are sprinkler systems, a gaseous system often is employed to protect the subfloor and equipment internals. These partial systems must be tested in a manner similar to that for total flooding systems.

Laboratories

Hazards in industrial laboratories can be classified as fire hazards and nonfire hazards. Industrial and academic laboratories have a wide range of potential hazards, including mechanical, electrical, biological, radiation (ionizing and nonionizing), hypobaric/hyperbaric, thermal, chemical, and fire hazards. All of these hazards have the potential to interact. The degree or severity of the hazard formed is driven by the function and details of a particular laboratory facility.

Nonfire hazards are those that can cause injury without ignition or flame. They include radiation and caustic, irritating, and toxic chemicals. Some of these can become more dangerous under fire conditions.

Fire hazards can include compressed gas cylinders, electrically operated laboratory equipment, and static electricity. Combustible or flammable liquids or vapors, reactive chemicals, and flammable solids also are fire hazards, as are furnishings, equipment, and paper products.

One way to reduce the fire hazard is to limit available fuel by excluding or protecting large glass containers of flammable chemicals, storing as much as possible in safety cabinets or rooms. The total amount of flammables should be limited to the quantity sufficient for convenient operation and what is allowed by applicable codes and standards. NFPA 45, *Standard on Fire Protection for Laboratories Using Chemicals,* sets limits on combustible liquids based on construction, compartmentation, fire protection, and arrangement of laboratory units and work areas. NFPA 30, *Flammable and Combustible Liquids Code,* allows up to 25 gallons of Class IA liquids and 120 gallons of Class IB through IIIA liquids to be kept in nonlaboratory spaces.

Ignition sources should be limited by prohibiting smoking and by frequently inspecting motors, switches, ovens, hot plates, and gas burners. Flammable chemicals should be stored in suitable compartments. Refrigerated compartments are considered hazardous locations if they are used to store flammable liquids that cannot be cooled below their flash points in ordinary refrigerators or freezers. Ethyl ether, pentane, and similar liquids should be stored in explosion-proof refrigerators or refrigerators approved for storing flammable materials.

Laboratory managers should strictly control welding, cutting, and other operations that might introduce ignition sources where combustible or flammable materials could be present (see NFPA 30). NFPA 45 is a particularly good reference for chemical lab safety. The NFPA *Industrial Fire Hazards Handbook* provides additional details.

Paint and Coating Plants

The production of nitrocellulose lacquer and the aerosol charging of containers present the most serious fire hazards in plants that make paints and coatings. The use of Class I solvents, with flash points below 100°F, and the production of varnish coating present a less serious fire hazard, as does the use of Class II solvents. Making waterborne coatings presents little fire hazard.

The accidental ignition of flammable vapors and the uncontrolled release of flammable or combustible liquids must be prevented. The most common cause of ignition is static sparks, so equipment must be bonded or grounded to prevent the generation of static electricity.

The storage and arrangement of raw materials present hazards typical of storing large quantities of flammable or combustible liquids. Quantities must be limited, and special fire protection systems must be in place (see NFPA 30 and 30B). However, special precautions must be taken for nitrocellulose.

Nitrocellulose presents special hazards in handling and storage whether it is alcohol-wet, water-wet, or in chips. It should be stored under cover in a cool place away from the plant. It is ignited easily by friction, and drums should never be skidded on the floor. All spilled residue should be swept up immediately with a natural bristle broom, deposited in a covered metal container, and wet with water. The container should be emptied each day and the nitrocellulose burned after it has dried.

Precautions with bulk solvent tanks, including separation venting, self-closing valves, spill and runoff control, control of ignition sources, among others, should conform to standard practice relevant to the liquid being stored.

The primary hazards associated with producing paint and coatings revolve around the storage and handling of flammable liquids. The most common ignition sources are static electricity, chemical heating, and chemical reaction hazards.

The primary safeguards include physical separation of hazardous processes and storage, electrical safeguards, ventilation, explosion venting, containment of spills and vapors, static electricity control such as bonding and grounding, mechanical spark control, spray booths, and inerting. There are special requirements for aerosol production facilities.

Consult NFPA 30, *Flammable and Combustible Liquids Code;* NFPA 30B, *Manufacture and Storage of Aerosol Products;* NFPA 33, *Standard for Spray Application Using Flammable and Combustible Materials;* and NFPA 35, *Standard for the Manufacture of Organic Coatings;* NFPA 68, *Guide for Venting of Deflagrations;* NFPA 497A, *Recommended Practice for Classification of Class I Hazardous (Classified) Locations for Electrical Installations in Chemical Process Areas.*

There often are special requirements for the fire protection systems for these facilities depending upon the materials used, how much of them are stored, and how they are arranged. You must carefully review the design and maintenance of these systems to ensure they provide adequate protection.

Areas that process nitrocellulose should be hosed down periodically or cleaned by an explosion-proof vacuum cleaner with a water chamber. Solidified residue on floors and equipment is highly combustible and difficult to extinguish. Tools used around nitrocellulose and flammable liquids should be nonsparking. Covers on mixing tanks also should be of nonferrous metal.

Aluminum Processing

The primary fire hazards in aluminum processing plants are the equipment for producing or regulating the large amounts of electric power. Other major hazards are hydraulic systems, conveyors, the use of combustible oils in rolling or forming, electrode production, and dust explosion or fire.

Alumina, a mixture of aluminum and oxygen, is precipitated out of a solution of bauxite and caustic soda. The alumina is dried in oil- or gas-fired kilns at 1,800°F. Combustion controls for this equipment require special maintenance efforts to keep them reliable from a safety standpoint.

The alumina is smelted, or reduced, to aluminum in electric furnaces, called pots, by a high-voltage, low-amperage direct current. The major transformers and rectifiers needed to provide the large amounts of current usually are located in a switchyard. There should be sufficient distance between them and oil-filled equipment.

The control building should be of noncombustible construction, and cable runs, pass-throughs, and openings should be firestopped. Cable trays should have noncombustible covers, or cables should be coated with an approved fire-retardant coating. Automatic sprinkler protection over cable trays also will help limit fire spread.

Electrodes for the furnaces are made from a mixture of inert carbon and combustible pitch in vessels heated by steam or oil. Hot-oil heating presents a fire hazard. The storage and handling of solid pitch also present fire and explosion hazards, as would any dust. Anodes are hardened in pits into which an oil or gas flame is introduced. Combustible, volatile products are given off, and fire in the exhaust duct and emission control system is a serious hazard. The baking process should be controlled carefully to prevent fire.

The primary hazard in smelting is the failure of a pot lining, which would permit a molten metal spill called a tap out. Utilities should be arranged so that they will not be damaged by a spill.

Large amounts of combustible oils are used in the rolling of finished aluminum. The oil used in cold rolling has ignition and burning characteristics similar to those of kerosene, and proper fire protection measures should be taken.

Hydraulic equipment using combustible oils usually is necessary to handle heavy ingots and coils. The oil pumps should have automatic shut-off devices. They should be maintained, and they should have a fire protection system.

Although aluminum is a metal, it will burn, especially if it is in a fine powder or dust form, which can be produced by scalping or planing rough ingots to give them a smooth surface. Shavings and fine particles can produce a fire or explosion in dust-collecting systems. Exhaust systems and collectors should meet the requirements of NFPA 65, *Standard for the Processing and Finishing of Aluminum.*

Asphalt Mixing Plants

Fire hazards in asphalt mixing plants generally are related to the aggregate dryer, the drum mix dryer, the pollution control system, and asphalt binder storage.

Tanks containing asphalt, cutbacks, and emulsion usually are heated by transfer oil. Transfer oil lines should be checked for damage that might contaminate the asphalt, thus reducing the flash point of the oil. If the heater is direct fired, it should be equipped with standard fuel burner safeguards and a high temperature shut-off device. The heater should be protected properly against low asphalt level because the greatest danger of fire and explosion occurs when the asphalt does not cover the heating tubes.

The aggregate dryer probably is the most vulnerable piece of equipment. It develops temperatures up to 1,600°F. Because it is subject to constant vibration, you should examine fuel lines, gas valves, flame guards, pumps, and motors for broken connections or leaks that might lead to fire or explosion. It also is important for you to verify that personnel are aware of the need and are trained to purge the heating and exhaust system after every shutdown. Spontaneous combustion can occur when there has been insufficient purging or when leaky valves or connections have allowed combustible gases to be drawn into the dryer.

Hot mix plants, whether portable or permanent, require constant preventive maintenance and must be inspected frequently. Check to see that the interlock system shuts down the burner and that the flow of asphalt is reduced when the flow of aggregate is lessened or stopped. Otherwise, the drum can overheat and the asphalt will ignite. The interlock also must prevent flames from being drawn into the exhaust system and igniting asphalt droplets.

Secondary collectors should be of the wet type to prevent spontaneous ignition of wood splinters or roots from bank-run gravel. Fuel tanks usually are below the ground, but posts or stanchions should be used to protect aboveground lines, valves, and couplings from damage from truck traffic. All general safety rules regarding welding and the use of solvents should be observed.

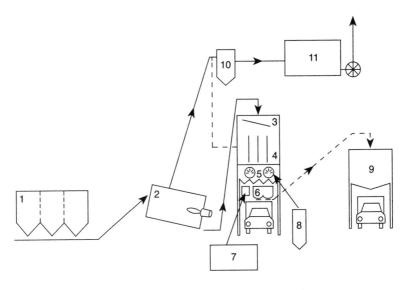

1. Aggregate cold feed
2. Aggregate dryer
3. Screens
4. Hot aggregate bins
5. Weigh hopper
6. Mixer

7. Asphalt cement storage
8. Mineral filler
9. Hot mix storage
10. Primary dust collector
11. Secondary dust collector

Figure 46-1. Flow diagram of materials used in an asphalt-batch plant process.

Plastics Fabrication Plants

There are two broad categories of plastic material processing. The first involves the synthesis or manufacture of a plastic from raw materials. Basically, these are chemical process plants with very specific and unique hazards that cannot be detailed here.

The second category involves the conversion of plastic materials into useful articles by molding, extrusion, or casting. These processes all involve heating the plastic material. This section covers the fire hazards of conversion or plastic processing.

Practically all plastics are combustible compounds that will burn under the right conditions. And the conversion of feedstock into finished articles involves combustible dusts, flammable solvents, and hydraulic fluids, along with the storage and handling of combustible raw material and finished goods.

Nearly all plastics will burn rapidly in the form of dust. If dispersed in air they can be explosively ignited by spark, flame, or metal surfaces heated above 700°F. Dust explosions are possible whenever plastics are pulverized, ground, machined, sanded, or compounded with dyes, fillers, lubricants, stabilizers, or modifiers. The basic chemical structure of the resin governs its explosiveness, and the addition of wood flour, cotton flock, or other combustible fillers usually increases explosiveness.

Fabrication plants have a variety of hazards that can cause fires or explosions. These include those mentioned above as well as high heat elements, heat-transfer fluids, static electricity, and poor storage and housekeeping practices.

Flammable solvents are used in nearly all plastic fabrication, and they must be stored and handled as carefully as they would be in any other processing plant. The solvents can be somewhat more hazardous when applied to plastics because plastics usually generate and retain static electricity more readily than do paper or cotton fabric. Static electricity can rapidly build up to spark discharge, a hazardous condition if dust or flammable vapors are present. High ambient humidity does not dissipate the static charge of plastic; therefore, equipment must be grounded, and the tinsel conductors must maintain contact with moving films.

Heat commonly is used in conversion processes. Interlocks required to ensure ovens, extruders, or molds do not exceed safe limits often are provided. Hydraulic systems used to compress or roll heated material that are in close proximity to heat sources are a potential fire hazard, and they present the same hazards in plastic fabrication as they do in other industrial processes.

Polyurethane, polyethylene, plasticized polyvinylchloride, and polyesters are severe fire hazards that are exceeded only by thermoplastics, such as polystyrene and acrylonitrile (ABS). These materials break down, act, and burn like flammable liquids. These plastics present the most severe fire hazard in the form of foamed material.

Rubber Products Plants

The principal hazards in the manufacture of rubber products involve storage of natural and synthetic rubber and compounds such as sulfur, oil, and hydrocarbon solvents; mixing of solvents and rubber; mixing rubber; spreading cement; spreading rubber on fabric; and dipping rubber fabric in cement because these processes involve a continual use of combustible materials.

Heat created in the mixing operation, static electricity, buffing, spontaneous combustion, and common operations such as welding and burning are the chief sources of ignition.

Baled raw rubber usually is shipped and stored in wood or cardboard containers. These materials, which are palletized and stored to a height of 12 to 14 feet, present a significant fire hazard.

Rubber is broken up and compounded with carbon black and oil in a Banbury mixer. Friction within the mill heats the compound to a predetermined level. Malfunction of the temperature indicator can allow the mixture to overheat and vaporize the oils to the point at which they ignite automatically. When exposed to air, the vapors ignite. Fire in the Banbury mixer can spread easily to the exhaust duct and dust collector. Periodic cleaning of the mixer is necessary to remove the oil-soaked residue that accumulates on the outside.

To improve adherence of rubber components, they are dipped or spread with a cement made of rubber, flammable liquids, and other compounds. The opening of the cement mixer can release flammable liquids or vapors, which, once ignited by static electricity or friction sparks, can cause a rapidly spreading fire. A humidity level of 50% or higher will help control static electricity.

If rubber cement with a low flash point is used for dipping, a flammable solvent is required, and the process is usually followed by drying in a heated oven. Therefore, adequate ventilation is necessary to keep the concentration of vapors below 25% of the lower explosive limit (LEL).

There are very specific requirements for the design and installation of fire protection systems in rubber manufacturing and storage. NFPA 231D, *Storage of Rubber Tires,* details the requirements for storing rubber tires in stacks higher than 20 feet indoors. Rubber-product manufacturing areas are classified as Extra Hazard Group 1 areas in NFPA 13, *Standard for the Installation of Sprinkler Systems.* Carbon black dust collectors should be protected in accordance with NFPA 654, *Standard for the Prevention of Fire and Dust Explosions in the Chemical, Dye, Pharmaceutical and Plastics Industries.*

Clay Products Plants

Many fires in clay products plants have common causes, such as high temperatures, improper storage and use of solid and liquid fuels, overheating due to insufficient clearance, and poor maintenance. The more unique hazards include small-particle combustibles, straw and other combustibles used for packing, welding, and careless smoking around combustibles that are more ignitible because they have been exposed to process heat.

Sawdust, ground nut shells, or similar substances are sometimes added to the clay mix. The handling and storage of them can create organic dust, which is an explosion hazard. Damp sawdust can heat spontaneously and should be disposed of properly.

Naphthalene, a combustible solid, is sometimes used to make bricks. It sublimes when the clay is fired and can be recovered and reused. Naphthalene vapors and dusts form explosive mixtures with air. Recovery equipment should be safely designed and have adequate ventilation. Naphthalene should be stored and handled in the same manner as other volatile combustible solids.

Oil of kerosene class often is used to prevent clay from sticking to molds. Oil-soaked floors and benches add to fire spread, thus safeguards against oil spills should be instituted.

The drying and firing of clay products require heat, often at high temperatures. There are the usual hazards of fuels, burners, and electrical and mechanical faults so combustible materials must be safely separated from heat and ignition sources. Examine chimneys and waste heat ducts for cracks and holes.

"Hot floor" drying is sometimes done on wood floors heated by low-pressure steam; such spaces need to be kept free of other combustibles, and proper clearance must be maintained. Slatted wood floors also are used in multiple levels. Prolonged exposure to elevated temperature and vertical updrafts pose the potential of rapid fire involvement.

These facilities require fuel for the heating processes used. Coal, fuel oils, and gases are used, and relevant precautions for handling them should be taken. Combustion safeguards for Dryers, kilns, ovens, and similar equipment also should have combustion safeguards.

All plants should have adequate Class A fire extinguishing equipment and employees should be trained to properly use fire fighting equipment.

Drycleaning Plants

The special fire hazards of drycleaning plants depend to a large extent on the class of solvent used. Systems using Class I solvents, such as low flash point naphtha, are now prohibited. Type II systems use solvents with flash points between 100°F and 140°F. Type III systems use solvents with flash points between 140°F and 200°F. Type IV and V systems use solvents considered to be noncombustible, but which can have toxic vapors that need to be adequately ventilated.

The fire hazards in drycleaning plants stem from poor housekeeping practices, lint and trash accumulation, and lack of cleanliness; improper wiring of equipment and overloading of circuits; failure to properly maintain and operate equipment; failure to maintain solvent temperatures at least 20°F below flash points; unsafe storage of chemicals and solvents; and static electricity, sparking from metal objects, and ignition of matches left in garments.

Type II and III plants should have scuppers, curbs, or special drainage systems that carry spilled or leaked solvents to a safe area. The exhaust system should have a capacity of 1 cubic foot per minute for each square foot of floor area. Ventilation pickup points should be within 6 inches of floor level. The amount of ventilation should keep solvent vapor concentration below 25 percent of its lower flammable limit.

Storage of combustible and flammable solvents in the cleaning room should be limited to a one-day supply. However, in plants that consume large amounts of solvents, the solvents can be stored in outside tanks or in cutoff enclosures with at least a 1-hour fire-resistance rating and then transferred as needed, to the cleaning room. The solvent transfer system should be adequately protected. (See NFPA 32, *Standard for Drycleaning Plants,* for more information.) Washing machines should have an automatic solvent shutoff device or overflow drains to an underground tank.

In Type IV plants, apparatus with open flames or exposed electric heating elements should be located so that cleaning vapors are not drawn over these apparatus and converted to phosgene, a toxic gas.

Grain Mill Products

Dust explosions are the most serious hazard in grain handling and storage. The greatest number of dust explosions have been of undetermined cause or in undetermined locations. However, where it has been possible to determine the location, the vertical bucket elevator is a common place for primary dust explosions. Where it has been possible to determine the cause, welding or cutting torches, friction in bucket elevators, and fire, other than welding, rank closely as the most common ignition sources. Spontaneous ignition of raw materials caused by microbiological spoilage is rare, but it has occurred.

Bucket elevators require constant care and maintenance to eliminate ignition sources, which can include bent or broken buckets, belt splice failures, electrical sparking resulting from overloading or grounding, open flames from smoking materials, and space heaters. Mechanically heated surfaces, such as bearings, sheet metal in contact with moving belts, and vibrating dissimilar materials can generate enough heat to ignite dust. Vehicles with internal combustion engines can have surface temperatures high enough to ignite dust-laden air. The primary fire hazards associated with belt conveyors are the rubber material of the belting and the potential dust production caused by the moving belt. Pneumatic conveyors can create static electrical charge buildup.

Dryers also present a significant hazard in grain handling. They are direct-fired with the heat of the burned fuel directed into a stream of air that is passed directly through the moist grain. Heated air leaving the dryer carries coarse dust and fine particles, and care must be taken to prevent them from re-entering the burner.

The grain-cleaning operation removes and concentrates extraneous materials from the grain. These materials, because of their dryness and high fiber content, are more prone to ignition than the grain itself.

Ventilation and dust-collection systems are the most important safeguards in grain mills. The difficulty in fighting grain fires, including the unique problems of access, the possibility of creating dust explosion hazards in fire fighting, and the management of fire water collection, require that adequate prefire planning and emergency procedures exist.

Special provisions for electric equipment (see Articles 500 and 502 of NFPA 70, *National Electrical Code*) in certain areas of the plant may be required. Equipment and process interlocks permitting automated safe shutdown typically are provided. Also see NFPA 61B, *Standard for the Prevention of Fires and Explosions in Grain Elevators and Facilities Handling Bulk Raw Agricultural Commodities,* and NFPA 61C, *Standard for the Prevention of Fire and Dust Explosions in Feed Mills.*

Vegetable- and Animal-Oil Processing

The fire hazards of processing vegetable and animal oils primarily involve the equipment and materials used as adjuncts to the main processing, such as the generation and use of hydrogen to harden fats and oils, the use of high temperatures and pressures, and the spray drying of soaps and detergents.

Fats and oils tend to solidify in storage and must be heated before being processed. Heating systems for storage tanks must enter at the top and extend to the bottom to provide a channel for the heated material to expand upward. Explosions can occur when tanks are heated improperly.

Disposal of the spent filter cake used in refining, degumming, and bleaching of oils and fats presents the hazard of spontaneous combustion. The filter cake should be removed from the plant and buried. If a flammable solvent is used to extract oil from the spent earth, all the required safeguards for the use and storage of such solvents must be observed, and the spent earth must be treated accordingly.

Because hydrogen has an extremely wide flammability range, there are fire hazards in the hydrogenation process. All electrical equipment should be suitable for Class I, Division 1 hazardous locations. Tools should be nonsparking, and employees should wear rubber-soled shoes.

The manufacture and storage of hydrogen require that all of the precautions for the hydrogenation process, and more, be taken. It is necessary to rely on the expertise of the plant designers and suppliers for full protection against fire and explosion.

Deodorizing requires temperatures of 410°F and 525°F. Boilers for heat-transfer systems employing the most frequently used mixture of diphenyl and diphenyl oxide are direct-fired with either gas or oil. Leaks between the firebox and the boiler can cause a fire or an explosion. Because of low surface tensions and viscosities of heat-transfer media, welded construction is recommended.

In addition to the above hazards, the manufacturing of soap has two more fire hazards. When soap is spray-dried to make beads, fire can occur in the spray tower or exhaust air ducts. Residue can stick to the tower walls and superheat to the point of ignition. Although periodic cleaning will minimize this hazard, automatic sprinkler protection is necessary. In addition, leaks in the fatty acids still and fractionating tower can permit the fatty acids to soak into the insulation. Where due to auto-oxidation, they can build up temperatures high enough to self-ignite.

Generally, the areas housing heat transfer boilers or vaporizers should be separated from the remainder of the plant by fire-resistive or noncombustible construction, and they should be sprinklered. Combustion safeguards on boilers or other fuel filled equipment should be provided.

The finished product should be stored away from the remainder of the plant. Palletized storage must be within the limits of the sprinkler system.

Furniture Manufacturing

Furniture manufacturing plants, except the most modern ones, present severe fire hazards. Usually the buildings are combustible. And wood, the primary raw material used to make furniture, normally is combustible and is made more so by being dried, in either the air or a kiln, until it has a moisture content of 7%. The process, which employs highly volatile and flammable solvents and finishes, produces shavings and dusts. It also requires a great deal of ventilation, which produces large airflows that spread fire rapidly.

Yard storage of raw material can be an obvious fire hazard. The arrangement of the storage piles with spacer sticks for drying make fires difficult to suppress once they have started. There should be adequate distance between these piles and the rest of the plant.

Fine dust produced by milling, veneering, finishing, or sanding must be removed by conveyor or pneumatic systems. These dusts and other scrap are often burned in the plant boiler room. Transporting the dust by conveyor to pulverizers has the typical hazards associated with conveyor belt systems.

Scraps and wood dust are collected by pneumatic conveyor and transported to filtration equipment. Often the pneumatic system air is recirculated to the plant. These systems should be designed and installed to meet the requirements of NFPA 91, *Standard for Exhaust Systems for Air Conveying of Materials;* and NFPA 664, *Standard for the Prevention of Fires and Explosions in Wood Processing and Woodworking Facilities.*

The primary hazards of furniture finishing operations are those associated with the spray application of flammable or combustible liquids and their associated mists and vapors. Spray booths, ventilation, and explosion-proof electrical equipment should be used to eliminate ignition sources in spray areas. Precautions against spontaneous heating must be taken. (See NFPA 33, *Standard for Spray Application Using Flammable and Combustible Materials*).

Curing ovens are generally Class A. Because there is a fire and explosion hazard inside the ovens, the installations should conform to the requirements of NFPA 86, *Standard for Ovens and Furnaces.*

Despite the hazards presented by the materials and processes, however, fires are most likely to occur from poor maintenance and repair practices involving welding and similar activities, saw or grinder sparks, or overheated motors. Contaminated rags, accumulations of overspray, and poor ventilation leading to a build-up of solvent vapors are other hazards.

Textile Manufacturing

The basic fire hazards in textile manufacturing are associated with the close proximity of machinery and materials, the ease of ignition of the material, and the potential rapid rate of fire spread. The leading causes of fire are electrical equipment failures, mechanical sparks, and friction heating.

Production processes in the textile industry differ between facilities because the raw materials used vary. However, there are common fire hazards, such as storage and opening of bales, cleaning raw stock, weaving, and finishing. The extent of the hazards will vary according to the inherent combustibility of the raw material.

Cotton fibers are ignited easily by sparks or open flame and burn readily. Synthetic fibers are less easily ignitible, but burn readily. Wool and other raw materials might not ignite or burn as easily as cotton, but collectively they present the same fire problems.

Cotton and other natural fibers are shipped and stored in rather loosely packed bales, which usually are covered with burlap. Often they are stacked up to 20 feet high (see NFPA 231E, *Recommended Practice for the Storage of Baled Cotton*). Fire from a smoldering, or firepacked, bale or from another source can ignite other bales and involve the entire stack.

Fires in the opener, or feeder, room can be caused by friction sparks from unremoved pieces of bale ties or from layering in the beaters. Lint accumulations on floors and machines are ready fuel for fires. Thus, the amount of opened material should be limited.

Card machines further clean and straighten the fibers, and fires in them usually are caused by friction sparks from tramp metal. Automated machines combining opening, picking, and carding are less susceptible to fire because they have incorporated fire safety measures. However, a fire in such equipment will spread through ducts to other machines or to the dust collector. Quick detection and suppression are necessary to avoid extensive damage.

In the combing, drawing, roving, and spinning operations, the bunching of fibers and ignition by friction can cause fires.

Starch is used in the sizing of warp or filler yarns. A dust explosion can occur if the dry starch is handled improperly (see NFPA 61A,

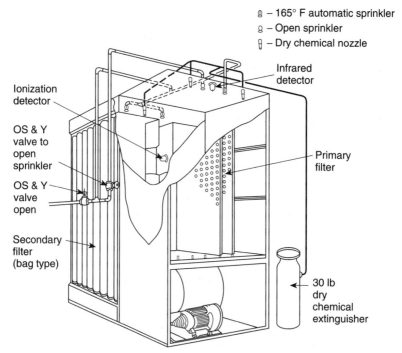

Figure 46-2. Arrangement of fire protection for a textile card filter unit. There are two basic extinguishing systems in this installation: water and dry chemical. (Factory Mutual System)

Standard for Prevention of Fire and Dust Explosions in Facilities Manufacturing and Handling Starch).

Fires in weaving rooms account for almost half of the fires in textile plants. The main cause of such fires is electrical. Vibration at the loom causes breaks in the wiring, resulting in short circuits and sparking. Lint and dust accumulations, unless periodically removed, provide fuel for such fires.

The manufacture of carpeting requires heat for setting the latex backing and setting the carpet width, which is done in carpet ovens. Malfunction of gas-fired equipment, lint build-up, and electrical arcing are the most frequent causes of fire in the ovens.

Paper Products Plants

Paper products include cardboard boxes, milk cartons, and a host of other products that start as rolled paper. The paper passes through machines that cut, shape, and convert the stock into finished goods. Regardless of the end product, the fire hazards for all are similar. They all involve large quantities of combustible stock and combustible waste in the form of paper dust and scrap. Idle wooden pallets also are a significant fire hazard.

Stock for shipping containers comes in rolls up to 120 inches wide. These rolls are stored in piles up to 25 feet high. The piles create flue spaces between the rolls, and fire spreads through them rapidly. The rate of fire spread is increased if the rolls are not prevented from unwinding, which exposes more unburned fuel (see NFPA 231F, *Standard for the Storage of Roll Paper*). And finished box blanks can be stored on rack storage shelves or on pallets piled one on top of another as high as necessary, as long as they are stable. The fire hazard is directly related to the storage heights of the combustible material, no matter what the storage method is.

Most modern container plants have pneumatic systems for conveying waste to the balers. In some plants, waste goes to the balers in bulk carts from localized collection points. Corrugated cardboard tends to bridge or hang up in waste accumulators, creating an additional fire hazard. Baled waste becomes mushy and difficult to handle when wetted, presenting the danger of collapse and structural damage.

Printing operations in container plants create the usual hazards of flammable inks, solvents, driers, and cleaners. Similar hazards are found in other paper products plants.

Printing and Publishing Plants

Hazards in the printing and publishing industry are due to the fact that the basic raw material, paper, is combustible. The oils and solvents used for printing and clean-up also are combustible and flammable, and the movement of paper through presses, folders, and collators generates static electricity, which can be an ignition source.

Letterpress operations produce an ink mist, which accumulates on building and equipment surfaces. Because of its oil content, the mist is a fire hazard.

Offset printing can use oil-fired, gas-fired, or electric heaters to obtain the proper humidity in the paper. Isopropyl alcohol, which has a flash point of 53°F, is used as a wetting agent in the water fountains of offset presses. Sheet-fed offset is dried with a cornstarch-based powder, which is more explosive than coal dust. This must be vacuumed up periodically, and the cleaner bags must be emptied immediately.

Practically all printing requires frequent washing and cleaning with highly volatile, flammable solvents, which can include lead-free gasoline. Silk-screen presses can be connected to drying ovens, which can create flammable vapor fires.

All solvents should be stored in safety cans, and data sheets should include flash points. Water-type extinguishers should not be permitted in press rooms because they are incompatible with flammable liquids and electrical equipment.

Stored rolled stock is a serious fire hazard because of the fluelike spaces that are created between rolls stored on end to heights of 20 feet or more. Stored rolled paper must be protected by automatic sprinklers. And although paper in sheet form stored on skids or pallets is not an unusual fire hazard, it should be protected by automatic sprinklers. Paper dust should not be allowed to accumulate on top of rolls or on building surfaces.

Good housekeeping is necessary throughout printing plants to remove paper dust and scraps, ink mist, or drying powder accumulations. Electrical equipment should be well maintained and grounded, and static electricity should be grounded. Smoking, the use of open flames, such as for cutting and welding, and hot surfaces should be controlled carefully.

Pulp and Paper Mills

Paper mills often are located in remote areas and rely on their own utility services, including power generation, steam production, and fire fighting water supply. Large boilers and chemical reactors form unique explosion hazards. The major hazard areas include black liquor recovery boilers, paper machines, roll paper storage, and process control centers and wiring. Other hazard areas include digestors, bailed paper storage, boilers, turbine generators, raw material storage, bleaching process areas, and cooling towers.

Log piles can be either ranked, as with cordwood, or stacked, such as dumped at random in cone-shaped piles. Dried wood and refuse combined with uncontrolled ignition sources such as welding, smoking, open burning, or poorly maintained handling equipment can cause a serious, difficult-to-control fire.

Debarkers and chippers produce large quantities of combustible material. Chief sources of ignition are careless welding, sparking, friction, and electrical defects.

Major hazards in the bleaching process involve the storage and handling of flammable liquids or toxic gases such as methanol and chlorine. Electrical cables required for power and control are subject to corrosive atmospheres and chemical spills. The use of fiber-reinforced plastics in ventilation and exhaust systems also poses a severe hazard.

A violent reaction can occur in the boiler in which process chemicals are recovered if water comes in contact with the hot smelt. Fire also can occur in combustible residues in the flue gas circuit.

Boilers for meeting the steam requirements of the mill can be fired by gas, oil, coal, bark, or a combination of these, and are subject to the hazards of similar boilers in other industrial plants. The lime kiln can be oil- or gas-fired and presents fuel-explosion hazards similar to those of the power boiler. Noncondensable gases, such as hydrogen sulfide, originating in various processes are collected and piped to the kiln for incineration.

Turbine generators are equipped with central lubricating and hydraulic systems. Oil leaks can present serious fire hazards so the generators should be properly protected.

The paper machine is a major fire hazard. Paper scraps, wool or synthetic felt, lint, and oily deposits can accumulate on the machine, hood, and duct surfaces. A break in the paper web can send large quantities of paper into the broke pit below the machine. Normally this is conveyed back for repulping, but it does present an added fire hazard. Dryers and coaters require heat that can ignite the paper if not controlled carefully. Flammable or combustible solvents used to clean calender rolls and other equipment are another hazard. Extrusion machines combine the hazards of paper, polyethylene, and lint with electrically heated dies and gas-fired flame impingement heaters. Large lube-oil and hydraulic-oil systems also are severe fire hazards.

Wood Products Manufacturing

Wood products plants include sawmills, which produce standard-sized lumber, and plywood and particle board plants. Because they use raw materials and produce wastes similar to those of the pulp and paper and furniture industries, their fire hazards are similar in many respects.

Sawmill logs are stored in ranked, or stacked, piles or floated in ponds. Fire hazards include ignition from grass, brush, or forest fires and sparks from refuse burners, boiler stacks, locomotives, and vehicle exhaust. Waste materials, sawdust, bark, and scraps are conveyed to wood hoggers; tramp metal entering the hogger can cause sparking, which will ignite the waste. Combustible hydraulic oil in process machinery, temporary heating devices, welding sparks, faulty electrical equipment, and smoking are all fire hazards. Good housekeeping is essential to reduce the amount of fuel available.

Stuck lumber in kilns and storage yards is a severe hazard because it creates horizontal flues, which increase the burning rate and make extinguishment difficult. Planing seasoned lumber creates combustible dusts and fine shavings.

Particle board and hardboard are made of sawdust, shavings, and chips. Dumping and retrieval of the raw materials can suspend wood dust and create an explosion hazard. Grinding raw materials to the desired size presents an explosion hazard from tramp metal. Drying the ground material, whether in direct or steam-heated dryers, basically is hazardous.

Hardboard and fiberboard are made from wood fiber, which is puffed in a steam chamber. Particle board is made of wood chips. The forming

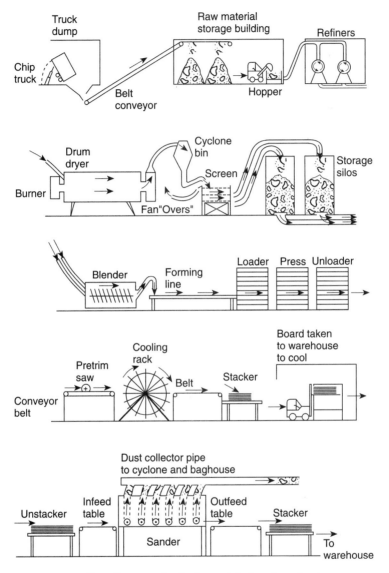

Figure 46-3. A flow diagram of a basic particle-board production process.

and pressing operations required for each produce explosion or fire hazards. After pressing, the boards are humidified in ovens, which also constitute a fire hazard. The dust-collecting systems and large belt sanders used in the finishing operation are particularly susceptible to fire and explosion.

Plywood plants do not have the same level of hazards as do particle board plants, but they do have similar dust hazards in finishing operations. Equipment such as hot presses, sanders, and dryers are potential ignition sources.

Lumber Storage Yards

Poor housekeeping, smoking, boiler room sparks, and portable heaters or barrel fires for warmth are the main hazards in lumber storage yards. Aisles in between storage piles should be wide enough for fire apparatus.

Waste material from rough milling is carried by belt conveyor to the wood hog, which cuts the waste into small pieces. The conveyor should have a magnetic separator to keep tramp metal from causing a fire in the hog, pneumatic conveying, and waste-storage silos. Waste material swept up and carried to the hog is a hazard because often it contains metal objects. Finer material is removed by air-moving equipment, cyclones, or bag filters. Some waste is used as fuel, and some might go to pulp or particle board manufacturers. Air-moving systems should be designed to remove transient flammable vapors.

Shipyards

Shipyards are threatened by many fire hazards that arise from the proximity of noncompatible processes such as welding and painting. Open-flame work is the prime hazard, so all welding and cutting must be monitored carefully (see NFPA 303, *Fire Protection Standard for Marinas and Boatyards*).

The materials used in the construction of ways partially determine the fire hazards (see NFPA 312, *Standard for Fire Protection of Vessels During Construction, Repair, and Lay-up*). When the ways are made of wood, exposure to open-flame and electric-arc welding is the primary concern. No stored materials or occupied structures should be permitted below the vessel being constructed. Accumulated flammable trash on or below the ways or aboard the vessel can lead to a catastrophic fire. Ways should be protected with adequate portable extinguishers, standpipes, and hoses. Automatic sprinklers for substructures and vertical draft stops are desirable.

Cylinders supplying welding torches should be restrained in an upright position, and lines should be protected against damage and leakage. Electrical cables also should be protected and generators secured. Generators, gas manifolds, and cylinders should be located on the open deck or over the side of the vessel.

Paints, solvents, adhesives, lumber, and other combustible materials should be limited aboard the vessel or closely adjacent to it. Crating and flammable packing materials should be removed immediately from the area.

When a vessel is ready for launching, all flame-producing work should cease, all flammable and volatile materials should be removed, and the ways should be greased properly. After the vessel is launched, skid grease should be removed immediately.

The fire hazards of shipyards will vary with the size of the yard and the types of construction materials. The major hazards arise from open-flame operations and the presence of large quantities of fuels such as flammable gases, liquids, solvents, adhesives, paints, and wood. All operations should be monitored carefully to see that they are compatible. Smoking should be confined to safe areas, and a high standard of house-keeping should be maintained.

Machine Shops

Metal machining might appear, at first sight, to have few, if any, fire hazards. However, many aspects of the operation are hazardous. Nearly all metals will burn in air under certain conditions, depending on size, shape, and quantity. And metals react differently with liquids used as coolants or lubricants. The metals most susceptible to ignition during milling or grinding are aluminum, magnesium, titanium, uranium, and zirconium. For most of these, Class D dry powder extinguishing agents should be readily available and carefully applied (see NFPA 480, *Standard for the Storage, Handling, and Processing of Magnesium Solids and Powders;* NFPA 481, *Standard for the Production, Processing, Handling, and Storage of Titanium;* and NFPA 482, *Standard for the Production, Processing, Handling, and Storage of Zirconium*).

The principal fire hazards in metal-working or machine shops include chip fires at the machine caused by heat or friction; spontaneous combustion of cuttings; combustion of coolants and lubricants; fine particles that are combustible or explosive; explosive hydrogen evolved from the reaction of metals such as uranium, aluminum, and magnesium with water; escape of pressurized hydraulic fluids from machine tools and accessories; combustion of oil vapors deposited on the building surfaces; and combustion of oil-saturated floors.

Often it is necessary to clean or degrease machined pieces. This often is done with flammable solvents, which can constitute a fire hazard. Trichloroethylene, a nonflammable solvent, will react with aluminum to form soft, burning carbon and great volumes of toxic and corrosive hydrochloric acid vapor. Proper safeguards should be provided for all types of degreasers.

Cuttings and chips should be collected in noncombustible containers and stored in safe locations. Cutting-fluid spills and drippage should be cleaned up and not allowed to accumulate. Building surfaces should be inspected frequently. Dust and oily residue should be cleaned as necessary.

Motor Vehicle Assembly

Plastics and flammable liquids are the cause of most of the fire hazards associated with the assembly of motor vehicles. Rubber tires and polyurethane foam seats are particularly difficult to protect in storage, and fire involving them is likely to be extensive and serious.

The flammable and combustible liquids include gasoline, lubricants, engine coolants, hydraulic fluid, paint, thinners, adhesives, cleaning solvents, and sealers. High-volume liquids such as gasoline, coolants, brake and hydraulic fluids, and paint often are pumped from a remote storage area to the point of use. Small quantities of flammable or combustible liquids can be kept in safety cans at work stations.

Probably the most common cause of fire in finished vehicles is electrical. Mistakes in the wiring assembly can result in crossed circuits and overheating of the wires. Metal-fastening clips can cut through insulation and cause a short-circuit fire. Another fire source is carburetor backfiring when engines are started with air cleaners removed and carburetors primed with gasoline.

Welding is a fairly common cause of fires in motor vehicle assembly. Large components are welded in machines using hydraulic clamps and pressure. Oil leaks are common and collected in a sump, which could contain other combustible debris. The welding arc is an ever-present ignition source. Cardboard cartons, wooden crates, and burlap bags used as containers for small parts often are brought to the welding area where they are a fire hazard. Body seams are sealed during and after welding. The sealant presents no special fire hazard, but solvents are required for cleaning up sealant spills. These solvents usually are flammable, so all solvent residue must be removed before welding is resumed.

Good maintenance and housekeeping practices are essential. Areas susceptible to fire include exhaust systems, electrical equipment, and paint overspray collectors. Rubber dust ground off on the test rolls is subject to spontaneous ignition.

Cleanrooms

Product development and quality control in many of today's industries require extremely clean work environments. Semiconductor manufacturing, pharmaceutical, and biomedical research facilities in particular operate under strict guidelines to avoid contamination. Critical research and development for these industries and others is performed in cleanrooms.

Cleanrooms are rooms in which the concentration of airborne particles is controlled to specified limits. These limits are defined in federal standard FED-STD-209D and are indicated by a class number. The number refers to the quantity of particles of a given size found in 1 cubic foot of air. Class 10,000 and 1,000 are fairly typical; class 100 is not uncommon. Many of these rooms may be further subdivided into clean zones with a designation of Class 10 or 1.

The fire hazards associated with a cleanroom will vary according to the functions performed and not all cleanrooms will contain the same hazards. A cleanroom designated for biomedical research may utilize only a small quantity of flammable liquids on a weekly basis. Alternatively, a semiconductor manufacturing cleanroom may utilize daily a substantial quantity of flammable liquids along with flammable, pyrophoric (gases which ignite spontaneously upon contact with air), and toxic gases. The most common flammable liquids encountered are alcohols or alcohol-based mixtures. Gases may include silane, arsine, dichlorosilane, and diborane.

Appropriate handling and storage procedures allow the use of the above materials without incident. Storage and handling of flammable liquids should follow the requirements of NFPA 30, *Flammable and Combustible Liquids Code,* except in the use of standard, metal, safety cans. Certain high purity chemicals may become contaminated from particles transferred from one container to another, or even from the liner of the container. In these instances, the flammable liquid is stored and dispensed from the original glass container in which it is received. In such cases, special carts designed to transport glass containers from the flammable liquid storage room are used. They support the containers and can hold their contents in the event of breakage. Flammable liquids should be placed in an approved flammable liquid storage cabinet when not in use.

Storage and handling of compressed gases should be in accordance with NFPA 55, *Standard for the Storage, Use, and Handling of Compressed and Liquefied Gases in Portable Cylinders.* Space limitations and safety concerns often will require that gases be piped into a cleanroom. Nonflammable gases such as oxygen and nitrogen may be in cylinders just outside the room and should be labeled and properly secured. Pyrophoric and toxic gases should be located outside of the building on concrete pads or in concrete vaults or bunkers. The process equipment or "tools" which use such gases are highly automated and incorporate various safety interlocks. Included are: pressure and temperature sensors, gas detectors, overpressure relief devices, and automatic shutoff valves. Maintenance and inspection files for this equipment should be available for review.

A wide variety of fire protection equipment will be found in cleanrooms. NFPA 318, *Standard for the Protection of Cleanrooms,* requires an automatic wet pipe sprinkler system. Appropriately spaced portable fire extinguishers also may be found. Halon extinguishers should not be used in cleanrooms where inorganic hydrides such as silane, diborane, dichlorosilane, and others are utilized. Halon is dangerously reactive with these materials.

Horizontal surfaces of wet benches or other "tools" should not be obstructed from coverage by ceiling sprinkler discharge. If obstructions exist, then sprinkler protection should be extended to cover the surface of the tool or a gaseous suppression system should be provided for it.

Due to unique airflow and filtering requirements, conventional spot-type smoke detectors will be ineffective for in-room detection. To overcome this, duct detectors are placed in the return air stream to sample for smoke. Some facilities utilize air sampling or particle counter-type smoke detection systems for in-room and return air stream sampling. Where the use of flammable liquids is extensive, optical flame detectors will be located strategically within the room.

Regardless of the type of early warning fire detection system employed, systems that exhaust toxic gases should not be interlocked so as to automatically shut down on activation of fire detection or alarm systems. Additionally, the exhaust ventilation system should have an automatic emergency back-up source of electrical power.

Bibliography

Cote, A. E., ed., *Fire Protection Handbook,* 17th edition, National Fire Protection Association, Quincy, MA, 1991. Discusses in detail many of the industrial occupancies covered in this chapter.

Linville, J. L. ed., *Industrial Fire Hazards Handbook,* 3rd edition, National Fire Protection Association, Quincy, MA, 1990. Provides a comprehensive description of the risks and hazards in the industrial environments discussed in this chapter.

NFPA Codes, Standards, and Recommended Practices

NFPA 10, *Standard for Portable Fire Extinguishers.* Contains criteria for the selection, installation, inspection, maintenance, and hydrostatic testing of portable fire extinguishers.

NFPA 13, *Standard for the Installation of Sprinkler Systems.* Contains illustrated descriptions, installations, and testing procedures for all types of sprinkler systems including wet pipe, dry pipe, deluge, and preaction.

NFPA 13A, *Recommended Practice for the Inspection, Testing, and Maintenance of Sprinkler Systems.* Gives practical advice for managers and property owners on how to keep sprinkler systems in proper operating condition.

NFPA 14, *Standard for the Installation of Standpipe and Hose Systems.* Presents minimum requirements for the design and installation of standpipe and hose systems; covers sizes, number, location, outlets, water supplies, and piping.

NFPA 30, *Flammable and Combustible Liquids Code.* Discusses requirements for tank storage, piping, valves and fittings, container storage, industrial plants, bulk plants, service stations, and processing plants for flammable liquids.

NFPA 32, *Standard for Drycleaning Plants.* Covers safeguards for drycleaning and drydyeing operations.

NFPA 33, *Standard for Spray Application Using Flammable and Combustible Materials.*

Addresses the application of flammable or combustible materials as a spray by compressed air, hydraulic atomization, steam, or electrostatic methods.

NFPA 34, *Standard for Dipping and Coating Processes Using Flammable or Combustible Liquids.* Covers requirements for coating, finishing, and treatment processes that use flammable or combustible liquids.

NFPA 45, *Standard on Fire Protection for Laboratories Using Chemicals.* Establishes basic requirements for the protection of life and property in laboratory work areas where hazardous chemicals are handled.

NFPA 51, *Standard for the Design and Installation of Oxygen-Fuel Gas Systems for Welding, Cutting, and Allied Processes.* Gives requirements for acetylene and oxygen cylinder storage and use; covers MAP, other stable gases, and acetylene generation.

NFPA 61A, *Standard for Prevention of Fire and Dust Explosions in Facilities Manufacturing and Handling Starch.* Covers the hazards of handling dried starch and precautions to prevent ignition.

NFPA 61B, *Standard for the Prevention of Fires and Explosions in Grain Elevators and Facilities Handling Bulk Raw Agricultural Commodities.* Covers prevention of dust explosions and ways to minimize the damage if an explosion should occur; also covers fumigation of commodities and storage spaces.

NFPA 61C, *Standard for the Prevention of Fire and Dust Explosions in Feed Mills.* Covers construction, ventilation, equipment, and miscellaneous precautions.

NFPA 61D, *Standard for the Prevention of Fire and Dust Explosions in the Milling of Agricultural Commodities for Human Consumption.* Covers prevention of fire and dust explosion hazards in the milling of wheat, rye, barley, corn, and other grains.

NFPA 65, *Standard for the Processing and Finishing of Aluminum.* Covers fire protection requirements for industrial operations in which fine metallic aluminum dust or powder is liberated.

NFPA 70, *National Electrical Code.* Specifies wiring and equipment requirements in domestic and industrial occupancies.

NFPA 75, *Standard for the Protection of Electronic Computer/Data Processing Equipment.* Contains requirements for installations needing fire protection or special construction, rooms, areas, or operating environments.

NFPA 77, *Recommended Practice on Static Electricity.* Explains the hazards of static accumulation and the means of diminishing or eliminating those hazards.

NFPA 90A, *Standard for the Installation of Air Conditioning and Ventilating Systems.* Specifies installation requirements to restrict the spread of smoke, heat, and fire through duct systems; to minimize ignition sources; and to permit use of the system for emergency smoke control.

NFPA 91, *Standard for Exhaust Systems for Air Conveying of Materials.* Provides the safety requirements for fans, ducts, direct clearances, system design, and dust-collecting system for removal or conveying of flammable vapors, corrosive fumes, dust stock, and refuse.

NFPA 120, *Standard for Coal Preparation Plants.* Specifies safety requirements for design, construction, and operation of coal preparation plants.

NFPA 231D, *Standard for Storage of Rubber Tires.* Covers indoor storage of rubber tires, including building construction, storage arrangement, and fire protection.

NFPA 231E, *Recommended Practice for the Storage of Baled Cotton.* Covers storage of baled cotton in buildings and yards.

NFPA 231F, *Standard for the Storage of Roll Paper.* Covers storage of roll paper in buildings or structures.

NFPA 303, *Fire Protection Standard for Marinas and Boatyards.* Contains fire protection requirements for locations used for the construction, repair, storage, launching, berthing, or fueling of small craft.

NFPA 307, *Standard for the Construction and Fire Protection of Marine Terminals, Piers, and Wharves.* Contains requirements for construction and fire protection at marine terminals, piers, and wharves, and for hazardous materials storage.

NFPA 312, *Standard for Fire Protection of Vessels During Construction, Repair, and Lay-up.* Covers fire protection for marine vessels during construction, conversion, repair, and lay-up.

NFPA 318, *Standard for the Protection of Cleanrooms.* Provides safeguards for the protection of semiconductor facilities containing cleanrooms from fire and related hazards.

NFPA 325M, *Fire Hazard Properties of Flammable Liquids, Gases, and Volatile Solids.* Summary of available data on the fire hazard properties of more than 1,600 substances.

NFPA 480, *Standard for the Storage, Handling, and Processing of Magnesium Solids and Powders.* Covers hazards in foundries, processing plants, and commercial storage, including machining, fabrication, scrap handling, and storage.

NFPA 481, *Standard for the Production, Processing, Handling, and Storage of Titanium.* Contains requirements for the firesafe use of titanium in operations including sponge production, melting powder, scrap production, and mill operations.

NFPA 482, *Standard for the Production, Processing, Handling, and Storage of Zirconium.* Gives a comprehensive plan for personnel safety and fire and explosion prevention and protection.

NFPA 650, *Standard for Pneumatic Conveying Systems for Handling Combustible Materials.* Covers requirements for pressure-type and suction-type systems with guidance on design safeguards of component parts.

NFPA 801, *Recommended Fire Protection Practice for Facilities Handling Radioactive Materials.* Covers practices aimed at reducing the risk of fire or explosion and the severity of contamination at facilities that handle radioactive materials.

NFPA 803, *Standard for Fire Protection for Light Water Nuclear Power Plants.* Gives fire safety guidelines for light water nuclear electric generating facilities, including operating personnel, equipment, and operations.

NFPA 850, *Recommended Practice for Fire Protection for Electric Generating Plants.* Provides recommendations for fire prevention and protection for gas-, oil-, or coal-fired steam electric generating plants during design, construction, and operation.

NFPA 851, *Recommended Practice for Fire Protection for Hydroelectric Generating Plants.* Gives recommendations for fire prevention and fire protection for hydroelectric generating plants during design, construction, and operation.

Venting Systems for Commercial Cooking Equipment

*A*s basic knowledge, familiarity with NFPA 96, *Standard for Ventilation Control and Fire Protection of Commercial Cooking Operations* and the appropriate NFPA fire suppression standard is a must for inspection of a kitchen exhaust system.

Ventilation components in a commercial cooking operation are designed to convey smoke, steam, grease-laden vapors, and condensed liquid to a safe disposal. Surface cooking operations producing grease-laden vapors consist of the following elements. *Appliances* are the locations where cooking takes place, utilizing electricity, gas, solid fuel, or a combination as the heat source. Consult the authority having jurisdiction (AHJ) for closed or non-grease vapor producing appliances. *Hood* is the area for containment and capture of smoke, steam, and grease-laden vapors. The hood consists of a shell that houses the filters, drip tray, and condensed grease container. It defines the location limits of the cooking operation. *Filters* must be listed for the removal of grease-laden vapors, and allow drainage of any condensed liquid. *Exhaust duct and fan* provide air movement from the hood to a safe termination area. *Replacement air* insures the proper air flow through the exhaust system. *Product* to be cooked is usually grease producing or cooked with the aid of grease.

Fire Hazards

Cooking grease is used in liquid state, and produces vapors while at cooking temperatures. It is a dangerous fuel when ignited, producing heavy, foul-smelling smoke with potential temperatures of 2,000°F. Autoignition is possible. The intense heat generated from flames, advancing through hood, filters, and exhaust duct, presents a serious threat to ignition of surrounding combustible materials and has the potential to spread fire to other parts of a structure.

Overview of Current Systems and Operations

The first step in any inspection is to examine the current equipment, systems, and space layouts to determine if any changes have been made since the last inspection. An inspection file should exist for each site with categories for cooking equipment, exhaust system, fire suppression system, operations, space layout, and maintenance. The first sheet or section of every category should list briefly the accepted standard that existed at the previous inspection(s). Where appropriate, this is facilitated with a picture or sketch of the areas of concern on which are identified all components or notes of relevance. A quick reference will identify whether these fundamental areas have changed and are now in need of special review for possible increased fire hazard. Only after this overview inspection confirms that there are no changes, or that the changes have been identified and handled as described below, should the inspection proceed with details of systems and components. The inspection file should also include the final conditions for approval determined by the local authorities, and this should be carefully reviewed at each inspection.

Any changes that have not increased the fire hazard should be noted and recorded as acceptable so they need not be reviewed at the next inspection. Any changes that have increased the fire hazard must be analyzed to determine what corrections or additions are required to bring the hazard within acceptable limits and in conformity with code requirements. Such requirements should be carefully detailed in the inspection report. Appropriate action should be taken under local enforcement measures to have the hazard brought into compliance. When compliance has been achieved, the follow-up inspection report should reflect the new changes as standard and acceptable.

There are three types of systems ordinarily encountered. *Recirculating systems* or ductless appliances are complete listed systems and should be serviced by qualified personnel in accordance with both the producer's and fire extinguisher manufacturer's instructions. The instructions and service record should be available for review. Also, the proximity to combustibles and/or any accumulation of grease outside the hood are areas of concern. Portability may allow inappropriate installation and use without the knowledge of the AHJ. *Listed, self-cleaning,* "water wash" hoods should be operated in accordance with the manufacturer's instructions and are not required to have conventional filters. However, other components and clearances are the same as those listed below. Manufacturer's instructions and the service record should be available for review. *Basic* surface cooking systems are composed of appliances, hood, filters, exhaust duct, fan, replacement air source, and automatic fire extinguishing equipment. Maintaining separation of the components from combustible materials or ignition hazards are prime concerns.

With all types of systems, grease and grease-laden vapors must be contained by the system design and operation. Precautions to avoid ignition also must be maintained and operators must understand the operation of the extinguishing system.

Cooking Equipment Review

Determine if the cooking equipment appears properly maintained and serviceable. If it has a high limit control and the facility is not unusually busy, have the temperatures increased to see that the device shuts off the cooking fuel. If not, indicate that it must be repaired or replaced.

Look at the power cord or gas line and the control cord, if any, to the cooking equipment, as well as end connectors and wall outlets to see if all appear to be in good condition. If any have frays, cracks, or breaks, list them to be repaired or replaced.

Check the location of the cooking equipment in relation to the exhaust hood and fire suppression nozzles. Appliances must be positioned entirely under the hood except for specially designed "back shelf" hoods. Deep fat fryers must be 16 inches from open flames and the required coverage of the fire extinguishing system must be maintained. No relocation or replacement of any equipment should be allowed without the approval of the AHJ. If the equipment should be in a particular location and with specific seals to the rear wall, end hood walls, or to other equipment, check that this is the case, and that some locating or locking device is used to keep the equipment in its proper location and fit-up.

Check to see if any cooking practices create a potential fire or personnel hazard. Storage of wipe towels, melted butter containers, shortening, or seasoning oils near open flames or above hot surfaces, placement of wooden utensils on hot surfaces, or storage of containers or utensils above deep fry vats where they might fall and cause hot oil to splash out, all are examples of hazardous practices.

Exhaust System Review

Hood

Look at the exhaust hood to see that it is well maintained and serviceable. Check that grease troughs and filters appear to be regularly maintained. If there are any service panels on the hood, check that they are in place and properly fitted and secured. If the hood has water spray or water wash down capabilities, check that detergent reservoirs are above minimum level, and have the operator demonstrate that the spray or wash down functions. This may require a visit during a slow business period.

Check to see if the exhaust hood is "listed" (both listed and non-listed hoods are allowed by NFPA 96). If the label lists any special criteria that are part of the listing, such as clearances to cooking equipment and combustibles, type of cooking equipment to be used under the hood, and other special features that are described on the label, see that these are met. All listed hoods of recent manufacture must have listed baffle filters unless they have special extraction elements that are part of the hood design. If the hood has a damper, be sure that the damper is cleaned regularly, operates automatically, is not blocked or wired open, and if equipped with a fusible link, that it is changed at the same interval as the fire extinguishing system fusible links, at least every 12 months.

If the hood is not listed it must comply with the material and construction of NFPA 96 and local code requirements. All outer seams of the exhaust section must be welded and only listed baffle filters and damper and hood collar assemblies can be installed.

If the hood is a compensating hood (having an integral supply air plenum) with some form of make-up air, it must comply with the requirements of Chapter 2 of NFPA 96. Pay special attention to damper requirements between the make-up air and exhaust air sections of the hood as described in Chapter 2 and as shown in examples in the Appendix of NFPA 96.

Lights and all possible sources of ignition within the hood must be listed for this use and maintained liquid tight.

Duct Systems

Check visible ductwork to determine if it has maintained its integrity. The original inspection during installation should have confirmed the integrity of all hidden ductwork. The concern now is whether any of the exposed ductwork has been damaged, compromising its ability to contain a fire. Check to see that all inspection/clean-out doors on the ductwork are in place, have proper gaskets, and are secured with all of their fasteners. Check that ductwork is regularly cleaned.

If the ductwork has a fire enclosure, check its integrity at all visible locations. All service access doors in the enclosure must be approved, self-closing fire doors in good working condition.

If the ductwork system is listed, check the integrity of its visible parts. If you question any part, check the literature for the system, which should be maintained by the operator, and compare its requirements to your observations.

Check that there are no combustibles within the required clearances around ductwork, which is 18 inches for standard ductwork, and somewhat less (6 inches minimum), for listed ductwork. The clearance should be indicated on listed ductwork or in its literature. If storage of supplies around or near exposed ductwork is common (such as in attics or closets), either require that the practice be stopped completely, or that a wire wall be installed to keep the supplies at the required distance from the ductwork and still permit its inspection. The wire must be readily removable for access to a service door if installed in the ductwork at that location.

Check that the duct systems are regularly cleaned by reviewing the invoice records for this work and by an occasional personal inspection inside some sections of the ductwork. When the system is used on a regular daily basis, the system should be inspected and cleaned if necessary on the following schedule. Systems utilizing solid cooking fuels or 24 hour high volume frying, charbroiling, or Oriental cooking - monthly. Systems utilizing high volumes of fast food frying, charbroiling or Oriental cooking - quarterly. Systems utilizing normal volumes of commercial cooking or baking - semi-annually. Systems utilizing low vapor producing cooking (pizza ovens, steam tables) - annually. Intervals between inspections and cleaning specified above will vary depending on types and volumes of use, conditions of equipment and efficiency of hood filtration. The AHJ may adjust the frequencies of cleaning required if conditions so warrant. Systems which are only used on a part-time or seasonal basis could require a reduced frequency.

Where manifold exhaust duct (common duct) systems are used to tie more than one hood or more than one restaurant together to a single fan, there is a greater possibility for improper operations. In such systems the correct airflows can exist (assuming that they were properly set up originally) only if all exhaust systems are in normal operating status with all filters in place. A hood without its filter in place will draw more air, and the remaining hoods will draw less air. Those moving less air will not capture all the grease vapors produced and there will be more grease deposits in their ductwork. Operators of such systems need to understand the importance of keeping the filters in place whenever any of the hoods on the manifold duct system are operating. Where multiple tenants are involved, it is best that each operation have adequate spare filters on hand so that spares can be put in place to keep the air balanced when any are removed from a hood for cleaning.

Fans

The ductwork-to-fan seal is one of the more common failures at a fan and therefore is important to inspect. If the seal is not in good condition, it can permit serious leaks of grease onto surrounding surfaces, which could seriously spread a fire that might emanate from the fan. Check the general condition of the fan to see if it appears in good shape and frequently and properly maintained. In addition to the duct seals, check that the belt is tight and that the grease drain and container are properly functioning. If the fan is the tilt-up type, this is a good opportunity to momentarily tip it up to inspect the condition of the gasket-to-fan seal, and the amount of grease build-up in the duct. If the fan cover is removed to check belt tension, it is also a good time to check that the fan is rotating in the proper direction by noting the arrow normally provided on the housing. Reverse rotation will dramatically reduce the amount of airflow through the system.

Roof-Mounted. Grease exhaust fans most commonly are located at the termination of the exhaust system on the roof. This is the best location for exhaust fans because it keeps all ductwork under a vacuum, thereby reducing the likelihood of many potential grease leaks. It also keeps leaks from the fan itself, a greater likelihood, outside of the building and more easily visible and serviceable, and it makes the choice of type of fan to be applied more flexible. Each fan should have a grease drain and a container to catch the grease. These drain systems should be designed to separate water from the grease, permitting rain water to run out, but retaining the grease in the container. If these are not functioning properly, the grease again will be spread over the adjoining surfaces. It is also possible that the separator drain will not work properly during winter when the water freezes. At such times more frequent maintenance is necessary to preclude a grease problem.

Check electric service to the fans to be sure it is still in original condition with no frays, cracks, or breaks in any of the flexible leads and that all covers are securely in place.

In-Line. These fans are usually found inside buildings and have ductwork connected to both ends of the fan. These duct connections are virtually always flanged, gasketed, and bolted so the fan can be removed for service. These are the most likely locations for grease leaks and should be inspected at each visit. The connection on the downstream side of the fan and all duct joints between the fan and the outside of the building are under pressure, and therefore more prone to grease leaks. These should be closely viewed at each inspection. Depending on the construction of the fan, leaks from joints or covers in the fan housing itself are possible. These also should be closely watched. These fans are heavy and require good support structure to hold them up and in alignment with the ends of the ductwork. Inspect these supports and the horizontal alignment of the ducts and fans to be sure that the supports are not deteriorating. Any sags, cracks, tears, or loose components in the support structure should be brought to the attention of the operator for immediate correction before a serious leak or support failure occurs.

Wall-Mounted. These fans are no longer as common as they were previously. They are prone to grease leaks both at the duct connection and at the fan discharge. It is not uncommon to see grease running down the inside or outside wall of the building under wall-mounted fans, but these leaks should not be accepted. It takes both a properly designed fan drain and duct-to-fan connection as well as fairly frequent maintenance to eliminate grease leaks. When these grease leaks become too great and are not kept constantly cleaned, the inspector should advise the operator to have the connections repaired. With wall-mounted fans it is more important to have the ductwork pitched down toward the hood to prevent grease leakage at the fan after it is shut off. On such fans the grease should drain to an indoor container or directly to a grease trap. NFPA 96 gives information on the ductwork arrangement and some added information on the location of wall exhaust termination in relation to fresh air intakes and other points on the outside of the building. Figures in NFPA 96 are helpful in these applications.

Fire Suppression System Review

General

Earlier overview and equipment inspections should have determined the appropriate fire suppression system application for the cooking equipment. It is necessary now to check only the components and condition of the suppression system itself. A good knowledge of the particular make and type of suppression system will greatly facilitate this portion of the inspection. These systems are referenced in NFPA 96 and complete descriptions may be found in NFPA 12, *Standard on Carbon Dioxide Extinguishing Systems;* NFPA 13, *Standard for the Installation of Sprinkler Systems;* NFPA 16, *Standard on the Installation of Deluge Foam-Water Sprinkler and Foam-Water Spray Systems;* NFPA 17, *Standard for Dry Chemical Extinguishing Systems;* and NFPA 17A, *Standard on Wet Chemical Extinguishing Systems.* Only the more important features of concern will be discussed here.

All of these systems should be inspected by a trained technician every six months to ascertain they are still in proper working order. Check that the agent tanks are full, and that the system is armed. Check that all fusible links are changed at least once a year. If possible (without discharging the system), check that the fuel to the cooking equipment shuts off when the system is tripped. Check whether the detector and fire suppression lines are secured adequately and that the nozzles are properly aimed.

Wet Chemical

By far the most common fire suppression system applied to restaurant cooking systems today is the wet chemical system. It has the feature of being able to saponify the greasy surface (as does dry chemical), to keep air away from the shortening, and prevent re-ignition. This is of critical importance in fry vats. It has the advantage over dry chemical of being able to more quickly lower the temperature of the shortening in deep fat fryers, and thus more quickly bring it below its re-ignition point and to a secured extinguishment. From the operator's viewpoint, its main advantage is that it makes far less mess than dry chemical and permits the cooking station to be put back in service sooner. The wet chemical drops are much heavier than the fine powder of the dry chemical. The wet chemical stays mainly in the limited area of application while the dry chemical can be carried by air handling systems throughout the restaurant, necessitating closure for a day or more while the entire building is cleaned. Wet chemical is lightly to mildly caustic and can cause skin irritations. Because it can corrode surfaces, it should be rinsed off as quickly as possible.

Dry Chemical

Dry chemical systems were applied for many years before wet chemical systems were developed. There are probably more dry than wet chemical systems still in use, but this will change in the near future. Dry chemicals are not as caustic to skin and surfaces as wet chemicals, but present a greater respiration hazard. In the event of a dry chemical discharge, the premises should be evacuated until the space and air handling systems can be cleared of the dry chemical powder.

Carbon Dioxide

Carbon dioxide systems are one of the oldest forms of fire suppression systems for restaurants but fell out of favor due to cost, space requirements, and the fact that it is difficult in the highly ventilated environment of a restaurant to keep the concentrations in place that are required to extinguish a fire and keep it out. This is especially true in the case of a deep fat fryer where it may be necessary to keep air away from the shortening for a period of 20 minutes or more until it has cooled sufficiently below its re-ignition point to be considered safe. Because carbon dioxide must be provided in relatively high concentrations to be effective and displace oxygen, it has the potential to suffocate humans. The premises should be evacuated immediately if a discharge of carbon dioxide occurs. A direct spray of carbon dioxide is also dangerous as it can cause severe frostbite.

Sprinkler Systems

Sprinkler systems previously have had limited applications in commercial cooking operations, but were quickly dropped in favor of the more simple, effective, and economical chemical systems. Also, sprinkler systems have always had a drawback in their application on deep fryer vats, where excess water or pressure could spread rather than control the fire.

Recently, a form of water sprinkler system has gained acceptance due to its apparent lower cost when viewed as part of an exhaust system that already has water spray or water wash as a feature of its hood. Virtually all of these hood systems are fed from the kitchen water system rather than from a dedicated sprinkler main. In this sense they are a variation from the standard sprinkler system, but are similar in their provision for the unlimited supply of plain water. It does not appear that full standard water sprinkler systems will return to favor because their installation and control supervision are too costly. New hood sprinkler systems for cooking operations are now being developed that have special considerations not yet accepted by the industry in general. Whereas regular sprinkler systems per NFPA 13 need to have sprinkler nozzles at each bend of duct and at the termination of the duct, the new sprinkler systems are being evaluated for unlimited duct coverage from just a single nozzle at the beginning of the duct, just as is done with dry and wet chemical systems. The new hood sprinkler systems are also being evaluated to determine if the standard spray or wash down they use in the hood is acceptable as fire suppression and can thus serve double duty.

Until recently only a standard sprinkler nozzle was available for appliance protection, including deep fat fryers. In about 1983 a special nozzle was developed for deep fat fryers that tended to be effective in suppressing the fire when the nozzle is applied over a vat from a canopy hood with adequate distance between the nozzle and the shortening surface. This nozzle is not adequate in most cases with a back shelf hood where the nozzle is too close to the shortening surface. In such applications it tends to push the fire out of the hood and thus is not recommended.

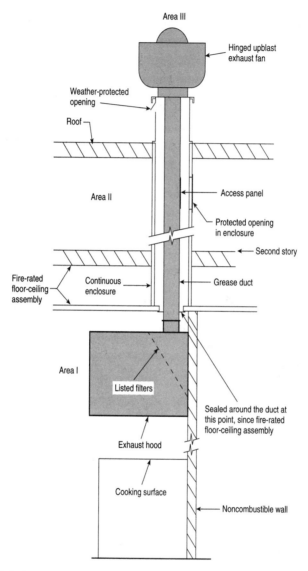

Area III

Hinged upblast
exhaust fan

Weather-protected
opening

Roof

Area II

Access panel

Protected opening
in enclosure

Second story

Fire-rated
floor-ceiling
assembly

Continuous
enclosure

Grease duct

Area I

Listed filters

Sealed around the duct at
this point, since fire-rated
floor-ceiling assembly

Exhaust hood

Cooking surface

Noncombustible wall

*Figure 47-1 shows a section view of a typical venting system installation in a
building with two or more stories with fire-rated floor-ceiling assemblies.
Source: NFPA 96,* **Standard for Ventilation Control and Fire Protection of
Commercial Cooking Operations,** *NFPA, Quincy, MA, 1994.*

Recirculating Systems

Recirculating systems are also known as ductless systems, ductless hoods, or ventless hoods. These units consist of cooking equipment and a hood with self-contained grease and odor control devices that claim to clean the air sufficiently to permit its return to the space in which the unit resides. Thus, the units do not have an external exhaust. They are all listed for their particular design and use and have some controls specified in NFPA 96.

All recirculating systems must be listed and labeled to indicate the specific equipment allowed under the hood. In a number of units the hood is directly attached to the cooking equipment so there can be no change of the equipment. The label will also indicate the CFM per lineal foot, the type of filters to be used, and other system specifications. The label also will indicate if the equipment is to be fixed to the building so it cannot be moved.

In all newer units, sensors prevent the unit from operating if filtration devices are not in position. All panels that access the interior grease-laden surfaces of the unit also have sensors that prevent operation if the panels are not in position. There are also special sensors that monitor minimum airflows and minimum electrostatic filter performance, which will shut off the unit if the threshold limits are exceeded. The inspector can test the filter and panel sensor operation by removing one or more sensors to see if the unit will not operate. The air flow sensor can be tested by restricting the hood filters with paper or cardboard to see that the unit shuts off.

Recirculating systems have installation limitations based on surrounding combustible materials, return and supply air grills, lower ceilings, and other conditions that may be fire or health concerns. Some of these restrictions may be indicated on the unit label, but most may have been determined by the local authorities and will only be found in the final condition of approval for the system. These should be a part of the inspector's file and should be carefully reviewed at each inspection. Some of these conditions could easily be violated unintentionally by the operator with potentially serious consequences.

Every recirculating system should have a detailed operation and maintenance manual, which not only covers all the standard material, but also addresses special features and concerns. It is advisable that the inspector be familiar with this manual to understand critical aspects of the unit and be able to review these at each inspection. These units all have built-in fire extinguishing systems though many of them are different from normal systems one would find with cooking equipment. Some have special nozzles that are not part of standard pre-engineered systems and some use water sprinkler detector/nozzles with wet chemical. These are specially listed for the applications and any differences that exist in these systems must be detailed in the system manual. The standard components and operations are the same as more standard systems and should be reviewed in the same manner.

A log must be kept to record all the required maintenance, and this log must be available to the AHJ. The inspector should ask to review this log and compare it to the condition of the equipment.

Maintenance Review

Maintenance review has been mentioned in each of the sections covered above and should have been a part of the inspector's comments recorded up to this point. If any of the maintenance has not been reviewed, it should be completed at this time. This review summarizes maintenance performance since the last inspection. If maintenance records are good, personnel are aware of what service is needed and has been performed, and the equipment looks clean, then it is likely that the quality of system maintenance was high and the equipment will be in good condition and providing the level of safety intended. If the opposite conditions are present, it is likely that the equipment is not in good shape and there is more reason to be concerned about its safety. Provide an overview of the maintenance status to the facility's manager and point out that this gives a strong indication of the status and safety of the equipment. By raising the issue of maintenance at each inspection, facility managers will begin to recognize its importance. Their increased concern will result in more favorable subsequent inspections.

Bibliography

NFPA 12, *Standard on Carbon Dioxide Extinguishing Systems*
NFPA 13, *Standard for the Installation of Sprinkler Systems*
NFPA 16, *Standard on the Installation of Deluge Foam-Water Sprinkler and Foam-Water Spray Systems*

NFPA 17, *Standard for Dry Chemical Extinguishing Systems*
NFPA 17A, *Standard on Wet Chemical Extinguishing Systems*
NFPA 80, *Standard for Fire Doors and Fire Windows*
NFPA 96, *Standard for Ventilation Control and Fire Protection of Commercial Cooking Operations*

SI Units

The following conversion factors are used to convert the English units used in this book to SI units.

1 in = 25.4 mm
1 ft = 0.3048 m
1 ft2 = 0.0929 m2
1 ft3 = 0.0283 m3
1 cfm = 0.0283 m3/min
1 gallon = 3.7854 liters
1 gpm = 3.7854 liters/min
1 gpm/ft2 = 40.746 liters/min/m2
1 lb = 0.4536 kg
1 Btu/lb = 2.326 kJ/kg
1 psi = 6.895 kPa
5/9 (°F - 32) = °C

Appendix

*T*he references that follow, all published by the National Fire Protection Association (Batterymarch Park, Quincy, MA 02269), will prove useful to the fire inspector. They are grouped under headings that indicate particular phases of the inspection process. The titles of NFPA codes, standards, and recommended practices and chapters in the *Fire Protection Handbook* are listed for each category. These titles and chapters contain information and guidance that will help the inspector evaluate specific hazards and occupancies, and make good recommendations to eliminate or protect against the hazards involved.

General Fire Protection

Carson, W. G. and Klinker, R. L., eds. *Fire Protection Systems: Inspection, Test and Maintenance Manual,* 2nd edition, 1992. A single source of information on the inspection, testing, and maintenance of fire detection and suppression systems.

Cote, A. E., ed. *Fire Protection Handbook*, 17th edition, 1991. An excellent handbook on the state of the art in fire protection and fire prevention practices and recommendations.

Cote, A. E. ed., *Industrial Fire Hazards Handbook*, 3rd edition, 1990. Identifies and discusses ways to control and eliminate fire hazards associated with industrial processes.

NFPA Codes, Standards, and Recommended Practices

NFPA 1, *Fire Prevention Code.* Provides comprehensive, user-friendly fire safety regulations for code enforcement and administration; references other NFPA standards and codes for detailed guidance.

NFPA 70, *National Electrical Code.* Contains comprehensive electrical safety requirements for all standard types of electrical installations; essential guide for anyone who specifies, certifies, or installs electrical jobs.

NFPA *101, Life Safety Code.* Addresses construction, protection, and occupancy features necessary to minimize danger to life from fire, smoke, fumes, and panic; identifies criteria for the design of egress facilities to permit prompt escape from buildings or, where desirable, into safe areas within the building.

Fire Protection Systems or Features

NFPA 10, *Standard for Portable Fire Extinguishers.* Criteria for the selection, installation, inspection, maintenance, and hydrostatic testing of portable fire extinguishers.

NFPA 11, *Standard for Low Expansion Foam and Combined Agent Systems.* Provides the minimum requirements for inside hazards, exterior storage tanks, indoor and outdoor processing areas, spray foam systems, and monitor and hose systems.

NFPA 11A, *Standard for Medium- and High-Expansion Foam Systems.* Outlines the minimum requirements for the design, installation, testing, operation, and maintenance of medium- and high-expansion foam systems.

NFPA 12, *Standard on Carbon Dioxide Extinguishing Systems.* Covers design, installation, testing, approval, operation, and maintenance for total flooding, local application, and hose line systems.

NFPA 12A, *Standard on Halon 1301 Fire Extinguishing Systems.* Provides the minimum requirements for design, installation, testing, inspection, and maintenance of bromotrifluoromethane systems.

NFPA 12B, *Standard on Halon 1211 Fire Extinguishing Systems.* Provides the minimum requirements for design, installation, testing, inspection, and maintenance of bromochlorodifluoromethane systems.

NFPA 13, *Standard for the Installation of Sprinkler Systems.* Illustrated description, installation, and testing procedures for all types of systems including wet pipe, dry pipe, deluge, and preaction.

NFPA 13D, *Standard for the Installation of Sprinkler Systems in One- and Two-Family Dwellings and Mobile Homes.* Covers the design and installation of automatic sprinkler systems and provides information on water supply, systems design, and other important technical considerations.

NFPA 13R, *Standard for the Installation of Sprinkler Systems in Residential Occupancies Up to and Including Four Stories in Height.* Provides installation requirements and covers systems design, water supply, and technical considerations.

NFPA 14, *Standard for the Installation of Standpipe and Hose Systems.* Presents minimum requirements for the design and installation of standpipe and hose systems; covers sizes, number, location, outlets, water supplies, and piping.

NFPA 15, *Standard for Water Spray Fixed Systems for Fire Protection.* Covers the design, installation, maintenance, and test requirements based on sound engineering principles, test data, and field experience.

NFPA 16, *Standard on the Installation of Deluge Foam-Water Sprinkler and Foam-Water Spray Systems.* Outlines requirements for system design, installation, components, and water supply.

NFPA 17, *Standard for Dry Chemical Extinguishing Systems.* Provides minimum requirements, plus discussion of total flooding, local application, hand hose line systems, and pre-engineered systems.

NFPA 17A, *Standard for Wet Chemical Extinguishing Systems.* Covers the design, installation, operation, testing, maintenance, and minimum requirements of wet chemical pre-engineered fire extinguishing systems that discharge wet chemical from fixed nozzles and piping by means of expellant gas.

NFPA 18, *Standard on Wetting Agents.* Covers uses, limitations, specifications, and test standards.

NFPA 20, *Standard for the Installation of Centrifugal Fire Pumps.* Provides guidelines for the design, installation, and maintenance of centrifugal fire pumps, pump drivers, horizontal pumps, and vertical shaft turbine-type pumps.

NFPA 22, *Standard for Water Tanks for Private Fire Protection.* Presents requirements for gravity and suction tanks, towers, foundations, piping, valves, heating, pressure tanks, and tank insulation.

NFPA 24, *Standard for the Installation of Private Fire Service Mains and Their Appurtenances.* Details of yard piping that supplies water to automatic sprinkler systems, yard hydrants, standpipes, and other systems.

NFPA 25, *Standard for the Inspection, Testing, and Maintenance of Water-Based Fire Protection Systems.* Provides the requirements on procedures and programs for conducting periodic inspection and testing as well as preventative maintenance.

NFPA 26, *Recommended Practice for the Supervision of Valves Controlling Water Supplies for Fire Protection.* Outlines the recommendations for identification and supervision of valve seals, valve tags, and valve index boards.

NFPA 69, *Standard on Explosion Prevention Systems.* Covers requirements for explosion prevention systems based on reducing the concentration of combustible materials or oxidants; also includes requirements for inert gas systems, explosion-suppression systems, and deflagration pressure containment.

NFPA 72, *National Fire Alarm Code.* This code deals with the application, installation, performance, and maintenance of fire signaling systems and their components.

NFPA 90A, *Standard for the Installation of Air Conditioning and Ventilating Systems.* Specifies installation requirements to restrict spread of smoke, heat, and fire through duct systems in order to minimize ignition sources and permit use of the system for emergency smoke control.

NFPA 90B, *Standard for the Installation of Warm Air Heating and Air Conditioning Systems.* Provides installation requirements for supply ducts, controls, clearances, heating panels, return ducts, air filters, heat pumps, and other components for one- and two-family dwellings or spaces not exceeding volumes of 25,000 cubic feet.

NFPA 110, *Standard for Emergency and Standby Power Systems.* Covers power sources, transfer equipment, controls, supervisory equipment, and all related electrical and mechanical auxiliary equipment for alternate electrical power systems.

NFPA 220, *Standard on Types of Building Construction.* Specifies types of building construction, including limited combustible and noncombustible building construction materials.

NFPA 231, *Standard for General Storage.* Recommended practices for storage of combustibles (Classes I through IV) and plastics (Groups A, B, and C).

NFPA 231C, *Standard for Rack Storage of Materials.* Applies to the broad range of combustible commodities stored in racks over 12 feet in height.

NFPA 231D, *Standard for Storage of Rubber Tires.* Covers indoor storage of rubber tires, including building construction, storage arrangement, and fire protection.

NFPA 231E, *Recommended Practice for the Storage of Baled Cotton.* Provides fire protection guidance for the storage of baled cotton in buildings and yards.

NFPA 231F, *Standard for the Storage of Roll Paper.* Covers storage of roll paper in buildings or structures.

NFPA 232, *Standard for the Protection of Records.* Outlines requirements for vaults, file rooms, safes, containers, and other devices, and for the management of records.

NFPA 780, *Lightning Protection Code.* Provides for the protection of people, buildings, special occupancies, heavy duty stacks, explosives, structures containing flammable liquids and gases, and other entities from lightning damage.

NFPA 1231, *Standard on Water Supplies for Suburban and Rural Fire Fighting.* Minimum requirements for fire fighting water supplies in areas without hydrants; also covers apparatus construction for water tankers.

NFPA 1961, *Standard for Fire Hose.* Covers construction, diameter and length, and hydrostatic pressure capacity for fire department, industrial, and forestry fire hose.

NFPA 1963, *Standard for Screw Threads and Gaskets for Fire Hose Connections.* Covers dimensions for screw threads, gauges, gaskets, and gasket seats.

Special Hazards

NFPA 30, *Flammable and Combustible Liquids Code.* Covers safe storage and handling requirements, including bulk storage in tanks, piping systems and valves, warehousing of containers, incidental use, and operations.

NFPA 31, *Standard for the Installation of Oil-Burning Equipment.* Covers requirements for stationary and portable oil-burning equipment, tanks, piping, and accessories.

NFPA 33, *Standard for Spray Application Using Flammable and Combustible Materials.* Requirements for the application of flammable or combustible materials when applied as a spray; covers spray painting and powder spray guns.

NFPA 34, S*tandard for Dipping and Coating Processes Using Flammable or Combustible Liquids.* Covers requirements for coating, finishing, and treatment processes that use flammable or combustible liquids.

NFPA 35, *Standard for the Manufacture of Organic Coatings.* Outlines the standard processes involving fire hazards in organic coating manufacturing.

NFPA 40, *Standard for the Storage and Handling of Cellulose Nitrate Motion Picture Film.* Provides data on film cabinets, vaults, archival vaults, projection rooms, and film exchanges.

NFPA 40E, *Code for the Storage of Pyroxylin Plastic.* Covers safe storage in manufacturing buildings, warehouses, jobbing shops, and retail outlets.

NFPA 43A, *Code for the Storage of Liquid and Solid Oxidizers.* Recommends practices for reducing hazards from fires and explosions when liquid and solid oxidizing materials are in storage.

NFPA 43B, *Code for the Storage of Organic Peroxide Formulations.* Covers the basic requirements, segregated storage, cutoff storage, anddetached storage of commercially available organic peroxide formulations in approved packages.

NFPA 43D, *Code for Storage of Pesticides in Portable Containers.* Covers both inside and outside storage of all forms of pesticides in portable containers other than fixed installations on transportation equipment.

NFPA 50, *Standard for Bulk Oxygen Systems at Consumer Sites.* Provides recommendations for location, distance between bulk systems and exposures, containers, and associated equipment.

NFPA 50A, *Standard for Gaseous Hydrogen Systems at Consumer Sites.* Requirements for containers, safety relief devices, piping, and other components.

NFPA 50B, *Standard for Liquefied Hydrogen Systems at Consumer Sites.* Requirements for containers, supports, marking, safety releases, piping, and other components.

NFPA 51, *Standard for the Design and Installation of Oxygen-Fuel Gas Systems for Welding, Cutting, and Allied Processes.* Applies to acetylene and oxygen cylinder storage and use; covers MAP, other stable gases, and acetylene generation.

NFPA 51A, *Standard for Acetylene Cylinder Charging Plants.* Safety requirements for design, construction, installation, operations, and fire protection.

NFPA 51B, *Standard for Fire Prevention in Use of Cutting and Welding Processes.* Covers practices and precautions for cutting and welding processes involving the use of electric arcs and oxyfuel gas flames.

NFPA 52, *Standard for Compressed Natural Gas (CNG) Vehicular Fuel Systems.* Applies to general CNG and equipment qualification, engine fuel systems, storage, and dispensing systems.

NFPA 54, *National Fuel Gas Code.* General criteria for safe design, installation, operation, and maintenance of gas piping in buildings and gas appliances in residential, commercial, and industrial applications.

NFPA 58, *Standard for the Storage and Handling of Liquefied Petroleum Gases.* Covers LP-Gas systems, liquid transfer, truck transportation, engine fuel systems, and buildings or structures housing LP-Gas distribution facilities.

NFPA 59, *Standard for the Storage and Handling of Liquefied Petroleum Gases at Utility Gas Plants.* Covers safe design, construction, and operation of LP-Gas equipment at plants supplying LP-Gas/air mixtures for utility application.

NFPA 59A, *Standard for the Production, Storage, and Handling of Liquefied Natural Gas (LNG).* Covers site selection, design, construction, and fire protection for LNG facilities.

NFPA 68, *Guide for Venting of Deflagrations.* Covers fundamentals of deflagration venting, important characteristics of ventdesign and vent closures, and interpreting test data.

NFPA 86, *Standard for Ovens and Furnaces.* Requirements for location, construction, operation, heating system, ventilation, safety control equipment, and fire protection for Class A and B ovens and furnaces.

NFPA 86C, *Standard for Industrial Furnaces Using a Special Processing Atmosphere.* Covers Class C industrial furnaces that utilize a special processing atmosphere, including salt baths and integral quench furnaces. Sets requirements for location, construction, heating system, safety controls, operation, and fire protection.

NFPA 86D, *Standard for Industrial Furnaces Using Vacuum as an Atmosphere.* Applies to the design, construction, and protection of Class D industrial furnaces that operate at above ambient temperatures to over 5,000°F and at pressures normally below atmosphere to 10-8 Torr.

NFPA 91, *Standard for Exhaust Systems for Air Conveying of Materials.* Covers safety requirements for fans, ducts, direct clearances, design, and dust-collecting systems for removal or conveying of flammable vapors, corrosive fumes, dust stock, and refuse.

NFPA 96, *Standard for Ventilation Control and Fire Protection of Commercial Cooking Operations.* Covers the design, installation, and use of exhaust-system hoods, grease-removal devices, ducts, dampers, air-moving devices, and fire extinguishing equipment.

NFPA 211, *Standard for Chimneys, Fireplaces, Vents, and Solid Fuel-Burning Appliances.* Covers requirements for safe installation and use in residential, commercial, and industrial applications.

NFPA 321, *Standard on Basic Classification of Flammable and Combustible Liquids.* Defines the physical and chemical properties of flammable and combustible liquids and establishes the classification system.

NFPA 385, *Standard for Tank Vehicles for Flammable and Combustible Liquids.* Requirements for the design and construction of tank vehicles used to transport asphalt or normally stable flammable and combustible liquids with a flash point below 200°F.

NFPA 386, *Standard for Portable Shipping Tanks for Flammable and Combustible Liquids.* Provides requirements for portable shipping tanks with capacity between 60 and 660 gallons used to transport normally stable flammable and combustible liquids with a flash point below 200°F.

NFPA 395, *Standard for the Storage of Flammable and Combustible Liquids at Farms and Isolated Sites.* Covers storage of hazardous materials in rural areas, where isolation from other structures makes it unnecessary to adhere to the more rigid requirements of NFPA 30.

NFPA 480, *Standard for the Storage, Handling and Processing of Magnesium Solids and Powders.* Deals with fire and explosion hazards in magnesium foundries and processing plants, as well as the commercial storage of magnesium.

NFPA 481, *Standard for the Production, Processing, Handling, and Storage of Titanium.* Governs the fire-safe use of titanium in operations including sponge production and melting powder and scrap production, and mill operations.

NFPA 482, *Standard for the Production, Processing, Handling, and Storage of Zirconium.* Provides a comprehensive plan for personnel safety, and fire and explosion prevention and protection.

NFPA 490, *Code for the Storage of Ammonium Nitrate.* Outlines safe storage procedures for fertilizer-grade ammonium nitrate in the form of crystals, flakes, grains, or prills.

NFPA 650, *Standard for Pneumatic Conveying Systems for Handling Combustible Materials.* Covers requirements for pressure-type and suction-type systems with guidance on design safeguards of component parts.

NFPA 655, *Standard for Prevention of Sulfur Fires and Explosions.* Methods to eliminate or reduce hazards encountered in the crushing and pulverizing of bulk and liquid sulfur.

NFPA 1122, *Code for Unmanned Rockets.* Designates requirements for the design, construction, limitation, and reliability of all rocket motors produced commercially for sale to the public.

NFPA 1123, *Code for the Outdoor Display of Fireworks.* Safety standards (including site selection criteria) for public fireworks displays for the protection of the operator as well as the viewing public.

NFPA 1124, *Code for the Manufacture, Transportation, and Storage of Fireworks.* Requirements for the safe manufacture, transport, and storage of fireworks (except for fireworks in retail stores and public displays, or those belonging to military agencies).

NFPA 1125, *Code for the Manufacture of Model Rocket Motors.* Specifies requirements for the safe manufacture of model rocket motors designed, sold, and used for the purpose of propelling recoverable aero models.

NFPA 1226, *Standard for the Use of Pyrotechnics before a Proximate Audience.* Provides requirements for reasonable protection for proximate audiences, pyrotechnic operators, performers, and support personnel where pyrotechnic special effects are used indoors or outdoors.

NFPA 8501, *Standard for Single Burner Boiler Operation.* Includes information on design, installation, operation, and maintenance on boilers with fuel input greater than 12,500,000 btu/hr that use single burners firing natural gas, fuel oil, or both.

NFPA 8503, *Standard for Pulverized Fuel Systems.* Details requirements for design, installation, operation, maintenance, and personal safety around pulverized fuel systems.

NFPA 8505, *Recommended Practice for Stoker Operation.* Details guidelines for the design, installation, and operation of stoker fired boiler-furnaces greater than 400,000 btu/hr.

Occupancies or Processes

NFPA 30A, *Automotive and Marine Service Station Code.* General provisions for piping, fuel dispensing systems, stations inside buildings, and operations.

NFPA 30B, *Code for the Manufacture and Storage of Aerosol Products.* Provides requirements for the safe manufacturing and storage of aerosol products, construction requirements for manufacturing plants and warehouses, special guidelines for flammable propellent filling operations, and fire protection and maximum storage requirements for storage rooms, warehouses, and retail outlets.

NFPA 32, *Standard for Drycleaning Plants.* Covers safeguards for drycleaning and dry dyeing operations.

NFPA 36, *Standard for Solvent Extraction Plants.* Suggests safeguards for the design and operation of solvent extraction processes that use hydrocarbon solvents.

NFPA 40E, *Code for the Storage of Pyroxylin Plastic.* Covers safe storage in manufacturing buildings, warehouses, jobbing shops, and retail outlets.

NFPA 43A, *Code for the Storage of Liquid and Solid Oxidizers.* Recommends practices for reducing hazards from fires and explosions when liquid and solid oxidizing materials are in storage.

NFPA 45, *Standard on Fire Protection for Laboratories Using Chemicals.* Basic requirements for protection of life and property in laboratory work areas where hazardous chemicals are handled.

NFPA 46, *Recommended Safe Practice for Storage of Forest Products.* Outlines the recommendations to minimize hazards and control fire in storage areas that contain lumber, timber, wood chips, logs, and similar products.

NFPA 61A, *Standard for Prevention of Fire and Dust Explosions in Facilities Manufacturing and Handling Starch.* Covers hazards of handling dried starch and precautions to prevent ignition.

NFPA 61B, *Standard for the Prevention of Fires and Explosions in Grain Elevators and Facilities Handling Bulk Raw Agricultural Commodities.* Covers prevention of dust explosions and ways to minimize the damage if an explosion should occur; also covers fumigation of commodities and storage spaces.

NFPA 61C, *Standard for the Prevention of Fire and Dust Explosions in Feed Mills.* Covers construction, ventilation, equipment, and miscellaneous precautions.

NFPA 61D, *Standard for the Prevention of Fire and Dust Explosions in the Milling of Agricultural Commodities for Human Consumption.*

Covers prevention of fire and dust explosion hazards in the milling of wheat, rye, barley, corn, and other grains.

NFPA 65, *Standard for the Processing and Finishing of Aluminum.* Outlines safety requirements for operations where fine aluminum dust or powder is liberated.

NFPA 75, *Standard for the Protection of Electronic Computer/Data Processing Equipment.* Covers requirements for installations needing fire protection or special building construction, rooms, areas, or operating environments.

NFPA 81, *Standard for Fur Storage, Fumigation and Cleaning.* Covers protective practices for fur storage vaults and cleaning plants.

NFPA 82, *Standard on Incinerators, Waste and Linen Handling Systems and Equipment.* Contains requirements for reducing fire hazards associated with the installation and use of compactors, incinerators, waste-handling and linen-handling systems, and waste storage rooms and containers.

NFPA 88A, *Standard for Parking Structures.* Covers construction and fire protection of parking garages.

NFPA 88B, *Standard for Repair Garages.* Covers construction and fire protection of repair garages for motorized vehicles.

NFPA 99, *Standard for Health Care Facilities.* Includes performance, maintenance, testing, and safe practices for facilities, materials, equipment, and appliances in order to minimize the hazards of fire, explosion, and electricity in health care facilities.

NFPA 99B, *Standard for Hypobaric Facilities.* Sets forth minimum safeguards for the protection of personnel involved in the use of facilities that contain an oxygen-enriched atmosphere.

NFPA 102, *Standard for Assembly Seating, Tents and Membrane Structures.* Safety requirements in grandstands, bleachers, mass folding, or telescopic seating, tents, and air-supported structures.

NFPA 120, *Standard for Coal Preparation Plants.* Specifies safety requirements for design, construction, and operation of coal preparation plants.

NFPA 130, *Standard for Fixed Guideway Transit Systems.* Covers fire protection requirements for underground, surface, and elevated fixed guideway transit systems and life safety in transit stations, trainways, vehicles, and storage areas.

NFPA 303, *Fire Protection Standard for Marinas and Boatyards.* Fire protection requirements for locations used for the construction, repair, storage, launching, berthing, or fueling of small craft.

NFPA 307, *Standard for the Construction and Fire Protection of Marine Terminals, Piers, and Wharves.* Outlines requirements for construction and fire protection of marine terminals, piers, and wharves, and for hazardous materials storage.

NFPA 312, *Standard for Fire Protection of Vessels During Construction, Repair, and Lay-up.* Covers fire protection for marine vessels during construction, conversion, repair, and lay-up.

NFPA 318, *Standard for the Protection of Cleanrooms.* Provides reasonable safeguards for the protection of semiconductor facilities containing cleanrooms from fire and related hazards.

NFPA 327, *Standard Procedures for Cleaning or Safeguarding Small Tanks and Containers without Entry.* Procedures for the safe removal of flammable vapors, liquids, gases, or solids from small tanks or containers that cannot be entered.

NFPA 407, *Standard for Aircraft Fuel Servicing.* Safety requirements for procedures, equipment, and installations during ground fueling of aircraft with liquid petroleum fuels.

NFPA 409, *Standard on Aircraft Hangars.* Covers specialized construction requirements and fire protection criteria for hangars designed to serve all types of aircraft.

NFPA 410, *Standard on Aircraft Maintenance.* Covers electrical and oxygen systems, fuel tank repairs, cabin cleaning, and refurbishing operations.

NFPA 415, *Standard on Aircraft Fueling Ramp Drainage.* Requirements for the drainage system of an aircraft fueling ramp to minimize the risk from spilled fuel.

NFPA 416, *Standard on Construction and Protection of Airport Terminal Buildings.* Covers fire safety in airport terminal buildings, including provisions for allowable modifications in smaller airports.

NFPA 418, *Standard for Heliports.* Fire protection of structures designed to accommodate operation of helicopters, with the exception of off-shore facilities.

NFPA 490, *Code for the Storage of Ammonium Nitrate.* Outlines safe storage procedures for fertilizer-grade ammonium nitrate in the form of crystals, flakes, grains, or prills.

NFPA 495, *Explosive Materials Code.* Identifies reasonable levels of safety for explosive materials, including small arms ammunition, exclusive of transportation of such materials for military purposes.

NFPA 498, *Standard for Explosives Motor Vehicle Terminals.* Requirements for fire and explosion prevention and fire protection at interchange and parking facilities for vehicles transporting explosives.

NFPA 501D, *Standard for Firesafety Criteria for Recreational Vehicle Parks and Campgrounds.* Criteria for general fire safety, fire detection, alarms, fire safety rules and regulations, and environmental health and sanitation in recreational vehicle parks and campgrounds.

NFPA 505, *Fire Safety Standard for Powered Industrial Trucks Including Type Designations, Areas of Use, Maintenance, and Operation.* Identifies type designations, areas of use, maintenance, and operation requirements for industrial trucks powered by electric motors or internal combustion engines.

NFPA 513, *Standard for Motor Freight Terminals.* Defines requirements for fire protection in motor freight terminals, including transfer areas, offices, employee facilities, and vehicle service areas.

NFPA 651, *Standard for the Manufacture of Aluminum Powder.* Covers the manufacture of aluminum and magnesium flakes, powders, pastes, or atomized granules and explosive aluminum or magnesium alloys.

NFPA 654, *Standard for the Prevention of Fire and Dust Explosions in the Chemical, Dye, Pharmaceutical, and Plastics Industries.* Methods for reducing the risk of fire and explosion in the manufacture, fabrication, or molding of plastics.

NFPA 664, *Standard for the Prevention of Fires and Explosions in Wood Processing and Woodworking Facilities.* Requirements for areas where finely divided wood particles are produced or handled.

NFPA 801, *Recommended Fire Protection Practice for Facilities Handling Radioactive Materials.* Specifies guidelines for reducing the risk of fire or explosion and the severity of contamination from a fire or explosion at facilities (except nuclear reactors) that handle radioactive materials.

NFPA 802, *Recommended Fire Protection Practice for Nuclear Research and Production Reactors.* Provides recommendations for the safe design, construction, operation, and protection of nuclear research and production facilities.

NFPA 803, *Standard for Fire Protection for Light Water Nuclear Power*

Plants. Provides fire safety guidelines for light water nuclear electric generating facilities, including operating personnel, equipment, and operations.

NFPA 820, *Recommended Practice for Fire Protection in Wastewater Treatment and Collection Facilities.* Provides recommended guidelines of protection against fire and explosion hazards in wastewater treatment facilities and associated collection systems.

NFPA 850, *Recommended Practice for Fire Protection for Electric Generating Plants.* Outlines fire safety recommendations for gas, oil, coal, and alternative fuel electric generating plants.

NFPA 851, *Recommended Practice for Fire Protection for Hydroelectric Generating Plants.* Recommendations to safeguard physical property and insure continuity of power production.

NFPA 910, *Recommended Practice for the Protection of Libraries and Library Collections.* Provides guidelines for fire safety, fire protection, and fire loss contingency planning for libraries.

NFPA 911, *Recommended Practice for the Protection of Museums and Museum Collections.* Offers guidance in fire prevention and protection in new and existing museums and during alterations and renovations.

NFPA 912, *Recommended Practice for Fire Protection in Places of Worship.* Specifies fire safety recommendations for churches, synagogues, and temples. Covers special hazards encountered in older buildings, arson, fire protection planning, detection and extinguishing systems.

NFPA 913, *Recommended Practice for the Protection of Historic Structures and Sites.* Recommends fire protection procedures and equipment for historic buildings. Describes common causes of fires and reasons for fire spread in historic buildings.

NFPA 914, *Recommended Practice for Fire Protection in Rehabilitation and Adaptive Reuse of Historic Structures.* Covers fire protection and prevention as it relates to all aspects of historic preservation.

Testing and Approval

NFPA 49, *Hazardous Chemicals Data.* Data involving chemicals that are a health hazard, have a reactivity rating, or have an unusual storage or fire fighting problem.

NFPA 80, *Standard for Fire Doors and Fire Windows.* Covers the use, installation, and maintenance of fire doors, windows, glass blocks, and shutters.

NFPA 92A, *Recommended Practice for Smoke-Control Systems.* Addresses smoke-control utilizing barriers, airflows, and pressure differentials in order to confine the smoke of a fire to the zone of fire origin and thus maintain a tenable environment in other zones.

NFPA 101M, *Manual on Alternative Approaches to Life Safety.* Contains several appendices formerly published in NFPA *101.* Provides an alternative method for calculating stair capacity; fire safety evaluation systems for health care, detention and correctional, board and care, and business occupancies; and a method for determining evacuation capability for board and care homes.

NFPA 203, *Guideline on Roof Coverings and Roof Deck Constructions.* Provides general information about roof coverings and their fire characteristics.

NFPA 204M, *Guide for Smoke and Heat Venting.* Defines principles of natural venting, type of vents, venting ratios, curtain boards, inspection and maintenance, and heat release data.

NFPA 251, *Standard Methods of Fire Tests of Building Construction and Materials.* Specifies methods for determining the fire-resistive abilities of building members and assemblies.

NFPA 252, *Standard Methods of Fire Tests of Door Assemblies.* Outlines methods of testing fire resistance of door assemblies in wall openings.

NFPA 253, *Standard Method of Test for Critical Radiant Flux of Floor Covering Systems Using a Radiant Heat Energy Source.* Provides a basis for estimating one aspect of the flame spread properties of floor covering systems in a building corridor or exit enclosure.

NFPA 255, *Standard Method of Test of Surface Burning Characteristics of Building Materials.* Guidelines for determining the comparative flame-spread rate and smoke density of building materials.

NFPA 256, *Standard Methods of Fire Tests of Roof Coverings.* Methods for measuring relative fire characteristics of roof coverings when fire originates outside the building.

NFPA 257, *Standard for Fire Tests of Window Assemblies.* Methods for testing glass block and other light-transmitting assemblies.

NFPA 260, *Standard Methods of Tests and Classification System for Cigarette Ignition Resistance of Components of Upholstered Furniture.*

Provides laboratory testing procedures for evaluating the performance of upholstered furniture components when exposed to smoldering cigarettes.

NFPA 261, *Standard Method of Test for Determining Resistance of Mockup Upholstered Furniture Material Assemblies to Ignition by Smoldering Cigarettes.* Provides laboratory testing procedures for evaluating the performance of mocked-up furniture.

NFPA 291, *Recommended Practice for Fire Flow Testing and Marking of Hydrants.* Covers testing procedures, classification, and color coding of hydrants.

NFPA 325M, *Fire Hazard Properties of Flammable Liquids, Gases, and Volatile Solids.* Summary of available data on the fire hazard properties of more than 1,600 substances.

NFPA 491M, *Manual of Hazardous Chemical Reactions.* Describes more than 3,500 potentially dangerous chemical reactions.

NFPA 701, *Standard Methods of Fire Tests for Flame-Resistant Textiles and Films.* Provides tests to determine flame-resistant properties of materials used in draperies and protective outdoor coverings.

NFPA 703, *Standard for Fire Retardant Impregnated Wood and Fire Retardant Coatings for Building Materials.* Criteria for defining and identifying certain types of wood that have undergone pressure impregnation or surface-coating processes to retard flame spread.

NFPA 704, *Standard System for the Identification of the Fire Hazards of Materials.* Describes key method of marking containers to indicate the relative reactivity, flammability, and health hazards of materials in storage.

NFPA 1962, *Standard for the Care, Use, and Service Testing of Fire Hose Including Couplings and Nozzles.* Defines requirements for use, inspection, storage, service testing, and record keeping for fire department, industrial, and forestry fire hose.

Life Safety Code Handbook, 5th edition. Extensively revised handbook gives all users of the *Life Safety Code* a clear, concise understanding of the code provisions to ensure they are applied correctly.

Organization

NFPA 10L, *Model Enabling Act for the Sale or Leasing and Servicing of Portable Fire Extinguishers (Including Recommended Rules and*

Regulations for the Administration of the Act). Regulations on the sale, leasing, and servicing of portable fire extinguishers.

NFPA 13E, *Recommendations for Fire Department Operations in Properties Protected by Sprinkler and Standpipe Systems.* Outlines fire department inspection, planning, water supply, operations, and reports.

NFPA 241, *Standard for Safeguarding Construction, Alteration, and Demolition Operations.* Covers fire safety procedures during the erection, alteration, or demolition of buildings.

NFPA 600, *Standard on Industrial Fire Brigades.* Explains how to organize, manage, train, inspect, maintain, and equip fire brigades.

NFPA 601, *Standard on Guard Service in Fire Loss Prevention.* Information that aids management in the selection and training of guards hired to protect a property against fire loss.

NFPA 901, *Uniform Coding for Fire Protection.* A common international language for the description of fire incidents and a method for classifying fire protection data.

NFPA 1031, *Standard for Professional Qualifications for Fire Inspector.* Specifies the minimum level of professional competence required for Fire Inspector I, II, and III.

NFPA 1452, *Guide for Training Fire Service Personnel to Make Dwelling Fire Safety Surveys.* Basic guide for establishing a local fire safety program for both single-and multi-family dwellings in rural and urban areas.

Index

Accessibility, as observation in inspection, 9
Acetaldehyde, 497
Acids, inorganic, 500
Acrylonitrile, 588
Additions, construction of, 40–41
Aerosols, storage of, 425
AFFF (aqueous film-forming foam), 188
After-burners (direct-flame incinerators), 536–537
Agricultural products, dryers for, 540, 542
Air carbon arc cutting process, 571
Air-cleaning equipment, 89–90
Air-conditioning systems
  components of, 88–93
  distribution equipment for, 90–93
  fire hazard potential and, 11
  maintenance of, 93
Air-conveying system, 411–412
Aircraft storage hangers, 353. *See also* Storage occupancies
Air-handling equipment rooms, 13
Air-intake system, 88
Air-sampling smoke detectors, 105
Air terminals, for lightning protection, 72–73
Alarm systems. *See also* Smoke detectors
  for apartment buildings, 274–275
  audible notification appliances for
    description of, 113–116
    room spacing allocation for, 116, 117
  for business occupancies, 330

differences among, 97–99
in hotels, 259
for industrial occupancies, 344
inspection of, 14
installation conductors, monitoring integrity of, 112–116
for lodging or rooming houses, 283
for mercantile occupancies, 315
monitoring for integrity, 95
for residential board and care occupancies, 295–297
for storage operations, 360
supervisory off-normal condition, 101
testing, 116–117
types of, 95–104. *See also specific types of alarm systems*
for vehicles and vessels, 374
wiring, inspection of, 111–115
Alkalies, 498
Alkylaluminums, 499
Alterations, construction, 40–41
Alumina, 585
Aluminum
  combustibility of, 483, 492–493
  dust, 473–474
  powdered, 496
  processing, fire hazards in, 584–586
Ambulatory health care center, 230. *See also* Health care occupancies
American National Standards Institute (ANSI)
  documents on gas appliances

American National Standards Institute (ANSI) *(cont.)*

and accessories, 468–469

gas appliances/accessories publications, 568–569

litigation and, 2

standards, 2, 462, 463

American Society of Mechanical Engineers (ASME), gas container safeguards, 458

Ammonia dissociators, 534

Ammonium nitrate, 520, 521–522

Amusement buildings, 212

Anhydrides, 499

Animal-oil processing, fire hazards of, 593–594

Annual test procedure, for water supplies, 130

ANSI. *See* American National Standards Institute (ANSI)

Apartment buildings

definition of, 264

dwelling units in, 271

for elderly, 275

existing, 263–264

alternative requirements, 268–269

inspection of, 265

exits for, 270–271

fire inspection form for, 276–277

fire protection for, 274

hazardous areas in, 273–274

inspection observations for, 265, 267, 269–270

interior finishes in, 273

lighting for, 275

new, 263–264

alternate requirements for, 266–267

high-rise type, 264–265

inspections of, 264–265

occupant load for, 270

openings, protection of, 272

waste chutes for, 272–273

Apparatus, electrical

damaged, electrical fires from, 61–67

grounding, 64–65

overcurrent protection for, 65–66

Application systems, for fire extinction, inspection and maintenance of, 168

Aqueous film-forming foam (AFFF), 188

Archives and records centers, 433–434

Arcing, electrical fires from, 61–62

Area separation walls. *See* Fire barriers

Arson, in storage areas, 421

ASME (American Society of Mechanical Engineers), gas container safeguards, 458

Asphalt mixing plants, fire hazards in, 586–587

Assembly occupancies

building services for, 210–211

characteristics of, 206–207

classifications of, 206

defined, 206

egress, means of, 208–209

fire inspection form for, 215–217

fire protection systems for, 214–215

interior finishes in, 209–210

occupant load for, 208

premises, inspection of, 207–211

smoking and, 211

special safeguards for, 211–213

ASTM E84 (Steiner Tunnel Test), 54, 507, 508

Atmosphere generators, 534

Atriums, 320

Attire, for fire inspector, 5

Autogenous ignition temperature, 439–440

Autoignition temperature, 439–440

Automatic-closing fire doors, 49

Automatic dry-pipe system, 162. *See also* Standpipe and hose systems

Automatic fire detectors, 101–103
Automatic sprinkler systems. *See*
    Sprinkler systems
Automatic wet system, 159. *See also*
    Standpipe and hose systems
Auxiliary fuel systems, for incinerator, 395

Backflow prevention devices, 121–122
Ballrooms, 255, 257. *See also* Assembly
    occupancies
Barium peroxide, 503
Barns. *See* Storage occupancies
Basements, in educational occupancies,
    221–222
Batch dryers, 540
BATF (Bureau of Alcohol, Tobacco and
    Firearms), 528, 529
Bathrooms, 264
Beams, 25
Bearing walls, 25
Bed and breakfasts, 278. *See also*
    Lodging or rooming houses
Belt conveyor, 408–409
Blasting agents, 520–521
    ammonium nitrate, 521–522
    defined, 516
    fire protection, 522
BLEVE (boiling liquid-expanding vapor
    explosion), 459, 546
Blow molding, 511
Boiler-furnaces. *See* Boilers
Boiler rooms, 78, 221–222, 248
Boilers
    burner controls and, 77–82
    explosions of, 579–580
    hazards of, 533
    installation of, 82–85, 532
    in large buildings, 76–77
    oil-fired, 579
    oil-fired steam, 78
    for pulp and paper mills, 599

types of, 531–533
Boiling liquid-expanding vapor explosion
    (BLEVE), 459, 546
Boiling point, 437
Bonding
    of lightning down conductors, 73
    vs. grounding, 70–72
Brazing, 572
Bromochlorodifluoromethane (halon
    1211), 170
Bromotrifluoromethane (halon 1301), 170
Bucket elevators, 410, 592
Building construction. *See* Construction
Building facilities, 11
Building separation walls. *See* Fire
    barriers
Building services
    for assembly occupancies, 210–211
    equipment rooms for, 258–259
    fire inspector's knowledge of, 3
Built-up roof covering, 28
Bulk dryers, 540
Bulkhead compactor, 396
Bulk storage, 417
Bulk storage elevators, exits for, 353
*The Bulletin of the Society of Fire
    Protection Engineers,* 30
Bunsen burner tests, 507–508
Bureau of Alcohol, Tobacco and Firearms
    (BATF), 528, 529
Burner controls, 77–82
Business occupancies
    building services for, 327–329
    cafeterias in, 328–329
    characteristics of, 319–321
    computer rooms in, 324–325
    defined, 319
    egress, means of, 321–323
    fire inspection form for, 331–333
    fire protection for, 329–330
    hazardous areas in, 324

openings, protection of, 323–324
operating features of, 330–331
records, protection of, 325–326
shafts and chases in, 329

Cables, common faults in, 62
Cafeterias, in business occupancies, 328–329
Calcium, 483, 492
Candles, 213–214
Carbide, 499
Carbon, burning, in boiler, 532
Carbon arc cutting air process, 571
Carbon black, 496
Carbon dioxide fire extinguishing
    systems, 168–169
    hand hose system with hose mounted
        on reel, 169
    inspection and maintenance, 170
    safety considerations, 169–170
    types of storage, 170
Carbon dioxide fire suppression systems,
    for commercial cooking operations,
    618–619
Carbon dioxide portable extinguishers,
    187–188, 189
Carbon dioxide systems, testing guidelines
    for, 171
Carbon monoxide, 13
Carousel bag packer, 396
Carpeting
    storage of, 426–427
    for use on wall or ceiling, 54
Cartridge fuses, 66
Cartridge-operated dry chemical
    extinguisher, 190
Cartridge-operated extinguishers, 191
Casting, 511
Catalytic combustion systems, 537
Cathodic protection, 134. *See also*
    Grounding

Caulking materials, 44
Ceiling finishes, 53–56
Ceiling height, smoke detector location
    and, 109–110
Ceiling tiles, 280
Cellulose nitrate, 507
Central station, auxiliary, remote station
    and proprietary systems, 96, 100
Centrifugal-type fire pumps, 126–127
Chain conveyors, 409
Charcoal, 499
Charging systems, for incinerator, 394–395
Chases, in business occupancies, 329
Check valves, 462
Chemically generated foam units, 189
Chemicals. *See also specific chemicals*
    corrosive materials, 500
    oxidizing, 501–504, 520
    solid combustible, 496–497
    toxic, 500–501
    unstable, 497–498
    water and air-reactive, 498–499
Chimneys
    defects, checklist of, 85–86
    types of, 84–85
    vent connectors, 83
Chlorates, 503
Chlorites, 503
Chutes. *See also* Waste chutes
    fire protection for, 44–45
    terminal enclosures for, 391
    termination bin for, 396
Cigarette ignition, of mattresses and
    upholstered furniture, 507
Circuit breakers, 61–62, 66
Circuit conductors, common faults in, 62
Civilian pyrotechnic products, 525
Clay products plants, fire hazards in, 590
Cleaning ducts, 328–329
Cleanliness, good housekeeping practice
    and, 381

Cleanrooms, fire hazards in, 605–607
Clean waste and rags, 384
Closets, 221–222, 264
Closing devices, for fire doors, 48–49
Clothing, protective
    for spray painting and powder coating, 566
    for welding and cutting, 572–573
Coal, 579
Coal and wood stoves, 305
Coal burning, in boiler, 533
Coast Guard stations, small sleeping accommodations in, 278. *See also* Lodging or rooming houses
Coating process, 511–512, 548
Coatings
    fire-retardant, 56
    housekeeping and, 384
    powder, 547–548
    solventborne, 546–547
    waterborne, 547, 583
Code of Federal Regulations, 459, 507
Cold storage warehouses, 426
Cold weather, water storage tank inspections and, 132, 134
College/university classrooms. See Business occupancies
Columns, 25
Combination heat detector, 104
Combustible gas detector, 6
Combustible liquids
    classification of, 440–441
    compressed gas displacement systems for, 450
    confinement of, 451
    dispensing systems for, 450–451
    drums and portable containers for, 447–448
    fire protection for, 452–453
    gravity systems for, 450
    identification of, 442

ignition sources, control of, 452
    outside aboveground tanks for, 444–446
    portable tanks for, 447
    pumping systems for, 450
    safety containers for, 449
    special occupancies for, 453–454
    storage of, 442–443
        tanks inside buildings for, 446–447
        underground tanks for, 443–444
        ventilation for, 451–452
    vs. flammable liquids, 436
Combustible materials. *See also specific combustible materials*
    class A, 178–179
    in fire-resistive construction, 29
    metal fires, extinguishing of, 484–486
    welding and cutting processes and, 573
Commissaries, in detention and correctional occupancies, 248
Commodity classification, for storage, 415–416
Common path of travel, 197–198, 199
Common walls, 25
Compactor and waste storage rooms, 396
Compactors, commercial-industrial, 396
Compartmentation
    in health care occupancies, 233–235
    in residential board and care occupancies, 294–295
Composite doors, 47
Composite propellants, 517
Compressed gas displacement systems, for combustible and flammable liquids, 450
Compression molding, 512
Computer rooms, in business occupancies, 324–325
Concealed spaces, 27, 32
Concrete construction, 29
Conditioning equipment, 88–90

Egress, means of. *See also* Escape, means
 of *(cont.)*
 travel distance and, 198, 200
 for vehicle or vessel, 373
 vs. means of escape, 264
Elastomeric coatings, for roofs, 28
Elderly, apartments for, 275
Electrical cabinets, common faults in, 63
Electrical distribution systems, 11
Electrical equipment maintenance, for
 prevention of dust explosions, 479
Electrical fires
 from arcing, 61–62
 causes of, 61
 from overheating, 61, 62
Electrical hazardous areas
 class I
 Division 1, 68–69
 Division 2, 69
 class II
 Division 1, 69
 Division 2, 69–70
 class III
 Division 1, 70
 Division 2, 70
Electrical inspectors, 61
Electrical installations, for lodging or
 rooming houses, 282
Electrical neutralizer, 72
Electrical systems, 61–73
Electric arc processes, for welding and
 cutting, 569–571
Electric generating stations, hazards of,
 578–581
Electric generators, 580
Electronic air cleaners, 90
Electroslag welding, 571
Embankment-supported rubberized-fabric
 tanks, 132, 133
Emergency lighting
 for business occupancies, 322

for industrial occupancies, 337
 for means of egress, 204
 for mercantile occupancies, 313
Emergency planning, for detention and
 correctional occupancies, 252–253
Employee locker rooms/cafeteria, 258
Engineered systems
 for fire extinguishing, 168
 for smoke control, 320
Engine generator sets, 131
Engines, internal combustion, 520
Environmental Protection Agency (EPA),
 443
Equipment. *See also specific equipment*
 good housekeeping practice and, 380–
 381
 industrial, 67–68
 maintenance, for prevention of dust
 explosions, 478–479
Equivalency concepts, in *Life Safety Code,*
 196
Escalators, fire protection for, 45
Escape, means of. *See also* Egress, means
 of
 for lodging or rooming houses, 280–281
 one-and two-family dwellings, 303–304
 for small residential board and care
 occupancies, 291–292
 vs. means of egress, 264
Ethylene oxide, 498
Evacuation capability, for residential
 board and care occupancies, 288–
 290
Evaporation, 437
Exhaust systems
 for commercial cooking operations,
 613–617
 for spray painting, 555
 for ventilation, 93
Exhibits, in assembly occupancies, 211–
 212

Fire hose. *See also* Standpipe and hose
  systems *(cont.)*
  inspection requirements for, 163–164
  testing requirements for, 164–165
Fire inspection form
  for apartment buildings, 276–277
  for assembly occupancies, 215–217
  for business occupancies, 331–333
  for detention and correctional
    occupancies, 253–254
  for educational occupancy, 228–229
  for health care occupancy, 238–240
  for hotel occupancy, 261–262
  for lodging or rooming houses, 285–
    286
  for residential board and care occupan-
    cies, 300–301
Fire inspector
  attire of, 5
  authority of, 12
  characteristics of, 1
  communication skills of, 1
  equipment for inspection procedures, 5
  identification, visible means of, 5
  knowledge of, 24
  physical condition of, 1
  tools/aids for, 56
Fire lanes, 9
Fire limits, in exterior protected,
    combustible construction, 31–32
Fire partitions. *See* Fire barriers
Fire point, 439
Fire Protection Handbook, 83
Fire protection systems. *See also under*
    specific occupancies
  for assembly occupancies, 214–215
  fire inspector's knowledge of, 3
  installation, during construction, 39–40
  for lodging or rooming houses, 283–
    284
  sprinklers. *See* Sprinkler systems

standpipe and hose systems. *See*
  Standpipe and hose systems
Fire pumps assembly, 127
  for industrial occupancies, 342
  inspecting, 126–131
  for storage operations, 359–360
Fire ratings
  class A, 173, 186
  class B, 173, 186
  class C, 173, 186
Fire-resistance rating
  of fire barriers, 26
  of fire walls, 26
  of floor/ceiling assemblies, 27
Fire-resistive construction, 29–30, 43–44
Fire-resistive walls, integrity of, 10
Fire service mains, private, inspecting,
    124–126
Fire shutters, 50, 338
Firestopping, 33, 43
Fire suppression equipment, inspection of,
    14
Fire wall, 26
Fire watchers, for welding and cutting
    processes, 574
Fireworks, 524. *See also* Pyrotechnics
  consumer, types of, 525, 526
  definitions, 525, 527
Fixed extinguishing systems, 3
Fixed fire protection, in demolition, 41
Fixed-temperature heat detectors, 103
Flame-failure gas shutoff devices, 462
Flame spread ratings
  classifications for, 55
  for duct materials, 92
  of interior finish in assembly occupan-
    cies, 209–210
  of interior finish material, 54
Flammability hazard rating, 428, 429, 431
Flammable limits, 440
Flammable liquids, 41

Flammable liquids *(cont.)*
classification of, 440–441
cleaning solvents, 386
in cleanrooms, 605–606
compressed gas displacement systems
for, 450
confinement of, 451
containers for
bonding of, 71–72
drums/portable, 447–448
safety types, 449
dispensing systems for, 450–451
fire protection for, 452–453
gravity systems for, 450
identification of, 442
ignition sources, control of, 452
pumping systems for, 450
special occupancies for, 453–454
spills of, 383
storage of, 425, 442–443
outside aboveground tanks for, 444–446
portable tanks for, 447
tanks inside buildings for, 446–447
underground tanks for, 443–444
ventilation for, 451–452
volatile, storage areas for, 69
vs. combustible liquids, 436
waste disposal for, 384
Flammable materials
class B, 179
in contents of detention and correctional
occupancies, 249
gases. *See* Gas(es), flammable
in laboratories of educational occupancies, 222
Flash arrestors, for welding and cutting
processes, 576
Flash point
of blasting agents, 520
of liquids, 438–439

test for, 442
Flexible cords, common faults in, 62–63
Flexible-plan buildings, as educational
occupancies, 224
Floor/ceiling assemblies
construction of, 27
for hotel, 258
integrity of, 10
penetrations in fire barriers, protection
for, 44
Flooring Radiant Panel Test Method, 56
Floor joists, 31, 33
Floor oils, 386
Floors
cleaning and treatment of, 386
interior finishes for, 56–57
Flow testing
of water main, 136–138
of yard system, 138–142
Fluid-filled transformers, 67
Flux-corded arc welding, 570
Foamed-in-place fire-resistant elastomers,
44
Foam extinguishing systems
description of, 156, 158–159
inspection, testing and maintenance
frequency, 160–161
Foam fire extinguishers, portable, 188
Footings, 25
Forbidden explosives, 518
Forced-circulation, double-track
compartment kiln, 539
Forced warm-air furnaces, 79–80
Foster homes, 278. *See also* Lodging or
rooming houses
Foundation, permanent for vehicle or
vessel, 372
Framing members, 24–25
Freight terminals. See Storage occupancies
Fuel dumps, 38

Guards *(cont.)*
 for stairs, 202
Guest houses, 278. *See also* Lodging or
 rooming houses
Guest rooms, 255. *See also* Residential
 board and care occupancies in
 hotels, 257

Hafnium, 483, 490
Halfway house, 242
Halogenated systems
 safety considerations, 171
 testing guidelines, 173
 types of storage, 172–173
Halogens, 170, 500. *See also specific*
 halons
Halon 1211 bromochlorodifluoromethane), 170
Halon 1301 (bromotrifluoromethane), 170
Hand hose line systems, for fire extinguishing, 168
Handrails, 202
Hartmann Apparatus, 474
Hazardous areas
 in apartment buildings, 264
 in business occupancies, 324
 in detention and correctional occupancies, 248
 in educational occupancies, 221–223
 electrical, classification of, 68–70
 in vehicles and vessels, 373–374
Hazardous materials. *See also specific*
 materials
 containers for, welding and cutting
 processes and, 574–575
 fire inspector's knowledge of, 3
 in industrial occupancies, 338–340
 types of, 3
Hazardous processes, 357–358
Hazards classification of, 178–179

distribution of portable fire
 extinguishers for, 180–185
 for storage occupancy contents, 350
of contents
 high, 11, 12
 level of, 11–14
 low, 11, 12
 ordinary, 11, 12–13
 in fire barrier openings, 43
 to health, ratings for, 428–430
Health care occupancies
 compartmentation of, 233–235
 defined, 230
 egress, means of, 235–236
 facility design, typical, 231
 fire inspection form for, 238–240
 fire protection in, 236–238
 openings, protection of, 232–233
 protecting patients in, 232–235
 subclassification of, 230
Health hazard rating, 428–430
Heat-actuated closing devices, for fire
 doors, 49
Heat detectors, 103–104
 location of, 108–109
 mounting, 106–108
 testing, 104
Heat distribution, 82
Heat exchangers, 537–538
Heating and cooling equipment, 89
Heating appliances, for lodging or
 rooming houses, 282
Heating systems, 11
 boilers. *See* Boilers
 furnaces. *See* Furnaces
 heat distribution, 82
 installation, 82–85
 for large buildings, 76–77
 for residential and small buildings, 77
Heat pump, 81–82
Heat recovery, 537–538

Incinerator and waste-handling room, 392–393
Incinerators
  auxiliary fuel systems, 395
  charging systems, 394–395
  commercial-industrial, 392
  direct-flame or after-burners, 536–537
  domestic, 395
  equipment design and construction, 393
  fire safety for, 392–393
  layout and arrangement, 393
Indoor storage, for industrial occupancies, 340–341
Industrial equipment
  medium voltage, 68
  motors, 67–68
  transformers, 67
Industrial occupancies
  building services for, 341–342
  classification of, 335
  defined, 334
  egress, means of, 336–337
  fire inspection form for, 345–347
  fire protection in, 342–344
    alarm systems for, 344
    special extinguishing systems for, 343
    sprinkler systems for, 343
    standpipe hose systems for, 343
    water supplies and fire pumps for, 342
  hazardous materials in, 338–340
  occupant load for, 335–336
  openings, protection of, 337–338
  storage for, 340–341
Industrial Risk Insurers (IRI), 463
Industrial trucks. See Trucks
Inns
  large. See Hotel occupancies
  small, 278. See also Lodging or rooming houses

Inorganic acids, 500
Inorganic peroxides, 503
Inspection(s)
  aids for, 56
  of assembly occupancies, 207–211
  of carbon dioxide fire extinguishing systems, 170
  cards for, 18
  closing interview for, 15
  daily, 18
  equipment for, 5
  exterior, 9
  external observations in, 7
  fieldnotes, 19–23
  of fire detection and alarm systems, 14
  of fire doors, 49–50
  of fire suppression equipment, 14
  introductions for, 78
  observations in, 8–18
  preparation for, 67
  sequence for, 9
Inspection reports, 16–18
  information in, 16–17
  purpose of, 17, 18
  for valve conditions, 147
Insulation
  failure, caused by overheating, 62
  roof, 27
Interior finishes
  in assembly occupancies, 209–210
  in day-care centers, 225–226
  in detention and correctional occupancies, 248–249
  in educational occupancies, 223
  for floors, 56–57
  furnishing/decorations and, 57–58
  for vehicles and vessels, 374
  for wall and ceiling, 53–56
Internal combustion engines, 520
Introductions, for inspections, 78
Inverting fire extinguishers, 189

Lithium *(cont.)*
  fire hazards of, 491
  process hazards of, 491
  storage of, 491–492
Litigation, 2
Live load, 24
Loaded stream extinguishers, 188
Load stream extinguishers, 191
Local and emergency voice/alarm
    communication systems, 96, 100
Local application systems, for fire
    extinguishing, 167–168
Lockers, 385
Locking devices
  for business occupancies, 322
  for exit doors, 353
  for health care occupancy doors, 236
  for industrial occupancies, 336
Lodging or rooming houses
  building services for, 281–283
  characteristics of, 278–279
  defined, 278
  fire inspection form for, 285–286
  fire protection systems for, 283–284
  interior finishes in, 279–280
  protection of exits in, 280–281
Loss control guidelines, for combustible
    and flammable liquids, 451–452
Lower explosive limit (LEL), 475
Low explosive materials, 517
Low-pressure extinguishers, cylinders of,
    193
LP-Gas, 79, 210
LP-Gas bulk plants, 463–467
Lube oil and hydraulic oil systems, 580
Lubricants, 384
Lumber kilns, 538–540
Lumber storage yards, fire hazards in, 602

Machines, radiation hazards, 400

Machine shops, fire hazards in, 603–604
Magnesium, 483
  dust, 473–474
  fire extinguishment for, 487–488
  ignition temperature of, 486
  powdered, 496
  process hazards, 486–487
  storage of, 487
Main drain test, 153
Maintenance
  of air conditioning systems, 93
  of carbon dioxide fire extinguishing
    systems, 170
  of fire doors, 49–50
  for spray painting/powder coating
    process, control of fire risk and,
    564–565
Maintenance services, for industrial
    occupancies, 341–342
Maintenance shops, 255. *See also*
    Industrial occupancies
  hotel, 258–259
Maintenance tags/labels, for portable fire
    extinguishers, 192
Maintenance workshops, educational and
    building, in educational occupan-
    cies, 222
Manual dry standpipe system, 162. *See
    also* Standpipe and hose systems
Manual fire alarm boxes, 100–101, 102
Manual incinerator charging system, 394
Manual wet standpipe system, 162. *See
    also* Standpipe and hose systems
Mapping, during initial inspection, 1415
Markers, for industrial truck identification,
    404–405
Markings, for means of egress, 204–205
Masonry chimneys, 84–85
Materials
  hazardous. *See* Hazardous materials
  for interior finishing, 53

Nitrates, 501–502
Nitric acid, 502
Nitrites, 503
Nitroaniline, 496
Nitrocellulose, 507, 583
Nitrochlorbenzenes, 496
Nitromethane, 498
Nitrous oxide, nonflammable medical gas systems, 466, 467
Noise-makers, trick, 525, 527
Noncombustible construction, 29, 30
Nonflammable medical gas systems, 466, 467
Nonrechargeable extinguishers, 192
Novelties and trick noise-makers, 525, 527
Nuclear energy plants, fire hazards of, 580–581
Nuclear Regulatory Commission (NRC), 398

Observations, in inspections, 8–18
Occupancies. *See also specific occupancies*
  classification of, as observation in inspection, 89
  hazard classifications
    extra, 145
    light, 145
    ordinary, 145
  in special structures. *See* Special structure occupancies
Occupancy separation walls. *See* Fire barriers
Occupant load. *See under specific occupancy*
  for apartment buildings, 270
  for assembly occupancies, 208
  for detention and correctional occupancies, 245
  for educational occupancies, 219
  for residential board and care occupancies, 291
Offices, 255. *See also* Business occupancies, 257
Oil
  floor, 386
  grades of, 78–79
  storage of, 520
Oil burning, in boiler, 532–533
Oil-filled transformers, 67
Oil-fired forced-air furnace, 79
Oil quenching, 542–543
Oily waste, 384, 385
One-family dwellings. *See* Family dwellings
Open-flame devices, 213
Open-flame equipment, 38
Open flames, 213–214
Openings, protection of. *See also* Horizontal openings; Vertical openings
  for conveyor systems, 410
  in detention and correctional occupancies, 248
  in health care occupancy, 232–233
Open-plan buildings, as educational occupancies, 224
Open-plan design, for business occupancies, 320
Open screw and yoke valves, 122, 123, 147
Open structures, 364, 366–367
Orderliness, good housekeeping practice and, 381
Ordinary construction (exterior protected, combustible construction), 31–32
Ordinary hazard occupancies, 179
Organic peroxides, 498
OS&Y valves, 122, 123, 147
Outdoor storage, 340, 427–428

NFPA INSPECTION MANUAL

Rack-supported structures, 419
Radiant energy sensing fire detectors, 106, 110
Radioactive materials
handling and storage of, 398–404
metals, 493–494
shipping labels for, 402
Rafter, 25
Rags and clean waste, 384
Railings, for fire doors, 49
Rate-of-rise-compensated fixed temperature detector, 103–104
Rate-of-rise heat detector, 104
Reactivity or instability hazard rating, 428–431
Recirculating systems, 611–612, 621–622
Records
protection of, in business occupancies, 325–326
storage of, 432
Reduced-pressure principle backflow prevention assembly devices (RPBA), 121
Reentry, for business occupancies, 322
Refrigerated storage, 425–426
Refuse and rubbish disposal, 388
Refuse-handling equipment, 11
Regulators, for welding and cutting processes, 575
Reinforced concrete construction, 29
Renovations, 40–41
Reports, inspection, 16–18
Residential and small buildings, heating systems for, 77
Residential board and care occupancies
compartmentation of, 294–295
defined, 287
detection and alarm systems for, 295–297
egress, means of, 291–293
evacuation capability for, 288–290

fire inspection form for, 300–301
fire suppression equipment for, 297–298
hazardous areas in, 295
occupancy characteristics of, 290
occupant load for, 291
operating features in, 298–299
vertical openings, protection of, 293
Resins, thermosetting, 511
Restaurants, 255, 257, 365. *See also* Assembly occupancies
Restrooms, hazards of contents classification, 13
Retail shops, 255. *See also* Mercantile occupancies
Rolled paper, 424–425, 598
Rolling steel doors, 47, 49–50
Roof/ceiling assembly, for hotel, 258
Roofing materials, 39
Roofing operations, fire-safe, 39
Roofs, 27–28
Room corner fire test, 54, 55
Rotational molding, 512
RPBA (reduced-pressure principle backflow prevention assembly devices), 121
Rubber
classification of, 509–510
fire protection for, 514
general uses of, 506–508
manufacturing of, 510–514
products plants for, fire hazards in, 588–589
tires, storage of, 424
warehousing of, 508–510

Safety containers, for flammable and combustible liquids, 449
Safety equipment, personal, 5
Sally ports, 247

Salute powder, 527
Sawdust, 222, 471, 590
Schools. *See* Educational occupancies
Self-ignition temperature, 439–440
Semiautomatic dry system, 159, 162. *See also* Standpipe and hose systems
Sensitivity, 517
Shafts
  in business occupancies, 329
  fire protection for, 44–45
Shear walls, 26
Sheathing, 31
Sheet Metal and Air Conditioning Contractors National Association (SMACNA), 90
Sheet metal doors, 47
Shielded metal arc welding, 570
Shipping labels, for radioactive materials, 402
Shipping/receiving areas, hotel, 258
Shipyards, fire hazards in, 602–603
Shopping centers. *See* Mercantile occupancies
Shredders, 396–397
Signs
  exit. *See* Exit signs
  floor level/terminus, 202
  permitting or forbidding smoking, 383
Sills, fire door, 51
Simple span beam, 25
Single-screw extruder, 513
Site plan, 15
Site preparation, fire protection during, 35–36
SI units, 624
Sketches, making for inspection purposes, 56, 207
Sliding doors, in detention and correctional occupancies, 246
Slow evacuation capability, 289
Smoke barriers, 26 in educational

occupancies, 221
  in health care occupancy, 234
  in residential board and care occupancies, 294–295
Smoke control, 92
Smoke detectors
  air conditioning equipment and, 88
  for apartment buildings, 264, 271
  for day-care centers, 226
  for guest room, 257
  in high air movement areas, 110
  location of, 109–111
  for lodging or rooming houses, 283
  mounting of, 106–108
  for one-and-two family dwellings, 306
  for residential board and care occupancies, 295–297
  testing, 105–106
  types of, 104–106
Smoke development value, 55
Smoking
  in assembly occupancies, 211
  control of, 381–383
  in health care occupancies, 237
  near storage areas, 421
  in residential board and care occupancies, 298–299
Soda-acid extinguishers, 189
Sodium, 483
  fire extinguishment for, 492
  fire hazards of, 491
  process hazards of, 491
  storage of, 491–492
Sodium-bicarbonate dry-chemical fire extinguishers, 173, 184
Sodium hydrosulfite, 499
Sodium peroxide, 503
Sodium-potassium alloy (NaK), 489
  fire extinguishment for, 492
  fire hazards of, 491
  process hazards of, 491

storage of, 491–492
Solid piling storage, 417–418
Spark-producing equipment, 38
Special agent extinguishing systems, 167–176
Special industrial explosive materials, 517
Special occupancies. *See also* Special
    structure occupancies
  for aluminum processing, 584–586
  asphalt mixing plants, 586–587
  computer centers, 581–582
  electric generating stations, 578–581
  for flammable and combustible liquids,
    453–454
  hazards of, 578–607
  laboratories, 582–583
  paint and coating plants, 583–584
  for special industrial purpose, 335
Special-purpose fire door assemblies, 48
Special structure occupancies, 145, 377
  characteristics of, 365–366
  fire inspection form for, 378–379
  open, 364, 366–367
  piers, 367–368
  towers, 364, 368–370
  types of, 364–365
  underground, 370–372
  vehicles, 364, 372–375
  vessels, 364, 372–375
  water-surrounded, 374–375
  windowless buildings, 375–376
Specific gravity, 438
Spontaneous ignition temperature, 439–440
Spray painting, 546
  control of fire risk for, 558–559
    explosion prevention and, 562–563
    extinguishment methods, 563–564
    fuel quantity limitations and, 561–562
    inspection of apparatus and procedures, 564

    isolation of process in, 562
    maintenance and, 564–565
    pressure relief venting and, 562–563
    protective clothing for, 566
    storage and handling of materials and
      residues for, 566
    training, 564
  differences between manual and
    automatic spray, 548
  dry filters for, 553
  electrostatics and, 548
  enclosed spray booths, 550–552
  exhaust system for, 555
  hazardous characteristics of, 546–548
  maze-type dry collectors, 553
  open-face spray booths, 549, 550
  open floor spraying, 556, 557
  overspray collector, 552–553
  spray apparatus for, 556, 558, 559
  spray booths for, 548–550
  spray rooms for, 555–556
  water wash collectors, 553–554
Sprinkler-draft curtain method, 45
Sprinkler systems, 14, 57, 144
  for apartment buildings, 264, 265, 274
  for bag-type dust collector, 480
  for business occupancies, 329–330
  for commercial cooking operations, 619
  in demolition, 41
  for detention and correctional
    occupancies, 250–251
  drain connection for, 149
  dry-pipe types, 150–151
  for flammable and combustible liquids,
    452–453
  foam, 156, 158–159
  gauges for, 153–154
  for health care occupancies, 231–232,
    236–237
  for hotel occupancies, 259–260
  for industrial occupancies, 343

Two-family dwellings. *See* Family
dwellings
Type S plug fuse, 66
Type V or wood frame construction, 33–
34

UL 181, 90, 92
UL 555, 92
UL 900, 90
UL 55–5S, 92
Underground structures, 364, 370–372
Underground tanks, for flammable and
combustible liquids, 443–444
Underwriters Laboratory (UL) standards,
462
Unit heaters, 80–81
Upholstered furniture, 57–58, 507
Uranium, 483, 493–494
Urea potassium bicarbonate, in dry
chemical extinguishing systems,
173
Utilities, for one-and-two-family
dwellings, 305

Valve pit or house, 132
Valves, for water supplies, inspections of,
122–123
Vandalism, during construction, 38
Vapor-air density, 437–438
Vapor pressure, 436–437
Vaults, 326, 432–433
Vegetable-oil processing, fire hazards of,
593–594
Vehicles, 364, 372–375
Vent connectors, 83
Ventilation systems, 93. *See also* Air-
conditioning systems
for commercial cooking equipment,
610–622

fire hazard potential and, 11
for flammable/combustible liquid
storage, 446–447, 451–452
installation of, 620
maintenance of, 93
for welding and cutting, 573
Vents, 83
Vertical openings, protection of
in apartment buildings, 272
in lodging or rooming houses, 280
in residential board and care occupancies, 293
in vehicles and vessels, 373
Vertical turbine pumps, 127
Vessels, 364, 372–375
Violations, written notices of, 2
Viscosity, 438
Voluntary inspections, for one-and-two-
family dwellings, 304–305

Wall and ceiling finishes, classification of,
54
Wall finishes, 53–56
Wall furnaces, 80
Wall hydrants, inspecting, 124–126
Walls
bearing, 25
common or party, 25
fire, 26
load-bearing, 25
shear, 26
veneered, 27
Warehouses. *See* Storage occupancies
Warm-air systems, 82
Waste chutes, 391. *See also* Chutes
for apartment buildings, 272–273
in business occupancies, 327–328
Waste compactors, 395–396
Waste disposal, for business occupancies,
327–328

Waste-handling systems, 390–391. *See
    also* Waste chutes
  compactors, 395–396
  incinerators, 392–395
  shredders, 396–397
Water-based fire protection systems, 144–
    165
  foam extinguishing systems, 156, 158–
    159
  inspection, testing and maintenance
    frequencies, 157–158
  occupancy classifications for, 145–146
  shut down of, 146
  steam smothering, 152–153
Water distribution systems, 11
Waterflow-actuated fire alarm initiating
    devices, 101
Waterflow measurements, 6
Water gel, 517
Water main, flow testing, 136–138
Water solubility, 438
Water spray sprinkler systems, 151–152,
    154, 156
Water-spray system, for escalator, 45
Water storage tanks, inspection of, 131–
    135
Water supplies, 119
  control valves, inspections of, 122–123
  fire department connections for,
    inspection of, 123–124
  fire pumps, inspections of, 126–131
  friction loss in pipe, 140–141
  for industrial occupancies, 342
  minimum, for fire fighting, 135–142
  private fire service mains, inspecting,
    124–126
  public, backflow protection for, 121–
    122
  sources, 120–122
  for sprinkler systems, 146–147
  temporary, during site preparation, 36

using NFPA 25, 119
  water tanks, inspections of, 131–135
  weekly inspections/tests, 128, 129
  yard hydrants, inspecting, 124–126
Water-surrounded structures, 364, 374–
    375
Water wash collectors, for spray painting,
    553–554
Weeds, control of, 388
Welding, 357–358, 568–576. *See also*
    Cutting operations
  in areas with combustibles, 573
  clothing for, 572–573
  fire protection for, 573–575
  hazards of, 568, 572–573
  inspection reminders for, 575–576
  for motor vehicle assembly, 605
  near conveyors, 409
  processes in, 569–572
  ventilation for, 573
Wet chemical fire suppression systems,
    176, 617–618
Windowless buildings/structures, 364,
    375–376
Windows
  in business occupancies, 323–324
  in educational occupancies, 221
Wired glass, 44, 50
Wiring, electrical
  for alarm system, checking, 112–113,
    114, 115
  damaged, electrical fires from, 61–67
  grounding of, 64–65
  inspection of, for fire alarm systems,
    111–112
  overcurrent protection and, 65–66
Wood core doors, 48
Wood frame construction, 33–34
Wood products manufacturing, fire
    hazards in, 600–602
Wood stoves, 305